CLASSICS Appreciation SOCIETY

LES MISERABLES
by Victor Hugo

The Autobiography of
BENJAMIN FRANKLIN

THE FRENCH REVOLUTION
by Thomas Carlyle

THE DIVINE COMEDY
by Dante Alighieri

and

THE CELEBRATED JUMPING FROG OF
CALAVERAS COUNTY *by Mark Twain*

A LETTER DESCRIBING THE ERUPTION OF
MOUNT VESUVIUS *by Pliny the Younger*

Andrew Hamilton's SPEECH DEFENDING
FREEDOM OF THE PRESS

CLASSICS Appreciation SOCIETY
CONDENSATIONS

CONTENTS

Each Home Course Appreciation precedes its work.

ILLUSTRATED BY WILLIAM SHARP

LES MISERABLES

by Victor Hugo

A CONDENSATION

HOME COURSE APPRECIATION

LIKE A COLOSSUS, Victor Hugo (1802–1885) stood astride his century. In his eighty-three years he helped to shape a tumultuous age—when democratic ideals, scientific discoveries, and new economic trends made everyday life infinitely more complex than it had ever been before.

When Hugo was born, Napoleon Bonaparte had not yet betrayed the French Republic and the democratic hopes of the world; two years later he was to seize the crown from the hands of Pope Pius VII and declare himself absolute Emperor. After Waterloo (Hugo was thirteen at the time) and Napoleon's banishment to St. Helena, came the restoration of ancient princely houses, bitter revolutions, upheavals, and rioting.

In time the second French Republic was betrayed by another Napoleon, Napoleon the Third, a man of decidedly limited abilities who nevertheless made Paris the most beautiful city in the world. He was bent on more glory and more conquest, but after the monumental failure of the Franco-Prussian War which he blundered into in 1870, he was captured at Sedan, interned in Germany and died thereafter as an exile in England.

As we look back upon it, we are amazed by the strides taken during that tremendous century. It was heroic in scale and its hero was the common man. It is not surprising, then, that the writers of that time were fascinated by issues which affected him, and none more so than Victor Hugo.

HUGO AS A SOCIAL FORCE

HUGO WOULD PROBABLY have made himself a social force in any age, for his energy was unbounded, his talent broad, and his feelings for his fellow men benevolent. He advanced the art of his time;

he stood up against armed mobs at the barricades; and he defied the Emperor himself. He was at the service of democracy everywhere and when he died at eighty-three, he was buried with national honors as a million people followed the procession.

As a writer, Hugo did not hesitate to deal with the actualities of daily life. It took him some time to disentangle his confused allegiances, and hostile critics have accused him of being insincere; but always he had before him a clear and sympathetic image of the common man, with all his woes and sufferings. This is what he wrote about in *Les Misérables*.

"So long as there shall exist, by reason of law and custom, a social condemnation, which, in the face of civilization, artificially creates hell on earth, and complicates a destiny that is divine, with human fatality; so long as the three problems of the age—the degradation of man by poverty, the ruin of woman by starvation, and the dwarfing of childhood by physical and spiritual night—are not solved; . . . so long as ignorance and misery remain on earth, books like this cannot be useless."

These words were written in 1862, at Hauteville House, on the Isle of Guernsey, where Victor Hugo was in exile for his well-publicized disdain of Napoleon III, whom he contemptuously called *le petit,* "the little one."

WHY THE BOOK IS CALLED "LES MISÉRABLES"

The French word *misérable* does not mean quite the same thing as the English "miserable." In addition to meaning "unfortunate," "filled with misery" or "pitiable," it carries the suggestion of wickedness. Thus the very title of the book expresses a judgment of the society of its time. With this in mind, we can better understand Hugo's remark, "Dante once made a Hell out of poetry. I shall write of the Hell that is the real life of our age."

He boldly brought into his plays and novels the laborer and the peasant, and made them the heroes. Although this may strike us as commonplace today, Hugo was defying the literary convention of his time in both subject and style. Feelings ran so high over his break with tradition that the Paris intellectuals resorted to riot.

In the literature on which he turned his back, the man of the lowest classes of society was a mere figure of comedy-relief—a clod or "stooge." Hugo made him humane and sympathetic, a figure capable of noble actions and inspiring emotions. His daily life, whether a success or failure, became as worthy of chronicling as the deeds of king or corsair.

THE GREATNESS OF THE BOOK

VICTOR HUGO called *Les Misérables* "a drama in which the hero is the infinite, the second character is Man." In it he mingles scenes of history and portraits of characters from many walks of life. The story has numerous improbabilities which strain our credulity, and at times the coincidences are just plain silly. Still, we are affected by some of the most tender writing, and some of the most monumental scenes in all literature.

Nobody who has read them in *Les Misérables* can ever quite forget Hugo's passages on children which, though at times very sentimental, carry us along with their intense love, "the perfume that was shed upon the air by a flowering shrub nearby seemed their own out-breathings . . . these delicate heads, molded in happiness and bathed in light. . . ."

In contrast, Hugo's pages on the battle of Waterloo are epic in stature. The vast panorama becomes so real that it takes on a nightmare horror: "The inexorable ravine could not yield until it was filled; riders and horses rolled in together pell-mell, grinding each other, making common flesh in this dreadful gulf, and when this grave was full of living men, the rest marched over them and passed on."

There is an immense amount of information on all sorts of subjects. We learn how it was to travel in France in the early nineteenth century by way of "some huge vehicle, painted yellow and black, heavily loaded, noisily harnessed, distorted with mails, awnings, and valises; full of heads that were constantly disappearing; grinding the curbstones, turning the pavements into flints. . . ."

We learn that ex-convicts must report to the police with their yellow passports immediately on arriving in a town, and must leave that town the next morning. We learn the extraordinary cheapness of human life and the brutality of contemporary "justice." This theme Hugo sears on the brain of the reader. Jean Valjean, the hero of the book, is sent to the galleys for five years for stealing a loaf of bread for his sister's starving children; and when he attempts to escape, his sentence is stiffened so that he has to serve nineteen years. Hugo drew on his own crowded memory for such details. A note in his memoirs recalls that on February 22, 1846, as he was going to his seat in the Chamber of Peers, he saw a young man taken in custody by two soldiers for having stolen a loaf of bread.

The early part of the novel is a grim indictment of punishment for the sake of vengeance. "The peculiarity of punishment of this kind, in which what is pitiless, that is to say, what is brutalizing, predominates, is to transform little by little, by a slow stupefaction, a man into an animal, sometimes into a wild beast." It leads only to "hatred of human law," then "hatred of the human race . . . and hatred of creation, and reveals itself by a vague and incessant desire to injure some living being, it matters not who."

Victor Hugo does not condemn justice. He believes that the individual must live within the law. Yet he also believes that the law should be just and the punishment humane. Above all, he insists that poverty and insecurity must be eradicated, for they are the cause of law-breaking. When there is prosperity for all, he wrote, "poverty disappears, and with poverty disappear debauchery, prostitution, theft, murder, all vices, all crimes!"

Hugo broadens this theme to expose the miseries and sufferings of the masses, and assails his society for its wickedness in identifying "the good" with the possession of money. The drive for money abases men and distorts human relationships. "We live in a sad society. Succeed; that is the advice which falls drop by drop, from the overhanging corruption. . . ."

HUGO IS A MASTER OF THE NARRATIVE

IT WOULD BE WRONG to create the impression that Victor Hugo has here given us only a vast description of social woes. For *Les Misérables* is one of the most thrilling stories ever written. The episodes roll on to dramatic, often melodramatic, climaxes, as in old-fashioned serials. There are hairbreadth escapes, last-minute arrivals, and sudden blackouts. This technique may not conform to our present-day taste, but because the book is as wild and powerful as nature itself, it overcomes us.

We follow innumerable characters through adventures of all kinds. There are many sub-plots, the most important of which is a first-rate love story. But reduced to simplest terms, *Les Misérables* is a detective story—one with a different twist. On one side there is Javert, the police inspector, who, the author says, made the good things he stood for evil by his exaggeration of them. On the other side is Jean Valjean, the reformed ex-convict, who spends the rest of his life trying to diminish suffering wherever he finds it. The relationship between these two men—Javert, who is going to "get" Jean Valjean, and Jean Val-

Javert added, "He was a convict."

jean, who has more important things to do than rot in prison—forms one of the most exciting plots in literature.

This relationship also brings out a note which Hugo keeps sounding throughout the book, namely, that much of human life is governed by chance. "A person seated instead of standing; fate hangs on such a thread as that." "Had it not rained on the night of the 17th of June, 1815, the future of Europe would have been changed." Over and over again, hazard shapes destiny.

"FIRST CITIZEN OF FRANCE"

As WE MIGHT EXPECT with so many-sided a figure, Hugo was hated, feared and loved with almost equal fervor. He was a man of so great an ego that he could seriously entertain the thought of Paris being renamed in his honor—or so the story goes. And yet, he had good grounds for his egotism, for more than once it seemed possible that he might become the chief executive of France. "Long live the defender of the free press! Long live the defender of the people! All honor to Victor Hugo!" cried workers in the streets in 1850, as they saluted "the first citizen of France."

His detractors considered him "a romantic fool" who "dreamed of being President." A paper which had formerly supported him, called him "the first demagogue in France, if not in Europe . . . always a socialist at heart." Royalists and extreme conservatives detested him because of his outspoken wrath at what he considered their betrayals of humanitarian hopes. Especially they hated him as a deserter of his earlier allegiances. For in his youth, because of his mother's influence, Victor Hugo's sympathies had been royalist enough for him to have accepted pensions granted by the throne. Later, in one of his tumultuous addresses to the French Assembly he said: "You monarchists—you are all dead! You do not belong in our century, in our world! . . . Silence! Do not resuscitate yourselves!" And he called for "the immense edifice of the future, which will be called some day the United States of Europe!"

No wonder liberals all over the world, weary of oppression and injustice, applauded him! Mazzini, the great Italian patriot, engaged in his desperate fight for Italian freedom, wrote in a fervent letter of admiration, "I have loved you since my days as a student; I admire you more than ever today for your burning words." And in 1865, the great American Emancipator sent a photograph of himself to the poet, autographed, "To Victor Hugo, Abraham Lincoln."

"Boundless" is an apt description of Victor Hugo. Whereas there seems to be more than a taint of the spoiled child or the disorganized rebel in so many of the creative spirits of Hugo's time—in Byron or Shelley, or Chopin—Hugo is an almost perfect example of a man of the so-called "Romantic Age."

He lived profusely, suffered greatly, reached heights of real glory and was guilty of foolish excesses. He adored nature and loved humanity. He was as healthy as an ox to almost the very end of his eighty-three years; and he lived his long years to their very fullest.

The aspects of his genius are remarkable: he was the greatest French lyric poet of his age; he was a dramatist of striking originality; he was a great novelist. None of the younger French writers escaped his influence, and for a while Hugo was in fact the virtual dictator of French literary expression.

Politically he went all the way from an early support of legitimate royalty, through Napoleonism, to find himself at last a believer in popular democracy and the advocate of world federation. He developed into one of the most fervent orators of the nineteenth century and a pamphleteer whose messages were sought by liberals everywhere. A newspaper edited by his sons was an outlet for his ideas.

His sharp business sense helped him to become a wealthy man, yet his strict personal habits remained extremely simple. He gave large sums to good causes, and supported households of needy people.

Though he was devoted to his wife throughout their forty-six years of married life, and was a fanatically proud and doting father and grandfather, he was passionately and profoundly attached to Juliette Drouet, a minor actress. So great was the force of character of this Jove-like figure that most of those who came under his influence remained fervently worshipful ever after. But if Hugo succeeded on a grander scale than most men, he also suffered more than did others. There were years of exile when he yearned for his home skies; and one by one he saw the passing of all who were most dear to him—his elder daughter, his wife, their two sons, and Juliette. His younger daughter was placed in an asylum in 1865, where she finally died in 1915. The old man went on to the end, alone.

SUCCESS ALMOST FROM THE START

VICTOR-MARIE HUGO was born February 26, 1802. His mother was from a royalist family. His father, an officer in Napoleon's army, held a command under Joseph Bonaparte when the latter was made

King of Spain. General Hugo took his family with him, and from the age of six weeks, Victor had a wandering, war-tinged childhood. He early knew the discomforts of constant shifting from place to place, amid scenes of cruelty and suffering. Nor was there a chance to enjoy even the limited stability a harmonious family would have provided; his parents' bitter quarreling drove him to seek security in his mother's arms.

When the family finally settled in Paris, ten-year-old Victor began to study and read widely and soon was busy turning out verses. Prizes and honors became common. He acquired the reputation of a poetic prodigy and with his brother he established a literary journal, for which he wrote voluminously.

From the grief and loneliness caused by his mother's death, he turned for comfort to marriage with his childhood friend, Adèle Foucher. He had just published his first volume of poems, which was warmly reviewed, and he received a pension from the King. At twenty, he had scored his first notable victory in the field of literature.

By the time he was twenty-five, his poetic prefaces and his play *Cromwell* announced his definition of the Romantic position in art and letters; gradually he was moving away from his early, conservative, royalist position to an admiration of Napoleon and a reconciliation with his warrior father.

His play, *Hernani,* about a heroic brigand, created riots in the theater. Both its subject and style broke away from the academic rules for correct drama. For ten years thereafter, Hugo was undisputed dictator of progressive French letters. His output in this decade was prolific: many plays, four important volumes of verse, and the very successful novel, *The Hunchback of Notre Dame.* His growing expression of democratic ideals gained him new friends— and made old ones uneasy.

In 1841, after several applications, he received the highest honor in the French literary world: election to the Academy.

THE POLITICAL LIFE OF A POET

After 1843, Hugo began to desert poetry for politics. Increasingly, he was moved by the struggles and miseries of the lower classes— even though at this very time the "citizen king," Louis Philippe, had just made him a Peer of France.

It was characteristic of the contradictions in his life that just when he became Viscount Hugo by royal proclamation, he should begin a long novel about the down-trodden. He supported Louis Napoleon for the Presidency in 1848, but when it became clear that Napoleon planned to restore the empire of his uncle, Hugo led a rebellion against him. When the coup-d'etat of December 1851 took place, the newly-installed telegraph bore the message to the Prefect of Police: "Use you own judgment about Hugo."

The poet fled the country, beginning an exile of almost nineteen years. First he stopped in Brussels, and then on the Isle of Jersey, where he attacked the emperor in *Napoleon the Little* and a collection of verse called *Chastisements*. Between 1855 and 1870, he lived on the Isle of Guernsey. There he finished *Les Misérables,* which he had begun in 1845. The novel was published in 1862 in nine European capitals. For it Hugo received the unprecedented advance payment of $60,000.

Three days after the Emperor surrendered to the Germans at Sedan, Hugo was back in Paris, where he was the object of wild enthusiasm. People saw in him both a hero and a prophet who had influenced much of French history, always to its glory. On his eightieth birthday, Paris held a great festival in his honor; and when he died on May 22, 1885, he was buried among the national heroes in the Pantheon.

ROMANTICISM IN LITERATURE

WHAT DOES THE LITERARY CRITIC MEAN when he calls Hugo a "Romantic" poet? Everyone has some idea of what "romantic" with a small "r" means: letters to a beautiful lady, the view of a crumbling farmhouse in the moonlight, or a shipboard flirtation. The word "romance" has to do with experiences that are sentimental by nature.

But "Romantic" and "Romanticism" as applied to literature—and music and art—are fairly precise terms. Generally speaking, Romanticism describes a kind of literature, or art, which tries to reach us through our feelings rather than through our reasoning. It puts emotion and senses above intellect. It creates anger by detailing something cruel and unjust, or it tries to make the reader compassionate by recreating a pathetic scene. It will sweep along in a passionate mood, or abruptly change pace, soothing our senses by a lyric strain.

The Romantic artist will not hesitate to use any device to play on his reader's emotions. He will use richly textured words and phrases, exaggerated figures of speech, all sorts of altering rhythms and cadences. Because he avoids any tight regularity of pattern, his work will

"But! I gave you the candlesticks also.

Why did you not take them along with your plates?"

be filled with thunderous waves of words that suddenly halt and whisper. For the Romantic artist time and place are never fixed; he jumps from present to past and from one place to another, without much attention to order. Everything is done for one end, which is always the *effect* his techniques will produce in the reader.

Romantic art, the most potent artistic mode after the French Revolution, reached its flowering during the second quarter of the nineteenth century. Victor Hugo was perhaps the greatest Romantic writer of France, sharing international honor with the Brontë sisters, Byron, Keats, and Shelley in England; Goethe, Shiller, and Heine in Germany; and Poe and Whitman in America.

Hugo had no hesitation about making literature deal with everyday problems and emotions. The situations, the events, even the speech of his characters reflect his own experiences. Understandably, a good deal of autobiography got into the work of the Romantics. Whose emotions, after all, were more interesting than their own? But as a group they were also passionately interested in man's relation to Nature. Disgusted by the corruption they found all around them in society, the Romantics sought peace by returning to nature. Hugo was among the most adept of the Romantics at making nature conform to the restlessness or quietude of his characters' emotions. Notice how he makes the reader feel the same sense of being absorbed in the natural harmony of things that Jean Valjean feels in the convent garden: "Everything around him, this quiet garden, these balmy flowers, these children, shouting with joy, these meek and simple women, this silent cloister, gradually entered into his being, and, little by little his soul subsided into silence like this cloister, into fragrance like these flowers, into peace like this garden, into simplicity like these women, into joy like these children."

SHIFTING MOODS AND EMOTIONS

The strength of this passage depends on its lyric structure. For among other achievements, Romantic writers, departing from the dryness of the eighteenth century rational traditions, brought music back to poetry and prose. Yet if Hugo can sing in the manner of Homer when he wants to glorify man's deeds, he can also cry out against man's follies. Here too the style is in keeping with Romantic sensibility: "His eye was full of the base delight of a feeble, cruel, and cowardly animal, which can finally prostrate that of which it has stood in awe . . . the joy of a jackal beginning to tear a sick bull, dead enough not to be able to defend himself, alive enough yet to suffer."

How Hugo loved the extremes of emotion! Though at times they may seem over-written, his scenes are undeniably powerful in calling forth the feelings he meant us to share. No one can forget Jean Valjean as he shows his contempt for his captors by burning himself with a glowing chisel, or the description of the lovers: "How was it that their lips met? How is it that the birds sing, that the snow melts, that the dawn whitens behind the black trees on the shivering summit of the hills?"

The novel mounts in intensity as Hugo brings into play his gifts as a story-teller, poet, and dramatist. He fashioned everything he had learned from life into the unforgettable characters who crowd the pages of *Les Misérables*. In doing so he made himself as unforgettable as any of them, a figure just a little larger than life whom our eyes are henceforth alert to discover on the highways of the world.

Fantine

A<small>N HOUR BEFORE SUNSET</small>, on the evening of a day in the beginning of October, 1815, a man traveling afoot entered the little town of D——. The few persons who at this time were at their windows or their doors, regarded this traveler with a sort of distrust. It would have been hard to find a passer-by more wretched in appearance. He was a man of middle height, stout and hardy, in the strength of maturity; he might have been forty-six or seven. A slouched leather cap half hid his face, bronzed by the sun and wind, and dripping with sweat. His shaggy breast was seen through the coarse yellow shirt which at the neck was fastened by a small silver anchor; he wore a cravat twisted like a rope; coarse blue trousers, worn and shabby, white on one knee, and with holes in the other; an old ragged gray blouse, patched on one side with a piece of green cloth sewed with twine. Upon his back was a well-filled knapsack, strongly buckled and quite new. In his hand he carried an enormous knotted stick; his stockingless feet were in hobnailed shoes; his hair was cropped and his beard long.

The sweat, the heat, his long walk, and the dust, added an indescribable meanness to his tattered appearance. His hair was shorn, but bristly, for it had begun to grow a little, and seemingly had not been cut for some time. Nobody knew him; he was evidently a traveler. Whence had he come? From the south—perhaps from the sea.

When he reached the corner of the Rue Poichevert he turned to the left and went towards the mayor's office. He went in, and a quarter of an hour afterwards he came out. The man raised his cap humbly and saluted a gendarme who was seated near the door, upon the stone bench. Without returning his salutation, the gendarme looked at him attentively, watched him for some distance, and then went into the city hall.

There was then in D——, a good inn called *La Croix de Colbas;* its host was named Jacquin Labarre, a man held in some consideration in the town. The traveler turned his steps towards this inn, which was the best in the place, and went at once into the kitchen, which opened out of the street. All the ranges were fuming, and a great fire was burning briskly in the chimney-place. Mine host, who was at the same time head cook, was going from the fire-place to the saucepans, very busy superintending an excellent dinner for some wagoners who were laughing and talking noisily in the next room.

The host, hearing the door open, and a new-comer enter, said, without raising his eyes from his ranges—

"What will monsieur have?"

"Something to eat and lodging."

"Nothing more easy," said mine host, but on turning his head and taking an observation of the traveler, he added, "for pay."

The man drew from his pocket a large leather purse, and answered, "I have money."

"Then," said mine host, "I am at your service."

However, as the host passed backwards and forwards, he kept a careful eye on the traveler.

"Is dinner almost ready?" said the man.

"Directly," said mine host.

While the new-comer was warming himself with his back turned, the worthy innkeeper, Jacquin Labarre, took a pencil from his pocket, and then tore off the corner of an old paper which he pulled from a little table near the window. On the margin he wrote a line or two, folded it, and handed the scrap of paper to a child, who appeared to serve him as lackey and scullion at the same time. The innkeeper whispered a word to the boy and he ran off in the direction of the mayor's office.

The traveler saw nothing of this.

He asked a second time: "Is dinner ready?"

"Yes; in a few moments," said the host.

The boy came back with the paper. The host unfolded it hurriedly, as one who is expecting an answer. He seemed to read with attention, then throwing his head on one side, thought for a moment. Then he took a step towards the traveler, who seemed drowned in troublous thought.

"Monsieur," said he, "I cannot receive you."

The traveler half rose from his seat.

"Why? Are you afraid I shall not pay you, or do you want me to pay in advance? I have money, I tell you."

"It is not that."

"What then?"

"You have money—"

"Yes," said the man.

"And I," said the host; "I have no room."

"Well, put me in the stable," quietly replied the man.

"I cannot."

"Why?"

"Because the horses take all the room."

"Well," responded the man, "a corner in the garret; a truss of straw: we will see about that after dinner."

"I cannot give you any dinner."

This declaration, made in a measured but firm tone, appeared serious to the traveler. He got up.

"Ah, bah! but I am dying with hunger. I have walked since sunrise; I have traveled twelve leagues. I will pay, and I want something to eat."

"I have nothing," said the host.

The man burst into a laugh, and turned towards the fire-place and the ranges.

"Nothing! and all that?"

"All that is engaged."

"By whom?"

"By those persons, the wagoners."

"How many are there of them?"

"Twelve."

"There is enough there for twenty."

"They have engaged and paid for it all in advance."

The man sat down again and said, without raising his voice: "I am at an inn. I am hungry, and I shall stay."

The host bent down his ear, and said in a voice which made him tremble:

"Go away! Shall I tell you your name? your name is Jean Valjean,

5

now shall I tell you *who* you are? When I saw you enter, I suspected something. I sent to the mayor's office, and here is the reply. Can you read?" So saying, he held towards him the open paper, which had just come from the mayor. The man cast a look upon it; the inn-keeper, after a short silence, said: "It is my custom to be polite to all: Go!"

The man bowed his head, picked up his knapsack, and went out. He took the principal street; he walked at random, slinking near the houses like a sad and humiliated man: he did not once turn around. He walked along in this way some time, going by chance down streets unknown to him, and forgetting fatigue, as is the case in sorrow. Suddenly he felt a pang of hunger; night was at hand, and he looked around to see if he could not discover a lodging. The good inn was closed against him: he sought some humble tavern, some poor cellar. Just then a light shone at the end of the street; he saw a pine branch, hanging by an iron bracket, against the white sky of the twilight. He went thither.

It was a tavern in the Rue Chaffaut. Some men were drinking and the host was warming himself; an iron pot hung over the fire seething in the blaze. The traveler did not dare to enter by the street door; he slipped into the court, stopped again, then timidly raised the latch, and pushed open the door.

"Who is it?" said the host.

"One who wants supper and a bed."

"All right: here you can sup and sleep."

He went in, all the men who were drinking turned towards him; the lamp shining on one side of his face, the firelight on the other, they examined him for some time as he was taking off his knapsack.

The host said to him: "There is the fire; the supper is cooking in the pot; come and warm yourself, comrade."

He seated himself near the fireplace and stretched his feet out towards the fire, half dead with fatigue: an inviting odor came from the pot. All that could be seen of his face under his slouched cap assumed a vague appearance of comfort, which tempered the sorrowful aspect given him by long-continued suffering. However, one of the men at the table was a fisherman who had put up his horse at the stable of Labarre's inn before entering the tavern of the Rue de Chaffaut. He beckoned to the tavern-keeper to come to him, which he did. They exchanged a few words in a low voice; the traveler had again relapsed into thought.

6

The tavern-keeper returned to the fire, and laying his hand roughly on his shoulder, said harshly:

"You are going to clear out from here!"

The stranger turned round and said mildly:

"Ah! Do you know?"

"Yes."

"They sent me away from the other inn."

"And we turn you out of this."

"Where would you have me go?"

"Somewhere else."

The man took up his stick and knapsack, and went off. As he went out, some children who had followed him from the *Croix de Colbas*, and seemed to be waiting for him, threw stones at him. He turned angrily and threatened them with his stick, and they scattered like a flock of birds. He passed the prison: an iron chain hung from the door attached to a bell. He rang. The grating opened.

"Monsieur Turnkey," said he, taking off his cap respectfully, "will you open and let me stay here to-night?"

A voice answered:

"A prison is not a tavern: get yourself arrested and we will open."

The grating closed.

Night came on; the cold Alpine winds were blowing; by the light of the expiring day the stranger perceived in one of the gardens which fronted the street a kind of hut which seemed to be made of turf; he boldly cleared a wooden fence and found himself in the garden. He neared the hut; its door was a narrow, low entrance; it resembled, in its construction, the shanties which the road-laborers put up for their temporary accommodation. He, doubtless, thought that it was, in fact, the lodging of a road-laborer. He was suffering both from cold and hunger. He had resigned himself to the latter; but there at least was a shelter from the cold. These huts are not usually occupied at night. He got down and crawled into the hut. It was warm there and he found a good bed of straw. He rested a moment upon his bed motionless from fatigue; then, as his knapsack on his back troubled him, and it would make a good pillow, he began to unbuckle the straps. Just then he heard a ferocious growling and looking up saw the head of an enormous bull-dog at the opening of the hut.

It was a dog-kennel!

He was himself vigorous and formidable; seizing his stick, he made a shield of his knapsack, and got out of the hut as best he could, but not without enlarging the rents of his already tattered garments. When he had, not without difficulty, got over the fence, he again found himself alone in the street without lodging, roof, or shelter, driven even from the straw-bed of that wretched dog-kennel. He threw himself rather than seated himself on a stone, and it appears that some one who was passing heard him exclaim, "I am not even a dog!"

Then he arose, and began to tramp again, taking his way out of the town, hoping to find some tree or haystack beneath which he could shelter himself. He walked on for some time, his head bowed down. When he thought he was far away from all human habitation he raised his eyes, and looked about him inquiringly. He was in a field: before him was a low hillock covered with stubble, which after the harvest looks like a shaved head. He retraced his steps; the gates of D——— were closed. He passed through a breach and entered the town. It was about eight o'clock in the evening: as he did not know the streets, he walked at hazard. So he came to the prefecture, then to the seminary; on passing by the Cathedral square, he shook his fist at the church. Exhausted with fatigue, and hoping for nothing better, he lay down on a stone bench. Just then an old woman came out of the church. She saw the man lying there in the dark and said:

"What are you doing there, my friend?"

He replied harshly, and with anger in his tone:

"You see, my good woman, I am going to sleep."

The good woman, who really merited the name, was Madame la Marquise de R———.

"Upon the bench?" said she.

"For nineteen years I have had a wooden mattress," said the man; "to-night I have a stone one."

"You have been a soldier?"

"Yes, my good woman, a soldier."

"Why don't you go to the inn?"

"Because I have no money."

"Alas!" said Madame de R———, "I have only four sous in my purse."

"Give them then." The man took the four sous, and Madame de R——— continued:

"You cannot find lodging for so little in an inn. But have you tried? You cannot pass the night so. You must be cold and hungry. They should give you lodging for charity."

"I have knocked at every door."

"Well, what then?"

"Everybody has driven me away."

The good woman touched the man's arm and pointed out to him, on the other side of the square, a little low house beside the bishop's palace.

"You have knocked at every door?" she asked.

"Yes."

"Have you knocked at that one there?"

"No."

"Knock there."

That evening, after his walk in the town, the Bishop of D—— remained quite late in his room. At eight o'clock he was still at work, writing with some inconvenience on little slips of paper, with a large book open on his knees, when Madame Magloire, as usual, came in to take the silver from the panel near the bed. A moment after, the bishop, knowing that the table was laid, and that his sister was perhaps waiting, closed his book and went into the dining room. Just as the bishop entered, Madame Magloire was speaking with some warmth. She was talking to Mademoiselle upon a familiar subject, and one to which the bishop was quite accustomed. It was a discussion on the means of fastening the front door.

It seems that while Madame Magloire was out making provision for supper, she had heard the news in sundry places. There was talk that an ill-favored runaway, a suspicious vagabond, had arrived and was lurking somewhere in the town; besides, that the police was very bad, as the prefect and the mayor did not like one another, and were hoping to injure each other by untoward events; that it was the part of wise people to be their own police, and to protect their own persons; and that every one ought to be careful to shut up, bolt, and bar his house properly, and *secure his door thoroughly*. At this moment there was a violent knock on the door.

"Come in!" said the bishop.

The door opened. It opened quickly, quite wide, as if pushed by some one boldly and with energy. A man entered. That man, we know already; it was the traveler we have seen wandering about in search of a lodging. He came in, took one step, and paused, leaving the door open behind him. He had his knapsack on his back, his stick in his hand, and a rough, hard, tired, and fierce look in his eyes, as seen by the firelight. He was hideous. It was an apparition of ill omen.

Madame Magloire had not even the strength to scream. She stood trembling with her mouth open. Mademoiselle Baptistine turned, saw the man enter, and started up half-alarmed; then, slowly turning back again towards the fire, she looked at her brother, and her face resumed its usual calmness and serenity. The bishop looked upon the man with a tranquil eye.

As he was opening his mouth to speak, doubtless to ask the stranger what he wanted, the man, leaning with both hands on his club, glanced from one to another in turn, and without waiting for the bishop to speak, said in a loud voice:

"See here! My name is Jean Valjean. I am a convict; I have been nineteen years in the galleys. Four days ago I was set free, and started for Pontarlier, which is my destination; during those four days I have walked from Toulon. To-day I have walked twelve leagues. When I reached this place this evening I went to an inn, and they sent me away on account of my yellow passport, which I had shown at the mayor's office, as was necessary. I went to another inn; they said: 'Get out!' It was the same with one as with another; nobody would have me. I went to the prison, and the turnkey would not let me in. I crept into a dog-kennel, the dog bit me, and drove me away as if he had been a man; you would have said that he knew who I was. I went into the fields to sleep beneath the stars: there were no stars; I thought it would rain, and there was no good God to stop the drops, so I came back to the town to get the shelter of some doorway. There in the square I lay down upon a stone; a good woman showed me your house, and said: 'Knock there!' I have knocked. What is this place? Are you an inn? I have money; my savings, one hundred and nine francs and fifteen sous which I have earned in the galleys by my work for nineteen years. I will pay. What do I care? I have money. I am very tired—twelve leagues on foot, and I am so hungry. Can I stay?"

"Madame Magloire," said the bishop, "put on another plate."

The man took three steps, and came near the lamp which stood on the table. "Stop," he exclaimed; as if he had not been understood, "not that, did you understand me? I am a galley-slave—a convict—I am just from the galleys." He drew from his pocket a large sheet of yellow paper, which he unfolded. "There is my passport, yellow as you see. That is enough to have me kicked out wherever I go. See, here is what they have put in the passport: 'Jean Valjean, a liberated convict, native of ——,' you don't care for that, 'has been nineteen years in the galleys; five years for burglary; fourteen years for having at-

10

tempted four times to escape. This man is very dangerous.' There you have it! Everybody has thrust me out; will you receive me? Is this an inn? Can you give me something to eat, and a place to sleep? Have you a stable?"

"Madame Magloire," said the bishop, "put some sheets on the bed in the alcove."

Madame Magloire went out to fulfill her orders. The bishop turned to the man:

"Monsieur, sit down and warm yourself: we are going to take supper presently, and your bed will be made ready while you sup."

At last the man quite understood; his face, the expression of which till then had been gloomy and hard, now expressed stupefaction, doubt and joy, and became absolutely wonderful. He began to stutter like a madman.

"True? What! You will keep me? you won't drive me away? a convict! I beg your pardon, Monsieur Innkeeper, what is your name? I will pay all you say. You are a fine man. You are an innkeeper, an't you?"

"I am a priest who lives here," said the bishop.

"A priest," said the man. "Oh, noble priest! Then you do not ask any money? You are the curé?"

"No," said the bishop, "keep your money. How much have you? You said a hundred and nine francs, I think."

"And fifteen sous," added the man.

"One hundred and nine francs and fifteen sous. And how long did it take you to earn that?"

"Nineteen years."

"Nineteen years!"

The bishop sighed deeply.

The man continued: "I have all my money yet. As you are an abbé, I must tell you, we have an almoner in the galleys. And then one day I saw a bishop. He said mass in the center of the place on an altar; he had a pointed gold thing on his head, that shone in the sun; it was noon. We were drawn up in line on three sides, with cannons and matches lighted before us. We could not see him well. He spoke to us, but he was not near enough, we did not understand him. That is what a bishop is."

While he was talking, the bishop shut the door, which he had left wide open.

Madame Magloire brought in a plate and set it on the table.

11

"Madame Magloire," said the bishop, "put his plate as near the fire as you can." Then turning towards his guest, he added: "The night wind is raw in the Alps; you must be cold, monsieur."

Every time he said this word monsieur, with his gently solemn, and heartily hospitable voice, the man's countenance lighted up. *Monsieur* to a convict, is a glass of water to a man dying of thirst at sea. Ignominy thirsts for respect.

"The lamp," said the bishop, "gives a very poor light."

Madame Magloire understood him, and going to his bedchamber, took from the mantel the two silver candlesticks, lighted the candles, and placed them on the table.

"Monsieur Curé," said the man, "you are good; you don't despise me. You take me into your house; you light your candles for me, and I haven't hid from you where I come from, and how miserable I am."

The bishop, who was sitting near him, touched his hand gently and said:

"You have seen much suffering?"

"Oh, the red blouse, the ball and chain, the plank to sleep on, the heat, the cold, the galley's crew, the lash, the double chain for nothing, the dungeon for a word—even when sick in bed, the chain. The dogs, the dogs are happier! nineteen years! and I am forty-six, and now a yellow passport. That is all."

"Yes," answered the bishop, "you have left a place of suffering. But listen, there will be more joy in heaven over the tears of a repentant sinner, than over the white robes of a hundred good men. If you are leaving that sorrowful place with hate and anger against men, you are worthy of compassion; if you leave it with goodwill, gentleness, and peace, you are better than any of us."

After having said good-night to his sister, Monseigneur Bienvenu took one of the silver candlesticks from the table, handed the other to his guest, and said to him:

"Monsieur, I will show you to your room."

The man followed him. The house was so arranged that one could reach the alcove in the oratory only by passing through the bishop's sleeping chamber. Just as they were passing through this room Madame Magloire was putting up the silver in the cupboard at the head of the bed. It was the last thing she did every night before going to bed. The bishop left his guest in the alcove, before a clean white bed. The man set down the candlestick upon a small table.

"Come," said the bishop, "a good night's rest to you: to-morrow morning, before you go, you shall have a cup of warm milk from our cows."

"Thank you, Monsieur l'Abbé," said the man.

Scarcely had he pronounced these words of peace, when suddenly he made a singular motion which would have chilled the two good women of the house with horror, had they witnessed it. . . . He turned abruptly towards the old man, crossed his arms, and casting a wild look upon his host, exclaimed in a harsh voice:

"Ah, now, indeed! You lodge me in your house, as near you as that!"

He checked himself, and added, with a laugh, in which there was something horrible:

"Have you reflected upon it? Who tells you that I am not a murderer?"

The bishop responded:

"God will take care of that."

Then with gravity, moving his lips like one praying or talking to himself, he raised two fingers of his right hand and blessed the man, who, however, did not bow; and without turning his head or looking behind him, went into his chamber. When the alcove was occupied, a heavy serge curtain was drawn in the oratory, concealing the altar. Before this curtain the bishop knelt as he passed out, and offered a short prayer. A moment afterwards he was walking in the garden, surrendering mind and soul to a dreamy contemplation of these grand and mysterious works of God, which night makes visible to the eye. As to the man, he was so completely exhausted that he did not even avail himself of the clean white sheets; he blew out the candle, and fell on the bed, dressed as he was, into a sound sleep. Midnight struck as the bishop came back to his chamber. A few moments afterwards all in the little house slept. . . .

Towards the middle of the night, Jean Valjean awoke. Jean Valjean was born of a poor peasant family of Brie. In his childhood he had not been taught to read: when he was grown up, he chose the occupation of a pruner at Faverolles. He earned in the pruning season eighteen sous a day: after that he hired out as a reaper, workman, teamster, or laborer. He did whatever he could find to do. His sister worked also, but what could she do with seven little children? It was a sad group, which misery was grasping and closing upon, little by little. There was a very severe winter; Jean had no work, the family had no bread; literally, no bread, and seven children.

One Sunday night, Maubert Isabeau, the baker on the Place de l'Eglise, in Faverolles, was just going to bed when he heard a violent blow against the barred window of his shop. He got down in time to see an arm thrust through the aperture made by the blow of a fist on the glass. The arm seized a loaf of bread and took it out. Isabeau rushed out; the thief used his legs valiantly; Isabeau pursued him and caught him. The thief had thrown away the bread, but his arm was still bleeding. It was Jean Valjean.

All that happened in 1795. Jean Valjean was brought before the tribunals of the time for "burglary at night, in an inhabited house." Jean Valjean was sentenced to five years in the galleys. Near the end of this fourth year, his chance of liberty came to Jean Valjean. His comrades helped him as they always do in that dreary place, and he escaped. He wandered two days in freedom through the fields. During the evening of the second day he was retaken; he had neither eaten nor slept for thirty-six hours. The maritime tribunal extended his sentence three years for this attempt, which made eight. In the sixth year his turn of escape came again; he tried it, but failed again. He did not answer at roll-call, and the alarm cannon was fired. At night the people of the vicinity discovered him hidden beneath the keel of a vessel on the stocks; he resisted the galley guard which seized him. Escape and resistance. This the provisions of the special code punished by an addition of five years, two with the double chain, thirteen years. The tenth year his turn came round again; he made another attempt with no better success. Three years for this new attempt. Sixteen years. And finally, I think it was in the thirteenth year, he made yet another, and was retaken after an absence of only four hours. Three years for these four hours. Nineteen years. In October, 1815, he was set at large: he had entered in 1796 for having broken a pane of glass, and taken a loaf of bread.

Jean Valjean entered the galleys sobbing and shuddering: he went out hardened; he entered in despair: he went out sullen.

He condemned society and sentenced it. He sentenced it to his hatred. He made it responsible for the doom which he had undergone, and promised himself that he, perhaps, would not hesitate some day to call it to an account. Thus, during those nineteen years of torture and slavery, did this soul rise and fall at the same time. Light entered on the one side, and darkness on the other.

We must not omit one circumstance, which is, that in physical strength he far surpassed all the other inmates of the prison. At hard work, at twisting a cable, or turning a windlass, Jean Valjean was equal to four men. He talked but little, and never laughed. Some extreme emotion was required to draw from him, once or twice a year, that lugubrious sound of the convict, which is like the echo of a demon's laugh. To those who saw him, he seemed to be absorbed in continually looking upon something terrible. From year to year this soul had withered more and more, slowly, but fatally. With this withered heart, he had a dry eye. When he left the galleys, he had not shed a tear for nineteen years. . . .

As the cathedral clock struck two, Jean Valjean awoke. What awakened him was, too good a bed. For nearly twenty years he had not slept in a bed, and, although he had not undressed, the sensation was too novel not to disturb his sleep. He had slept something more than four hours. His fatigue had passed away. He was not accustomed to give many hours to repose. He could not get to sleep again, and so he began to think.

Those six silver plates took possession of him. There they were, within a few steps. His mind wavered a whole hour, and a long one, in fluctuation and in struggle. The clock struck three. He opened his eyes, rose up hastily in bed, reached out his arm and felt his haversack, which he had put into the corner of the alcove, then he thrust out his legs and placed his feet on the ground, and found himself, he knew not how, seated on his bed. All was still in the house. With stealthy steps, he moved towards the door of the next room, which was the bishop's, as we know. On reaching the door, he found it unlatched. The bishop had not closed it. He took one step and was in the room.

A deep calm filled the chamber. Here and there indistinct, confused forms could be distinguished; which by day, were papers scattered over a table, open folios, books piled on a stool, an armchair with clothes on it, a *prie-dieu,* but now were only dark corners and whitish spots. Jean Valjean advanced, carefully avoiding the furniture. At the further end of the room he could hear the equal and quiet breathing of the sleeping bishop.

He did not remove his eyes from the old man. The only thing which was plain from his attitude and his countenance was a strange indecision. You would have said he was hesitating between two realms, that of the doomed and that of the saved. He appeared ready either to cleave this skull, or to kiss this hand.

In a few moments he raised his left hand slowly to his forehead and took off his hat; then, letting his hand fall with the same slowness, Jean

15

Valjean resumed his contemplations, his cap in his left hand, his club in his right, and his hair bristling on his fierce-looking head.

Under this frightful gaze the bishop still slept in profoundest peace.

The crucifix above the mantelpiece was dimly visible in the moonlight, apparently extending its arms towards both, with a benediction for one and a pardon for the other.

Suddenly Jean Valjean put on his cap, then passed quickly, without looking at the bishop, along the bed, straight to the cupboard which he perceived near its head; he raised the drill to force the lock; the key was in it; he opened it; the first thing he saw was the basket of silver, he took it, crossed the room with hasty stride, careless of noise, reached the door, entered the oratory, took his stick, stepped out, put the silver in his knapsack, threw away the basket, ran across the garden, leaped over the wall like a tiger, and fled. . . .

The next day at sunrise, Monseigneur Bienvenu was walking in the garden. Madame Magloire ran towards him quite beside herself.

"Monseigneur, monseigneur," cried she, "does your greatness know where the silver basket is?"

"Yes," said the bishop.

"God be praised!" said she, "I did not know what had become of it."

The bishop had just found the basket on a flower-bed. He gave it to Madame Magloire and said: "There it is."

"Yes," said she, "but there is nothing in it. The silver?"

"Ah!" said the bishop, "it is the silver then that troubles you. I do not know where that is."

"Good heavens! it is stolen. That man who came last night stole it."

And in the twinkling of an eye, with all the agility of which her age was capable, Madame Magloire ran to the oratory, went into the alcove, and came back to the bishop. The bishop was bending with some sadness over a cochlearia des Guillons, which the basket had broken in falling. He looked up at Madame Magloire's cry:

"Monseigneur, the man has gone! the silver is stolen!"

While she was uttering this exclamation her eyes fell on an angle of the garden where she saw traces of an escalade. A capstone of the wall had been thrown down.

"See, there is where he got out; he jumped into Cochefilet lane. The abominable fellow! he has stolen our silver!"

The bishop was silent for a moment, then raising his serious eyes, he said mildly to Madame Magloire:

16

"Now first, did this silver belong to us?"

Madame Magloire did not answer; after a moment the bishop continued:

"Madame Magloire, I have for a long time wrongfully withheld this silver; it belonged to the poor. Who was this man? A poor man evidently."

In a few minutes he was breakfasting at the same table at which Jean Valjean sat the night before. While breakfasting, Monseigneur Bienvenu pleasantly remarked to his sister who said nothing, and Madame Magloire who was grumbling to herself, that there was really no need even of a wooden spoon or fork to dip a piece of bread into a cup of milk. Just as the brother and sister were rising from the table, there was a knock at the door.

"Come in," said the bishop.

The door opened. A strange, fierce group appeared on the threshold. Three men were holding a fourth by the collar. The three men were gendarmes; the fourth Jean Valjean. A brigadier of gendarmes, who appeared to head the group, was near the door. He advanced towards the bishop, giving a military salute.

"Monseigneur," said he—

At this word Jean Valjean, who was sullen and seemed entirely cast down, raised his head with a stupefied air—

"Monseigneur!" he murmured, "then it is not the curé!"

"Silence!" said a gendarme, "it is monseigneur, the bishop."

In the meantime Monsieur Bienvenu had approached as quickly as his great age permitted:

"Ah, there you are!" said he, looking towards Jean Valjean, "I am glad to see you. But! I gave you the candlesticks also, which are silver like the rest, and would bring two hundred francs. Why did you not take them along with your plates?"

Jean Valjean opened his eyes and looked at the bishop with an expression which no human tongue could describe.

"Monseigneur," said the brigadier, "then what this man said was true? We met him. He was going like a man who was running away, and we arrested him in order to see. He had this silver."

"And he told you," interrupted the bishop, with a smile, "that it had been given him by a good old priest with whom he had passed the night. I see it all. And you brought him back here? It is all a mistake."

"If that is so," said the brigadier, "we can let him go."

"Certainly," replied the bishop.

The gendarmes released Jean Valjean, who shrank back.

"Is it true that they let me go?" he said in a voice almost inarticulate, as if he were speaking in his sleep.

"My friend," said the bishop, "before you go away, here are your candlesticks; take them."

He went to the mantelpiece, took the two candlesticks, and brought them to Jean Valjean. The two women beheld the action without a word, or gesture, or look, that might disturb the bishop. Jean Valjean was trembling in every limb. He took the two candlesticks mechanically, and with a wild appearance.

"Now," said the bishop, "go in peace."

Then turning to the gendarmes, he said:

"Messieurs, you can retire." The gendarmes withdrew.

Jean Valjean felt like a man who is just about to faint.

The bishop approached him, and said, in a low voice:

"Forget not, never forget that you have promised me to use this silver to become an honest man."

Jean Valjean, who had no recollection of this promise, stood confounded. The bishop had laid much stress upon these words as he uttered them. He continued, solemnly:

"Jean Valjean, my brother: you belong no longer to evil, but to good. It is your soul that I am buying for you. I withdraw it from dark thoughts and from the spirit of perdition, and I give it to God!"

Jean Valjean went out of the city as if he were escaping. He made all haste to get into the open country, taking the first lanes and by-paths that offered, without noticing that he was every moment retracing his steps. He wandered thus all the morning. He had eaten nothing, but he felt no hunger. He was the prey of a multitude of new sensations. As the sun was sinking towards the horizon, lengthening the shadow on the ground of the smallest pebble, Jean Valjean was seated behind a thicket in a large reddish plain, an absolute desert. There was no horizon but the Alps. Not even the steeple of a village church. In the midst of this meditation, which would have heightened not a little the frightful effect of his rags to any one who might have met him, he heard a joyous sound.

He turned his head, and saw coming along the path a little Savoyard, a dozen years old, singing, with his hurdygurdy at his side, and his marmot box on his back. One of those pleasant and gay youngsters who go from place to place, with their knees sticking through their trousers. Still singing, the boy stopped from time to time, and played

18

at tossing up some pieces of money that he had in his hand, probably his whole fortune. Among them there was one forty-sous piece. The boy stopped by the side of the thicket without seeing Jean Valjean, and tossed up his handful of sous; until this time he had skillfully caught the whole of them upon the back of his hand.

This time the forty-sous piece escaped him, and rolled towards the thicket, near Jean Valjean. Jean Valjean put his foot upon it. The boy, however, had followed the piece with his eye, and had seen where it went. He was not frightened, and walked straight to the man.

"Monsieur," said the little Savoyard, with that childish confidence which is made up of ignorance and innocence, "my piece?"

"What is your name?" said Jean Valjean.

"Petit Gervais, monsieur."

"Get out," said Jean Valjean.

"Monsieur," continued the boy, "give me my piece."

Jean Valjean did not appear to understand. The boy took him by the collar of his blouse and shook him. And at the same time he made an effort to move the big, iron-soled shoe which was placed upon his treasure.

"I want my piece! my forty-sous piece!"

The child began to cry. Jean Valjean raised his head. He still kept his seat. His look was troubled. He looked upon the boy with an air of wonder, then reached out his hand towards his stick, and exclaimed in a terrible voice: "Who is there?"

"Me, monsieur," answered the boy. "Petit Gervais! me! me! give me my forty sous, if you please! Take away your foot, monsieur, if you please!" Then becoming angry, small as he was, and almost threatening:

"Come, now, will you take away your foot? Why don't you take away your foot?"

"Ah! you here yet!" said Jean Valjean, and rising hastily to his feet, without releasing the piece of money, he added: "You'd better take care of yourself!"

The boy looked at him in terror, then began to tremble from head to foot, and after a few seconds of stupor, took to flight and ran with all his might without daring to turn his head or to utter a cry. At a little distance, however, he stopped for want of breath, and Jean Valjean in his reverie heard him sobbing. In a few minutes the boy was gone.

The sun had gone down. The shadows were deepening around Jean

Valjean. He had not eaten during the day; probably he had some fever. He pulled his cap down over his forehead, sought mechanically to fold and button his blouse around him, stepped forward and stooped to pick up his stick. At that instant he perceived the forty-sous piece which his foot had half buried in the ground, and which glistened among the pebbles. It was like an electric shock. "What is that?" said he, between his teeth. He drew back a step or two, then stopped without the power to withdraw his gaze from this point which his foot had covered the instant before, as if the thing that glistened there in the obscurity had been an open eye fixed upon him.

After a few minutes, he sprang convulsively towards the piece of money, seized it, and, rising, looked away over the plain, straining his eyes towards all points of the horizon, standing and trembling like a frightened deer which is seeking a place of refuge. He saw nothing. Night was falling, the plain was cold and bare, thick purple mists were rising in the glimmering twilight. He said: "Oh!" and began to walk rapidly in the direction in which the child had gone. After some thirty steps, he stopped, looked about, and saw nothing.

Then he called with all his might: "Petit Gervais! Petit Gervais!"

And then he listened. There was no answer. Jean Valjean began to run again in the direction which he had first taken. Finally, at a place where three paths met, he stopped. The moon had risen. He strained his eyes in the distance, and called out once more: "Petit Gervais! Petit Gervais! Petit Gervais!" His cries died away into the mist, without even awakening an echo. Again he murmured: "Petit Gervais!" but with a feeble, and almost inarticulate voice. That was his last effort; his knees suddenly bent under him, as if an invisible power overwhelmed him at a blow, with the weight of his bad conscience; he fell exhausted upon a great stone, his hands clenched in his hair, and his face on his knees, and exclaimed: "What a wretch I am!"

Then his heart swelled, and he burst into tears. It was the first time he had wept for nineteen years.

While he wept, the light grew brighter and brighter in his mind— an extraordinary light, a light at once transporting and terrible. His past life, his first offense, his long expiation, his brutal exterior, his hardened interior, his release made glad by so many schemes of vengeance, what had happened to him at the bishop's, his last action, this theft of forty sous from a child, a crime meaner and the more monstrous that it came after the bishop's pardon, all this returned and appeared to him, clearly, but in a light that he had never seen before.

He beheld his life, and it seemed to him horrible; his soul, and it seemed to him frightful. There was, however, a softened light upon that life and upon that soul. It seemed to him that he was looking upon Satan by the light of Paradise.

How long did he weep thus? What did he do after weeping? Where did he go? Nobody ever knew. It is known simply that, on that very night, the stage-driver who drove at that time on the Grenoble route, and arrived at D—— about three o'clock in the morning, saw, as he passed through the bishop's street, a man in the attitude of prayer, kneel upon the pavement in the shadow, before the door of Monseigneur Bienvenu.

Fantine was one of those beings who are brought forth from the heart of the people. Sprung from the most unfathomable depths of social darkness, she bore on her brow the mark of the anonymous and unknown. She was born at M—— sur M——. Who were her parents? None could tell, she had never known either father or mother. She was called Fantine—why so? because she had never been known by any other name. At the time of her birth, the Directory was still in existence. She could have no family name, for she had no family; she could have no baptismal name, for then there was no church. She was named after the pleasure of the first passer-by who found her, a mere infant, straying barefoot in the streets. She received a name as she received the water from the clouds on her head when it rained. She was called Fantine. Nobody knew anything more of her. Such was the manner in which this human being had come into life. At the age of ten, Fantine left the city and went to service among the farmers of the suburbs. At fifteen, she came to Paris, "to seek her fortune." Fantine was beautiful and remained pure as long as she could. She was a pretty blonde with fine teeth. She had gold and pearls for her dowry; but the gold was on her head and the pearls in her mouth.

She worked to live; then, also to live, for the heart too has its hunger, she loved. She loved Tholomyès. To him, it was an amour; to her a passion. The streets of the Latin Quarter saw the beginning of this dream. Fantine in those labyrinths of the hill of the Pantheon, where so many ties are knotted and unloosed, long fled from Tholomyès, but in such a way as always to meet him again. There is a way of avoiding a person which resembles a search. In short, the eclogue took place.

[*Tholomyès deserts Fantine. Ten months later, having borne his child, Fantine returns to her birthplace. On the way, she stops at Montfermeil.*]

There was, during the first quarter of the present century, at Montfermeil, near Paris, a sort of chop-house; it is not there now. It was kept by a man and his wife, named Thénardier, and was situated in the Lane Boulanger.

Towards noon, after having, for the sake of rest, traveled from time to time at a cost of three or four cents a league, in what they called then the Petites Voitures of the environs of Paris, Fantine reached Montfermeil, and stood in Boulanger Lane. As she was passing by the Thénardier chop-house, two little children sitting in delight on their swing, had a sort of dazzling effect upon her, and she paused before this joyous vision. There are charms. These two little girls were one for this mother. She beheld them with emotion. The presence of angels is a herald of paradise. She thought she saw above this inn the mysterious "HERE" of Providence. These children were evidently happy: she gazed upon them, she admired them, so much affected that at the moment when the mother was taking breath between the verses of her song, she could not help saying what we have been reading.

"You have two pretty children there, madame."

The most ferocious animals are disarmed by caresses to their young. The mother raised her head and thanked her, and made the stranger sit down on the stone step, she herself being on the doorsill: the two women began to talk together.

"My name is Madame Thénardier," said the mother of the two girls: "we keep this inn."

The traveler told her story, a little modified. She said she was a working woman, and her husband was dead. Not being able to procure work in Paris she was going in search of it elsewhere; in her own province; that she had left Paris that morning on foot; that carrying her child she had become tired, and meeting the Villemomble stage had got in; that from Villemomble she had come on foot to Montfermeil; that the child had walked a little, but not much, she was so young; that she was compelled to carry her, and the jewel had fallen asleep.

She seized the hand of Madame Thénardier and said:

"Will you keep my child for me?"

Madame Thénardier made a motion of surprise, which was neither consent nor refusal.

Cosette's mother continued:

"You see I cannot take my child into the country. Work forbids it. With a child I could not find a place there; they are so absurd in that district. It is God who has led me before your inn. The sight of your little ones, so pretty, and clean, and happy, has overwhelmed me. I said: there is a good mother; they will be like three sisters, and then it will not be long before I come back. Will you keep my child for me?"

"I must think over it," said Madame Thénardier.

"I will give six francs a month."

Here a man's voice was heard from within:

"Not less than seven francs, and six months paid in advance."

"Six times seven are forty-two," said Madame Thénardier.

"I will give it," said the mother.

"And fifteen francs extra for the first expenses," added the man.

"That's fifty-seven francs," said Madame Thénardier.

"I will give it," said the mother; "I have eighty francs. That will leave me enough to go into the country if I walk. I will earn some money there, and as soon as I have I will come for my little love."

The man's voice returned:

"Has the child a wardrobe?"

"That is my husband," said Madame Thénardier.

"Certainly she has, the poor darling. I knew it was your husband. And a fine wardrobe it is too, an extravagant wardrobe, everything in dozens, and silk dresses like a lady. They are there in my carpetbag."

"You must leave that here," put in the man's voice.

"Of course I shall give it to you," said the mother; "it would be strange if I should leave my child naked."

The face of the master appeared.

"It is all right," said he.

The bargain was concluded. The mother passed the night at the inn, gave her money and left her child, fastened again her carpetbag, diminished by her child's wardrobe, and very light now, and set off next morning, expecting soon to return. These partings are arranged tranquilly, but they are full of despair.

Thanks to Fantine's fifty-seven francs, Thénardier had been able to avoid a protest and to honor his signature. The next month they were still in need of money, and the woman carried Cosette's wardrobe to Paris and pawned it for sixty francs. When this sum was spent, the

Thénardiers began to look upon the little girl as a child which they sheltered for charity, and treated her as such. Her clothes being gone, they dressed her in the cast-off garments of the little Thénardiers, that is in rags. They fed her on odds and ends, a little better than the dog, and a little worse than the cat. The dog and cat were her messmates. Cosette ate with them under the table in a wooden dish like theirs.

Cosette was made to run errands, sweep the rooms, the yard, the street, wash the dishes, and even carry burdens. The Thénardiers felt doubly authorized to treat her thus, as the mother, who still remained at M—— sur M——, began to be remiss in her payments. Some months remained due.

Had this mother returned to Montfermeil, at the end of three years, she would not have known her child. Cosette, so fresh and pretty when she came to that house, was now thin and wan. She had a peculiar restless air. Sly! said the Thénardiers. Injustice had made her sullen, and misery had made her ugly. Her fine eyes only remained to her, and they were painful to look at, for, large as they were, they seemed to increase the sadness. It was a harrowing sight to see in the winter time the poor child, not yet six years old, shivering under the tatters of what was once a calico dress, sweeping the street before daylight with an enormous broom in her little red hands and tears in her large eyes. In the place she was called the Lark. Only the poor lark never sang.

What had become of this mother, in the meanwhile, who, according to the people of Montfermeil, seemed to have abandoned her child? where was she? what was she doing? After leaving her little Cosette with the Thénardiers, she went on her way and arrived at M—— sur M——. This, it will be remembered, was in 1818.

Fantine had left the province some twelve years before, and M—— sur M—— had greatly changed in appearance. While Fantine had been slowly sinking deeper and deeper into misery, her native village had been prosperous. Within about two years there had been accomplished there one of those industrial changes which are the great events of small communities. This circumstance is important and we think it well to relate it, we might even say to italicize it.

From time immemorial the special occupation of the inhabitants of M—— sur M—— had been the imitation of English jets and German black glass trinkets. The business had always been dull in consequence of the high price of the raw material, which reacted upon the manufacture. At the time of Fantine's return to M—— sur M—— an entire transformation had been effected in the production of these 'black goods.' Towards the end of the year 1815, an unknown man had established himself in the city, and had conceived the idea of substituting gum-lac for resin in the manufacture; and for bracelets, in particular, he made the clasps by simply bending the ends of the metal together instead of soldering them.

This very slight change had worked a revolution.

This very slight change had in fact reduced the price of the raw material enormously, and this had rendered it possible, first, to raise the wages of the laborer—a benefit to the country—secondly, to improve the quality of the goods—an advantage for the consumer—and thirdly, to sell them at a lower price even while making three times the profit—a gain for the manufacturer.

In less than three years the inventor of this process had become rich, which was well, and had made all around him rich, which was better. He was a stranger in the Department. Nothing was known of his birth, and but little of his early history.

The story went that he came to the city with very little money, a few hundred francs at most.

It seems that the very day on which he thus obscurely entered the little city of M—— sur M——, just at dusk on a December evening, with his bundle on his back, and a thorn stick in his hand, a great fire had broken out in the town-house. This man rushed into the fire, and saved, at the peril of his life, two children, who proved to be those of the captain of the gendarmerie, and in the hurry and gratitude of the moment no one thought to ask him for his passport. He was known from that time by the name of Father Madeleine. . . .

The profits of Father Madeleine were so great that by the end of the second year he was able to build a large factory, in which there were two immense workshops, one for men and the other for women: whoever was needy could go there and be sure of finding work. Before the arrival of Father Madeleine, the whole region was languishing; now it was all alive with the healthy strength of labor. An active circulation kindled everything and penetrated everywhere. Idleness and misery were unknown. There was no pocket so obscure that it did not contain some money and no dwelling so poor that it was not the abode of some joy.

Father Madeleine employed everybody; he had only one condition, "Be an honest man!" "Be an honest woman!"

As we have said, in the midst of this activity, of which he was the cause and the pivot, Father Madeleine had made his fortune, but, very strangely for a mere man of business, that did not appear to be his principal care. It seemed that he thought much for others, and little for himself. In 1820, it was known that he had six hundred and thirty thousand francs standing to his credit in the banking-house of Laffitte; but before setting aside this six hundred and thirty thousand francs for himself, he had expended more than a million for the city and for the poor.

At first, when he began to attract the public attention, the good people would say: "This is a fellow who wishes to get rich." When they saw him enrich the country before he enriched himself, the same good people said: "This man is ambitious." This seemed the more probable, since he was religious and observed the forms of the church, to a certain extent, a thing much approved in those days. He went regularly to hear mass every Sunday.

At length, in 1819, it was reported in the city one morning, that upon the recommendation of the prefect, and in consideration of the services he had rendered to the country, Father Madeleine had been appointed by the king, Mayor of M—— sur M——. Those who had pronounced the new-comer "an ambitious man," eagerly seized this opportunity, which all men desire, to exclaim:

"There! what did I tell you?"

M—— sur M—— was filled with the rumor, and the report proved to be well founded, for, a few days afterwards, the nomination appeared in the *Moniteur*. The next day Father Madeleine declined.

As we have seen, the country owed a great deal to this man, and the poor owed him everything; he was so useful that all were compelled to honor him, and so kind that none could help loving him; his workmen in particular adored him, and he received their adoration with a sort of melancholy gravity. After he became rich, those who constituted "society" bowed to him as they met, and, in the city, he began to be called Monsieur Madeleine—but his workmen and the children continued to call him *Father Madeleine,* and at that name his face always wore a smile. As his wealth increased, invitations rained in on him. "Society" claimed him. A thousand advances were made to him, but he refused them all.

And again the gossips were at no loss. "He is an ignorant man, and of poor education. No one knows where he came from. He does not know how to conduct himself in good society, and it is by no means certain that he knows how to read."

When they saw him making money, they said, "He is a merchant." When they saw the way in which he scattered his money, they said, "He is ambitious." When they saw him refuse to accept honors, they said, "He is an adventurer." When they saw him repel the advances of the fashionable, they said, "He is a brute."

In 1820, five years after his arrival at M—— sur M——, the services that he had rendered to the region were so brilliant, and the wish of the whole population was so unanimous, that the king again appointed him mayor of the city. He refused again; but the prefect resisted his determination, the principal citizens came and urged him to accept, and the people in the streets begged him to do so; all insisted so strongly that at last he yielded. It was remarked that what appeared most of all to bring him to this determination was the almost angry exclamation of an old woman belonging to the poorer class, who cried out to him from her door-stone, with some temper:

"A good mayor is a good thing. Are you afraid of the good you can do?"

This was the third step in his ascent. Father Madeleine had become Monsieur Madeleine, and Monsieur Madeleine now became Monsieur the Mayor. . . .

Nevertheless he remained as simple as at first. He had gray hair, a serious eye, the brown complexion of a laborer, and the thoughtful countenance of a philosopher. He usually wore a hat with a wide brim, and a long coat of coarse cloth, buttoned to the chin. He fulfilled his duties as mayor, but beyond that his life was isolated. He talked with very few persons.

He always took his meals alone with a book open before him in which he read. His library was small but well selected. He loved books; books are cold but sure friends. As his growing fortune gave him more leisure, it seemed that he profited by it to cultivate his mind. Since he had been at M—— sur M——, it was remarked from year to year that his language became more polished, choicer, and more gentle.

Although he was no longer young, it was reported that he was of prodigious strength. He would offer a helping hand to any one who needed it, help up a fallen horse, push at a stalled wheel, or seize by the horns a bull that had broken loose. He always had his pockets full of money when he went out, and empty when he returned. He did a multitude of good deeds as secretly as bad ones are usually done.

He would steal into houses in the evening, and furtively mount the stairs. A poor devil, on returning to his garret, would find that his door had been opened, sometimes even forced, during his absence. The poor man would cry out: "Some thief has been here!" When he got in, the first thing that he would see would be a piece of gold lying on the table. "The thief" who had been there was Father Madeleine.

He was affable and sad. The people used to say: "There is a rich man who does not show pride. There is a fortunate man who does not appear contented."

Some pretended that he was a mysterious personage, and declared that no one ever went into his room, which was a true anchorite's cell furnished with hour-glasses, and enlivened with death's heads and cross-bones. So much was said of this kind that some of the more mischievous of the elegant young ladies of M—— sur M—— called on him one day and said: "Monsieur Mayor, will you show us your room? We have heard that it is a grotto." He smiled, and introduced them on the spot to this "grotto." They were well punished for their curiosity. It was a room very well fitted up with mahogany furniture, ugly as all furniture of that kind is, and the walls covered with shilling paper. They could see nothing but two candlesticks of antique form that stood on the mantel, and appeared to be silver.

It was also whispered that he had "immense" sums deposited with Laffitte, with the special condition that they were always at his immediate command, in such a way, it was added, that Monsieur Madeleine might arrive in the morning at Laffitte's, sign a receipt and carry away his two or three millions in ten minutes. In reality these "two or three millions" dwindled down, as we have said, to six hundred and thirty or forty thousand francs. . . .

Near the beginning of the year 1821, the journals announced the decease of Monsieur Myriel, Bishop of D——, "surnamed *Monseigneur Bienvenu,*" who died in the odor of sanctity at the age of eighty-two years.

The announcement of his death was reproduced in the local paper of M—— sur M——. Monsieur Madeleine appeared next morning dressed in black with crape on his hat.

This mourning was noticed and talked about all over the town. It appeared to throw some light upon the origin of Monsieur Madeleine. The conclusion was that he was in some way related to the venerable bishop. *"He wears black for the Bishop of D——,"* was the talk of the drawing-rooms; it elevated Monsieur Madeleine very much, and gave him suddenly, and in a trice, marked consideration in the noble world of M—— sur M——. It was also remarked that whenever there passed through the city a young Savoyard who was tramping about the country in search of chimneys to sweep, the mayor would send for him, ask his name and give him money. The little Savoyards told each other, and many of them passed that way.

Little by little in the lapse of time all opposition had ceased. At first there had been, as always happens with those who rise by their own efforts, slanders and calumnies against Monsieur Madeleine, soon this was reduced to satire, then it was only wit, then it vanished entirely. People came from thirty miles around to consult Monsieur Madeleine. He settled differences, he prevented lawsuits, he reconciled enemies. Everybody, of his own will, chose him for judge. He seemed to have the book of the natural law by heart. A contagion of veneration had, in the course of six or seven years, step by step, spread over the whole country.

One man alone, in the city and its neighborhood, held himself entirely clear from this contagion, and, whatever Father Madeleine did, he remained indifferent, as if a sort of instinct, unchangeable and imperturbable, kept him awake and on the watch.

Often, when Monsieur Madeleine passed along the street, calm, affectionate, followed by the benedictions of all, it happened that a tall man, wearing a flat hat and an iron-gray coat, and armed with a stout cane, would turn around abruptly behind him, and follow him with his eyes until he disappeared, crossing his arms, slowly shaking his head, and pushing his upper with his under lip up to his nose, a sort of significant grimace which might be rendered by: "But what is that man? I am sure I have seen him somewhere. At all events, I at least am not his dupe."

His name was Javert, and he was one of the police.

He exercised at M—— sur M—— the unpleasant but useful function of inspector. He was not there at the date of Madeleine's arrival. When Javert arrived at M—— sur M—— the fortune of the great manufacturer had been made already, and Father Madeleine had become Monsieur Madeleine.

It will be easily understood that Javert was the terror of all that class which the annual statistics of the Minister of Justice include under the heading: *People without a fixed abode*. To speak the name of Javert would put all such to flight; the face of Javert petrified them. Javert was like an eye always fixed on Monsieur Madeleine; an eye full of suspicion and conjecture. Monsieur Madeleine finally noticed it, but seemed to consider it of no consequence. He treated Javert as he did everybody else, at ease and with kindness.

Javert was evidently somewhat disconcerted by the completely natural air and the tranquillity of Monsieur Madeleine.

One day, however, his strange manner appeared to make an impression upon Monsieur Madeleine. The occasion was this:

Monsieur Madeleine was walking one morning along one of the unpaved alleys of M—— sur M——; he heard a shouting and saw a crowd at a little distance. He went to the spot. An old man, named Father Fauchelevent, had fallen under his cart, his horse being thrown down.

This Fauchelevent was one of the few who were still enemies of Monsieur Madeleine at this time. When Madeleine arrived in the place, the business of Fauchelevent, who was a notary of long standing, and very well-read for a rustic, was beginning to decline. Fauchelevent had seen this mere artisan grow rich, while he himself, a professional man, had been going to ruin. This had filled him with jealousy, and he had done what he could on all occasions to injure Madeleine. Then came bankruptcy, and the old man, having nothing but a horse and cart, as he was without family, and without children, was compelled to earn his living as a cartman.

The horse had his thighs broken, and could not stir. The old man was caught between the wheels. Unluckily he had fallen so that the whole weight rested upon his breast. The cart was heavily loaded. Father Fauchelevent was uttering doleful groans. They had tried to pull him out, but in vain. An unlucky effort, inexpert help, a false push, might crush him. It was impossible to extricate him otherwise than by raising the wagon from beneath. Javert, who came up at the moment of the accident, had sent for a jack.

Monsieur Madeleine came. The crowd fell back with respect.

He turned towards the bystanders:

"Has anybody a jack?"

"They have gone for one," replied a peasant.

"How soon will it be here?"

"We sent to the nearest place, to Flachot Place, where there is a blacksmith; but it will take a good quarter of an hour at least."

"A quarter of an hour!" exclaimed Madeleine.

It had rained the night before, the road was soft, the cart was sinking deeper every moment, and pressing more and more on the breast of the old cartman. It was evident that in less than five minutes his ribs would be crushed.

"We cannot wait a quarter of an hour," said Madeleine to the peasants who were looking on.

"Listen," resumed Madeleine, "there is room enough still under the wagon for a man to crawl in, and lift it with his back. In half a minute we will have the poor man out. Is there nobody here who has strength and courage? Five louis d'ors for him!"

Nobody stirred in the crowd.

"Ten louis," said Madeleine.

The bystanders dropped their eyes.

"Come," said Madeleine, "twenty louis."

The same silence.

"It is not willingness which they lack," said a voice.

Monsieur Madeleine turned and saw Javert. He had not noticed him when he came.

Javert continued:

"It is strength. He must be a terrible man who can raise a wagon like that on his back."

Then, looking fixedly at Monsieur Madeleine, he went on emphasizing every word that he uttered:

"Monsieur Madeleine, I have known but one man capable of doing what you call for."

Madeleine shuddered.

Javert added, with an air of indifference, but without taking his eyes from Madeleine:

"He was a convict."

"Ah!" said Madeleine.

"In the galleys at Toulon."

Madeleine became pale.

Meanwhile the cart was slowly settling down. Father Fauchelevent roared and screamed:

"I am dying! my ribs are breaking! a jack! anything! oh!"

Madeleine looked around him:

"Is there nobody, then, who wants to earn twenty louis and save this poor old man's life?"

None of the bystanders moved. Javert resumed:

"I have known but one man who could take the place of a jack; that was that convict."

"It is crushing me!" cried the old man.

Madeleine raised his head, met the falcon eye of Javert still fixed upon him, looked at the immovable peasants, and smiled sadly. Then, without saying a word, he fell on his knees, and even before the crowd had time to utter a cry, he was under the cart. There was an awful moment of suspense and of silence. The bystanders held their breath. The wheels were still sinking and it had now become almost impossible for Madeleine to extricate himself. All at once the enormous mass started, the cart rose slowly, the wheels came half out of the ruts. A smothered voice was heard, crying: "Quick! help!" It was Madeleine, who had just made a final effort.

They all rushed to the work. The devotion of one man had given strength and courage to all. The cart was lifted by twenty arms. Old Fauchelevent was safe. Father Madeleine had him carried to an infirmary that he had established for his workmen in the same building with his factory, which was attended by two Sisters of Charity. The next morning the old man found a thousand franc bill upon the stand by the side of the bed, with this note in the handwriting of Father Madeleine: *I have purchased your horse and cart.* The cart was broken and the horse was dead. Fauchelevent got well, but he had a stiff knee. Monsieur Madeleine, through the recommendations of the sisters and the curé, got the old man a place as gardener at a convent in the Quartier Saint Antoine at Paris.

It was some time afterwards that Monsieur Madeleine was appointed mayor. The first time that Javert saw Monsieur Madeleine clothed with the scarf which gave him full authority over the city, he felt the same sort of shudder which a bull-dog would feel who should scent a wolf in his master's clothes. From that time he avoided him as much as he could. When the necessities of the service imperiously demanded it, and he could not do otherwise than come in contact with the mayor, he spoke to him with profound respect.

[*Meantime, Fantine, who has become a prostitute, is arrested by Javert. When M. Madeleine intervenes and sets her at liberty, Javert becomes more suspicious of him than ever.*]

One morning Monsieur Madeleine was in his office arranging for some pressing business of the mayoralty, in case he should decide to go to Montfermeil himself, when he was informed that Javert, the inspector of police, wished to speak with him. On hearing this name spoken, Monsieur Madeleine could not repress a disagreeable impression. Since the affair of the Bureau of Police, Javert had more than ever avoided him, and Monsieur Madeleine had not seen him at all.

"Let him come in," said he.

Javert entered.

Monsieur Madeleine remained seated near the fire, looking over a bundle of papers upon which he was making notes, and which contained the returns of the police patrol. He did not disturb himself at all for Javert: he could not but think of poor Fantine, and it was fitting that he should receive him very coldly.

Javert respectfully saluted the mayor, who had his back towards him. The mayor did not look up, but continued to make notes on the papers.

Javert advanced a few steps, and paused without breaking silence.

At last the mayor laid down his pen and turned partly round:

"Well, what is it? What is the matter, Javert?"

Javert remained silent a moment as if collecting himself; then raised his voice with a sad solemnity which did not, however, exclude simplicity: "There has been a criminal act committed, Monsieur Mayor."

"What act?"

"An inferior agent of the government has been wanting in respect to a magistrate, in the gravest manner. I come, as is my duty, to bring the fact to your knowledge."

"Who is this agent?" asked Monsieur Madeleine.

"I," said Javert.

"You?"

"I."

"And who is the magistrate who has to complain of this agent?"

"You, Monsieur Mayor."

Monsieur Madeleine straightened himself in his chair. Javert continued, with serious looks and eyes still cast down.

"Monsieur Mayor, I come to ask you to be so kind as to make charges and procure my dismissal."

Monsieur Madeleine, amazed, opened his mouth. Javert interrupted him:

"You will say that I might tender my resignation, but that is not enough. To resign is honorable; I have done wrong. I ought to be punished. I must be dismissed."

And after a pause he added:

"Monsieur Mayor, you were severe to me the other day, unjustly. Be justly so to-day."

33

Javert sighed deeply.

"Monsieur Mayor, six weeks ago, after that scene about that girl, I was enraged and I denounced you."

"Denounced me?"

"To the Prefecture of Police at Paris."

Monsieur Madeleine, who did not laugh much oftener than Javert, began to laugh:

"As a mayor having encroached upon the police?"

"As a former convict."

The mayor became livid.

Javert, who had not raised his eyes, continued:

"I believed it. For a long while I had had suspicions. A resemblance, your immense strength; the affair of old Fauchelevent; your leg which drags a little—and in fact I don't know what other stupidities; but at last I took you for a man named Jean Valjean."

"Named what? How did you call that name?"

"Jean Valjean. He was a convict I saw twenty years ago, when I was adjutant of the galley guard at Toulon. After leaving the galleys this Valjean, it appears, robbed a bishop's palace, then he committed another robbery with weapons in his hands, in a highway, on a little Savoyard. For eight years his whereabouts have been unknown, and search has been made for him. I fancied—in short, I have done this thing. Anger determined me, and I denounced you to the prefect."

M. Madeleine, who had taken up the file of papers again, a few moments before, said with a tone of perfect indifference: "And what answer did you get?"

"That I was crazy."

"Well!"

"Well; they were right."

"It is fortunate that you think so!"

"It must be so, for the real Jean Valjean has been found."

The paper that M. Madeleine held fell from his hand; he raised his head, looked steadily at Javert, and said in an inexpressible tone:

"Ah!"

Javert continued:

"I will tell you how it is, Monsieur Mayor. There was, it appears, in the country, a simple sort of fellow who was called Father Champmathieu. Finally, this last fall, Champmathieu was arrested. The rogue was caged. So far, it was nothing more than a penitentiary matter.

34

But here comes in the hand of Providence. The jail being in a bad condition, the police justice thought it best to take him to Arras, where the prison of the department is. In this prison at Arras there was a former convict named Brevet, who is there for some trifle, and who, for his good conduct, has been made turnkey. No sooner was Champmathieu set down, than Brevet cried out: 'Ha, ha! I know that man. He is a *fagot*' (ex-convict)."

" 'Look up here, my good man. You are Jean Valjean.' 'Jean Valjean, who is Jean Valjean?' Champmathieu plays off the astonished. 'Don't play ignorance,' said Brevet. 'You are Jean Valjean; you were in the galleys at Toulon. It is twenty years ago. We were there together.' Champmathieu denied it all. Besides Brevet there are only two convicts who have seen Jean Valjean. They are convicts for life; their names are Cochepaille and Chenildieu. These men were brought from the galleys and confronted with the pretended Champmathieu. They did not hesitate. To them as well as to Brevet it was Jean Valjean. Same age; fifty-four years old; same height; same appearance, in fact the same man; it is he. At this time it was that I sent my denunciation to the Prefecture at Paris. They replied that I was out of my mind, and that Jean Valjean was at Arras in the hands of justice. You may imagine how that astonished me; I who believed that I had here the same Jean Valjean. I wrote to the justice; he sent for me and brought Champmathieu before me."

"Well," interrupted Monsieur Madeleine.

Javert replied, with an incorruptible and sad face:

"Monsieur Mayor, truth is truth. I am sorry for it, but that man is Jean Valjean. I recognized him also."

Monsieur Madeleine had turned again to his desk, and was quietly looking over his papers, reading and writing alternately, like a man pressed with business. He turned again towards Javert:

"That will do, Javert. Indeed all these details interest me very little. We are wasting time, and we have urgent business. Did you not tell me you were going to Arras in eight or ten days on this matter?"

"Sooner than that, Monsieur Mayor."

"What day then?"

"I think I told monsieur that the case would be tried to-morrow, and that I should leave by the diligence to-night."

Monsieur Madeleine made an imperceptible motion.

"And how long will the matter last?"

"One day at longest. Sentence will be pronounced at latest to-morrow evening. But I shall not wait for the sentence, which is certain; as soon as my testimony is given I shall return here."

"Very well," said Monsieur Madeleine.

And he dismissed him with a wave of his hand.

Javert did not go.

"Your pardon, monsieur," said he.

"What more is there?" asked Monsieur Madeleine.

"Monsieur Mayor, there is one thing more to which I desire to call your attention."

"What is it?"

"It is that I ought to be dismissed."

Monsieur Madeleine arose.

"Javert, you are a man of honor and I esteem you. You exaggerate your fault. Besides, this is an offense which concerns me. You are worthy of promotion rather than disgrace. I desire you to keep your place."

"Monsieur Mayor, I cannot agree to that."

"I repeat," said Monsieur Madeleine, "that this matter concerns me."

But Javert, with his one idea, continued:

"As to exaggerating, I do not exaggerate. This is the way I reason. I have unjustly suspected you. That is nothing. It is our province to suspect, although it may be an abuse of our right to suspect our superiors. But without proofs and in a fit of anger, with revenge as my aim, I denounced you as a convict—you, a respectable man, a mayor, and a magistrate. This is a serious matter, very serious. I have committed an offense against authority in your person, I, who am the agent of authority. If one of my subordinates had done what I have, I would have pronounced him unworthy of the service, and sent him away. Well, listen a moment, Monsieur Mayor; I have often been severe in my life towards others. It was just. I did right. Now if I were not severe towards myself, all I have justly done would become injustice. Should I spare myself more than others? No. What! if I should be prompt only to punish others and not myself, I should be a wretch indeed! They who say: 'That blackguard, Javert,' would be right. Monsieur Mayor, I do not wish you to treat me with kindness. Your kindness, when it was for others, enraged me; I do not wish it for myself. Monsieur Mayor, the good of the service demands an example. I simply ask the dismissal of Inspector Javert."

All this was said in a tone of proud humility, a desperate and resolute tone, which gave an indescribably whimsical grandeur to this oddly honest man.

"We will see," said Monsieur Madeleine.

And he held out his hand to him.

Javert started back, and said fiercely:

"Pardon, Monsieur Mayor, that should not be. A mayor does not give his hand to a spy."

He added between his teeth:

"Spy, yes; from the moment I abused the power of my position, I have been nothing better than a spy!"

Then he bowed profoundly, and went towards the door. There he turned around: his eyes yet downcast.

"Monsieur Mayor, I will continue in the service until I am relieved."

He went out. Monsieur Madeleine sat musing, listening to his firm and resolute step as it died away along the corridor.

[*M. Madeleine (who is, of course, Jean Valjean) passes a dreadful night but sets out promptly for Arras, where the trial is being held, in order to save an innocent man by giving himself up. He arrives as the defense plea is ended.*]

A buzz ran through the crowd and almost invaded the jury. It was evident that the man was lost.

"Officers," said the judge, "enforce order. I am about to sum up the case."

At this moment there was a movement near the judge. A voice was heard exclaiming:

"Brevet, Chenildieu, Cochepaille, look this way!"

So lamentable and terrible was this voice that those who heard it felt their blood run cold. All eyes turned towards the spot whence it came. A man, who had been sitting among the privileged spectators behind the court, had risen, pushed open the low door which separated the tribunal from the bar, and was standing in the center of the hall. The judge, the prosecuting attorney, Monsieur Bamatabois, twenty persons recognized him, and exclaimed at once:

"Monsieur Madeleine!"

It was he, indeed. The clerk's lamp lighted up his face. He held his hat in hand; there was no disorder in his dress; his overcoat was carefully buttoned. He was very pale, and trembled slightly. His hair, already gray when he came to Arras, was now perfectly white. It had become so during the hour that he had been there. All eyes were strained towards him.

The sensation was indescribable. There was a moment of hesitation in the hall. The voice had been so thrilling, the man standing there appeared so calm, that at first nobody could comprehend it. They asked who had cried out. They could not believe that this tranquil man had uttered that fearful cry. This indecision lasted but few seconds. Before even the judge and prosecuting attorney could say a word, before the gendarmes and officers could make a sign, the man, whom all up to this moment had called Monsieur Madeleine, had advanced towards the witnesses, Cochepaille, Brevet, and Chenildieu.

"Do you not recognize me?" said he.

All three stood confounded, and indicated by a shake of the head that they did not know him. Cochepaille, intimidated, gave the military salute. Monsieur Madeleine turned towards the jurors and court, and said in a mild voice:

"Gentlemen of the jury, release the accused. Your honor, order my arrest. He is not the man whom you seek; it is I. I am Jean Valjean."

Not a breath stirred. To the first commotion of astonishment had succeeded a sepulchral silence. That species of religious awe was felt in the hall which thrills the multitude at the accomplishment of a grand action. Nevertheless, the face of the judge was marked with sympathy and sadness; he exchanged glances with the prosecuting attorney, and a few whispered words with the assistant judges. He turned to the spectators and asked in a tone which was understood by all:

"Is there a physician here?"

The prosecuting attorney continued:

"Gentlemen of the jury, the strange and unexpected incident which disturbs the audience inspires us, as well as yourselves, with a feeling we have no need to express. You all know, at least by reputation, the honorable Monsieur Madeleine, Mayor of M—— sur M——. If there be a physician in the audience, we unite with his honor the judge in entreating him to be kind enough to lend his assistance to Monsieur Madeleine and conduct him to his residence."

Monsieur Madeleine did not permit the prosecuting attorney to finish, but interrupted him with a tone full of gentleness and authority. These are the words he uttered; we give them literally, as they were written down immediately after the trial, by one of the witnesses of the scene—as they still ring in the ears of those who heard them, now nearly forty years ago.

"I thank you, Monsieur Prosecuting Attorney, but I am not mad. You shall see. You were on the point of committing a great mistake; release that man. I am accomplishing a duty; I am the unhappy convict. I am the only one who sees clearly here, and I tell you the truth. What I do at this moment, God beholds from on high, and that is sufficient. You can take me, since I am here. Nevertheless, I have done my best. I have disguised myself under another name, I have become rich, I have become a mayor, I have desired to enter again among honest men. It seems that this cannot be. In short, there are many things which I cannot tell. I shall not relate to you the story of my life: some day you will know it. I did rob Monseigneur the Bishop—that is true; I did rob Petit Gervais—that is true. They were right in telling you that Jean Valjean was a wicked wretch. But all the blame may not belong to him. The galleys make the galley-slave. Receive this in kindness, if you will. Before the galleys, I was a poor peasant, unintelligent, a species of idiot; the galley changed me. I was stupid, I became wicked; I was a log, I became a firebrand. Later, I was saved by indulgence and kindness, as I had been lost by severity. I have nothing more to add. Take me."

Nothing could express the kindly yet terrible melancholy of the tone which accompanied these words.

He turned to the three convicts:

"Well! I recognize you, Brevet, do you remember—"

He paused, hesitated a moment, and said:

"Do you remember those checkered, knit suspenders that you had in the galleys?"

Brevet started as if struck with surprise, and gazed wildly at him from head to foot. He continued:

"Chenildieu, surnamed by yourself Je-nie-Dieu, the whole of your left shoulder has been burned deeply, from laying it one day on a chafing dish full of embers, to efface the three letters T. F. P., which yet are still to be seen there. Answer me, is this true?"

"It is true!" said Chenildieu.

He turned to Cochepaille:

"Cochepaille, you have on your left arm, near where you have been bled, a date put in blue letters with burnt powder. It is the date of the landing of the emperor at Cannes, *March 1st,* 1815. Lift up your sleeve."

Cochepaille lifted up his sleeve; all eyes around him were turned to his naked arm. A gendarme brought a lamp; the date was there. The

39

unhappy man turned towards the audience and the court with a smile, the thought of which still rends the hearts of those who witnessed it. It was the smile of triumph; it was also the smile of despair.

"You see clearly," said he, "that I am Jean Valjean."

There were no longer either judges, or accusers, or gendarmes in the hall; there were only fixed eyes and beating hearts. Nobody remembered longer the part which he had to play; the prosecuting attorney forgot that he was there to prosecute, the judge that he was there to preside, the counsel for the defense that he was there to defend. Strange to say no question was put, no authority intervened. It was evident that Jean Valjean was before their eyes. That fact shone forth. Without need of any further explanation, the multitude, as by a sort of electric revelation, comprehended instantly, and at a single glance, this simple and magnificent story of a man giving himself up that another might not be condemned in his place.

"I will not disturb the proceeding further," continued Jean Valjean. "I am going, since I am not arrested. I have many things to do. Monsieur the prosecuting attorney knows where I am going, and will have me arrested when he chooses."

He walked towards the outer door. Not a voice was raised, not an arm stretched out to prevent him. . . . He passed through the throng with slow steps. It was never known who opened the door, but it is certain that the door was open when he came to it. On reaching it he turned and said:

"Monsieur the Prosecuting Attorney, I remain at your disposal."

He then addressed himself to the assembled people.

"You all, all who are here, think me worthy of pity, do you not? Great God! when I think of what I have been on the point of doing, I think myself worthy of envy. Still, would that all this had not happened!"

He went out, and the door closed as it had opened.

Less than an hour afterwards, the verdict of the jury discharged from all accusation the said Champmathieu.

[*The mayor returns home and visits Fantine who is dying at the hospital. He had promised to search for her child. Javert arrives to arrest the mayor.*]

Fantine had not seen Javert since the day the mayor had wrested her from him. Her sick brain accounted for nothing, only she was sure that he had come for her. She could not endure this hideous face, she felt as if she were dying, she hid her face with both hands, and shrieked in anguish:

"Monsieur Madeleine, save me!"

Jean Valjean, we shall call him by no other name henceforth, had risen. He said to Fantine in his gentlest and calmest tone:

"Be composed; it is not for you that he comes."

He then turned to Javert and said:

"I know what you want."

Javert answered:

"Hurry along."

There was in the manner in which these two words were uttered, an inexpressible something which reminded you of a wild beast and of a madman. At the exclamation of Javert, Fantine had opened her eyes again. But the mayor was there, what could she fear? Javert advanced to the middle of the chamber, exclaiming:

"Hey, there; are you coming?"

The unhappy woman looked around her. Then she saw a mysterious thing, so mysterious that its like had never appeared to her in the darkest delirium of fever. She saw the spy Javert seize Monsieur the Mayor by the collar; she saw Monsieur the Mayor bow his head. The world seemed vanishing before her sight. Javert, in fact, had taken Jean Valjean by the collar. Javert burst into a horrid laugh, displaying all his teeth.

"There is no Monsieur the Mayor here any longer!" said he.

Jean Valjean did not attempt to disturb the hand which grasped the collar of his coat. He said:

"Javert—"

Javert interrupted him: "Call me Monsieur the Inspector!"

"Monsieur," continued Jean Valjean, "I would like to speak a word with you in private."

"Aloud, speak aloud," said Javert, "people speak aloud to me."

Jean Valjean went on, lowering his voice.

"It is a request that I have to make of you—"

"I tell you to speak aloud."

"But this should not be heard by any one but yourself."

"What is that to me? I will not listen."

Jean Valjean turned to him and said rapidly and in a very low tone:

"Give me three days! Three days to go for the child of this unhappy woman! I will pay whatever is necessary. You shall accompany me if you like."

"Are you laughing at me!" cried Javert. "Hey! I did not think you so stupid! You ask for three days to get away, and tell me that you are going for this girl's child! Ha, ha, that's good! That is good!"

Fantine shivered.

"My child!" she exclaimed, "going for my child! Then she is not here! Sister, tell me, where is Cosette? I want my child! Monsieur Madeleine, Monsieur the Mayor!"

Javert stamped his foot.

"There is the other now! Hold your tongue, hussy! Miserable country, where galley slaves are magistrates and women of the town are nursed like countesses! Ha, but all this will be changed; it was time!"

He gazed steadily at Fantine, and added, grasping anew the cravat, shirt, and coat collar of Jean Valjean:

"I tell you that there is no Monsieur Madeleine, and that there is no Monsieur the Mayor. There is a robber, there is a brigand, there is a convict called Jean Valjean, and I have got him! That is what there is!"

Fantine started upright, supporting herself by her rigid arms and hands; she looked at Jean Valjean, then at Javert, and then at the nun; she opened her mouth as if to speak; a rattle came from her throat, her teeth struck together, she stretched out her arms in anguish, convulsively opening her hands, and groping about her like one who is drowning; then sank suddenly back upon the pillow. Her head struck the head of the bed and fell forward on her breast, the mouth gaping, the eyes open and glazed. She was dead. Jean Valjean put his hand on that of Javert which held him, and opened it as he would have opened the hand of a child; then he said:

"You have killed this woman."

"Have done with this!" cried Javert, furious, "I am not here to listen to sermons; save all that; the guard is below; come right along, or the handcuffs!"

There stood in a corner of the room an old iron bedstead in a dilapidated condition, which the sisters used as a camp-bed when they watched. Jean Valjean went to the bed, wrenched out the rickety head bar—a thing easy for muscles like his—in the twinkling of an eye, and with the bar in his clenched fist, looked at Javert. Javert recoiled towards the door. Jean Valjean, his iron bar in hand, walked slowly towards the bed of Fantine. On reaching it, he turned and said to Javert in a voice that could scarcely be heard:

"I advise you not to disturb me now."

Nothing is more certain than that Javert trembled. He had an idea of calling the guard, but Jean Valjean might profit by his absence to escape. He remained, therefore, grasped the bottom of his cane, and leaned against the framework of the door without taking his eyes from Jean Valjean. Jean Valjean rested his elbow upon the post, and his head upon his hand, and gazed at Fantine, stretched motionless before him. He remained thus, mute and absorbed, evidently lost to everything of this life. His countenance and attitude bespoke nothing but inexpressible pity. After a few moments' reverie, he took Fantine's head in his hands and arranged it on the pillow, as a mother would have done for her child, then fastened the string of her night-dress, and replaced her hair beneath her cap. This done, he closed her eyes.

The face of Fantine, at this instant, seemed strangely illumined. Death is the entrance into the great light. Fantine's hand hung over the side of the bed. Jean Valjean knelt before this hand, raised it gently, and kissed it. Then he rose, and, turning to Javert, said:

"Now, I am at your disposal."

Javert put Jean Valjean in the city prison. The arrest of Monsieur Madeleine produced a sensation, or rather an extraordinary commotion, at M—— sur M——. We are sorry not to be able to disguise the fact that, on this single sentence, *he was a galley slave,* almost everybody abandoned him. In less than two hours, all the good he had done was forgotten, and he was "nothing but a galley slave." It is just to say that the details of the scene at Arras were not yet known. In this manner the phantom which had been called Monsieur Madeleine was dissipated at M—— sur M——. Three or four persons alone in the whole city remained faithful to his memory. The old portress who had been his servant was among the number.

On the evening of this same day, the worthy old woman was sitting in her lodge, still quite bewildered and sunk in sad reflections. The factory had been closed all day, the carriage doors were bolted, the street was deserted. There was no one in the house but the two nuns, Sister Perpétue and Sister Simplice, who were watching the corpse of Fantine. Towards the time when Monsieur Madeleine had been accustomed to return, the honest portress rose mechanically, took the key of his room from a drawer, with the taper-stand that he used at night to light himself up the stairs, then hung the key on a nail from which he had been in the habit of taking it, and placed the taper-stand by its side, as if she were expecting him. She then seated herself again in her chair, and resumed her reflections. The poor old woman had done all this without being conscious of it. More than two hours had elapsed when she started from her reverie and exclaimed, "Why, bless me! I have hung his key on the nail!"

Just then, the window of her box opened, a hand passed through the opening, took the key and stand, and lighted the taper at the candle which was burning. The portress raised her eyes; she was transfixed with astonishment; a cry rose to her lips, but she could not give it utterance. She knew the hand, the arm, the coat-sleeve. It was M. Madeleine.

"My God! Monsieur Mayor!" she exclaimed, "I thought you were—"

She stopped; the end of her sentence would not have been respectful to the beginning. To her, Jean Valjean was still Monsieur the Mayor. He completed her thought.

"In prison," said he. "I was there; I broke a bar from a window, let myself fall from the top of a roof, and here I am. I am going to my room; go for Sister Simplice. She is doubtless beside this poor woman."

The old servant hastily obeyed. He cast a glance about him, over his table, his chair, his bed, which had not been slept in for three days. There remained no trace of the disorder of the night before the last. The portress had "put the room to rights."

He took from a wardrobe an old shirt which he tore into several pieces and in which he packed the two silver candlesticks. In all this there was neither haste nor agitation. Two gentle taps were heard at the door.

"Come in," said he.

It was Sister Simplice. She was pale, her eyes were red, and the candle which she held trembled in her hand. Jean Valjean had written a few lines on a piece of paper, which he handed to the nun, saying: "Sister, you will give this to the curé."

The paper was not folded. She cast her eyes on it.

"You may read it," said he.

She read: "I beg Monsieur the Curé to take charge of all that I leave here. He will please defray therefrom the expenses of my trial, and of the burial of the woman who died this morning. The remainder is for the poor."

"Does not Monsieur the Mayor wish to see this poor unfortunate again for the last time?"

"No," said he, "I am pursued; I should only be arrested in her chamber; it would disturb her."

He had scarcely finished when there was a loud noise on the staircase. They heard a tumult of steps ascending, and the old portress exclaiming in her loudest and most piercing tones:

"My good sir, I swear to you in the name of God, that nobody has come in here the whole day, and the whole evening; that I have not even once left my door!"

A man replied: "But yet, there is a light in this room."

They recognized the voice of Javert. The chamber was so arranged that the door in opening covered the corner of the wall to the right. Jean Valjean blew out the taper, and placed himself in this corner. Sister Simplice fell on her knees near the table. The door opened. Javert entered.

The whispering of several men, and the protestations of the portress were heard in the hall. The nun did not raise her eyes. She was praying. The candle was on the mantel, and gave but a dim light. Javert perceived the sister, and stopped abashed. It will be remembered that the very foundation of Javert, his element, the medium in which he breathed, was veneration for all authority. On perceiving the sister, his first impulse was to retire. But there was also another duty which held him, and which urged him imperiously in the opposite direction. His second impulse was to remain, and to venture at least one question.

"Sister," said he, "are you alone in this room?"

There was a fearful instant during which the poor portress felt her limbs falter beneath her. The sister raised her eyes, and replied: "Yes."

Then continued Javert—"Excuse me if I persist, it is my duty—you have not seen this evening a person, a man—he has escaped, and we are in search of him—Jean Valjean—you have not seen him?"

The sister answered—"No."

She lied. Two lies in succession, one upon another, without hesitation, quickly, as if she were an adept in it.

"Your pardon!" said Javert, and he withdrew, bowing reverently.

Oh, holy maiden! for many years thou hast been no more in this world; thou hast joined the sisters, the virgins, and thy brethren, the angels, in glory; may this falsehood be remembered to thee in Paradise.

The affirmation of the sister was to Javert something so decisive that he did not even notice the singularity of this taper, just blown out, and smoking on the table.

An hour afterwards, a man was walking rapidly in the darkness beneath the trees from M—— sur M—— in the direction of Paris. This man was Jean Valjean. It has been established, by the testimony of two or three wagoners who met him, that he carried a bundle, and was dressed in a blouse. Where did he get this blouse? It was never known. An old artisan had died in the infirmary of the factory a few days before, leaving nothing but his blouse. This might have been the one.

A last word in regard to Fantine.

We have all one mother—the earth. Fantine was restored to this mother. The curé thought best, and did well perhaps, to reserve out of what Jean Valjean had left, the largest amount possible for the poor. After all, who were in question?—a convict and a woman of the town. This was why he simplified the burial of Fantine, and reduced it to that bare necessity called the Potter's field.

And so Fantine was buried in the common grave of the cemetery, which is for everybody and for all, and in which the poor are lost. Happily, God knows where to find the soul.

Cosette

THE FIELD OF Waterloo to-day has that calm which belongs to the earth, impassive support of man; it resembles any other plain.

At night, however, a sort of visionary mist arises from it, and if some traveler be walking there, if he looks, if he listens, if he dreams like Vergil in the fatal plain of Philippi, he becomes possessed by the hallucination of the disaster. The terrible 18th of June is again before him; the artificial hill of the monument fades away, this lion, whatever it be, is dispelled; the field of battle resumes its reality; the lines of infantry undulate in the plain, furious gallops traverse the horizon; the bewildered dreamer sees the flash of sabers, the glistening of bayonets, the bursting of shells, the awful intermingling of the thunders; he hears, like a death-rattle from the depths of a tomb, the vague clamor of the phantom battle; these shadows are grenadiers; these gleams are cuirassiers; this skeleton is Napoleon; that skeleton is Wellington; all this is unreal, and yet it clashes and combats; and the ravines run red, and the trees shiver, and there is fury even in the clouds, and, in the darkness, all those savage heights, Mont Saint Jean, Hougomont, Frischemont, Papelotte, Planchenoit, appear confusedly crowned with whirlwinds of specters exterminating each other. . . .

We are not of those who glorify war; when the opportunity presents itself we describe its realities. War has frightful beauties which we have not concealed; it has also, we must admit, some deformities. One of the most surprising is the eager spoliation of the dead after a victory. The day after a battle dawns upon naked corpses. One thing is certain, that, after the conquerors, come the robbers. But let us place the soldier, especially the soldier of to-day, beyond this charge.

Every army has a train, and there the accusation should lie. Bats, half-brigand and half-valet, all species of night bird engendered by this twilight which is called war, bearers of uniforms who never fight, sham invalids, formidable cripples, interloping sutlers, traveling, sometimes with their wives, on little carts and stealing what they sell, beggars offering themselves as guides to officers, army-servants, marauders; armies on the march formerly were followed by all these, to such an extent that, in technical language, they are called "camp-followers."

Towards midnight a man was prowling or rather crawling along the sunken road of Ohain. He was, to all appearance, one of those whom we have just described, neither English nor French, peasant nor soldier, less a man than a ghoul, attracted by the scent of the corpses, counting theft for victory, coming to rifle Waterloo. He looked about. He passed an indescribably hideous review of the dead. He walked with his feet in blood.

Suddenly he stopped. A few steps before him, in the sunken road, at a point where the mound of corpses ended, from under this mass of men and horses appeared an open hand, lighted by the moon. This hand had something upon a finger which sparkled; it was a gold ring. The man stooped down, remained a moment, and when he rose again there was no ring upon that hand.

He did not rise up precisely; he remained in a sinister and startled attitude, turning his back to the pile of dead, scrutinizing the horizon, on his knees, all the front of his body being supported on his two forefingers, his head raised just enough to peep above the edge of the hollow road. The four paws of the jackal are adapted to certain actions.

Then, deciding upon his course, he arose.

At this moment he experienced a shock. He felt that he was held from behind.

He turned; it was the open hand, which had closed, seizing the lapel of his coat.

An honest man would have been frightened. This man began to laugh.

"Oh," said he, "it's only the dead man. I like a ghost better than a gendarme."

47

However, the hand relaxed and let go its hold. Strength is soon exhausted in the tomb.

"Ah ha!" returned the prowler, "is this dead man alive? Let us see."

He bent over again, rummaged among the heap, removed whatever impeded him, seized the hand, laid hold of the arm, disengaged the head, drew out the body, and some moments after dragged into the shadow of the hollow road an inanimate man, at least one who was senseless. It was a cuirassier, an officer; an officer, also, of some rank; a great gold epaulet protruded from beneath his cuirass, but he had no casque. A furious saber cut had disfigured his face, where nothing but blood was to be seen. It did not seem, however, that he had any limbs broken; and by some happy chance, if the word is possible here, the bodies were arched above him in such a way as to prevent his being crushed. His eyes were closed.

He had on his cuirass the silver cross of the Legion of Honor. The prowler tore off this cross, which disappeared in one of the gulfs which he had under his capote. After which he felt the officer's fob, found a watch there, and took it. Then he rummaged in his vest and found a purse, which he pocketed. When he had reached this phase of the succor he was lending the dying man, the officer opened his eyes.

"Thanks," said he feebly.

The rough movements of the man handling him, the coolness of the night, and breathing the fresh air freely, had roused him from his lethargy.

The prowler answered not. He raised his head. The sound of a footstep could be heard on the plain; probably it was some patrol who was approaching.

The officer murmured, for there were still signs of suffering in his voice:

"Who has gained the battle?"

"The English," answered the prowler.

The officer replied:

"Search my pockets. You will there find a purse and a watch. Take them."

This had already been done. The prowler made a pretense of executing the command, and said:

"There is nothing there."

"I have been robbed," replied the officer; "I am sorry. They would have been yours."

The step of the patrol became more and more distinct.

"Somebody is coming," said the prowler, making a movement as if he would go.

The officer, raising himself up painfully upon one arm, held him back.

"You have saved my life. Who are you?"

The prowler answered quick and low:

"I belong, like yourself, to the French army. I must go. If I am taken I shall be shot. I have saved your life. Help yourself now."

"What is your grade?"

"Sergeant."

"What is your name?"

"Thénardier."

"I shall not forget that name," said the officer. "And you, remember mine. My name is Pontmercy."

Jean Valjean has been retaken.

We shall be pardoned for passing rapidly over the painful details. We shall merely reproduce a couple of items published in the newspapers of that day, some few months after the remarkable events that occurred at M—— sur M——.

The articles referred to are somewhat laconic. It will be remembered that the *Gazette des Tribunaux* had not yet been established.

We copy the first from the *Drapeau Blanc*. It is dated the 25th of July, 1823:

"A district of the Pas-de-Calais has just been the scene of an extraordinary occurrence. A stranger in that department, known as Monsieur Madeleine, had, within a few years past, restored, by means of certain new processes, the manufacture of jet and black glass ware —a former local branch of industry. He had made his own fortune by it, and, in fact, that of the entire district. In acknowledgment of his services he had been appointed mayor. The police has discovered that Monsieur Madeleine was none other than an escaped convict, condemned in 1796 for robbery, and named Jean Valjean. This Jean Valjean has been sent back to the galleys. It appears that previous to his arrest, he succeeded in withdrawing from Laffitte's a sum amounting to more than half a million which he had deposited there, and which it is said, by the way, he had very legitimately realized in his business. Since his return to the galleys at Toulon, it has been impossible to discover where Jean Valjean concealed this money."

The second article, which enters a little more into detail, is taken from the *Journal de Paris* of the same date:

"An old convict, named Jean Valjean, has recently been brought before the Var Assizes, under circumstances calculated to attract attention. This villain had succeeded in eluding the vigilance of the police; he had changed his name, and had even been adroit enough to procure the appointment of mayor in one of our small towns in the North. He had established in this town a very considerable business, but was, at length, unmasked and arrested, thanks to the indefatigable zeal of the public authorities. He kept, as his mistress, a prostitute, who died of the shock at the moment of his arrest. This wretch, who is endowed with herculean strength, managed to escape, but, three or four days afterwards, the police retook him, in Paris, just as he was getting into one of the small vehicles that ply between the capital and the village of Montfermeil (Seine-et-Oise). It is said that he had availed himself of the interval of these three or four days of freedom, to withdraw a considerable sum deposited by him with one of our principal bankers. This bandit attempted no defense. It was proven by the able and eloquent representative of the crown that the robbery was shared in by others, and that Jean Valjean formed one of a band of robbers in the South. Consequently, Jean Valjean, being found guilty, was condemned to death. The criminal refused to appeal to the higher courts, and the king, in his inexhaustible clemency, deigned to commute his sentence to that of hard labor in prison for life. Jean Valjean was immediately forwarded to the galleys at Toulon."

Toward the end of October, in that same year, 1823, the inhabitants of Toulon saw coming back into their port, in consequences of heavy weather, and in order to repair some damages, the ship *Orion,* which formed a part of the Mediterranean squadron.

She was moored near the arsenal, and they were repairing her. One morning, the throng which was gazing at her witnessed an accident. The crew was engaged in furling sail. The topman, whose duty it was to take in the starboard upper corner of the main topsail, lost his balance. He was seen tottering; he whirled over the yard, his arms outstretched toward the deep; as he went over, he grasped the manropes, first with one hand, and then with the other, and hung suspended in that manner. The sea lay far below him at a giddy depth. The shock of his fall had given to the manropes a violent swinging motion, and the poor fellow hung dangling to and fro at the end of this line, like a stone in a sling.

To go to his aid was to run a frightful risk. None of the crew, who were all fishermen of the coast recently taken into service, dared attempt it. In the meantime, the poor topman was becoming exhausted; his increasing weakness could be detected in the movements of all his limbs.

Suddenly, a man was discovered clambering up the rigging with the agility of a wildcat. This man was clad in red—it was a convict; he wore a green cap—it was a convict for life. As he reached the round top, a gust of wind blew off his cap and revealed a head entirely white: it was not a young man. In a twinkling he was upon the yard. He paused a few seconds, and seemed to measure it with his glance. At length, the convict raised his eyes to heaven, and took a step forward. He was seen to run along the yard. Not a cry, not a word was uttered; the same emotion contracted every brow. Every man held his breath. Finally, he was seen reascending to the yard, and hauling the sailor after him; he supported him there, for an instant, and then, lifting him in his arms, carried him, as he walked along the yard, to the crosstrees, and from there to the round top, where he left him in the hands of his mess-mates.

Then the throng applauded. He, however, had made it a point of duty to descend again immediately, and go back to his work. All eyes were following him. There was a certain moment when everyone felt alarmed; whether it was that he felt fatigued, or because his head swam, people thought they saw him hesitate and stagger. Suddenly, the throng uttered a thrilling outcry: the convict had fallen into the sea. He had disappeared in the sea, without making even a ripple, as though he had fallen into a cask of oil. They sounded and dragged the place. It was in vain. The search was continued until night, but not even the body was found.

The next morning, the *Toulon Journal* published the following lines:—"November 17, 1823. Yesterday, a convict at work on board the *Orion,* on his return from rescuing a sailor, fell into the sea, and was drowned. His body was not recovered. It is presumed that it has been caught under the piles at the pier-head of the arsenal. This man was registered by the number 9430, and his name was Jean Valjean."

[*Cosette lives a wretched life with the Thénardiers who continue to mistreat her. Late in December, a stranger spends the night at Montfermeil, pays fifteen hundred francs to the Thénardiers, and takes Cosette away with him.*]

Jean Valjean was not dead.

When he fell into the sea, or rather when he threw himself into it, he was free from his irons. He swam under water to a ship at anchor to which a boat was fastened. He found means to conceal himself in this boat until evening. At night he betook himself again to the water, and reached the land a short distance from Cape Brun. There, as he did not lack for money, he could procure clothes.

His first care, on reaching Paris, had been to purchase a mourning dress for a little girl of eight years, then to procure lodgings. That done, he had gone to Montfermeil.

He was believed to be dead, and that thickened the obscurity which surrounded him. At Paris there fell into his hands a paper which chronicled the fact. He felt reassured, and almost as much at peace as if he really had been dead.

On the evening of the same day that Jean Valjean had rescued Cosette from the clutches of the Thénardiers, he entered Paris again. He entered the city at night-fall, with the child, by the barrière de Monceaux. There he took a cabriolet, which carried him as far as the esplanade of the Observatory. There he got out, paid the driver, took Cosette by the hand, and both in the darkness of the night, through the deserted streets in the vicinity of l'Ourcine and la Glacière, walked towards the boulevard de l'Hôpital. Before an old, ruined building called the Gorbeau tenement Jean Valjean stopped. Like the birds of prey, he had chosen this lonely place to make his nest. He fumbled in his waistcoat and took from it a sort of night-key, opened the door, entered, then carefully closed it again and ascended the stairway, still carrying Cosette.

At the top of the stairway he drew from his pocket another key, with which he opened another door. The chamber which he entered was a sort of garret, rather spacious, furnished only with a mattress spread on the floor, a table, and a few chairs. A stove containing a fire, the coals of which were visible, stood in one corner. The street lamp of the boulevards shed a dim light through this poor interior. At the further extremity there was a little room containing a cot bed. On this Jean Valjean laid the child without waking her.

He struck a light with a flint and steel and lit a candle, which, with his tinder-box, stood ready, beforehand, on the table; and, as he had done on the preceding evening, he began to gaze upon Cosette with a look of ecstasy, in which the expression of goodness and tenderness went almost to the verge of insanity. He knelt down by the bedside of

Cosette. It was broad daylight, and yet the child slept on. A pale ray from the December sun struggled through the garret window and traced upon the ceiling long streaks of light and shade. Suddenly a carrier's wagon, heavily laden, trundled over the cobble-stones of the boulevard, and shook the old building like the rumbling of a tempest, jarring it from cellar to roof-tree.

"Yes, madame!" cried Cosette, starting up out of sleep, "here I am! here I am!"

And she threw herself from the bed, her eyelids still half closed with the weight of slumber, stretching out her hand towards the corner of the wall.

"Oh! what shall I do? Where is my broom?" said she.

By this time her eyes were fully open, and she saw the smiling face of Jean Valjean.

"Oh! yes—so it is!" said the child. "Good morning, monsieur."

Children at once accept joy and happiness with quick familiarity, being themselves naturally all happiness and joy. Cosette asked Jean Valjean a thousand questions.—Where was she? Was Paris a big place? Was Madame Thénardier really very far away? Wouldn't she come back again, etc., etc. All at once she exclaimed, "How pretty it is here!"

It was a frightful hovel, but she felt free.

"Must I sweep?" she continued at length.

"Play!" replied Jean Valjean.

And thus the day passed by. Cosette, without troubling herself with trying to understand anything about it, was inexpressibly happy with her doll and her good friend. . . .

The dawn of the next day found Jean Valjean again near the bed of Cosette. He waited there, motionless, to see her wake. Something new was entering his soul. Jean Valjean had never loved anything. For twenty-five years he had been alone in the world. He had never been a father, lover, husband or friend. At the galleys, he was cross, sullen, obstinate, ignorant, and intractable. The heart of the old convict was full of freshness. His sister and her children had left in his memory only a vague and distant impression, which had finally almost entirely vanished. He had made every exertion to find them again, and, not succeeding, had forgotten them. Human nature is thus constituted. The other tender emotions of his youth, if any such he had, were lost in an abyss. Poor old heart, so young! But, as he was fifty-five and Cosette was but eight years old, all that he might have felt of love in his entire life melted into a sort of ineffable radiance. This was the second white vision he had seen. The bishop had caused the dawn of virtue on his horizon; Cosette evoked the dawn of love.

On her part, Cosette, too, unconsciously underwent a change, poor little creature! She was so small when her mother left her that she could not recollect her now. As all children do, like the young shoots of the vine that cling to everything, she had tried to love. She had not been able to succeed. Everybody had repelled her—the Thénardiers, their children, other children. She had loved the dog; it died, and after that no person and no thing would have aught to do with her. Mournful thing to tell, and one which we have already hinted, at the age of eight her heart was cold. This was not her fault; it was not the faculty of love that she lacked; alas! it was the possibility. And so, from the very first day, all that thought and felt in her began to love this kind old friend. She now felt a sensation utterly unknown to her before—a sensation of budding and of growth.

Her friend no longer impressed her as old and poor. In her eyes Jean Valjean was handsome, just as the garret had seemed pretty. The apartment with the side chamber which he occupied with Cosette, was the one whose window looked out upon the boulevard. This window being the only one in the house, there was no neighbor's prying eye to fear from that side or opposite. The upper floor contained, as we have said, several rooms and a few lofts, only one of which was occupied—by an old woman, who was maid of all work to Jean Valjean. All the rest was uninhabited. It was this old woman, honored with the title of landlady, but, in reality, entrusted with the functions of portress, who had rented him these lodgings on Christmas Day. He had passed himself off to her as a gentleman of means, ruined by the Spanish Bonds, who was going to live there with his granddaughter.

Weeks rolled by. These two beings led in that wretched shelter a happy life. From the earliest dawn, Cosette laughed, prattled, and sang. Children have their morning song, like birds. Jean Valjean had begun to teach her to read. Sometimes, while teaching the child to spell, he would remember that it was with the intention of accomplishing evil that he had learned to read, in the galleys. This intention had now been changed into teaching a child to read. Then the old convict would smile with the pensive smile of angels.

To teach Cosette to read, and to watch her playing, was nearly all Jean Valjean's life. And then, he would talk to her about her mother, and teach her to pray. She called him *Father,* and knew him by no other name. He spent hours seeing her dress and undress her doll, and listening to her song and prattle. From that time on, life seemed full of interest to him, men seemed good and just; he no longer, in his thoughts, reproached anyone with any wrong; he saw no reason, now, why he should not live to grow very old, since his child loved him. Jean Valjean was prudent enough never to go out in the daytime. Every evening, however, about twilight, he would walk for an hour or two, sometimes alone, often with Cosette.

They lived frugally, always with a little fire in the stove, but like people in embarrassed circumstances. Jean Valjean made no change in the furniture. He still wore his yellow coat, his black pantaloons, and his old hat. On the street he was taken for a beggar. It sometimes happened that kind-hearted dames, in passing, would turn and hand him a penny. Jean Valjean accepted the penny and bowed humbly. It chanced, sometimes, also, that he would meet some wretched creature begging alms, and then, glancing about him to be sure no one was looking, he would stealthily approach the beggar, slip a piece of money, often silver, into his hand, and walk rapidly away. This had its inconveniences. He began to be known in the quarter as *the beggar who gives alms.*

The old landlady, a crabbed creature, fully possessed with that keen observation as to all that concerned her neighbors, which is peculiar to the suburbs, watched Jean Valjean closely without exciting his suspicion. She was a little deaf, which made her talkative. She had questioned Cosette, who, knowing nothing, could tell nothing, further than that she came from Montfermeil. One morning this old female spy saw Jean Valjean go, with an appearance which seemed peculiar to the old busybody, into one of the uninhabited apartments of the building. She followed him with the steps of an old cat, and could see him without herself being seen, through the chink of the door directly opposite. She saw him fumble in his pocket, and take from it a needle case, scissors, and thread, and then proceed to rip open the lining of one lapel of his coat and take from under it a piece of yellowish paper, which he unfolded. The beldame remarked with dismay that it was a bank bill for a thousand francs. It was the second or third one only that she had ever seen. She ran away very much frightened.

A moment afterwards, Jean Valjean accosted her, and asked her to get this thousand-franc bill changed for him, adding that it was the half-yearly interest on his property which he had received on the previous day. "Where?" thought the old woman. He did not go out until six o'clock, and the government treasury is certainly not open at that hour. The old woman got the note changed, all the while forming her conjectures. . . .

There was, in the neighborhood of Saint Médard, a mendicant who sat crouching over the edge of a condemned public well near by, and to whom Jean Valjean often gave alms. He never passed this man without giving him a few pennies. Sometimes he spoke to him. One evening, as Jean Valjean was passing that way, unaccompanied by Cosette, he noticed the beggar sitting in his usual place, under the street lamp which had just been lighted. Jean Valjean walked up to him, and put a piece of money in his hand, as usual. The beggar suddenly raised his eyes, gazed intently at Jean Valjean, and then quickly dropped his head. This movement was like a flash; Jean Valjean shuddered. He recoiled, horror-stricken and petrified, daring neither to breathe nor to speak, to stay nor to fly, but gazing upon the beggar who had once more bent down his head, with its tattered covering, and seemed to be no longer conscious of his presence. At this singular moment, an instinct, perhaps the mysterious instinct of self-preservation, prevented Jean Valjean from uttering a word. The beggar had the same form, the same rags, the same general appearance as on every other day. "Pshaw!" said Jean Valjean to himself, "I am mad! I am dreaming! It cannot be!" And he went home, anxious and ill at ease. He scarcely dared to admit, even to himself, that the countenance he thought he had seen was the face of Javert.

Some days after, it might be eight o'clock in the evening, he was in his room, giving Cosette her spelling lesson, which the child was repeating in a loud voice, when he heard the door of the building open and close again. Jean Valjean remained silent and motionless, his back turned towards the door, still seated on his chair from which he had not moved, and holding his breath in the darkness. After a considerable interval, not hearing anything more, he turned round without making any noise, and as he raised his eyes towards the door of his room, he saw a light through the keyhole. There was, evidently, somebody outside with a candle who was listening.

A few minutes elapsed, and the light disappeared. But he heard no sound of footsteps, which seemed to indicate that whoever was listening at the door had taken off his shoes. Jean Valjean threw himself on his bed without undressing, but could not shut his eyes that night.

At daybreak, as he was sinking into slumber from fatigue, he was aroused, again, by the creaking of the door of some room at the end of the hall, and then he heard the same footstep which had ascended the stairs, on the preceding night. The step approached. He started from his bed and placed his eye to the keyhole, hoping to get a glimpse of the person, whoever it might be, who had made his way into the building in the night-time and had listened at his door. It was a man, indeed, who passed by Jean Valjean's room, this time without stopping. The hall was still too dark for him to make out his features; but, when the man reached the stairs, a ray of light from without made his figure stand out like a profile, and Jean Valjean had a full view of his back. The man was tall, wore a long frock-coat, and had a cudgel under his arm. It was the redoubtable form of Javert.

At dusk, he went to the street-door and looked carefully up and down the boulevard. No one was to be seen. The boulevard seemed to be utterly deserted. It is true that there might have been someone hidden behind a tree. He went upstairs again.

"Come," said he to Cosette.

He took her by the hand and they both went out. Cosette walked without asking any questions. The sufferings of the first six years of her life had introduced something of the passive into her nature. Besides—and this is a remark to which we shall have more than one occasion to return—she had become familiar, without being fully conscious of them, with the peculiarities of her good friend and the eccentricities of destiny. And then she felt safe, being with him. Jean Valjean knew, no more than Cosette, where he was going. He trusted in God, as she trusted in him.

As eleven o'clock struck in the tower of Saint Etienne du Mont, he crossed the Rue de Pontoise in front of the bureau of the Commissary of Police, which is at No. 14. At this moment he saw distinctly—thanks to the commissary's lamp which revealed them—three men following him quite near, pass one after another under this lamp on the dark side of the street. One of these men entered the passage leading to the commissary's house. The one in advance appeared to him decidedly suspicious.

They stopped in the center of the square and formed a group like people consulting. They appeared undecided. The man who seemed to be the leader turned and energetically pointed in the direction in which Jean Valjean was; one of the others seemed to insist with some obstinacy on the contrary direction. At the instant when the leader turned, the moon shone full in his face. Jean Valjean recognized Javert perfectly. Uncertainty was at an end for Jean Valjean. Cosette began to be tired; he took her in his arms, and carried her. There was nobody in the streets, and the lamps had not been lighted on account of the moon.

A little street, the Rue de Chemin Vert Saint Antoine, opened between two wood-yards enclosed by walls. This street was narrow, obscure, and seemed made expressly for him. Before entering it, he looked back. From the point where he was, he could see the whole length of the bridge of Austerlitz. Four shadows, at that moment, entered upon the bridge. These shadows were coming from the Jardin des Plantes towards the right bank. These four shadows were the four men. Jean Valjean felt a shudder like that of the deer when he sees the hounds again upon his track. There was now no time to turn back. What he had seen moving in the obscurity some distance behind him, the moment before, was undoubtedly Javert and his squad. . . .

At the rate at which they were marching, and the stops they were making, it would take them about a quarter of an hour to arrive at the spot where Jean Valjean was. It was a frightful moment. A few minutes separated Jean Valjean from that awful precipice which was opening before him for the third time. And the galleys now were no longer simply the galleys, they were Cosette lost for ever; that is to say, a life in death. There was now only one thing possible.

Among other resources, thanks to his numerous escapes from the galleys at Toulon, he had become master of that incredible art of raising himself, in the right angle of a wall, if need be to the height of a sixth story. Jean Valjean measured with his eyes the wall above which he saw the lime tree. It was about eighteen feet high. The angle that it made with the gable of the great building was filled in its lower part with a pile of masonry of triangular shape. This pile was about five feet high. From its top the space to climb to get upon the wall was hardly more than fourteen feet.

The difficulty was Cosette. Cosette did not know how to scale a wall. Abandon her? Jean Valjean did not think of it. To carry her was impossible. He needed a cord. Jean Valjean had none. Truly at that instant, if Jean Valjean had had a kingdom, he would have given it for a rope.

All extreme situations have their flashes which sometimes make us blind, sometimes illuminate us. The despairing gaze of Jean Valjean encountered the lamp-post in the Cul-de-sac Genrot. At this epoch there were no gas-lights in the streets of Paris. At nightfall they lighted the street lamps, which were placed at intervals, and were raised and lowered by means of a rope traversing the street from end to end, running through the grooves of posts. The reel on which this rope was wound was enclosed below the lantern in a little iron box, the key of which was kept by the lamp-lighter, and the rope itself was protected by a casing of metal.

Jean Valjean, with the energy of a final struggle, crossed the street at a bound, entered the cul-de-sac, sprang the bolt of the little box with the point of his knife, and an instant after was back at the side of Cosette. He had a rope. Then, without any haste, but without doing anything a second time, with a firm and rapid decision, so much the more remarkable at such a moment when the patrol and Javert might come upon him at any instant, he took off his cravat, passed it around Cosette's body under the arms, attached this cravat to an end of the rope, took the other end of the rope in his teeth, took off his shoes and stockings and threw them over the wall, climbed upon the pile of masonry and began to raise himself in the angle of the wall and the gable with as much solidity and certainty as if he had the rounds of a ladder under his heels and his elbows. Half a minute had not passed before he was on his knees on the wall.

Cosette watched him, stupefied, without saying a word. All at once, she heard Jean Valjean's voice calling to her in a low whisper:

"Put your back against the wall."

And she felt herself lifted from the ground.

Before she had time to think where she was she was at the top of the wall. Jean Valjean seized her, put her on his back, took her two little hands in his left hand, lay down flat and crawled along the top of the wall as far as the cut-off corner. As he had supposed, there was a building there, the roof of which sloped from the top of the wooden casing we have mentioned very nearly to the ground, with a gentle inclination, and just reaching to the lime tree. He had just reached the inclined plane of the roof, and had not yet left the crest of the wall, when a violent uproar proclaimed the arrival of the patrol. He heard the thundering voice of Javert:

"Search the cul-de-sac!"

The soldiers rushed into the Cul-de-sac Genrot.

Jean Valjean slid down the roof, keeping hold of Cosette, reached the lime tree, and jumped to the ground. He found himself in a sort of garden, very large and of a singular appearance; one of those gloomy gardens which seem made to be seen in the winter and at night. He had on one side the building, down the roof of which he had come, a wood-pile, and behind the wood, against the wall, a stone statue. The building was in ruins, but some dismantled rooms could be distinguished in it, one of which was well filled, and appeared to serve as a shed.

Jean Valjean's first care had been to find his shoes, and put them on; then he entered the shed with Cosette. A man trying to escape never thinks himself sufficiently concealed. The child, thinking constantly of the Thénardiers, shared his instinct, and cowered down as closely as she could. Cosette trembled, and pressed closely to his side. They heard the tumultuous clamor of the patrol ransacking the cul-de-sac and the street, the clatter of their muskets against the stones, the calls of Javert to the watchmen he had stationed, and his imprecations mingled with words which they could not distinguish.

At the end of a quarter of an hour it seemed as though this stormy rumbling began to recede. Jean Valjean did not breathe. Suddenly, in the midst of this deep calm, a new sound arose; a celestial, divine, ineffable sound, as ravishing as the other was horrible. It was a hymn which came forth from the darkness, a bewildering mingling of prayer and harmony in the obscure and fearful silence of the night. This song came from the gloomy building which overlooked the garden. At the moment when the uproar of the demons receded, one would have said, it was a choir of angels approaching in the darkness. Cosette and Jean Valjean fell on their knees.

The chant ceased. Perhaps it had lasted a long time. Jean Valjean could not have told. Hours of ecstasy are never more than a moment. All had again relapsed into silence. There was nothing more in the street, nothing more in the garden. That which threatened, that which reassured, all had vanished. The wind rattled the dry grass on the top of the wall, which made a low, soft, and mournful noise. The night wind had risen, which indicated that it must be between one and two o'clock in the morning. Poor Cosette did not speak. The ground was damp, the shed open on all sides, the wind freshened every moment. The man took off his coat and wrapped Cosette in it.

"Are you warmer, so?"

"Oh! yes, Father!"

"Well, wait here a moment for me. I shall soon be back."

60

He went out of the ruin, and along by the large building, in search of some better shelter. He found doors, but they were all closed. All the windows of the ground-floor were barred. Where was he? who would ever have imagined anything equal to this species of sepulcher in the midst of Paris? what was this strange house? A building full of nocturnal mystery, calling to souls in the shade with the voice of angels, and, when they came, abruptly presenting to them this frightful vision— promising to open the radiant gate of Heaven and opening the horrible door of the tomb. And that was in fact a building, a house which had its number in a street? It was not a dream? He had to touch the walls to believe it.

The cold, the anxiety, the agitation, the anguish of the night, were giving him a veritable fever, and all his ideas were jostling in his brain. He went to Cosette. She was sleeping. Meanwhile, through the reverie into which he had fallen, he had heard for some time a singular noise. It sounded like a little bell that someone was shaking. This noise made Jean Valjean turn. He looked, and saw that there was someone in the garden. Something which resembled a man was walking among the glass cases of the melon patch, rising up, stooping down, stopping, with a regular motion, as if he were drawing or stretching something upon the ground. This being appeared to limp.

He fell again from chimerical terrors into real terrors. He said to himself that perhaps Javert and his spies had not gone away, that they had doubtless left somebody on the watch in the street; that, if this man should discover him in the garden, he would cry thief, and would de- liver him up. He took the sleeping Cosette gently in his arms and carried her into the farthest corner of the shed behind a heap of old furniture. Cosette did not stir.

While he was revolving these questions, he touched Cosette's hands. They were icy.

"Oh! God!" said he.

He called to her in a low voice:

"Cosette!"

She did not open her eyes.

He shook her smartly.

She did not wake.

"Could she be dead?" said he, and he sprang up, shuddering from head to foot.

He listened for her breathing; she was breathing with a respira- tion that appeared feeble and about to stop. How should he get her warm again? how rouse her? All else was banished from his thoughts. He rushed desperately out of the ruin. It was absolutely necessary that in less than a quarter of an hour Cosette should be in bed and before a fire. He walked straight to the man whom he saw in the garden. He had taken in his hand the roll of money which was in his vest-pocket. This man had his head down, and did not see him coming. A few strides and Jean Valjean was at his side.

Jean Valjean approached him, exclaiming:

"A hundred francs!"

The man started and raised his eyes.

"A hundred francs for you," continued Jean Valjean, "if you will give me refuge to-night."

The moon shone full in Jean Valjean's bewildered face.

"What, it is you, Father Madeleine!" said the man.

This name, thus pronounced, at this dark hour, in this unknown place, by this unknown man, made Jean Valjean start back. He was ready for anything but that. The speaker was an old man, bent and lame, dressed much like a peasant, who had on his left knee a leather knee-cap from which hung a bell. His face was in the shade, and could not be distinguished. Meanwhile the man had taken off his cap, and was exclaiming, tremulously:

"Ah! my God! how did you come here, Father Madeleine? How did you get in, O Lord? Did you fall from the sky? There is no doubt, if you ever do fall, you will fall from there. And what has happened to you? You have no cravat, you have no hat, you have no coat?"

"Who are you? and what is this house?" asked Jean Valjean.

"Oh! indeed, that is good now," exclaimed the old man. "I am the one you got the place for here, and this house is the one you got me the place in. What! you don't remember me?"

"No," said Jean Valjean. "And how does it happen that you know me?"

"You saved my life," said the man.

He turned, a ray of the moon lighted up his side face, and Jean Valjean recognized old Fauchelevent.

"Ah!" said Jean Valjean, "it is you? Yes, I remember you."

"That is good!" said the old man, in a reproachful tone.

"And what are you doing here?" added Jean Valjean.

"Oh! I am covering my melons.

"I said to myself: the moon is bright, there is going to be a frost. Suppose I put their jackets on my melons? And," added he, looking at Jean Valjean, with a loud laugh, "you would have done well to do as much for yourself. But how did you come here?"

Jean Valjean, finding that he was known by this man, at least under his name of Madeleine, went no further with his precautions. He multiplied questions.

"And what is this bell you have on your knee?"

"That!" answered Fauchelevent, "that is so that they may keep away from me."

"How! keep away from you?"

Old Fauchelevent winked in an indescribable manner.

"Ah! Bless me! there's nothing but women in this house; plenty of young girls. It seems that I am dangerous to meet. The bell warns them. When I come they go away."

"What is this house?"

"The Convent of the Petit Picpus!

"But now, really," resumed Fauchelevent, "how the deuce did you manage to get in, you, Father Madeleine? It is no use for you to be a saint, you are a man; and no men come in here."

"But," resumed Jean Valjean, "I must stay here."

"Oh! my God," exclaimed Fauchelevent.

Jean Valjean approached the old man, and said to him in a grave voice:

"Father Fauchelevent, I saved your life."

"I was first to remember it," answered Fauchelevent.

"Well, you can now do for me what I once did for you."

"What do you want me to do?" he added.

"I will explain. You have a room?"

"I have a solitary shanty, over there, behind the ruins of the old convent, in a corner that nobody ever sees. There are three rooms."

"Very well. But now come with me. We will go for the child."

"Ah!" said Fauchelevent, "there is a child!"

He said not a word more, but followed Jean Valjean as a dog follows his master.

In half an hour Cosette, again become rosy before a good fire, was asleep in the old gardener's bed.

Into this house it was that Jean Valjean had, as Fauchelevent said, "fallen from heaven." He had crossed the garden wall at the corner of the Rue Polonceau. That angels' hymn which he had heard in the middle of the night, was the nuns chanting matins; that bell the sound of which had so strangely surprised him was the gardener's bell fastened to old Fauchelevent's knee.

When Cosette had been put to bed, Jean Valjean and Fauchelevent had taken a glass of wine and a piece of cheese before a blazing fire; then, the only bed in the shanty being occupied by Cosette, they had thrown themselves each upon a bundle of straw. Before closing his eyes, Jean Valjean had said: "Henceforth I must remain here." These words were chasing one another through Fauchelevent's head the whole night. To tell the truth, neither of them had slept.

Jean Valjean, feeling that he was discovered and Javert was upon his track, knew full well that he and Cosette were lost should they return into the city. Since the new blast which had burst upon him had thrown him into this cloister, Jean Valjean had but one thought, to remain there. Now, for one in his unfortunate position, this convent was at once the safest and the most dangerous place; the most dangerous, for, no man being allowed to enter, if he should be discovered, it was a flagrant crime, and Jean Valjean would take but one step from the convent to prison; the safest, for if he succeeded in getting permission to remain, who would come there to look for him? To live in an impossible place; that would be safety.

For his part, Fauchelevent was racking his brains. He began by deciding that he was utterly bewildered. How did Monsieur Madeleine come there, with such walls! The walls of a cloister are not so easily crossed. How did he happen to be with a child? Fauchelevent said to himself: "One does not question a saint." To him Monsieur Madeleine had preserved all his prestige. He said aside to himself: It is my turn now. He added in his conscience: Monsieur Madeleine did not deliberate so long when the question was about squeezing himself under the cart to draw me out. He decided that he would save Monsieur Madeleine.

[*As it happens, the nuns have decided to bury the body of one of their number, Mother Crucifixion, who has just died, in a vault in the church instead of having the body carried outside for burial in the cemetery. Jean Valjean, who is anxious to escape from Javert by remaining inside the convent, realizes that he must somehow get outside in order to re-enter as the supposed brother of the gardener. He does so in a coffin believed to contain the body of the deceased nun, and immediately after the interment, the old gardener digs up the coffin and releases him. Next morning he is introduced to the nuns as Ultimus Fauchelevent and allowed to remain as gardener's helper. Cosette becomes a boarder at the convent school.]*

God has his own ways. The convent contributed, like Cosette, to confirm and complete, in Jean Valjean, the work of the bishop. He had before his eyes the sublime summit of self-denial, the loftiest possible height of virtue; innocence forgiving men their sins and expiating them in their stead; servitude endured, torture accepted, chastisement and misery invoked by souls that had not sinned in order that these might not fall upon souls which had; the love of humanity losing itself in the love of God, but remaining there, distinct and suppliant; sweet, feeble beings supporting all the torments of those who are punished, yet retaining the smile of those who are rewarded. And then he remembered that he had dared to complain. Often, in the middle of the night, he would rise from his bed to listen to the grateful anthem of these innocent beings thus overwhelmed with austerities, and he felt the blood run cold in his veins as he reflected that they who were justly punished never raised their voices towards heaven excepting to blaspheme, and that he, wretch that he was, had uplifted his clenched fist against God.

This house, also, was a prison, and bore dismal resemblance to the other from which he had fled, and yet he had never conceived anything like it. He once more saw gratings, bolts and bars of iron—to shut in whom? Angels. Those lofty walls which he had seen surrounding tigers, he now saw encircling lambs.

It was a place of expiation, not of punishment; and yet it was still more austere, more somber and more pitiless than the other. These virgins were more harshly bent down than the convicts. A harsh, cold blast, the blast that had frozen his youth, careered across that grated moat and manacled the vultures; but a wind still more biting and more cruel beat upon the dove cage. And why? When he thought of these things, all that was in him gave way before this mystery of sublimity. In these meditations, pride vanished. He reverted, again and again, to himself; he felt his own pitiful unworthiness, and often wept. All that had occurred in his existence, for the last six months, led him back towards the holy injunctions of the bishop; Cosette through love, the convent through humility.

Sometimes, in the evening, about dusk, at the hour when the garden was solitary, he was seen kneeling, in the middle of the walk that ran along the chapel, before the window through which he had looked, on the night of his first arrival, turned towards the spot where he knew that the sister who was performing the reparation was prostrate in prayer. Thus he prayed kneeling before this sister.

It seemed as though he dared not kneel directly before God.

Everything around him, this quiet garden, these balmy flowers, these children, shouting with joy, these meek and simple women, this silent cloister, gradually entered into all his being, and, little by little, his soul subsided into silence like this cloister, into fragrance like these flowers, into peace like this garden, into simplicity like these women, into joy like these children. And then he reflected that two houses of God had received him in succession at the two critical moments of his life, the first when every door was closed and human society repelled him; the second, when human society again howled upon his track, and the galleys once more gaped for him; and that, had it not been for the first, he should have fallen back into crime, and had it not been for the second, into punishment. His whole heart melted in gratitude, and he loved more and more. Several years passed thus. Cosette was growing.

Marius

PARIS HAS A CHILD, and the forest has a bird; the bird is called the sparrow; the child is called the *gamin*.

This little creature is full of joy. He has not food to eat every day, yet he goes to the show every evening, if he sees fit. He has no shirt to his back, no shoes to his feet, no roof over his head; he is like the flies in the air who have none of all these things. He is from seven to thirteen years of age, lives in troops, ranges the streets, sleeps in the open air, wears an old pair of his father's pantaloons down about his heels, an old hat of some other father, which covers his ears, and a single suspender of yellow listing, runs about, is always on the watch and on the search, kills time, colors pipes, swears like an imp, hangs about the wine-shop, knows thieves and robbers, is hand in glove with the street-girls, rattles off slang, sings smutty songs, and, withal, has nothing bad in his heart. The *gamin* of Paris is the dwarf of the giantess. . . .

About eight or nine years after the events narrated in the second part of this story, there was seen, on the Boulevard du Temple, and in the neighborhood of the Château d'Eau, a little boy of eleven or twelve years of age, who would have realized with considerable accuracy the ideal of the *gamin* previously sketched, if, with the laughter of his youth upon his lips, his heart had not been absolutely dark and empty. This child was well muffled up in a man's pair of pantaloons, but he had not got them from his father, and in a woman's chemise, which was not an inheritance from his mother. Strangers had clothed him in these rags out of charity. Still, he had a father and a mother. But his father never thought of him, and his mother did not love him. He was one of those children so deserving of pity from all, who have fathers and mothers, and yet are orphans. This little boy never felt so happy as when in the street. The pavement was not so hard to him as the heart of his mother.

He was a boisterous, pallid, nimble, wide-awake, roguish urchin, with an air at once vivacious and sickly. He went, came, sang, played pitch and toss, scraped the gutters, stole a little, but he did it gaily, like the cats and the sparrows, laughed when people called him an errand-boy, and got angry when they called him a ragamuffin. He had no shelter, no food, no fire, no love, but he was light-hearted because he was free.

However, deserted as this lad was, it happened sometimes, every two or three months, that he would say to himself: "Come, I'll go and see my mother!" Then he would leave the Boulevard, the Cirque, the Porte Saint Martin, go down along the quays, cross the bridges, reach the suburbs, walk as far as the Salpêtrière, and arrive—where? Precisely at that double number, 50-52, which is known to the reader, the Gorbeau building.

At that period referred to, the tenement No. 50-52, usually empty, and permanently decorated with the placard "Rooms to let," was, for a wonder, tenanted by several persons who, in all other respects, as is always the case at Paris, had no relation to or connection with each other. They all belonged to that indigent class which begins with the small bourgeois in embarrassed circumstances, and descends, from grade to grade of wretchedness, through the lower strata of society, until it reaches those two beings in whom all the material things of civilization terminate, the scavenger and the ragpicker.

The landlady of the time of Jean Valjean was dead, and had been replaced by another exactly like her. The new old woman was called Madame Burgon, and her life had been remarkable for nothing except a dynasty of three paroquets, which had in succession wielded the scepter of her affections. Among those who lived in the building, the wretchedest of all were a family of four persons, father, mother, and two daughters nearly grown, all four lodging in the same garret room, one of those cells of which we have already spoken. This family at first sight presented nothing very peculiar but its extreme destitution; the father, in renting the room, had given his name as Jondrette. Some time after his moving in, which had singularly resembled, to borrow the memorable expression of the landlady, the entrance of *nothing at all,* this Jondrette said to the old woman, who, like her predecessor, was, at the same time, portress and swept the stairs: "Mother So-and-So, if anybody should come and ask for a Pole or an Italian or, perhaps, a Spaniard, that is for me."

Now, this family was the family of our sprightly little bare-footed urchin. When he came there, he found distress and, what is sadder still, no smile; a cold hearthstone and cold hearts. When he came in, they would ask: "Where have you come from?" He would answer: "From the street." When he was going away they would ask him: "Where are you going to?" He would answer: "Into the street." His mother would say to him: "What have you come here for?"

We had forgotten to say that on the Boulevard du Temple this boy went by the name of little Gavroche. Why was his name Gavroche? Probably because his father's name was Jondrette. To break all links seems to be the instinct of some wretched families.

The room occupied by the Jondrettes in the Gorbeau tenement was the last at the end of the hall. The adjoining cell was tenanted by a very poor young man who was called Monsieur Marius.

[*The father of Marius, Colonel Pontmercy, had been one of Napoleon's officers. He believed that he owed his life to Thénardier who, as we know, was actually robbing him as he lay wounded on the battlefield of Waterloo. Young Marius lived with his maternal grandfather, M. Gillenormand, who idolized him but who hated the boy's father and refused to allow his name to be mentioned. When the Colonel died, he left a letter for his son telling him that Napoleon had created him Baron Pontmercy. Marius quarreled with M. Gillenormand, left his house, and tried to earn his living in Paris.*]

It is with misery as with everything else. It gradually becomes endurable. It ends by taking form and becoming fixed. You vegetate, that is to say you develop in some wretched fashion, but sufficient for existence. This is the way in which Marius Pontmercy's life was arranged.

By the side of his father's name, another name was engraven upon Marius' heart, the name of Thénardier. Marius, in his enthusiastic yet serious nature, surrounded with a sort of halo the man to whom, as he thought, he owed his father's life, that brave sergeant who had saved the colonel in the midst of the balls and bullets of Waterloo. He never separated the memory of this man from the memory of his father, and he associated them in his veneration. It was a sort of worship with two steps, the high altar for the colonel, the low one for Thénardier. The idea of the misfortune into which he knew that Thénardier had fallen and been engulfed, intensified his feeling of gratitude. Marius had learned at Montfermeil of the ruin and bankruptcy of the unlucky innkeeper. Since then, he had made untold efforts to get track of him, and to endeavor to find him, in that dark abyss of misery in which Thénardier had disappeared.

Nobody could give him any news of Thénardier; it was thought he had gone abroad. His creditors had sought for him, also, with less love than Marius, but with as much zeal, and had not been able to put their hands on him. Marius blamed and almost hated himself for not succeeding in his researches. This was the only debt which the colonel had left him, and Marius made it a point of honor to pay it. "What," thought he, "when my father lay dying on the field of battle, Thénardier could find him through the smoke and the grape, and bring him off on his shoulders, and yet he owed him nothing; while I, who owe so much to Thénardier, I cannot reach him in that darkness in which he is suffering, and restore him, in my turn, from death to life. Oh! I will find him!"

Marius was now twenty years old. It was three years since he had left his grandfather. It was Marius' delight to take long walks alone on the outer boulevards, or in the Champ de Mars, or in the less frequented walks of the Luxembourg. He sometimes spent half a day in looking at a vegetable garden, at the beds of salad, the fowls on the dung-heap, and the horse turning the wheel of the pump. The passers-by looked at him with surprise, and some thought that he had a suspicious appearance and an ill-omened manner. He was only a poor young man, dreaming without an object. It was in one of these walks that he had discovered the Gorbeau tenement, and its isolation and cheapness being an attraction to him, he had taken a room in it. He was only known in it by the name of Monsieur Marius.

69

Towards the middle of this year, 1831, the old woman who waited upon Marius told him that his neighbors, the wretched Jondrette family, were to be turned into the street. Marius, who passed almost all his days out of doors, hardly knew that he had any neighbors.

"Why are they turned out?" said he.

"Because they do not pay their rent; they owe for two terms."

"How much is that?"

"Twenty francs," said the old woman.

Marius had thirty francs in reserve in a drawer.

"Here," said he to the old woman, "there are twenty-five francs. Pay for these poor people, give them five francs, and do not tell them that it is from me."

Marius was now a fine-looking young man, of medium height, with heavy jet-black hair, a high intelligent brow, large and passionate nostrils, a frank and calm expression, and an indescribable something beaming from every feature, which was at once lofty, thoughtful and innocent. At the time of his most wretched poverty, he noticed that girls turned when he passed, and with a deathly feeling in his heart he fled or hid himself. He thought they looked at him on account of his old clothes, and that they were laughing at him; the truth is, that they looked at him because of his graceful appearance, and that they dreamed over it. This wordless misunderstanding between him and the pretty girls he met had rendered him hostile to society.

For more than a year Marius had noticed in a retired walk of the Luxembourg, the walk which borders the parapet of the Pépinière, a man and a girl quite young, nearly always sitting side by side, on the same seat, at the most retired end of the walk. The man might be sixty years old; he seemed sad and serious; his whole person presented the robust but wearied appearance of a soldier retired from active service.

This man and this young girl, though they appeared, and perhaps because they appeared, to avoid observation, had naturally excited the attention of the five or six students, who decided to name the daughter *Mademoiselle Lanoire* [*Black*] and the father *Monsieur Leblanc* [*White*]; and so, as nobody knew them otherwise, in the absence of a name, this surname had become fixed. The students said: "Ah! Monsieur Leblanc is at his seat!" and Marius, like the rest, had found it convenient to call this unknown gentleman M. Leblanc. The second year, it so happened that Marius broke off this habit of going to the Luxembourg, without really knowing why himself, and there were nearly six months during which he did not set foot in his walk. At last he went back there again one day; it was a serene summer morning, Marius was as happy as one always is when the weather is fine. It seemed to him as if he had in his heart all the bird songs which he heard, and all the bits of blue sky which he saw through the trees.

He went straight to his walk, and as soon as he reached it, he saw, still on the same seat, this well-known pair. When he came near them, however, he saw that it was indeed the same man, but it seemed to him that it was no longer the same girl. The woman whom he now saw was a noble, beautiful creature, with all the most bewitching outlines of woman, at the precise moment at which they are yet combined with all the most charming graces of childhood—that pure and fleeting moment which can only be translated by these two words: sweet sixteen.

At the first instant Marius thought it was another daughter of the same man, a sister doubtless of her whom he had seen before. But when the invariable habit of his promenade led him for the second time near the seat, and he had looked at her attentively, he recognized that she was the same. In six months the little girl had become a young woman; that was all. The second time that Marius came near her, the young girl raised her eyes; they were of a deep celestial blue, but in this veiled azure was nothing yet beyond the look of a child. She looked at Marius with indifference. . . .

One day the air was mild, the Luxembourg was flooded with sunshine and shadow, the sky was as clear as if the angels had washed it in the morning, the sparrows were twittering in the depths of the chestnut trees, Marius had opened his whole soul to nature, he was thinking of nothing, he was living and breathing, he passed near this seat, the young girl raised her eyes, their glances met. There is a time when every young girl looks thus. Woe to him upon whom she looks!

At night, on returning to his garret, Marius cast a look upon his dress, and for the first time perceived that he had the slovenliness, the indecency, and the unheard-of stupidity, to promenade in the Luxembourg with his "every day" suit, a hat broken near the band, coarse teamsters' boots, black pantaloons shiny at the knees, and a black coat threadbare at the elbows. The next day, at the usual hour, Marius took from his closet his new coat, his new pantaloons, his new hat, and his new boots; he dressed himself in this panoply complete, put on his gloves, prodigious prodigality, and went to the Luxembourg.

Thus a fortnight rolled away. Marius went to the Luxembourg, no longer to promenade, but to sit down, always in the same place, and without knowing why. Once there he did not stir. Every morning he put on his new suit, not to be conspicuous, and he began again the next morning. He was desperately in love. A whole month passed during which Marius went every day to the Luxembourg. He finally grew bolder, and approached nearer to the seat.

We must, however, suppose that M. Leblanc perceived something of this at last, for often when Marius came, he would rise and begin to promenade. He had left their accustomed place, and had taken the seat at the other end of the walk, near the Gladiator, as if to see whether Marius would follow them. Marius did not understand it, and committed that blunder. "The father" began to be less punctual and did not bring "his daughter" every day. Sometimes he came alone. Then Marius did not stay. Another blunder.

Marius took no note of these symptoms. From the phase of timidity he had passed, a natural and inevitable progress, to the phase of blindness. His love grew. He dreamed of her every night. And then there came to him a good fortune for which he had not even hoped, oil upon the fire, double darkness upon his eyes. One night, at dusk, he found on the seat, which "M. Leblanc and his daughter" had just left, a handkerchief, a plain handkerchief without embroidery, but white, fine, and which appeared to him to exhale ineffable odors. He seized it in transport. This handkerchief was marked with the letters U.F.: Marius knew nothing of this beautiful girl, neither her family, nor her name, nor her dwelling; these two letters were the first thing he had caught of her, adorable initials upon which he began straightway to build his castle. It was evidently her first name. Ursula, thought he, what a sweet name! He kissed the handkerchief, inhaled its perfume, put it over his heart, on his flesh in the day-time, and at night went to sleep with it on his lips. . . .

Hunger comes with love. To know that her name was Ursula had been much; it was little. In three or four weeks Marius had devoured this piece of good fortune. He desired another. He wished to know where she lived. From that moment Marius added to his happiness in seeing her at the Luxembourg, the happiness of following her home. One night after he had followed them home, and seen them disappear at the porte-cochère, he entered after them, and said boldly to the porter:

"Is it the gentleman on the first floor who has just come in?"

"No," answered the porter. "It is the gentleman on the third."

Another fact. This success made Marius still bolder.

"In front?" he asked.

"Faith!" said the porter, "the house is only built on the street."

"And what is this gentleman?"

"He lives on his income, monsieur. A very kind man, who does a great deal of good among the poor, though not rich."

"What is his name?" continued Marius.

The porter raised his head, and said:

"Is monsieur a detective?"

Marius retired, much abashed, but still in great transports. He was getting on. On the morrow—for he lived only from morrow to morrow; there was no longer any to-day, so to speak, to him—on the morrow he found nobody at the Luxembourg; he waited; at dusk he went to the house. No light in the windows; the blinds were closed; the third story was entirely dark. Marius knocked at the porte-cochère; went in and said to the porter:

"The gentleman of the third floor?"

"Moved," answered the porter.

Marius tottered, and said feebly:

"Since when?"

"Yesterday."

"Where does he live now?"

"I don't know anything about it."

"He has not left his new address, then?"

"No."

And the porter, looking up, recognized Marius.

"What! it is you!" said he, but decidedly now, "you do keep a bright look-out."

Summer passed, then autumn; winter came. Neither M. Leblanc nor the young girl had set foot in the Luxembourg. Marius had now but one thought, to see that sweet, that adorable face again. He searched continually; he searched everywhere: he found nothing. He fell into a melancholy. It was all over with him. Work disgusted him, walking fatigued him, solitude wearied him. He reproached himself a hundred times. Why did I follow her? I was so happy in seeing her only! She looked upon me; was not that infinite? She had the appearance of loving me. Was not that everything? I desired to have what? There is nothing more after that. I was a fool. He lived more and more alone, bewildered, overwhelmed, given up to his inward anguish, walking to and fro in his grief like a wolf in a cage, seeking everywhere for the absent, stupefied with love.

One day, in the course of this winter, Marius went slowly up the boulevard towards the barrière, on the way to the Rue Saint Jacques. He was walking thoughtfully, with his head down.

Suddenly he felt that he was elbowed in the dusk; he turned, and saw two young girls in rags, one tall and slender, the other a little shorter, passing rapidly by, breathless, frightened, and apparently in flight; they had met him, had not seen him, and had jostled him in passing. Marius could see in the twilight their livid faces, their hair tangled and flying, their frightful bonnets, their tattered skirts, and their naked feet. As they ran they were talking to each other. The taller one said in a very low voice:

"The *cognes* came. They just missed *pincer* me at the *demi-cercle.*"

The other answered: "I saw them. I *cavalé, cavalé, cavalé.*"

Marius understood, through this dismal argot, that the gendarmes, or the city police, had not succeeded in seizing these two girls, and that the girls had escaped. They plunged in under the trees of the boulevard behind him, and for a few seconds made a kind of dim whiteness in the obscurity which soon faded out. Marius stopped for a moment. He was about to resume his course when he perceived a little grayish packet on the ground at his feet. He stooped down and picked it up. It was a sort of envelope which appeared to contain papers.

"Good," said he, "those poor creatures must have dropped this!"

He retraced his steps, he called, he did not find them; he concluded they were already beyond hearing, put the packet in his pocket and went to dinner.

In the evening, as he was undressing to go to bed, he happened to feel in his coat-pocket the packet which he had picked up on the boulevard. He had forgotten it. He thought it might be well to open it, and that the packet might perhaps contain the address of the young girls, if, in reality, it belonged to them, or at all events the information necessary to restore it to the person who had lost it.

He opened the envelope. It was unsealed and contained four letters, also unsealed. The addresses were upon them. All four exhaled an odor of wretched tobacco. The first letter was addressed: *To Madame, Madame the Marchioness de Grucheray, Square opposite the Chamber of Deputies, No. ——.*

No address was added to the signature. Marius hoped to find the address in the second letter the superscription of which ran: *To Madame, Madame the Countess de Montvernet, Rue Cassette.*

Marius passed to the third letter, which was, like the preceding, a begging one.

He finally opened the fourth letter. There was on the address: *To the beneficent gentleman of the church of Saint Jacques du Haut Pas.* It contained these few lines:

"Beneficent man.

"If you will deign to accompany my daughter, you will see a miserable calamity, and I will show you my certificates.

"At the sight of these writings your generous soul will be moved with a sentiment of lively benevolence, for true philosophers always experience vivid emotions.

"Agree, compassionate man, that one must experience the most cruel necessity, and that it is very painful, to obtain relief, to have it attested by authority, as if we were not free to suffer and to die of inanition while waiting for someone to relieve our misery. The fates are very cruel to some and too lavish or too careful to others.

"I await your presence or your offering, if you deign to make it, and I pray you to have the kindness to accept the respectful sentiments with which I am proud to be,

"Truly magnanimous man,
        "Your very humble
                And very obedient servant,
                        "P. FABANTOU, dramatic artist."

After reading these four letters, Marius did not find himself much wiser than before. In the first place none of the signers gave his address. Then they seemed to come from four different individuals, Don Alvarès, Mother Balizard, the poet Genflot, and the dramatic artist Fabantou; but, strangely enough, these letters were all four written in the same hand. What was the conclusion from that, unless that they came from the same person? Marius put them back into the envelope, threw it into a corner, and went to bed. About seven o'clock in the morning, he had got up and breakfasted, and was trying to set about his work when there was a gentle rap at his door. . . .

A girl who was quite young was standing in the half-opened door. It was a pale, puny, meager creature, nothing but a chemise and a skirt covered a shivering and chilly nakedness, one of those beings who are both feeble and horrible at once, and who make those shudder whom they do not make weep.

"What do you wish, mademoiselle?" asked he.

The young girl answered with her voice like a drunken galley-slave's:

"Here is a letter for you, Monsieur Marius."

She had really in her hand a letter which she presented to Marius. Marius, in opening this letter, noticed that the enormously large wafer was still wet. The message could not have come far. He read:

"My amiable neighbor, young man!

"I have lerned your kindness towards me, that you have paid my rent six months ago. I bless you, young man. My eldest daughter will tell you that we have been without a morsel of bread for two days, four persons, and my spouse sick. If I am not desseived by my thoughts, I think I may hope that your generous heart will soften at this exposure and that the desire will subjugate you of being propitious to me by deigning to lavish upon me some light gift.

"I am with the distinguished consideration which is due to the benefactors of humanity,

"JONDRETTE

"P. S. My daughter will await your orders, dear Monsieur Marius."

This letter, in the midst of the obscure accident which had occupied Marius' thoughts since the previous evening, was a candle in a cave. Everything was suddenly cleared up. This letter came from the same source as the other four. It was the same writing, the same style, the same orthography, the same paper, the same odor of tobacco. There were five missives, five stories, five names, five signatures, and a single signer. The Spanish Captain Don Alvarès, the unfortunate mother Balizard, the dramatic poet Genflot, the old comedy writer Fabantou, were all four named Jondrette, if indeed the name of Jondrette himself was Jondrette. Now he saw everything clearly. He understood that the occupation of his neighbor Jondrette in his distress was to work upon the sympathies of benevolent persons; that he procured their addresses, and that he wrote under assumed names letters to people whom he deemed rich and compassionate, which his daughters carried, at their risk and peril.

Meantime, while Marius fixed upon her an astonished and sorrowful look, the young girl was walking to and fro in the room with the boldness of a specter. She bustled about regardless of her nakedness. At times, her chemise, unfastened and torn, fell almost to her waist. She moved the chairs, she disarranged the toilet articles on the bureau, she felt of Marius' clothes, she searched over what there was in the corners.

She went to the table.

"Ah!" said she, "books!"

A light flashed through her glassy eye. She resumed, and her tone expressed that happiness of being able to boast of something, to which no human creature is insensible:

"I can read, I can."

She put down the book, took up a pen, and exclaimed:

"And I can write, too!"

She dipped the pen in the ink, and turning towards Marius:

"Would you like to see? Here, I am going to write a word to show."

And before he had had time to answer, she wrote upon a sheet of blank paper which was on the middle of the table: *The Cognes [cops] are here.*"

Marius had drawn back quietly.

"Mademoiselle," said he, with his cold gravity, "I have here a packet, which is yours, I think. Permit me to return it to you."

And he handed her the envelope, which contained the four letters.

She clapped her hands and exclaimed:

"We have looked everywhere!"

Then she snatched the packet, and opened the envelope, saying:

"Lordy, Lordy, haven't we looked, my sister and I? And you have found it! on the boulevard, didn't you? It must have been on the boulevard?" The young girl continued to talk as if she were no longer conscious that Marius was there present. After a thorough exploration of his pockets, Marius had at last got together five francs and sixteen sous. This was at the time all that he had in the world. "That is enough for my dinner to-day," thought he, "to-morrow we will see." He took the sixteen sous, and gave the five francs to the young girl. She took the piece eagerly.

"Good," said she, "there is some sunshine!" Then she went out.

For five years Marius had lived in poverty, in privation, in distress even, but he perceived that he had never known real misery. Real misery he had just seen. It was this sprite which had just passed before his eyes. In fact, he who has seen the misery of man only has seen nothing, he must see the misery of woman; he who has seen the misery of woman only has seen nothing, he must see the misery of childhood.

She revealed to him an entire and hideous aspect of the darkness. Marius almost reproached himself with the fact that he had been so absorbed in his reveries and passion that he had not until now cast a glance upon his neighbors. Paying their rent was a mechanical impulse; everybody would have had that impulse; but he, Marius, should have done better. What! a mere wall separated him from these abandoned beings, who lived by groping in the night without the pale of the living; he came in contact with them, he was in some sort the last link of the human race which they touched, he heard them live or rather breathe beside him, and he took no notice of them! every day at every moment, he heard them through the wall, walking, going, coming, talking, and he did not lend his ear! and in these words there were groans, and he did not even listen, his thoughts were elsewhere, upon dreams, upon impossible glimmerings, upon loves in the sky, upon infatuations; and all the while human beings, his brothers in Jesus Christ, his brothers in the people, were suffering death agonies beside him! agonizing uselessly; he even caused a portion of their suffering, and aggravated it.

While he thus preached to himself, for there were times when Marius, like all truly honest hearts, was his own monitor, and scolded himself more than he deserved, he looked at the wall which separated him from the Jondrettes, as if he could send his pitying glance through that partition to warm those unfortunate beings. The wall was a thin layer of plaster, upheld by laths and joists, through which, as we have just seen, voices and words could be distinguished perfectly. None but the dreamer, Marius, would not have perceived this before. There was no paper hung on this wall, either on the side of the Jondrettes, or on Marius' side; its coarse construction was bare to the eye. Almost unconsciously, Marius examined this partition; sometimes reverie examines, observes, and scrutinizes, as thought would do. Suddenly he arose. He noticed towards the top, near the ceiling, a triangular hole, where three laths left a space between them. The plaster which should have stopped this hole was gone, and by getting upon the bureau he could see through that hole into the Jondrettes' garret. Pity has and should have its curiosity. This hole was a kind of Judas. It is lawful to look upon misfortune like a betrayer for the sake of relieving it. "Let us see what these people are," thought Marius, "and to what they are reduced."

He climbed upon the bureau, put his eye to the crevice, and looked. What Marius saw was a hole. Marius was poor and his room was poorly furnished, but even as his poverty was noble, his garret was clean. The den into which his eyes were at that moment directed, was abject, filthy, fetid, infectious, gloomy, unclean. All the furniture was a straw chair, a rickety table, a few old broken dishes, and in two of the corners two indescribable pallets; all the light came from a dormer window of four panes, curtained with spiders' webs.

By the table, upon which Marius saw a pen, ink, and paper, was seated a man of about sixty, small, thin, livid, haggard, with a keen, cruel, and restless air; a hideous harpy. This man had a long gray beard. He was dressed in a woman's chemise, which showed his shaggy breast and his naked arms bristling with gray hairs. Below this chemise were a pair of muddy pantaloons and boots from which the toes stuck out. He had a pipe in his mouth, and was smoking. There was no more bread in the den, but there was tobacco. He was writing, probably some such letter as those which Marius had read.

Marius, with a heavy heart, was about to get down from the sort of observatory which he had extemporized, when a sound attracted his attention, and induced him to remain in his place. The door of the garret was hastily opened. The eldest daughter appeared upon the threshold.

The father turned his eyes, the woman turned her head, the younger sister did not stir.

"Who?" asked the father.

"The gentleman!"

"The philanthropist?"

"Yes."

The man sprang up. There was a sort of illumination on his face.

"Wife!" cried he, "you hear. Here is the philanthropist. Put out the fire."

The astounded woman did not stir. The father, with the agility of a mountebank, caught a broken pot which stood on the mantel, and threw some water upon the embers.

Then turning to his elder daughter:

"You! unbottom the chair!"

His daughter did not understand him at all. He seized the chair, and with a kick he ruined the seat. His leg went through it.

As he drew out his leg, he asked his daughter:

"Is it cold?"

"Very cold. It snows."

The father turned towards the younger girl, who was on the pallet near the window, and cried in a thundering voice:

"Quick! off the bed, good-for-nothing! will you never do anything? break a pane of glass!"

The little girl sprang off the bed trembling.

"Break a pane of glass!" said he again.

The child was speechless.

"Do you hear me?" repeated the father, "I tell you to break a pane!"

The child, with a sort of terrified obedience, rose up on tiptoe and struck her fist into a pane. The glass broke and fell with a crash. The mother, who had not yet said a word, got up and asked in a slow, muffled tone, her words seeming to come out as if curdled:

"Dear, what is it you want to do?"

"Get into bed," answered the man.

His tone admitted of no deliberation. The mother obeyed, and threw herself heavily upon one of the pallets. Meanwhile a sob was heard in a corner.

"What is that?" cried the father.

The younger daughter, without coming out of the darkness into which she had shrunk, showed her bleeding fist. In breaking the glass she had cut herself; she had gone to her mother's bed, and she was weeping in silence. It was the mother's turn to rise and cry out.

"You see now! what stupid things you are doing? breaking your glass, she has cut herself!"

"So much the better!" said the man. "I knew she would."

"How! so much the better?" resumed the woman.

"Silence!" replied the father. "I suppress the liberty of the press."

Then tearing the chemise which he had on, he made a bandage with which he hastily wrapped up the little girl's bleeding wrist.

An icy wind whistled at the window and came into the room. The mist from without entered and spread about like a whitish wadding picked apart by invisible fingers. Through the broken pane the falling snow was seen. . . .

"Do you know," resumed the father, "that it is as cold as a dog in this devilish garret? If this man should not come! Oh! that is it! he makes us wait for him! he says: Well! they will wait for me! that is what they are for!—Oh! how I hate them, and how I would strangle them with joy and rejoicing, enthusiasm and satisfaction, these rich men! all the rich! these professed charitable men."

Just then there was a light rap at the door, the man rushed forward and opened it, exclaiming with many low bows and smiles of adoration:

"Come in, monsieur! deign to come in, my noble benefactor, as well as your charming young lady."

A man of mature age and a young girl appeared at the door of the garret. Marius had not left his place. What he felt at that moment escapes human language.

It was She.

Whoever has loved, knows all the radiant meaning contained in the three letters of this word: She.

She appeared again in this gloom, in this garret, in this shapeless den, in this horror! She was still the same, a little paler only; her delicate face was set in a violet velvet hat, her form was hidden under a black satin pelisse, below her long dress he caught a glimpse of her little foot squeezed into a silk buskin. She was still accompanied by Monsieur Leblanc. She stepped into the room and laid a large package on the table. Monsieur Leblanc approached with his kind and compassionate look, and said to the father:

"Monsieur, you will find in this package some new clothes, some stockings, and some new coverlids."

"Our angelic benefactor overwhelms us," said Jondrette, bowing down to the floor. "Look, my benefactor, no bread, no fire. My poor darlings have no fire! My only chair unseated! A broken window! in such weather as is this! My spouse in bed! sick!"

"Poor woman!" said Monsieur Leblanc.

"My child injured!" added Jondrette.

The child, whose attention had been diverted by the arrival of the strangers, was staring at "the young lady," and had ceased her sobbing.

"Why don't you cry? why don't you scream?" said Jondrette to her in a whisper.

At the same time he pinched her injured hand. All this with the skill of a juggler. The little one uttered loud cries. The adorable young girl whom Marius in his heart called "his Ursula" went quickly to her:

"Poor, dear child!" said she.

"Look, my beautiful young lady," pursued Jondrette, "her bleeding wrist! It is an accident which happened in working at a machine by which she earned six sous a day. It may be necessary to cut off her arm."

"Indeed!" said the old gentleman alarmed.

The little girl, taking this seriously, began to sob again beautifully.

"Alas, yes, my benefactor!" answered the father.

For some moments, Jondrette had been looking at "the philanthropist" in a strange manner. Even while speaking, he seemed to scrutinize him closely as if he were trying to recall some reminiscence. Suddenly, taking advantage of a moment when the newcomers were anxiously questioning the smaller girl about her mutilated hand, he passed over to his wife who was lying in her bed, appearing to be overwhelmed and stupid, and said to her quickly and in a very low tone:

"Notice that man!"

Then turning towards M. Leblanc, and continuing his lamentation:

"You see, monsieur! my whole dress is nothing but a chemise of my wife's! and that all torn! in the heart of winter. I cannot go out, for lack of a coat. If I had a sign of a coat, I should go to see Mademoiselle Mars, who knows me, and of whom I am a great favorite. Well, monsieur, my worthy monsieur, do you know what is going to happen to-morrow? To-morrow is the 4th of February, the fatal day, the last delay that my landlord will give me; if I do not pay him this evening, to-morrow my eldest daughter, myself, my spouse with her fever, my child with her wound, we shall all four be turned out of doors, and driven off into the street, upon the boulevard, without shelter, into the rain, upon the snow. You see, monsieur, I owe four quarters, a year! that is sixty francs."

Jondrette lied. Four quarters would have made but forty francs, and he could not have owed for four, since it was not six months since Marius had paid for two.

M. Leblanc took five francs from his pocket and threw them on the table. He had also taken off a large brown overcoat, which he wore over his blue surtout, and hung it over the back of the chair.

"Monsieur Fabantou," said he, "I have only these five francs with me; but I am going to take my daughter home, and I will return this evening; is it not this evening that you have to pay?"

Jondrette's face lighted up with a strange expression. He answered quickly:

"Yes, my noble monsieur. At eight o'clock I must be at my landlord's."

"I will be here at six o'clock, and I will bring you the sixty francs."

"My benefactor!" cried Jondrette, distractedly.

And he added in an undertone:

"Take a good look at him, wife!"

M. Leblanc took the arm of the beautiful young girl, and turned towards the door:

"Till this evening, my friends," said he.

"Six o'clock," said Jondrette.

"Six o'clock precisely."

Just then the overcoat on the chair caught the eye of the elder daughter.

"Monsieur," said she, "you forget your coat."

Jondrette threw a crushing glance at his daughter, accompanied by a terrible shrug of the shoulders.

M. Leblanc turned and answered with a smile:

"I do not forget it, I leave it."

"O my patron," said Jondrette, "my noble benefactor, I am melting into tears! Allow me to conduct you to your carriage."

"If you go out," replied M. Leblanc, "put on this overcoat. It is really very cold."

Jondrette did not make him say it twice. He put on the brown overcoat very quickly. And they went out all three, Jondrette preceding the two strangers.

[*Marius learns of a plot being hatched by Jondrette against M. Leblanc and his daughter. At the office of the Commissary of Police, an inspector, after listening to his story, tells him to keep watch at the hole in the wall and to signal the police at the proper moment by firing one of the two small pistols which he gives him. The inspector tells Marius that his name is Javert.*]

Marius judged that the time had come to resume his place at his observatory. In a twinkling, and with the agility of his age, he was at the hole in the partition. He looked in.

The interior of the Jondrette apartment presented a singular appearance. The entire den was, as it were, illuminated by the reflection of a large sheet-iron furnace in the fireplace, which was filled with lighted charcoal. The charcoal was burning and the furnace was red hot, a blue flame danced over it and helped to show the form of a chisel which was growing ruddy among the coals. In a corner near the door, and arranged as if for anticipated use, were two heaps which appeared to be, one a heap of old iron, the other a heap of ropes.

The Jondrette lair was, if the reader remembers what we have said of the Gorbeau house, admirably chosen for the theater of a deed of darkness and violence, and for the concealment of a crime. It was the most retired room of the most isolated house of the most solitary boulevard in Paris.

Jondrette had lighted his pipe, sat down on the dismantled chair, and was smoking. His wife was speaking to him in a low tone. Suddenly Jondrette raised his voice:

"Do you know? we must have two chairs here."

Marius felt a shiver run down his back on hearing the woman make this quiet reply:

"Pardieu! I will get our neighbor's."

And with rapid movement she opened the door of the den, and went out into the hall.

Marius heard the heavy hand of mother Jondrette groping after his key in the dark. The door opened. The woman came in.

The gable window let in a ray of moonlight, between two great sheets of shadow. One of these sheets of shadow entirely covered the wall against which Marius was leaning, so as to conceal him. The mother Jondrette raised her eyes, did not see Marius, took the two chairs, the only chairs which Marius had, and went out, slamming the door noisily behind her. She went back into the den.

Jondrette arranged the two chairs on the two sides of the table, turned the chisel over in the fire, put an old screen in front of the fireplace, which concealed the furnace, then went to the corner where the heap of ropes was, and stooped down, as if to examine something. Marius then perceived that what he had taken for a shapeless heap, was a rope ladder, very well made, with wooden rounds, and two large hooks to hang it by. This ladder and a few big tools, actual masses of iron, which were thrown upon the pile of old iron heaped up behind the door, were not in the Jondrette den in the morning, and had evidently been brought there in the afternoon, during Marius' absence.

Jondrette had let his pipe go out—a sure sign that he was intensely absorbed—and had come back and sat down. The candle made the savage ends and corners of his face stand out prominently. There were contractions of his brows, and abrupt openings of his right hand, as if he were replying to the last counsels of a dark interior monologue. In one of these obscure replies which he was making to himself, he drew the table drawer out quickly towards him, took out a long carving knife which was hidden there, and tried its edge on his nail. This done, he put the knife back into the drawer, and shut it. Just then the distant and melancholy vibration of a bell shook the windows. Six o'clock struck on Saint Médard. Jondrette marked each stroke with a nod of his head. At the sixth stroke, he snuffed the candle with his fingers. Then he began to walk about the room, listened in the hall, walked, listened again: "Provided he comes!" muttered he; then he returned to his chair. He had hardly sat down when the door opened.

The mother Jondrette had opened it, and stood in the hall making a horrible, amiable grimace, which was lighted up from beneath by one of the holes of the dark lantern.

"Walk in," said she.

"Walk in, my benefactor," repeated Jondrette, rising precipitately.

Monsieur Leblanc appeared. He had an air of serenity which made him singularly venerable. He laid four louis upon the table.

"Monsieur Fabantou," said he, "that is for your rent and your pressing wants. We will see about the rest."

"God reward you, my generous benefactor!" said Jondrette, and rapidly approaching his wife:

"Send away the fiacre!"

She slipped away, while her husband was lavishing bows and offering a chair to Monsieur Leblanc. A moment afterwards she came back and whispered in his ear:

"It is done."

The snow which had been falling ever since morning, was so deep that they had not heard the fiacre arrive, and did not hear it go away. Meanwhile Monsieur Leblanc had taken a seat. Jondrette had taken possession of the other chair opposite Monsieur Leblanc. No sooner was Monsieur Leblanc seated than he turned his eyes towards the empty pallets.

"How does the poor little injured girl do?" he inquired.

"Badly," answered Jondrette with a doleful yet grateful smile, "very badly, my worthy monsieur. Her eldest sister has taken her to the Bourbe to have her arm dressed. You will see them, they will be back directly."

"Madame Fabantou appears to me much better," resumed Monsieur Leblanc, casting his eyes upon the grotesque accouterment of the female Jondrette, who, standing between him and the door, as if she were already guarding the exit, was looking at him in a threatening and almost a defiant posture.

"She is dying," said Jondrette. "But you see, monsieur! she has so much courage, that woman! She is not a woman, she is an ox."

The woman, touched by the compliment, retorted with the smirk of a flattered monster:

"You are always too kind to me, Monsieur Jondrette."

"Jondrette!" said M. Leblanc, "I thought that your name was Fabantou?"

"Fabantou or Jondrette!" replied the husband hastily. "Sobriquet as an artist!"

And, directing a shrug of the shoulders towards his wife, which M. Leblanc did not see, he continued with an emphatic and caressing tone of voice:

"Ah! how long we have always got along together, this poor dear and I! What would be left to us, if it were not for that? We are so unfortunate, my respected monsieur! We have arms, no labor! We have courage, no work! Now, for example, I wanted to have my girls learn the trade of making card boxes. You will say: What! a trade? Yes! a trade! a simple trade! a living! What a fall, my benefactor! What a degradation, when one has been what we were! Alas! we have nothing left from our days of prosperity! Nothing but one single thing, a painting, to which I cling, but yet which I shall have to part with, for we must live!"

While Jondrette was talking, with an apparent disorder which detracted nothing from the crafty and cunning expression of his physiognomy, Marius raised his eyes, and perceived at the back of the room somebody whom he had not before seen. A man had come in so noiselessly that nobody had heard the door turn on its hinges. He sat down in silence and with folded arms on the nearest bed, and as he kept behind the woman, he was distinguished only with difficulty.

"Who is that man?" said M. Leblanc.

"That man?" said Jondrette, "that is a neighbor. Pay no attention to him."

M. Leblanc resumed: "Pardon me; what were you saying to me, Monsieur Fabantou?"

"I was telling you, monsieur and dear patron," replied Jondrette, leaning his elbows on the table, and gazing at M. Leblanc with fixed and tender eyes, similar to the eyes of a boa constrictor, "I was telling you that I had a picture to sell."

He got up, went to the wall, at the foot of which stood something, in fact, that resembled a picture and which the candle scarcely revealed. Marius could make nothing out of it, Jondrette being between him and the picture; he merely caught a glimpse of a coarse daub, with a sort of principal personage colored in the crude and glaring style of strolling panoramas and paintings upon screens.

"What is that?" asked M. Leblanc.

Jondrette exclaimed:

"A painting by a master; a picture of great price, my benefactor! I cling to it as to my two daughters, it calls up memories to me! but I am so unfortunate that I would part with it."

Whether by chance, or whether there was some beginning of distrust, while examining the picture, M. Leblanc glanced towards the back of the room. There were now four men there, three seated on the bed, one standing near the door-casing; all four bare-armed, motionless, and with blackened faces. Jondrette noticed that M. Leblanc's eye was fixed upon these men.

"They are friends. They live near by," said he. "They are dark because they work in charcoal. They are chimney doctors. Do not occupy your mind with them, my benefactor, but buy my picture. Take pity on my misery. I shall not sell it to you at a high price. How much do you estimate it worth?"

"But," said M. Leblanc, looking Jondrette full in the face and like a man who puts himself on his guard, "this is some tavern sign, it is worth about three francs."

Jondrette answered calmly:

"Have you your pocket-book here? I will be satisfied with a thousand crowns."

M. Leblanc rose to his feet, placed his back to the wall, and ran his eye rapidly over the room. He had Jondrette at his left on the side towards the window, and his wife and the four men at his right on the side towards the door. The four men did not stir, and had not even the appearance of seeing him; Jondrette had begun again to talk in a plaintive key, with his eyes so wild and his tones so mournful, that M. Leblanc might have thought that he had before his eyes nothing more nor less than a man gone crazy from misery.

While speaking Jondrette did not look at M. Leblanc, who was watching him. M. Leblanc's eye was fixed upon Jondrette, and Jondrette's eye upon the door. Marius' breathless attention went from one to the other. M. Leblanc appeared to ask himself, "Is this an idiot?" Jondrette repeated two or three times with all sorts of varied inflections in the drawling and begging style: "I can only throw myself into the river! I went down three steps for that the other day by the side of the bridge of Austerlitz!"

Suddenly his dull eye lighted up with a hideous glare, this little man straightened up and became horrifying, he took a step towards M. Leblanc and cried to him in a voice of thunder:

"But all this is not the question! do you know me?"

The door of the garret had been suddenly flung open, disclosing three men in blue blouses with black paper masks. The first was spare and had a long iron-bound cudgel; the second, who was a sort of colossus, held by the middle of the handle, with the axe down, a butcher's pole-axe. The third, a broad-shouldered man, not so thin as the first, nor so heavy as the second, held in his clenched fist an enormous key stolen from some prison door. It appeared that it was the arrival of these men for which Jondrette was waiting. A rapid dialogue commenced between him and the man with the cudgel, the spare man. Jondrette, after his colloquy with the man who had the cudgel, turned again towards M. Leblanc and repeated his question, accompanying it with that low, smothered, and terrible laugh of his:

"You do not recognize me, then?"

M. Leblanc looked him in the face, and answered:

"No."

Then Jondrette came up to the table. He leaned forward over the candle, folding his arms, and pushing his angular and ferocious jaws up towards the calm face of M. Leblanc, as nearly as he could without forcing him to draw back, and in that posture, like a wild beast just about to bite, he cried:

"My name is not Fabantou, my name is not Jondrette, my name is Thénardier! I am the innkeeper of Montfermeil! do you understand me? Thénardier! now do you know me?"

When Jondrette had said: *My name is Thénardier,* Marius had trembled in every limb, and supported himself against the wall as if he had felt the chill of a sword-blade through his heart. Then his right arm, which was just ready to fire the signal shot, dropped slowly down, and at the moment that Jondrette had repeated: *Do you understand me, Thénardier?* Marius' nerveless fingers had almost dropped the pistol. Jondrette, in unveiling who he was, had not moved M. Leblanc, but he had completely unnerved Marius. That name of Thénardier, which M. Leblanc did not seem to know, Marius knew. Remember what that name was to him! that name he had worn on his heart, written in his father's will! he carried it in the innermost place of his thoughts, in the holiest spot of his memory, in that sacred command: "A man named Thénardier saved my life. If my son should meet him, he will do him all the good he can." His father's life, saved in a storm of grape upon the heroic field of Waterloo, he was at last about to reward this man for, and to reward him with the scaffold! He had resolved, if ever he found this Thénardier, to accost him in no other wise than by throwing himself at his feet, and now he found him indeed, but to deliver him to the executioner! His father had said to him: Aid Thénardier! and he was answering that adored and holy voice by crushing Thénardier! But on the other hand, to see him ambuscade and not prevent it! to condemn the victim and spare the assassin, could he be bound to any gratitude towards such a wretch? All the ideas which Marius had had for the last four years were, as it were, pierced through and through by this unexpected blow. He shuddered. Everything depended upon him. He held in his hand, they all unconscious, those beings who were moving there before his eyes. If he fired the pistol, M. Leblanc was saved and Thénardier was lost; if he did not, M. Leblanc was sacrificed, and, perhaps, Thénardier escaped. To hurl down the one, or to let the other fall! remorse on either hand. What was to be done? which should he choose? be wanting to his most imperious memories, to so many deep resolutions, to his most sacred duty, to that most venerated paper! be wanting to his father's will, or suffer a crime to be accomplished? He seemed on the one hand to hear "his Ursula" entreating him for her father, and on the other the colonel commending Thénardier to him. He felt that he was mad. His knees gave way beneath him. He was on the point of fainting.

Meanwhile Thénardier, we will call him by no other name henceforth, was walking to and fro before the table in a sort of bewilderment and frenzied triumph. He clutched the candle and put it on the mantel with such a shock that the flame was almost extinguished and the tallow was spattered upon the wall. Then he turned towards M. Leblanc.

"Ha!" cried he, "I have found you again at last, monsieur philanthropist! monsieur threadbare millionaire! old marrow-bones! ha! you do not know me? no, it was not you who came to Montfermeil, to my inn, eight years ago, the night of Christmas, 1823! it was not you who took away Fantine's child from my house! the Lark! it was not you who had a yellow coat! no! and a package of clothes in your hand just as you came here this morning! Ah! you are going to find out at last that it is not all roses to go into people's houses like that, under pretext of their being inns, with worn-out clothes, with the appearance of a pauper, to whom anybody would have given a sou, to deceive persons, to act the generous, take their help away, and threaten them in the woods, and that you do not get quit of it by bringing back afterwards, when people are ruined, an overcoat that is too large and two paltry hospital coverlids, old beggar, child-stealer!"

Thénardier stopped. He was out of breath. His little narrow chest was blowing like a blacksmith's bellows. His eye was full of the base delight of a feeble, cruel, and cowardly animal, which can finally prostrate that of which it has stood in awe, and insult what it has flattered, the joy of a dwarf putting his heel upon the head of Goliath, the joy of a jackal beginning to tear a sick bull, dead enough not to be able to defend himself, alive enough yet to suffer.

M. Leblanc did not interrupt him but said when he stopped: "I see that you are a bandit."

Who has not noticed it, hateful beings have their tender points; monsters are easily annoyed. At this word bandit, Madame Thénardier sprang off the bed. Thénardier seized his chair as if he were going to crush it in his hands: "Don't you stir," cried he to his wife, and turning towards M. Leblanc:

"Bandit! Yes, I know that you call us so, you rich people! Yes! It is true I have failed; I am in concealment, I have no bread; I have not a sou, I am a bandit. Here are three days that I have eaten nothing, I am a bandit! Ah! you warm your feet; you have wadded overcoats like archbishops, you eat truffles, you eat forty-franc bunches of asparagus in the month of January, and green peas, you stuff yourselves, and when you want to know if it is cold you look in the newspaper to see at what degree the thermometer stands. And you come into our caverns, yes, into our caverns, and call us bandits."

Here Thénardier took a step towards the men who were before the door, and added with a shudder:

"When I think that he dares to come and talk to me, as if I were a cobbler!"

For some moments, Monsieur Leblanc had seemed to follow and to watch all the movements of Thénardier, who, blinded and bewildered by his own rage, was walking to and fro in the den with the confidence inspired by the feeling that the door was guarded, having armed possession of a disarmed man, and being nine to one, even if the Thénardiers should count but for one man. In his apostrophe to the man with the pole-axe, he turned his back to Monsieur Leblanc.

Monsieur Leblanc seized this opportunity, pushed the chair away with his foot, the table with his hand, and at one bound, with a marvelous agility, before Thénardier had had time to turn around he was at the window. To open it, get up and step through it, was the work of a second. He was half outside when six strong hands seized him, and drew him forcibly back into the room. The three "chimney doctors" had thrown themselves upon him. At the same time the Thénardiers had clutched him by the hair.

Marius could not endure this sight. "Father," thought he, "pardon me!" And his finger sought the trigger of the pistol. The shot was just about to be fired, when Thénardier's voice cried:

"Do him no harm!"

This desperate attempt of the victim, far from exasperating Thénardier, had calmed him.

"Do him no harm!" he repeated, and without suspecting it, the first result of this was to stop the pistol which was just ready to go off, and paralyze Marius, to whom the urgency seemed to disappear, and who, in view of this new phase of affairs, saw no impropriety in waiting longer. Who knows but some chance may arise which will save him from the fearful alternative of letting the father of Ursula perish, or destroying the savior of the colonel!

A herculean struggle had commenced. With one blow full in the chest M. Leblanc had sent the old man sprawling into the middle of the room, then with two back strokes had knocked down two other assailants, whom he held one under each knee; the wretches screamed under the pressure as if they had been under a granite mill-stone; but the four others had seized the formidable old man by the arms and the back, and held him down over the two prostrate "chimney doctors." They succeeded in throwing him over upon the bed nearest to the window and held him there in awe. Madame Thénardier had not let go of his hair.

"Here," said Thénardier, "let it alone."

"Now, the rest of you," continued Thénardier, "search him."

M. Leblanc seemed to have given up all resistance. They searched him. There was nothing upon him but a leather purse which contained six francs, and his handkerchief. Thénardier put the handkerchief in his pocket, went to the corner by the door, and took a bundle of ropes which he threw to them.

"Tie him to the foot of the bed," said he. The brigands bound him firmly, standing, with his feet to the floor, by the bed-post farthest from the window and nearest to the chimney.

When the last knot was tied, Thénardier took a chair and came and sat down nearly in front of M. Leblanc. Thénardier looked no longer like himself; in a few seconds the expression of his face had passed from unbridled violence to tranquil and crafty mildness. Marius hardly recognized in that polite, clerkly smile the almost beastly mouth which was foaming a moment before; he looked with astonishment upon this fantastic and alarming metamorphosis, and he experienced what a man would feel who should see a tiger change itself into an attorney.

"Monsieur," said Thénardier.

And with a gesture dismissing the brigands who still had their hands upon M. Leblanc:

"Move off a little, and let me talk with monsieur."

They all retired towards the door. He resumed:

"Monsieur, you were wrong in trying to jump out the window. You might have broken your leg. Now, if you please, we will talk quietly. Let us arrange this amicably. I was wrong to fly into a passion just now. I do not know where my wits were, I went much too far, I talked extravagantly. For instance, because you are a millionaire, I told you that I wanted money, a good deal of money, an immense deal of money. That would not be reasonable. My God, rich as you may be, you have your expenses; who does not have them? I do not want to ruin you, I am not a catch-poll, after all. I am not one of those people who, because they have the advantage in position, use it to be ridiculous. Here, I am willing to go halfway and make some sacrifice on my part. I need only two hundred thousand francs. You will say: but I have not two hundred thousand francs with me. Oh! I am not exacting. I do not require that. I only ask one thing. Have the goodness to write what I shall dictate."

Here Thénardier paused, then he added, emphasizing each word and casting a smile towards the furnace:

"I give you notice that I shall not admit that you cannot write."

Thénardier pushed the table close up to Monsieur Leblanc, and took the inkstand, a pen, and a sheet of paper from the drawer, which he left partly open, and from which gleamed the long blade of the knife. He laid the sheet of paper before Monsieur Leblanc.

"Write," said he.

The prisoner spoke at last:

"How do you expect me to write? I am tied."

"That is true; pardon me!" said Thénardier, "you are quite right."

And turning towards one of his men, Bigrenaille, he said:

"Untie monsieur's right arm."

When the prisoner's right hand was free, Thénardier dipped the pen into the ink, and presented it to him.

"Remember, monsieur, that you are in our power, at our discretion, that no human power can take you away from here, and that we should be really grieved to be obliged to proceed to unpleasant extremities. I know neither your name nor your address, but I give you notice that you will remain tied until the person whose duty it will be to carry the letter which you are about to write, has returned. Have the kindness now to write."

"What?" asked the prisoner.

"I will dictate."

M. Leblanc took the pen.

Thénardier began to dictate:

"My daughter—

"Come immediately, I have imperative need of you. The person who will give you this note is directed to bring you to me. I am waiting for you. Come with confidence."

Thénardier resumed:

"Sign it. What is your name?"

"Urbain Fabre," said the prisoner.

Thénardier, with the movement of a cat, thrust his hand into his pocket and pulled out the handkerchief taken from M. Leblanc. He looked for the mark upon it and held it up to the candle.

"U. F. That is it. Urbain Fabre. Well, sign U. F."

The prisoner signed.

"As it takes two hands to fold the letter, give it to me, I will fold it."

This done, Thénardier resumed:

"Put on the address, *Mademoiselle Fabre,* at your house."

The prisoner remained thoughtful for a moment, then he took the pen and wrote:

"Mademoiselle Fabre, at Monsieur Urbain Fabre's, Rue Saint Dominique d'Enfer, No. 17."

Thénardier seized the letter with a sort of feverish convulsive movement.

"Wife!" cried he.

She sprang forward.

"Here is the letter. You know what you have to do. There is a fiacre below. Go right away, and come back ditto."

And addressing the man with the pole-axe:

"Here, since you have taken off your hide-your-nose, go with the woman. You will get up behind the fiacre. You know where you left the *maringotte.*"

"Yes," said the man.

And, laying down his pole-axe in a corner, he followed Madame Thénardier.

[*The Thénardier woman goes out carrying the letter. An hour later she returns, crying out: "False address!"*]

Marius breathed. She, Ursula or the Lark, she whom he no longer knew what to call, was safe.

While his exasperated wife was vociferating, Thénardier had seated himself on the table; he sat a few seconds without saying a word, swinging his right leg, which was hanging down, and gazing upon the furnace with a look of savage reverie. At last he said to the prisoner with a slow and singularly ferocious inflexion:

"A false address! what did you hope for by that?"

"To gain time!" cried the prisoner with a ringing voice.

And at the same moment he shook off his bonds; they were cut. The prisoner was no longer fastened to the bed save by one leg. Before the seven men had had time to recover themselves and spring upon him, he had bent over to the fireplace, reached his hand towards the furnace, then rose up, and now Thénardier, his wife, and the bandits, thrown by the shock into the back part of the room, beheld him with stupefaction, holding above his head the glowing chisel, from which fell an ominous light, almost free and in a formidable attitude.

At the judicial inquest, to which the ambuscade in the Gorbeau tenement gave rise, it appeared that a big sou, cut and worked in a peculiar fashion, was found in the garret, when the police made a descent upon it; this big sou was one of those marvels of labor which the patience of the galleys produces in the darkness and for the darkness, marvels which are nothing else but instruments of escape. The unhappy man who aspires to deliverance finds the means, sometimes without tools, with a folding knife, with an old case knife, to split a sou into two thin plates, to hollow out these two plates without touching the stamp of the mint, and to cut a screw-thread upon the edge of the sou, so as to make the plates adhere anew. This screws and unscrews at will; it is a box. In this box, they conceal a watch-spring, and this watch-spring, well handled, cuts off rings of some size and bars of iron. The unfortunate convict is supposed to possess only a sou; no, he possesses liberty. A big sou of this kind, on subsequent examination by the police, was found open and in two pieces in the room under the pallet near the window. There was also discovered a little saw of blue steel which could be concealed in the big sou. It is probable that when the bandits were searching the prisoner's pockets, he had this big sou upon him and succeeded in hiding it in his hand; and that afterwards, having his right hand free, he unscrewed it and used the saw to cut the ropes by which he was fastened. Being unable to stoop down for fear of betraying himself, he had not cut the cords on his left leg. The prisoner now raised his voice:

"You are pitiable, but my life is not worth the trouble of so long a defense. As to your imagining that you could make me speak, that you could make me write what I do not wish to write, that you could make me say what I do not wish to say——"

He pulled up the sleeve of his left arm, and added:

"Here."

At the same time he extended his arm, and laid upon the naked flesh the glowing chisel, which he held in his right hand, by the wooden handle.

They heard the hissing of the burning flesh; the odor peculiar to chambers of torture spread through the den. Marius staggered, lost in horror; the brigands themselves felt a shudder; the face of the won-derful old man hardly contracted, and while the red iron was sinking into the smoking wound, he turned upon Thénardier his fine face, in which there was no hatred, and in which suffering was swallowed up in a serene majesty.

"Wretches," said he, "have no more fear for me than I have of you."

And drawing the chisel out of the wound, he threw it through the window, which was still open; the horrible glowing tool disappeared, whirling into the night, and fell in the distance, and was quenched in the snow.

The prisoner resumed:

"Do with me what you will."

He was disarmed.

"Lay hold of him," said Thénardier.

Two of the brigands laid their hands upon his shoulders.

At the same time Marius heard beneath him, at the foot of the par-tition, but so near that he could not see those who were talking, this colloquy, exchanged in a low voice:

"There is only one thing more to do."

"To kill him!"

"That is it."

It was the husband and wife who were holding counsel. Thénardier walked with slow steps towards the table, opened the drawer, and took out the knife. Marius cast his eyes wildly about him; the last mechanical resource of despair. Suddenly he started. At his feet, on the table, a clear ray of the full moon illuminated and seemed to point out to him a sheet of paper. Upon that sheet he read this line, written in large letters that very morning, by the elder of the Thérnardier girls:

"THE COGNES ARE HERE."

An idea, a flash crossed Marius' mind; that was the means which he sought; the solution of this dreadful problem which was torturing him, to spare the assassin and to save the victim. He knelt down upon his bureau, reached out his arm, caught up the sheet of paper, quietly detached a bit of plaster from the partition, wrapped it in the paper, and threw the whole through the crevice into the middle of the den.

It was time. Thénardier had conquered his last fears, or his last scruples, and was moving towards the prisoner.

96

"Something fell!" cried the Thénardier woman.

"What is it?" said the husband.

The woman had sprung forward, and picked up the piece of plaster wrapped in the paper. She handed it to her husband. Thénardier hurriedly unfolded the paper, and held it up to the candle.

"It is Eponine's writing. The devil!"

He made a sign to his wife, who approached quickly, and he showed her the line written on the sheet of paper; then he added in a hollow voice:

"Quick! the ladder! leave the meat in the trap, and clear the camp!" This was like the signal to clear the decks in a fleet. The brigands, who were holding the prisoner, let go of him; in the twinkling of an eye, the rope ladder was unrolled out of the window, and firmly fixed to the casing by the two iron hooks.

The prisoner paid no attention to what was passing about him. He seemed to be dreaming or praying. As soon as the ladder was fixed, Thénardier cried:

"Come!"

And he rushed towards the window.

But as he was stepping out, Bigrenaille seized him roughly by the collar.

"No; wait now, old joker! after us."

"After us!" howled the bandits.

"You are children," said Thénardier. "We are losing time. The *railles* are at our heels."

"Well," said one of the bandits, "let us draw lots who shall go out first."

Thénardier exclaimed:

"Are you fools? are you cracked? You are a mess of *jobards!* Losing time, isn't it? drawing lots, isn't it? with a wet finger! for the short straw! write our names! put them in a cap!——"

"Would you like my hat?" cried a voice from the door.

They all turned round. It was Javert.

He had his hat in his hand, and was holding it out smiling. . . .

Javert, at nightfall, had posted his men and hid himself behind the trees on the other side of the boulevard. He put himself in rest, and listened for the signal agreed upon. At last, he became impatient, and finally decided to go up without waiting for the pistol shot. He had come at the right time. The frightened bandits rushed for the arms

97

which they had thrown down anywhere when they had attempted to escape. Javert put on his hat again, and stepped into the room, his arms folded, his cane under his arm, his sword in its sheath.

"Halt there," said he. "You will not pass out through the window, you will pass out through the door. It is less unwholesome. There are seven of you, fifteen of us."

And turning round and calling behind him:

"Come in now!"

A squad of sergeants de ville with drawn swords, and officers armed with axes and clubs, rushed in at Javert's call. They bound the bandits. This crowd of men, dimly lighted by a candle, filled the den with shadow.

"Handcuffs on all!" cried Javert. In a few seconds Javert's order was executed. The Thénardier woman, completely crushed, looked at her manacled hands and those of her husband, dropped to the floor and exclaimed, with tears in her eyes:

"My daughters!"

"They are provided for," said Javert.

Just then he perceived the prisoner of the bandits, who, since the entrance of the police, had not uttered a word, and had held his head down.

"Untie monsieur!" said Javert, "and let nobody go out."

This said, he sat down with authority before the table, on which the candle and the writing materials still were, drew a stamped sheet from his pocket, and commenced his police report. When he had written the first lines, a part of the formula, which is always the same, he raised his eyes:

"Bring forward the gentleman whom these gentlemen had bound."

The officers looked about them.

"Well," asked Javert, "where is he?"

The prisoner of the bandits, M. Leblanc, M. Urbain Fabre, the father of Ursula, or the Lark, had disappeared.

The door was guarded, but the window was not. As soon as he saw that he was unbound, and while Javert was writing, he had taken advantage of the disturbance, the tumult, the confusion, the obscurity, and a moment when their attention was not fixed upon him, to leap out of the window.

An officer ran to the window, and looked out; nobody could be seen outside.

The rope ladder was still trembling.

"The devil!" said Javert, between his teeth, "that must have been the best one."

Saint Denis and Idyl of the Rue Plumet

MARIUS HAD SEEN the unexpected outcome of the ambush upon the track of which he had put Javert; but hardly had Javert left the old ruin, carrying away his prisoners in three coaches, when Marius also slipped out of the house. It was only nine o'clock in the evening. Marius went to Courfeyrac's in the Rue de la Verrerie. This quarter was one of those in which the insurrection was fond of installing itself in those days. Marius said to Courfeyrac: "I have come to sleep with you." Courfeyrac drew a mattress from his bed, where there were two, laid it on the floor, and said: "There you are."

The next day, by seven o'clock in the morning, Marius went back to the tenement, paid his rent, and what was due to Ma'am Bougon, had his books, bed, table, bureau, and his two chairs loaded upon a hand-cart, and went off without leaving his address, so that when Javert came back in the forenoon to question Marius about the events of the evening, he found only Ma'am Bougon, who answered him, "moved!"

A month rolled away, then another. Marius was still with Courfeyrac. He knew from a young attorney, an habitual attendant in the ante-rooms of the court, that Thénardier was in solitary confinement. Every Monday Marius sent to the clerk of La Force five francs for Thénardier.

It happened one day that Marius' solitary walks conducted him to a spot near a pond. That day there was a rarity on the boulevard, a passer. Marius, vaguely struck with the almost sylvan charm of the spot, asked this traveler: "What is the name of this place?"

The traveler answered: "It is the Field of the Lark."

And he added: "It was here that Ulbach killed the shepherdess of Ivry."

But after that word, "the Lark," Marius had heard nothing more. There are such sudden congelations in the dreamy state, which a word is sufficient to produce. The whole mind condenses abruptly about one idea, and ceases to be capable of any other perception. The Lark was the appellation which, in the depths of Marius' melancholy, had replaced Ursula. "Yes," said he in the kind of unreasoning stupor pe-

99

culiar to these mysterious asides, "this is her field. I shall learn here where she lives." This was absurd, but irresistible. And he came every day to this Field of the Lark.

Javert's triumph in the Gorbeau tenement had seemed complete, but it was not so. In the first place, and this was his principal regret, Javert had not made the prisoner prisoner. The victim who slips away is more suspicious than the assassin; and it was probable that this personage, so precious a capture to the bandits, would be a not less valuable prize to the authorities. As to Eponine, Javert "nabbed" her; trifling consolation.

Marius now visited nobody. He lived in the Field of the Lark rather than in Courfeyrac's room. This was his real address: Boulevard de la Santé, seventh tree from the Rue Croulebarbe. He was thinking of "Her!" All at once, in the midst of his ecstasy of exhaustion, he heard a voice which was known to him say:

"Ah! there he is!"

He raised his eyes and recognized the unfortunate child who had come to his room one morning, the elder of the Thénardier girls, Eponine; he now knew her name. Singular fact, she had become more wretched and more beautiful.

She stood for a few seconds, as if she could not speak.

"I have found you, then?" said she at last. "How I have looked for you! if you only knew! Do you know? I have been in the jug. A fortnight! They have let me out! seeing that there was nothing against me, and then I was not of the age of discernment. It lacked two months. Oh! how I have looked for you! it is six weeks now. You don't live down there any longer?"

"No," said Marius.

She looked into Marius' eyes and said:

"I have the address."

Marius turned pale. All his blood flowed back to his heart.

"What address?"

"Of the young lady!"

Marius sprang up from the bank on which he was sitting, and took her wildly by the hand.

"Oh! come! show me the way, tell me! ask me for whatever you will! Where is it?"

"Come with me," she answered. "I am not sure of the street and the number; it is away on the other side from here, but I know the house very well. I will show you."

A cloud passed over Marius' brow. He seized Eponine by the arm: "Swear to me one thing!"

"Swear?" said she. "What does that mean? Ah! you want me to swear?"

And she laughed.

"Your father! promise me, Eponine! swear to me that you will not give this address to your father!"

"Let me go then!" said she, bursting into a laugh. "How you shake me! Yes! yes! I promise you that! I swear to you that! What is it to me? I won't give the address to my father. There! will that do? is that it?"

"Nor to anybody?" said Marius.

"Nor to anybody."

"Now," added Marius, "show me the way."

[*Jean Valjean, known to Marius only as M. Leblanc, left the convent after the death of Fauchelevent. In order not to attract attention by always being seen in the same section of Paris, he hired a house on Rue Plumet, faubourg Saint Germain and two other lodgings elsewhere, one in the Rue de l'Ouest and the other in the Rue de l'Homme Armé. Thanks to Thénardier's daughter Eponine, Marius has found "the Lark" once more. He writes her a strange sort of love letter which Cosette finds one day on a bench in the garden.*]

During the reading, Cosette entered gradually into reverie. These lines, fallen one by one upon the paper, were what might be called drops of soul. Now these pages, from whom could they come? Who could have written them? Cosette did not hesitate for a moment. One single man.

He!

Day had revived in her mind; all had appeared again. She felt a wonderful joy and deep anguish. It was he! he who wrote to her! he who was there! he whose arm had passed through that grating! While she was forgetting him, he had found her again! But had she forgotten him? No, never!

When evening came, Jean Valjean went out; Cosette dressed herself. She arranged her hair in the manner which best became her, and she put on a dress the neck of which, as it had received one cut of the scissors too much, and as, by this slope, it allowed the turn of the neck to be seen, was, as young girls say "a little immodest." It was not the least in the world immodest, but it was prettier than otherwise. She did all this without knowing why.

Did she intend to go out? no.

Did she expect a visit? no.

At dusk, she went down to the garden. Toussaint was busy in her kitchen, which looked out upon the back-yard. She began to walk under the branches, putting them aside with her hand from time to time, because there were some that were very low. She thus reached the seat. The stone was still there. She sat down, and laid her soft white hand upon that stone as if she would caress it and thank it.

All at once, she had that indefinable impression which we feel, though we see nothing, when there is somebody standing behind us. She turned her head and arose. It was he.

Cosette, ready to faint, did not utter a cry. She drew back slowly, for she felt herself attracted forward. He did not stir. Through the sad and ineffable something which enwrapped him, she felt the look of his eyes, which she did not see.

Cosette, in retreating, encountered a tree, and leaned against it. But for this tree, she would have fallen.

Then she heard his voice, that voice which she had never really heard, hardly rising above the rustling of the leaves, and murmuring:

"Pardon me, I am here. My heart is bursting, I could not live as I was, I have come. Have you read what I placed there, on this seat? do you recognize me at all? do not be afraid of me. It is a long time now, do you remember the day when you looked upon me? it was at the Luxembourg, near the Gladiator. And the day when you passed before me? it was the 16th of June and the 2nd of July. It will soon be a year. For a very long time now, I have not seen you at all. See, you are my angel, let me come sometimes; I believe I am going to die. If you but knew! I adore you! Forgive me, I do not know what I am saying to you, perhaps I annoy you. Do I annoy you?"

"O mother!" said she.

And she sank down upon herself as if she were dying.

He caught her, she fell, he caught her in his arms, he grasped her tightly, unconscious of what he was doing. He supported her even while tottering himself. He felt as if his head were enveloped in smoke; flashes of light passed through his eyelids; his ideas vanished; it seemed to him that he was performing a religious act, and that he was committing a profanation. Yet he felt no passionate emotion for this ravishing woman, whom he held against his heart. He was lost in love.

She took his hand and laid it on her heart. He felt the paper there, and stammered:

"You love me, then?"

She answered in a voice so low that it was no more than a breath which could scarcely be heard:

"Hush! you know it!"

And she hid her blushing head on the chest of the proud and intoxicated young man.

He fell upon the seat, she by his side. There were no more words. The stars were beginning to shine. How was it that their lips met? How is it that the birds sing, that the snow melts, that the rose opens, that May blooms, that the dawn whitens behind the black trees on the shivering summit of the hills? Gradually they began to talk. These two beings, pure as spirits, told each other all their dreams, their frenzies, their ecstasies, their chimeras, their despondencies, how they had adored each other from afar, how they had longed for each other, their despair when they had ceased to see each other. When they had finished, when they had told each other everything, she laid her head upon his shoulder, and asked him:

"What is your name?"

"My name is Marius," said he. "And yours?"

"My name is Cosette."

[*Thénardier and his gang escape and their plot to rob the house of Jean Valjean is thwarted by Eponine. Valjean, however, determines to move and tells Cosette to be ready to leave at a moment's notice. Marius is in despair when Cosette tells him. Before he leaves her, he scratches his address on the plaster of the wall: 16, Rue de la Verrerie. Next day he visits his grandfather in an attempt to be reconciled with him. The visit is a failure. Meanwhile insurgents against the government are building barricades in the streets.*]

That very day, towards four o'clock in the afternoon, Jean Valjean was sitting alone upon one of the most solitary embankments of the

Champ de Mars, revolving all manner of thoughts in his mind: Thénardier, the police, the journey, and the difficulty of procuring a passport. On all these points he was anxious.

Finally, an inexplicable circumstance which had just burst upon him, and with which he was still warm, had added to his alarm. On the morning of that very day, being the only one up in the house, and walking in the garden before Cosette's shutters were open, he had suddenly come upon this line scratched upon the wall, probably with a nail.

16, *Rue de la Verrerie*.

It had probably been written during the night. What was it? an address? a signal for others? a warning for him? At all events, it was evident that the garden had been violated, and that some persons unknown had penetrated into it. His mind worked upon this canvas. He took good care not to speak to Cosette of the line written on the wall, for fear of frightening her.

In the midst of these meditations, he perceived, by a shadow which the sun had projected, that somebody had just stopped upon the crest of the embankment immediately behind him. He was about to turn round, when a folded paper fell upon his knees, as if a hand had dropped it from above his head. He took the paper, unfolded it, and read on it this word, written in large letters with a pencil:

REMOVE.

Jean Valjean rose hastily. There was no longer anybody on the embankment; he looked about him, and perceived a species of being larger than a child, smaller than a man, dressed in a gray blouse, and trousers of dirt-colored cotton velvet, which jumped over the parapet and let itself slide into the ditch of the Champ de Mars. Jean Valjean returned home immediately, full of thought. . . .

Marius had left M. Gillenormand's home, feeling desolate. He had entered with a very small hope; he came out with an immense despair. He rambled about all day without knowing where; it rained at intervals, he did not perceive it; for his dinner he bought a penny roll at a baker's, put it in his pocket, and forgot it. It would appear that he took a bath in the Seine without being conscious of it. There are moments when a man has a furnace in his brain. Marius was in one of those moments. He hoped nothing more, he feared nothing more; he had reached this condition since the evening before. He waited for night with feverish impatience, he had but on clear idea; that was, that at nine o'clock he should see Cosette. This last happiness was now his whole future; afterwards, darkness. At intervals, while walking along the most deserted boulevards, he seemed to hear strange sounds in Paris. He roused himself from his reverie, and said: "Are they fighting?"

At nightfall, at precisely nine o'clock, as he had promised Cosette, he was in the Rue Plumet. When he approached the grating he forgot everything else. It was forty-eight hours since he had seen Cosette, he was going to see her again, every other thought faded away, and he felt now only a deep and wonderful joy. Those minutes in which we live centuries always have this sovereign and wonderful peculiarity, that for the moment while they are passing, they entirely fill the heart.

Marius displaced the grating, and sprang into the garden. Cosette was not at the place where she usually waited for him. He crossed the thicket and went to the recess near the steps. "She is waiting for me there," said he. Cosette was not there. He raised his eyes, and saw the shutters of the house were closed. He took a turn around the garden; the garden was deserted. Then he returned to the house, and, mad with love, intoxicated, dismayed, exasperated with grief and anxiety, like a master who returns home in an untoward hour, he rapped on the shutters. He rapped, he rapped again, at the risk of seeing the window open and the forbidding face of the father appear and ask him: "What do you want?" This was nothing compared with what he now began to see. When he had rapped, he raised his voice and called Cosette. "Cosette!" cried he. "Cosette!" repeated he imperiously. There was no answer. It was settled. Nobody in the garden; nobody in the house.

Suddenly he heard a voice which appeared to come from the street, and which cried through the trees:

"Monsieur Marius!"

He arose.

"Hey?" said he.

"Monsieur Marius, is it you?"

"Yes."

"Monsieur Marius," added the voice, "your friends are expecting you at the barricade, in the Rue de la Chanvrerie."

This voice was not entirely unknown to him. It resembled the harsh and roughened voice of Eponine. Marius ran to the grating, pushed aside the movable bar, passed his head through, and saw somebody who appeared to him to be a young man rapidly disappearing in the twilight.

The place was indeed admirably chosen, the entrance of the street wide, the farther end contracted and like a cul-de-sac, Corinth throttling it, Rue Mondétour easy to bar at the right and left, no attack possible except from the Rue Saint Denis, that is from the front, and without cover.

At the irruption of the mob, dismay seized the whole street, not a passer but had gone into eclipse. In a flash, at the end, on the right, on the left, shops, stalls, alley gates, windows, blinds, dormer-windows, shutters of every size, were closed from the ground to the roofs. One frightened old woman had fixed a mattress before her window on two clothes poles, as a shield against the musketry. The wine-shop was the only house which remained open; and that for a good reason, because the band had rushed into it. The rain had ceased. Recruits had arrived. Some working-men had brought under their blouses a keg of powder, a hamper containing bottles of vitriol, two or three carnival torches.

Courfeyrac and his men Enjolras and Combeferre directed everything. Two barricades were now building at the same time, both resting on the house of Corinth and making a right angle; the larger one closed the Rue de la Chanvrerie, the other closed the Rue Mondétour in the direction of the Rue du Cygne. This last barricade, very narrow, was constructed only of casks and paving stones. There were about fifty laborers there, some thirty armed with muskets, for on their way they had effected a wholesale loan from an armorer's shop.

Nothing could be more fantastic and more motley than this band. One had a short jacket, a cavalry, and two horse-pistols; another was in shirt sleeves, with a round hat, and a powder-horn hung at his side; a third had a breast-plate of nine sheets of brown paper, and was armed with a saddler's awl. There was one of them who cried: *"Let us exterminate to the last man, and die on the point of our bayonets!"* This man had no bayonet. Another displayed over his coat a cross-belt and cartridge-box of the National Guard, with the box cover adorned with this inscription in red cloth: *Public Order.* Many muskets bearing the numbers of their legions, few hats, no cravats, many bare arms, some pikes. Add to this all ages, all faces, small pale young men, bronzed wharfmen. All were hurrying, and, while helping each other, they talked about the possible chances—that they would have help by three o'clock in the morning—that they were sure of one regiment—that Paris would rise. Terrible subjects, with which were mingled a sort of cordial joviality. One would have said they were brothers, they did not know each other's names. Great perils have this beauty, that they bring to light the fraternity of strangers.

A fire had been kindled in the kitchen, and they were melting pitchers, dishes, forks, all the pewter ware of the wine-shop into bullets. They drank through it all. Percussion-caps and buck-shot rolled pell-mell upon the tables with glasses of wine.

The man of tall stature whom Courfeyrac, Combeferre and Enjolras had noticed, at the moment he joined the company at the corner of the Rue des Billettes, was working on the little barricade, and making himself useful there. Gavroche worked on the large one.

The two barricades finished, the flag run up, a table was dragged out of the wine-shop; and Courfeyrac mounted upon the table. Enjolras brought the square box and Courfeyrac opened it. This box was filled with cartridges. When they saw the cartridges, there was a shudder among the bravest, and a moment of silence. Courfeyrac distributed them with a smile. Each one received thirty cartridges. Many had powder and set about making others with the balls which they were molding. As for the keg of powder, it was on a table by itself near the door, and it was reserved.

The long roll which was running through all Paris was not discontinued, but it had got to be only a monotonous sound to which they paid no more attention, with melancholy undulations. They loaded their muskets and their carbines all together, without precipitation, with a solemn gravity. Enjolras placed three sentinels outside the barricades, one in the Rue de la Chanvrerie, the second in the Rue des Prêcheurs, the third at the corner of la Petite Truanderie.

Then, the barricades built, the posts assigned, the muskets loaded, the videttes placed, alone in these fearful streets in which there were now no passers, surrounded by these dumb, and as it were dead houses, which throbbed with no human motion, enwrapped by the deepening shadows of the twilight, which was beginning to fall, in the midst of this obscurity and this silence, through which they felt the advance of something inexpressibly tragical and terrifying, isolated, armed, determined, tranquil, they waited. It was now quite night. Nothing came. There were only confused sounds, and at intervals volleys of musketry; but rare, ill-sustained, and distant. This respite, which was thus prolonged, was a sign that the government was taking its time, and massing its forces. These fifty men were awaiting sixty thousand. Gavroche at this moment was very much engaged, not exactly with his cartridges.

The man from the Rue des Billettes had just entered the basement room and had taken a seat at the table which was least lighted. An infantry musket of large model had fallen to his lot, and he held it between his knees. Gavroche hitherto, distracted by a hundred "amusing" things, had not even seen this man. When he came in, Gavroche mechanically followed him with his eyes, admiring his musket, then, suddenly, when the man had sat down, the *gamin* arose. Gavroche balanced himself upon his heels, clenched both fists in his pockets, twisted his neck like a bird, expended in one measureless pout all the sagacity of his lower lip. He was stupefied, uncertain, credulous, convinced, bewildered.

It was in the deepest of this meditation that Enjolras accosted him.

"You are small," said Enjolras, "nobody will see you. Go out of the barricades, glide along by the houses, look about the streets a little, and come and tell me what is going on."

Gavroche straightened himself up.

"Little folks are good for something then! that is very lucky! I will go! meantime, trust the little folks, distrust the big——" And Gavroche, raising his head and lowering his voice, added, pointing to the man of the Rue des Billettes:

"You see that big fellow there?"

"Well?"

"He is a spy."

"You are sure?"

"It isn't a fortnight since he pulled me by the ear off the cornice of the Pont Royal where I was taking the air."

Enjolras approached the man and asked him:

"Who are you?"

At this abrupt question, the man gave a start. He looked straight to the bottom of Enjolras' frank eye and appeared to catch his thought. He smiled with a smile which, of all things in the world, was the most disdainful, the most energetic, and the most resolute, and answered with a haughty gravity:

"I see how it is——Well, yes!"

"You are a spy?"

"I am an officer of the government."

"Your name is?"

"Javert."

Enjolras made a sign to the four men. In a twinkling, before Javert had had time to turn around, he was collared, thrown down, bound, searched. All this was executed so rapidly that it was finished as soon as it was perceived about the wine-shop. Javert had not uttered a cry. Seeing Javert tied to the post, Courfeyrac, Bossuet, Joly, Combeferre and the men scattered about the two barricades ran in.

Javert, backed up against the post, and so surrounded with ropes that he could make no movement, held up his head with the intrepid serenity of the man who has never lied.

"It is a spy," said Enjolras.

And turning towards Javert:

"You will be shot ten minutes before the barricade is taken."

Javert replied in his most imperious tone:

"Why not immediately?"

"We are economizing powder."

"Then do it with a knife."

"Spy," said the handsome Enjolras, "we are judges, not assassins."

That voice which through the twilight had called Marius to the barricade of the Rue de la Chanvrerie sounded to him like the voice of destiny. He wished to die, the opportunity presented itself; he was knocking at the door of the tomb, a hand in the shadow held out the key. These dreary clefts in the darkness before despair are tempting. Marius pushed aside the bar which had let him pass so many times, came out of the garden, and said: "Let us go!"

Mad with grief, feeling no longer anything fixed or solid in his brain, incapable of accepting anything henceforth from fate, after these two months passed in the intoxications of youth and of love, whelmed at once beneath all the reveries of despair, he had now but one desire: to make an end of it very quick.

He began to walk rapidly. It happened that he was armed, having Javert's pistols with him. A little beyond the black corner of the alley and the Rue de la Chanvrerie, which threw a broad shadow, in which he was himself buried, he perceived a light upon the pavement, a portion of the wine-shop, and behind, a lamp twinkling in a kind of shapeless wall, and men crouching down with muskets on their knees. All this was within twenty yards of him. It was the interior of the barricade. The houses on the right of the alley hid from him the rest of the wine-shop, the great barricade, and the flag. Marius had but one step more to take. Then the unhappy young man sat down upon a stone, folded his arms, and thought of his father.

Still hidden in the corner of the Rue Mondétour, he watched the first phase of the combat, irresolute and shuddering. At the shots, at the cries of the wounded Guards, the assailants had scaled the entrenchment, upon the summit of which could now be seen thronging Municipal Guards, soldiers of the Line, National Guards of the banlieue, musket in hand. They already covered more than two-thirds of the wall, but they did not leap into the enclosure; they seemed to hesitate, fearing some snare. They looked into the obscure barricade as one would look into a den of lions. The light of the torch only lighted up their bayonets, their bearskin caps, and the upper part of their anxious and angry faces.

Marius had now no arms, he had thrown away his pistols, but he had noticed the keg of powder in the basement room near the door.

As he turned half round, looking in that direction, a soldier aimed at him. At the moment the soldier aimed at Marius, a hand was laid upon the muzzle of the musket, and stopped it. It was somebody who had sprung forward, the young working-man with velvet pantaloons. The shot went off, passed through the hand, and perhaps also through the working-man, for he fell, but the ball did not reach Marius. All this in the smoke, rather guessed than seen. Marius, who was entering the basement room, hardly noticed it. Still he had caught a dim glimpse of that musket directed at him, and that hand which had stopped it, and he had heard the shot. But in moments like that the things which we see waver and rush headlong, and we stop for nothing. We feel ourselves vaguely pushed towards still deeper shadow, and all is cloud.

The insurgents, surprised, but not dismayed, had rallied. Enjolras had cried: "Wait! don't fire at random!" In the first confusion, in fact, they might hit one another. Most of them had gone up to the window of the second story and to the dormer windows, whence they commanded the assailants. The most determined, with Enjolras, Courfeyrac, Jean Prouvaire and Combeferre, had haughtily placed their backs to the houses in the rear, openly facing the ranks of soldiers and guards which crowded the barricade.

All this was accomplished without precipitation, with that strange and threatening gravity which precedes melees. On both sides they were taking aim, the muzzles of the guns almost touching; they were so near that they could talk with each other in an ordinary tone. Just as the spark was about to fly, an officer in a gorget and with huge epaulets, extended his sword and said:

"Take aim!"

"Fire!" said Enjolras.

The two explosions were simultaneous, and everything disappeared in the smoke. A stinging and stifling smoke amid which writhed, with dull and feeble groans, the wounded and the dying. When the smoke cleared away, on both sides the combatants were seen, thinned out, but still in the same places, and reloading their pieces in silence. Suddenly, a thundering voice was heard, crying:

"Begone, or I'll blow up the barricade!"

All turned in the direction whence the voice came.

Marius had entered the basement room, and had taken the keg of powder, then he had profited by the smoke and the kind of obscure fog which filled the entrenched enclosure, to glide along the barricade as far as that cage of paving-stones in which the torch was fixed. To pull out the torch, to put the keg of powder in its place, to push the pile of paving-stones upon the keg, which stove it in, with a sort of terrible self-control—all this had been for Marius the work of stooping down and rising up; and now all, National Guards, Municipal Guards, officers, soldiers, grouped at the other extremity of the barricade, beheld him with horror, his foot upon the stones, the torch in his hand, his stern face lighted by a deadly resolution, bending the flame of the torch towards that formidable pile in which they discerned the broken barrel of powder, and uttering that terrific cry:

"Begone, or I'll blow up the barricade!"

Marius upon this barricade, after the octogenarian, was the vision of the young revolution after the apparition of the old.

"Blow up the barricade!" said a sergeant, "and yourself also!"

Marius answered:

"And myself also."

And he approached the torch to the keg of powder.

But there was no longer anybody on the wall. The assailants, leaving their dead and wounded, fled pell-mell and in disorder towards the extremity of the street, and were again lost in the night. It was a rout.

The barricade was redeemed.

[*Marius discovers that the young man who saved his life is Eponine, disguised as a boy. Before she dies, she gives him a letter from Cosette.*]

Marius kissed that livid forehead from which oozed an icy sweat. This was not infidelity to Cosette; it was a thoughtful and gentle farewell to an unhappy soul. He had not taken the letter which Eponine had given him without a thrill. He had felt at once the presence of an event. He was impatient to read it. The heart of man is thus made; the unfortunate child had hardly closed her eyes when Marius thought to unfold this paper. He laid her gently upon the ground, and went away. Something told him that he could not read that letter in sight of this corpse.

He went to a candle in the basement-room. It was a little note, folded and sealed with the elegant care of woman. The address was in a woman's hand, and ran:

"To Monsieur, Monsieur Marius Pontmercy, at M. Courfeyrac's, Rue de la Verrerie, No. 16."

He broke the seal and read:

"My beloved, alas! my father wishes to start immediately. We shall be to-night in the Rue de l'Homme Armé, No. 7. In a week we shall be in England. COSETTE. June 4th."

Such was the innocence of this love that Marius did not even know Cosette's handwriting.

What happened may be told in a few words. Eponine had done it all. After the evening of the 3rd of June, she had had a double thought, to thwart the projects of her father and the bandits upon the house in the Rue Plumet, and to separate Marius from Cosette. She had changed rags with the first young rogue who thought it amusing to dress as a woman while Eponine disguised herself as a man. It was she who, in the Champ de Mars, had given Jean Valjean the expressive warning: *Remove.* Jean Valjean returned home, and said to Cosette: *We start to-night, and we are going to the Rue de l'Homme Armé with Toussaint. Next week we shall be in London.* Cosette, prostrated by this unexpected blow, had hastily written two lines to Marius. But how should she get the letter to the post? She did not go out alone, and Toussaint, surprised at such an errand, would surely show the letter to M. Fauchelevent. In this anxiety, Cosette saw, through the grating, Eponine in men's clothes, who was now prowling continually about the garden. Cosette called "this young working-man" and handed him five francs and the letter, saying to him: "Carry this letter to its address right away." Eponine put the letter in her pocket. The next day, June 5th, she went to Courfeyrac's to ask for Marius, not to give him the letter, but, a thing which every jealous and loving soul will understand, "to see." There she waited for Marius, or, at

112

least, for Courfeyrac—still to see. When Courfeyrac said to her: we are going to the barricades, an idea flashed across her mind. To throw herself into that death as she would have thrown herself into any other, and to push Marius into it. She followed Courfeyrac, made sure of the post where they were building the barricade; and very sure, since Marius had received no notice, and she had intercepted the letter, that he would at nightfall be at his usual evening rendezvous, she went to the Rue Plumet, waited there for Marius, and sent him, in the name of his friends, that appeal which must, she thought, lead him to the barricade. She counted upon Marius' despair when he should not find Cosette; she was not mistaken. She returned herself to the Rue de la Chanvrerie. We have seen what she did there. She died with that tragic joy of jealous hearts which drag the being they love into death with them, saying: nobody shall have him!

Marius covered Cosette's letter with kisses. She loved him then? He had for a moment the idea that now he need not die. Then he said to himself: "She is going away. Her father takes her to England, and my grandfather refuses to consent to the marriage. Nothing is changed in the fatality." Then he thought that there were two duties remaining for him to fulfill: to inform Cosette of his death and to send her a last farewell, and to save from the imminent catastrophe which was approaching this poor child, Eponine's brother and Thénardier's son.

He had a pocket-book with him; the same that had contained the pages upon which he had written so many thoughts of love for Cosette. He tore out a leaf and wrote with a pencil these few lines:

"Our marriage was impossible. I have asked my grandfather, he has refused; I am without fortune, and you also. I ran to your house, I did not find you, you know the promise that I gave you? I keep it, I die, I love you. When you read this, my soul will be near you, and will smile upon you."

Having nothing to seal this letter with, he merely folded the paper, and wrote upon it this address:

"To Mademoiselle Cosette Fauchelevent, at M. Fauchelevent's, Rue de l'Homme Armé, No. 7."

The letter folded, he remained a moment in thought, took his pocket-book again, opened it, and wrote these lines on the first page with the same pencil:

"My name is Marius Pontmercy. Carry my corpse to my grandfather's, M. Gillenormand, Rue des Filles du Calvaire, No. 6, in the Marais."

He put the book into his coat-pocket, then he called Gavroche. The *gamin,* at the sound of Marius' voice, ran up with his joyous and devoted face.

"Will you do something for me?"

"Anything," said Gavroche.

"You see this letter?"

"Yes."

"Take it. Go out of the barricade immediately" (Gavroche, disturbed, began to scratch his ear), "and to-morrow morning you will carry it to its address, to Mademoiselle Cosette, at M. Fauchelevent's, Rue de l'Homme Armé, No. 7."

"All right," said he.

And he started off on a run by the little Rue Mondétour.

What are the convulsions of a city compared with those of the soul? Man is of a still deeper depth than the people. Jean Valjean, at that very moment, was a prey to a frightful uprising. All the gulfs were re-opened within him. He also, like Paris, was shuddering on the threshold of a formidable and obscure revolution. A few hours had sufficed. His destiny and his conscience were suddenly covered with shadow. Of him also, as of Paris, we might say: the two principles are face to face. The angel of light and the angel of darkness are to wrestle on the bridge of the abyss. Which of the two shall hurl down the other? which shall sweep him away?

On the eve of that same day, June 5th, Jean Valjean, accompanied by Cosette and Toussaint, had installed himself in the Rue de l'Homme Armé. A sudden turn of fortune awaited him there.

Jean Valjean had brought Toussaint, which he had never done in his preceding absences. He saw that possibly he should not return to the Rue Plumet, and he could neither leave Toussaint behind, nor tell her his secret. Besides he felt that she was devoted and safe. Between servant and master, treason begins with curiosity. But Toussaint, as if she had been predestined to be the servant of Jean Valjean, was not curious. She said through her stuttering, "I am so; I do my work! the rest is not my affair."

In this departure from the Rue Plumet, which was almost a flight, Jean Valjean carried nothing but the little valise christened by Cosette the *inseparable*. Full trunks would have required porters, and porters are witnesses. They had a coach come to the door on the Rue Babylone, and they went away. It was with great difficulty that Toussaint obtained permission to pack up a little linen and clothing and a few toilet articles. Cosette herself carried only her writing case and her blotter.

Jean Valjean, to increase the solitude and mystery of this disappearance, had arranged so as not to leave the cottage on the Rue Plumet till the close of the day, which left Cosette time to write her note to Marius. They arrived in the Rue de l'Homme Armé after nightfall.

We are reassured almost as foolishly as we are alarmed; human nature is so constituted. Hardly was Jean Valjean in the Rue de l'Homme Armé, before his anxiety grew less, and by degrees was dissipated.

His first care was to place the *inseparable* by his side. He slept well. Night counsels; we may add: night calms. Next morning he awoke almost cheerful. He thought the dining-room charming, although it was hideous, furnished with an old round table, a low sideboard surmounted by a hanging mirror, a worm-eaten armchair, and a few other chairs loaded down with Toussaint's bundles. Through an opening in one of these bundles, Jean Valjean's National Guard uniform could be seen. As for Cosette, she had Toussaint bring a bowl of soup to her room, and did not make her appearance till evening.

About five o'clock, Toussaint, who was coming and going, very busy with this little removal, set a cold fowl on the dining-room table, which Cosette, out of deference to her father, consented to look at. This done, Cosette, upon pretext of a severe headache, said good night to Jean Valjean, and shut herself in her bedroom. Jean Valjean ate a chicken's wing with a good appetite, and, leaning on the table, clearing his brow little by little, was regaining his sense of security. While he was making this frugal dinner, he became confusedly aware, on two or three occasions, of the stammering of Toussaint, who said to him: "Monsieur, there is a row; they are fighting in Paris." But, absorbed in a multitude of interior combinations, he paid no attention to it. To tell the truth, he had not heard. He arose and began to walk from the window to the door, and from the door to the window, growing calmer and calmer. While yet walking up and down, with

115

slow steps, his eye suddenly met something strange. He perceived facing him, in the inclined mirror which hung above the sideboard, and he distinctly read the lines which follow:

"My beloved, alas! my father wishes to start immediately. We shall be to-night in the Rue de l'Homme Armé, No. 7. In a week we shall be in London. COSETTE. June 4th."

Jean Valjean stood aghast.

Cosette, on arriving, had laid her blotter on the sideboard before the mirror, and, wholly absorbed in her sorrowful anguish, had forgotten it there, without even noticing that she left it wide open, and open exactly at the page upon which she had dried the five lines written by her, and which she had given in charge to the young workman passing through the Rue Plumet. The writing was imprinted upon the blotter.

The mirror reflected the writing. There resulted what is called in geometry the symmetrical image; so that the writing reversed on the blotter was corrected by the mirror, and presented its original form; and Jean Valjean had beneath his eyes the letter written in the evening by Cosette to Marius. It was simple and withering.

Jean Valjean went to the mirror. He read the five lines again, but he did not believe it. They produced upon him the effect of an apparition in a flash of lightning. It was a hallucination. It was impossible. It was not true.

Little by little his perception became more precise; he looked at Cosette's blotter, and the consciousness of the real fact returned to him. Jean Valjean tottered, let the blotter fall, and sank down into the old armchair by the sideboard, his head drooping, his eye glassy, bewildered. He said to himself that it was clear, and that the light of the world was for ever eclipsed, and that Cosette had written that to somebody. Then he heard his soul, again become terrible, given a sullen roar in the darkness. Go, then, and take from the lion the dog which he has in his cage.

A circumstance strange and sad, Marius at that moment had not yet Cosette's letter; chance had brought it, like a traitor, to Jean Valjean before delivering it to Marius.

Jean Valjean til this day had never been vanquished when put to the proof. He had been subjected to fearful trials; no violence of ill fortune had been spared him; the ferocity of fate, armed with every vengeance and with every scorn of society, had taken him for a subject and had greedily pursued him. He had neither recoiled nor flinched before anything. He had accepted, when he must, every extremity; he had sacrificed his reconquered inviolability of manhood, given up his liberty, risked his head, lost all, suffered all, and he had remained so disinterested and stoical that at times one might have believed him translated, like a martyr. His conscience, inured to all possible assaults of adversity, might seem for ever impregnable. Well, he who could have seen his inward monitor would have been compelled to admit that at this hour it was growing feeble.

For, of all the tortures which he had undergone in that inquisition of destiny, this was the most fearful. Never had such pincers seized him. He felt the mysterious quiver of every latent sensibility. He felt the laceration of the unknown fiber. Alas, the supreme ordeal, let us say rather, the only ordeal, is the loss of the beloved being.

His instinct did not hesitate. He put together certain circumstances, certain dates, certain blushes, and certain pallors of Cosette, and he said to himself: "It is he." The divination of despair is a sort of mysterious bow which never misses its aim. With his first conjecture, he hit Marius. He did not know the name, but he found the man at once. He perceived distinctly, at the bottom of the implacable evocation of memory, the unknown prowler of the Luxembourg, that wretched seeker of amours, that romantic idler, that imbecile, that coward, for it is cowardice to come and make sweet eyes at girls who are beside their father who loves them.

While he was thinking, Toussaint entered. Jean Valjean arose, and asked her:

"Didn't you tell me just now that they were fighting?"

"Oh! yes, monsieur," answered Toussaint. "It is over by Saint Merry."

There are some mechanical impulses which come to us, without our knowledge even, from our deepest thoughts. It was doubtless under the influence of an impulse of this kind, and of which he was hardly conscious, that Jean Valjean five minutes afterwards found himself in the street.

He was bare-headed, seated upon the stone block by the door of his house. He seemed to be listening. The night had come. . . .

The street was empty. A few anxious bourgeois, who were rapidly returning home, hardly perceived him. Every man for himself in times of peril. The lamplighter came as usual to light the lamp which hung exactly opposite the door of No. 7, and went away. Jean Valjean, to one who had examined him in that shadow, would not have seemed a living man. However, almost at that very moment, there was a sharp explosion in the direction of the markets, a second followed, more violent still; it was probably that attack on the barricade of the Rue de la Chanvrerie which we have just seen repulsed by Marius. At this double discharge, the fury of which seemed increased by the stupor of the night, Jean Valjean was startled; he looked up in the direction whence the sound came; then he sank down upon the block, folded his arms, and his head dropped slowly upon his breast. He resumed his dark dialogue with himself.

Suddenly he raised his eyes; somebody was walking in the street; he heard steps near him; he looked, and, by the light of the lamp, in the direction of the Archives, he perceived a livid face, young and radiant.

Gavroche had just arrived in the Rue de l'Homme Armé. Gavroche was looking in the air, and appeared to be searching for something. He saw Jean Valjean perfectly, but he took no notice of him. Jean Valjean, who, the instant before, in the state of mind in which he was, would not have spoken nor even replied to anybody, felt irresistibly impelled to address a word to this child.

"Small boy," said he, "what is the matter with you?"

"The matter is that I am hungry," answered Gavroche tartly. And he added: "Small yourself."

Jean Valjean felt in his pocket and took out a five-franc piece.

"Poor creature," said he, in an undertone, and speaking to himself, "he is hungry."

And he put the hundred-sous piece into his hand.

Gavroche cocked up his nose, astonished at the size of this big sou; he looked at it in the dark, and the whiteness of the big sou dazzled him. He knew five-franc pieces by hearsay; their reputation was agreeable to him; he was delighted to see one so near.

"You are a fine fellow," said Gavroche.

And he put the five-franc piece into one of his pockets.

His confidence increasing, he added:

"Do you belong in the street?"

"Yes; why?"

"Could you show me number seven?"

"What do you want with number seven?"

Here the boy stopped; he feared that he had said too much; he plunged his nails vigorously into his hair, and merely answered:

"Ah! that's it."

118

An idea flashed across Jean Valjean's mind. Anguish has such lucidities. He said to the child:

"Have you brought the letter I am waiting for?"

"You?" said Gavroche. "You are not a woman."

"The letter is for Mademoiselle Cosette; isn't it?"

"Cosette?" muttered Gavroche. "Yes, I believe it is that funny name."

"Well," resumed Jean Valjean, "I am to deliver the letter to her. Give it to me."

"The fact is," continued Gavroche, "you look to me like a fine fellow."

"Give it to me quick."

"Take it."

And he handed the paper to Jean Valjean.

"And hurry yourself, Monsieur What's-your-name, for Mamselle What's-her-name is waiting."

This said, Gavroche went away, or rather, resumed his flight like an escaped bird towards the spot whence he came. He replunged into the obscurity as if he made a hole in it, with the rapidity and precision of a projectile.

Jean Valjean went in with Marius' letter. He groped his way upstairs, pleased with the darkness like an owl which holds his prey, opened and softly closed the door, listened to see if he heard any sound, decided that, according to all appearances, Cosette and Toussaint were asleep, plunged three or four matches into the bottle of the Fumade tinder-box before he could raise a spark, his hand trembled so much; there was theft in what he was about to do. At last, his candle was lighted, he leaned his elbows on the table, unfolded the paper, and read. In Marius' note to Cosette, Jean Valjean saw only these words.

"—I die. When you read this, my soul will be near you."

Before these two lines he was horribly dazzled; he sat a moment as if crushed by the change of emotion which was wrought within him. He had only to keep the note in his pocket. Cosette would never know what had become of "that man." "I have only to let things take their course. That man cannot escape. If he is not dead yet, it is certain that he will die. What happiness!"

All this said within himself, he became gloomy. Then he went down and waked the porter. About an hour afterwards, Jean Valjean went out in the full dress of a National Guard, and armed.

Jean Valjean

THE INSURGENTS put the barricade in order, cleared up the basement room, took the kitchen for a hospital, completed the dressing of the wounds; gathered up the powder scattered over the floor and the tables, cast bullets, made cartridges, scraped lint, distributed the arms of the fallen, cleaned the interior of the redoubt, picked up the fragments, carried away the corpses.

They deposited the dead in a heap in the little Rue Mondétour, of which they were still masters. The pavement was red for a long time at that spot. Among the dead were four National Guards of the suburbs. Enjolras had their uniforms laid aside. About two o'clock in the morning, they took a count. There were left thirty-seven of them. Marius, fasting, feverish, successively driven from every hope, stranded upon grief, most dismal of shipwrecks, saturated with violent emotions and feeling the end approach, was sinking deeper and deeper into that visionary stupor which always precedes the fatal hour when voluntarily accepted.

He raised his voice:

"Enjolras and Combeferre are right," said he; "no useless sacrifice. I add my voice to theirs, and we must hasten. Combeferre has given the criteria. There are among you some who have families, mothers, sisters, wives, children. Let those leave the ranks."

Nobody stirred.

"Married men and supports of families, out of the ranks!" repeated Marius.

His authority was great. Enjolras was indeed the chief of the barricade, but Marius was its savior.

"I order it," cried Enjolras.

"I beseech you," said Marius.

They obeyed. In a few minutes five were unanimously designated and left the ranks.

"There are five!" exclaimed Marius.

There were only four uniforms.

Marius raised his eyes and saw M. Fauchelevent. Jean Valjean had just entered the barricade. Whether by information obtained, or by instinct, or by chance, he came by the little Rue Mondétour. Thanks to his National Guard dress, he had passed easily.

At the moment Jean Valjean entered the redoubt, nobody had

noticed him, all eyes being fixed upon the five chosen ones and upon the four uniforms. Jean Valjean, himself, saw and understood, and, silently, he stripped off his coat, and threw it upon the pile with the others.

The commotion was indescribable.

"Who is this man?" asked Bossuet.

"He is," answered Combeferre, "a man who saves others."

Marius added in a grave voice:

"I know him."

This assurance was enough for all.

Enjolras turned towards Jean Valjean:

"Citizen, you are welcome."

And he added:

"You know that we are going to die."

Jean Valjean, without answering, helped the fifth insurgent to put on his uniform.

[*Jean Valjean, as a reward for giving up his uniform so that the fifth citizen could escape, claims the privilege of putting Javert to death.*]

When Jean Valjean was alone with Javert, he untied the rope that held the prisoner by the middle of the body, the knot of which was under the table. Then he motioned to him to get up. Javert obeyed, with that undefinable smile into which the supremacy of enchained authority is condensed. Jean Valjean took Javert by the strap as you would take a beast of burden and, drawing him after him, went out of the wine-shop slowly, for Javert, with his legs fettered, could take only very short steps. Jean Valjean had the pistol in his hand.

They crossed thus the interior trapezium of the barricade. The insurgents, intent upon the imminent attack, were looking the other way. Jean Valjean, with some difficulty, bound as Javert was, but without letting go of him for a single instant, made him scale the little entrenchment on the Rue Mondétour. When they had climbed over this wall, they found themselves alone in the little street. Nobody saw them now. The corner of the house hid them from insurgents. The corpses carried out from the barricades made a terrible mound a few steps off. Jean Valjean put the pistol under his arm, and fixed upon Javert a look which had no need of words to say: "Javert, it is I."

Javert answered.

"Take your revenge."

Jean Valjean took a knife out of his pocket, and opened it.

"A *surin!*" exclaimed Javert. "You are right. That suits you better."

Jean Valjean cut the martingale which Javert had about his neck, then he cut the ropes which he had on his wrists, then, stooping down, he cut the cord which he had on his feet; and, rising, he said to him:

"You are free."

Javert was not easily astonished. Still, complete master as he was of himself, he could not escape an emotion. He stood aghast and motionless.

Jean Valjean continued:

"I don't expect to leave this place. Still, if by chance I should, I live, under the name of Fauchelevent, in the Rue de l'Homme Armé, Number Seven."

Javert had the scowl of a tiger half opening the corner of his mouth, and he muttered between his teeth:

"Take care."

"Go," said Jean Valjean.

Javert resumed:

"You said Fauchelevent, Rue de l'Homme Armé?"

"Number seven."

Javert repeated in an undertone: "Number seven." He buttoned his coat, restored the military stiffness between his shoulders, turned half round, folded his arms, supporting his chin with one hand, and walked off in the direction of the markets. Jean Valjean followed him with his eyes. When Javert was gone, Jean Valjean fired the pistol in the air. Then he re-entered the barricade and said: "It is done."

The death-agony of the barricade was approaching. Suddenly the drum beat the charge. The attack was a hurricane. In the evening, in the obscurity, the barricade had been approached silently as if by a boa. Now, in broad day, in this open street, surprise was entirely impossible; the strong hand, moreover, was unmasked, the cannon had commenced the roar, the army rushed upon the barricade. A powerful column of infantry of the line, intersected at equal intervals by National Guards and Municipal Guards on foot, and supported by deep masses heard but unseen, turned into the street at a quick step, drums beating, trumpets sounding, bayonets fixed, sappers at their head, and, unswerving under the projectiles, came straight upon the barricade with the weight of a bronze column upon a wall. The wall held well.

The insurgents fired impetuously. The barricade scaled was like a mane of flashes. The assault was so sudden that for a moment it was overflowed by assailants; but it shook off the soldiers as the lion does the dogs, and it was covered with besiegers only as a cliff is with foam, to reappear, a moment afterwards, steep, black and formidable. There was assault after assault. The horror continued to increase. Then resounded over this pile of paving-stones, in this Rue de la Chanvrerie, a struggle worthy the walls of Troy. These men, wan, tattered and exhausted, who had not eaten for twenty-four hours, who had not slept, who had but a few more shots to fire, who felt their pockets empty of cartridges, nearly all wounded, their heads or arms bound with a smutty and blackened cloth, with holes in their coats whence the blood was flowing, scarcely armed with worthless muskets and with old hacked swords, became Titans. A final assault was now attempted, and this assault succeeded. The mass bristling with bayonets and hurled at a double-quick step, came on irresistible, and the dense battle-front of the attacking column appeared in the smoke at the top of the escarpment. This time, it was finished. The group of insurgents who defended the center fell back pell-mell to the high six-story house which formed the rear of the redoubt.

Marius remained without. A ball had broken his shoulder-blade; he felt that he was fainting, and that he was falling. At that moment, his eyes already closed, he experienced the shock of a vigorous hand seizing him, and his fainting fit, in which he lost consciousness, left him hardly time for this thought, mingled with the last memory of Cosette: "I am taken prisoner. I shall be shot."

Marius was in fact a prisoner. Prisoner of Jean Valjean. The hand which had seized him from behind at the moment he was falling, and the grasp of which he had felt in losing consciousness, was the hand of Jean Valjean.

Jean Valjean had taken no other part in the combat than to expose himself. Save for him, in that supreme phase of the death-struggle, nobody would have thought of the wounded. Thanks to him, everywhere present in the carnage like a providence, those who fell were taken up, carried into the basement-room, and their wounds dressed. In the intervals, he repaired the barricade. But nothing which could resemble a blow, an attack, or even a personal defense came from his hands. He was silent, and gave aid.

Jean Valjean, in the thick cloud of the combat, did not appear to see Marius; the fact is, that he did not take his eyes from him. When a shot struck down Marius, Jean Valjean bounded with the agility of a tiger, dropped upon him as upon a prey, and carried him away.

The whirlwind of the attack at that instant concentrated so fiercely upon Enjolras and the door of the wine-shop that nobody saw Jean Valjean cross the unpaved field of the barricade, holding the senseless Marius in his arms, and disappear behind the corner of the house. There Jean Valjean stopped; he let Marius slide to the ground, set his back to the wall, and cast his eyes about him. The situation was appalling.

For the moment, for two or three minutes, perhaps, this skirt of wall was a shelter; but how escape from this massacre? He remembered the anguish in which he was in the Rue Polonceau, eight years before, and how he had succeeded in escaping; that was difficult then, to-day it was impossible. Before him he had that deaf and implacable house of six stories, which seemed inhabited only by the dead man, leaning over his window; on his right he had the low barricade, which closed the Petite Truanderie; to clamber over this obstacle appeared easy, but above the crest of the wall a range of bayonet-points could be seen. A company of the line was posted beyond this barricade, on the watch. It was evident that to cross the barricade was to meet the fire of a platoon, and that every head which should venture to rise above the top of the wall of paving-stones would serve as a target for sixty muskets. At his left he had the field of combat. Death was behind the corner of the wall.

What should he do?

A bird alone could have extricated himself from that place.

And he must decide upon the spot, find an expedient, adopt his course. They were fighting a few steps from him; by good luck all were fiercely intent upon a single point, the door of the wine-shop; but let one soldier, a single one, conceive the idea of turning the house, of attacking it in flank, and all was over.

Jean Valjean looked at the house in front of him, he looked at the barricade by the side of him, then he looked upon the ground, with the violence of the last extremity, in desperation, and as if he would have made a hole in it with his eyes.

Beneath his persistent look, something vaguely tangible in such an agony outlined itself and took form at his feet, as if there were a power in the eye to develop the thing desired. He perceived a few steps from him, at the foot of the little wall so pitilessly watched and guarded on the outside, under some fallen paving-stones which partly hid it, an iron grating laid flat and level with the ground. This grating, made of strong transverse bars, was about two feet square. The stone frame which held it had been torn up, and it was as it were unset. Through the bars a glimpse could be caught of an obscure opening, something like the flue of a chimney or the main of a cistern. Jean Valjean sprang forward. His old science of escape mounted to his brain like a flash. To remove the stones, to lift the grating, to load Marius, who was as inert as a dead body, upon his shoulders, to descend, with that burden upon his back, by the aid of his elbows and knees, into this kind of well, fortunately not very deep, to let fall over his head the heavy iron trapdoor upon which the stones were shaken back again, to find a foothold upon a flagged surface ten feet below the ground, this was executed like what is done in delirium, with the strength of a giant and the rapidity of an eagle; it required but very few moments.

Jean Valjean found himself, with Marius still senseless, in a sort of long underground passage. There, deep peace, absolute silence, night.

For ten centuries, the cloaca has been the disease of Paris. The sewer is the taint which the city has in her blood. The popular instinct is never mistaken. The trade of sewerman was formerly almost as perilous, and almost as repulsive to the people, as the trade of knacker so long stricken with horror, and abandoned to the executioner. It required high wages to persuade a mason to disappear in that fetid ooze; the well-digger's ladder hesitated to plunge into it; it was said proverbially: *to descend into the sewer is to enter the grave;* and all manner of hideous legends covered this colossal drain with dismay.

It was in the sewer of Paris that Jean Valjean found himself. Further resemblance of Paris with the sea. As in the ocean, the diver can disappear.

The transition was marvelous. From the very center of the city, Jean Valjean had gone out of the city, and, in the twinkling of an eye, the time of lifting a cover and closing it again, he had passed from broad day to complete obscurity, from noon to midnight, from uproar to silence, from the whirl of the thunder to the stagnation of the tomb, and, by a mutation much more prodigious still than that of the Rue Polonceau, from the most extreme peril to the most absolute security. Only, the wounded man did not stir, and Jean Valjean did not know whether what he was carrying away in this grave were alive or dead.

His first sensation was blindness. Suddenly he saw nothing more. It seemed to him also that in one minute he had become deaf. He heard nothing more. The frenzied storm of murder which was raging a few feet above him only reached him, as we have said, thanks to the thickness of the earth which separated him from it, stifled and indistinct, and like a rumbling at a great depth. He felt that it was solid under his feet; that was all; but that was enough. A whiff of fetidness informed him where he was.

After a few moments, he ceased to be blind. A little light fell from the air-hole through which he had slipped in, and his eye became accustomed to this cave. He began to distinguish something. The passage in which he was earthed, no other word better expresses the condition, was walled up behind him. It was one of those cul-de-sacs technically called branchments. Before him, there was another wall, a wall of night. The light from the air-hole died out ten or twelve paces from the point at which Jean Valjean stood, and scarcely produced a pallid whiteness over a few yards of the damp wall of the sewer. Beyond, the opaqueness was massive; to penetrate it appeared horrible, and to enter it seemed like being engulfed. He could, however, force his way into that wall of mist, and he must do it. He must even hasten. There was not a minute to be lost. He had laid Marius upon the ground; he gathered him up, this is again the right word; replaced him upon his shoulders, and began his journey. He resolutely entered that obscurity.

The track of the sewers echoes, so to speak, the track of the streets which overlie them. There were in the Paris of that day two thousand two hundred streets. Picture to yourselves below then that forest of dark branches which is called the sewer. The sewers existing at that epoch, placed end to end, would have given a length of thirty miles.

He went forward, with anxiety, but with calmness, seeing nothing, knowing nothing, plunged into chance, that is to say, swallowed up in Providence. At a certain moment he felt that he was getting away from under the Paris which was petrified by the rebellion, in which the barricades had suppressed the circulation, and that he was com-

126

ing beneath the Paris which was alive and normal. He heard suddenly above his head a sound like thunder, distant, but continuous. It was the rumbling of the vehicles.

He had been walking for about half an hour, at least by his own calculation, and had not yet thought of resting; only he had changed the hand which supported Marius. The darkness was deeper than ever, but this depth reassured him.

All at once he saw his shadow before him. It was marked out on a feeble ruddiness almost indistinct, which vaguely empurpled the floor at his feet, and the arch over his head, and which glided along at his right and his left on the two slimy walls of the corridor. In amazement he turned round.

Behind him, in the portion of the passage through which he had passed, at a distance which appeared to him immense, flamed, throwing its rays into the dense obscurity, a sort of horrible star which appeared to be looking at him.

It was the gloomy star of the police which was rising in the sewer. Behind this star were moving without order eight or ten black forms, straight, indistinct, terrible. . . .

During the day of the 6th of June, a search of the sewers had been ordered. It was feared that they would be taken as a refuge by the vanquished. Three platoons of officers and sewermen explored the subterranean streets of Paris. The officers were armed with carbines, clubs, swords, and daggers. That which was at this moment directed upon Jean Valjean was the lantern of the patrol.

Luckily, if he saw the lantern well, the lantern saw him badly. It was light and he was shadow. He was far off, and merged in the blackness of the place. He drew close to the side of the wall, and stopped. The men of the patrol listened and heard nothing; they looked and saw nothing. They consulted. The result of this council held by the watch-dogs was that they had been mistaken, that there had been no noise, that there was nobody there.

Before going away, the sergeant, to ease the police conscience, discharged his carbine in the direction they were abandoning, towards Jean Valjean. The detonation rolled from echo to echo in the vault like the rumbling of this titanic bowel. Some plastering which fell into the stream and spattered the water a few steps from Jean Valjean made him aware that the ball had struck the arch above his head.

Slow and measured steps resounded upon the floor for some time, more and more deadened by the progressive increase of the distance,

127

the group of black forms sank away, a glimmer oscillated and floated, making a ruddy circle in the vault, which decreased, then disappeared, the silence became deep again, the obscurity became again complete. Jean Valjean had resumed his advance.

He had to stoop every second, then rise up, to grope incessantly for the wall. The moisture of the stones and the sliminess of the floor made them bad points of support, whether for the hand or for the foot. He was wading in the hideous muck of the city. The occasional gleams from the air-holes appeared only at long intervals, and so ghastly were they that the noonday seemed but moonlight; all the rest was mist, miasma, opacity, blackness. Jean Valjean was hungry and thirsty; thirsty especially; and this place, like the sea, is one full of water where you cannot drink. His strength, which was prodigious, and very little diminished by age, thanks to his chaste and sober life, began to give way notwithstanding. Fatigue grew upon him, and as his strength diminished the weight of his load increased. Marius, dead perhaps, weighed heavily upon him as inert bodies do. Jean Valjean supported him in such a way that his breast was not compressed and his breathing could always be as free as possible. He felt the rapid gliding of the rats between his legs. One of them was so frightened as to bite him. There came to him from time to time through the aprons of the mouths of the sewer a breath of fresh air which revived him.

In opening Marius' clothes, he had found two things in his pockets, the bread which had been forgotten there since the day previous, and Marius' pocket-book. He ate the bread and opened the pocket-book. On the first page he found the lines written by Marius. They will be remembered.

"My name is Marius Pontmercy. Carry my corpse to my grandfather's, M. Gillenormand, Rue des Filles du Calvaire, No. 6, in the Marais."

By the light of the air-hole, Jean Valjean read these lines, and stopped a moment as if absorbed in himself, repeating in an undertone: "Rue des Filles du Calvaire, Number Six, Monsieur Gillenormand." He replaced the pocket-book in Marius' pocket. He had eaten; strength had returned to him; he took Marius on his back again, laid his head carefully upon his right shoulder, and began to descend the sewer. . . .

He walked with desperation, almost with rapidity. He had reached an angle of the sewer and, down there before him, far, very far away, he perceived a light. This time, it was not the terrible light; it was the good and white light. It was the light of day. Jean Valjean saw the outlet.

It was indeed the outlet, but it did not let him out. The arch was closed by a strong grating, and the grating which, according to all appearance, rarely turned upon its rusty hinges, was held in its stone frame by a stout lock which, red with rust, seemed an enormous brick. He could see the keyhole, and the strong bolt deeply plunged into the iron staple. The lock was plainly a double-lock. It was one of those Bastille locks of which the old Paris was so lavish.

Beyond the grating were the open air, the river, the daylight; the beach, very narrow, but sufficient to get away. The distant quays, Paris, that gulf in which one is so easily lost, the wide horizon, liberty. He distinguished at his right, below him, the Pont d'Iéna, and at his left, above, the Pont des Invalides; the spot would have been propitious for awaiting night and escaping. It was one of the most solitary points in Paris; the beach which fronts on the Gros Caillou. The flies came in and went out through the bars of the grating. It might have been half-past eight o'clock in the evening. The day was declining.

Jean Valjean laid Marius along the wall on the dry part of the floor, then walked to the grating and clenched the bars with both hands; the shaking was frenzied, the shock nothing. The grating did not stir. Jean Valjean seized the bars one after another, hoping to be able to tear out the least solid one, and to make a lever of it to lift the door or break the lock. Not a bar yielded. A tiger's teeth are not more solid in their sockets. No lever; no possible purchase. The obstacle was invincible. No means of opening the door. He had only succeeded in escaping into a prison.

It was over. All that Jean Valjean had done was useless. Exhaustion ended in abortion. He turned his back to the grating, and dropped upon the pavement, rather prostrate than sitting, beside the yet motionless Marius and his head sank between his knees. No exit. This was the last drop of anguish.

Of whom did he think in this overwhelming dejection? Neither of himself nor of Marius. He thought of Cosette. In the midst of this annihilation, a hand was laid upon his shoulder, and a voice which spoke low, said to him:

"Go halves."

Somebody in that darkness? Nothing is so like a dream as despair; Jean Valjean thought he was dreaming. He had heard no steps. Was it possible? He raised his eyes.

A man was before him.

This man was dressed in a blouse; he was barefooted; he held his shoes in his left hand; he had evidently taken them off to be able to reach Jean Valjean without being heard. Jean Valjean had not a moment's hesitation. Unforeseen as was the encounter, this man was known to him. This man was Thénardier.

Although wakened, so to speak, with a start, Jean Valjean, accustomed to be on the alert and on the watch for unexpected blows which he must quickly parry, instantly regained possession of all his presence of mind. Besides, the condition of affairs could not be worse; a certain degree of distress is no longer capable of crescendo, and Thénardier himself could not add to the blackness of this night. There was a moment of delay.

[*Thénardier does not recognize Jean Valjean. He demands a share in the money for which he believes Valjean has murdered the man he is carrying. In return, he unlocks the grille and the two fugitives are at last able to leave the sewer.*]

Jean Valjean found himself outside. He let Marius slide down upon the beach. They were outside!

The miasmas, the obscurity, the horror, were behind him. The balmy air, pure, living, joyful, freely respirable, flowed around him. Everywhere about him silence, but the charming silence of a sunset in a clear sky. Twilight had fallen; night was coming, the great liberatress, the friend of all those who need a mantle of darkness to escape from an anguish. It was the undecided and exquisite hour which says neither yes nor no. There was already night enough for one to be lost in it at a little distance, and still day enough for one to be recognized near at hand.

Jean Valjean was for a few seconds irresistibly overcome by all this august and caressing serenity. Then, hastily, as if a feeling of duty came back to him, he bent over Marius, and, dipping up some water in the hollow of his hand, he threw a few drops gently into his face. Marius' eyelids did not part; but his half-open mouth breathed. Jean Valjean was plunging his hand into the river again, when suddenly he felt an indescribable uneasiness, such as we feel when we have somebody behind us, without seeing him. He turned round. As just before, somebody was indeed behind him.

A man of tall stature, wrapped in a long overcoat, with folded arms, and holding in his right hand a club, the leaden knob of which could be seen, stood erect a few steps in the rear of Jean Valjean, who was stooping over Marius. It was, with the aid of the shadow, a sort of apparition. A simple man would have been afraid on account of the twilight, and a reflective man on account of the club.

Jean Valjean recognized Javert.

Javert, after his unhoped-for departure from the barricade, had gone to the prefecture of police, had given an account verbally to the prefect in person in a short audience, had then immediately returned to his duty, which implied a certain surveillance of the shore on the right bank of the Champs Elysées, which for some time had excited the attention of the police. There he had seen Thénardier, and had followed him. The rest is known.

Jean Valjean had passed from one shoal to another. These two encounters, blow on blow—to fall from Thénardier to Javert—were hard to bear.

Javert did not recognize Jean Valjean, who no longer resembled himself. He did not unfold his arms, he secured his club in his grasp by an imperceptible movement, and said in a quick and calm voice:

"Who are you?"

"I."

"What you?"

"Jean Valjean."

Javert put the club between his teeth, bent his knees, inclined his body, laid his two powerful hands upon Jean Valjean's shoulders, which they clamped like two vises, examined him, and recognized him. Their faces almost touched. Javert's look was terrible. Jean Valjean stood inert under the grasp of Javert like a lion who should submit to the claw of a lynx.

"Inspector Javert," said he, "you have got me. Besides, since this morning, I have considered myself your prisoner. I did not give you my address to try to escape you. Take me. Only grant me one thing."

Javert seemed not to hear. At last, he let go of Jean Valjean, rose up as straight as a stick, took his club firmly in his grasp, and, as if in a dream, murmured rather than pronounced this question:

"What are you doing here? and who is this man?"

Jean Valjean answered, and the sound of his voice appeared to awaken Javert:

"It is precisely of him that I wished to speak. Dispose of me as you please; but help me first to carry him home. I only ask that of you."

Javert's face contracted, as it happened to him whenever anybody seemed to consider him capable of a concession. Still he did not say no. He seized Marius' hand, seeking for his pulse.

"He is wounded," said Jean Valjean.

"He is dead," said Javert.

Jean Valjean answered:

"No. Not yet."

"You have brought him, then, from the barricade here?" observed Javert.

His preoccupation must have been deep, as he did not dwell longer upon this perplexing escape through the sewer, and did not even notice Jean Valjean's silence after his question. Jean Valjean, for his part, seemed to have but one idea. He resumed:

"He lives in the Marais, Rue des Filles du Calvaire, at his grandfather's—I forget the name."

Jean Valjean felt in Marius' coat, took out the pocket-book, opened it at the page penciled by Marius, and handed it to Javert. There was still enough light floating in the air to enable one to read. Javert, moreover, had in his eye the feline phosphorescence of the birds of the night. He deciphered the few lines written by Marius, and muttered: "Gillenormand, Rue des Filles du Calvaire, No. 6."

Then he cried to a fiacre: "Driver?" Javert kept Marius' pocket-book.

A moment later, the carriage, descending by the slope of the watering-place, was on the beach. Marius was laid upon the back seat, and Javert sat down by the side of Jean Valjean on the front seat. When the door was shut, the fiacre moved rapidly off, going up the quays in the direction of the Bastille. . . .

It was after nightfall when the fiacre arrived at No. 6, in the Rue des Filles du Calvaire. Everybody in the house was asleep. People go to bed early in the Marais, especially on days of civil trouble. That good old quarter, startled by the Revolution, takes refuge in slumber, as children, when they hear Bugaboo coming, hide their heads very quickly under their coverlets.

Jean Valjean and the driver lifted Marius out of the coach, Jean Valjean supporting him by the armpits, and the coachman by the knees. Javert called out to the porter in the tone which befits the government, in presence of the porter of a factious man.

"Somebody whose name is Gillenormand?"

"It is here. What do you want with him?"

"His son is brought home."

"His son?" said the porter with amazement.

"He is dead."

Jean Valjean, who came ragged and dirty, behind Javert, and whom the porter beheld with some horror, motioned to him with his head that he was not. The porter did not appear to understand either Javert's words, or Jean Valjean's signs.

The porter merely woke Basque. Basque woke Nicolette; Nicolette woke Aunt Gillenormand. As to the grandfather, they let him sleep, thinking that he would know it soon enough at all events. They carried Marius up to the first story, without anybody perceiving it in the other portions of the house, and they laid him on an old couch in M. Gillenormand's ante-chamber; and, while Basque went for a doctor and Nicolette was opening the linen closets, Jean Valjean felt Javert touch him on the shoulder. He understood, and went downstairs, having behind him Javert's following steps. The porter saw them depart as he had seen them arrive, with drowsy dismay.

They got into the fiacre again, and the driver mounted upon his box.

"Inspector Javert," said Jean Valjean, "grant me one thing more."

"What?" asked Javert roughly.

"Let me go home a moment. Then you shall do with me what you will."

Javert remained silent for a few seconds, his chin drawn back into the collar of his overcoat, then he let down the window in front.

"Driver," said he, "Rue de l'Homme Armé, No. 7."

What did Jean Valjean desire? To finish what he had begun; to inform Cosette, to tell her where Marius was, to give her perhaps some other useful information, to make, if he could, certain final dispositions. As to himself, as to what concerned him personally, it was all over; he had been seized by Javert and did not resist. At the entrance of the Rue de l'Homme Armé, the fiacre stopped, this street being too narrow for carriages to enter. Javert and Jean Valjean got out. They entered the street. It was, as usual, empty. Javert followed Jean Valjean. They reached No. 7. Jean Valjean rapped. The door opened.

"Very well," said Javert. "Go up."

He added with a strange expression and as if he were making an effort in speaking in such a way:

"I will wait here for you."

Jean Valjean looked at Javert. This manner of proceeding was little in accordance with Javert's habits. Still, that Javert should now have a sort of haughty confidence in him, the confidence of the cat which grants the mouse the liberty of the length of her claw, resolved as Jean Valjean was to deliver himself up and make an end of it, could not surprise him very much. He opened the door, went into the house, cried to the porter who was in bed and who had drawn the cord without getting up: "It is I!" and mounted the stairs.

On reaching the first story, he paused. All painful paths have their halting-places. The window on the landing, which was a sliding window, was open. As in many old houses, the stairway admitted the light, and had a view upon the street.

Jean Valjean, either to take breath or mechanically, looked out of this window. He leaned over the street. It is short, and the lamp lighted it from one end to the other. Jean Valjean was bewildered with amazement; there was nobody there.

Javert was gone.

Basque and the porter had carried Marius into the parlor, still stretched motionless upon the couch on which he had been first laid. The doctor, who had been sent for, had arrived. Aunt Gillenormand had got up.

On the doctor's order, a cot-bed had been set up near the couch. The doctor examined Marius, and, after having determined that the pulse still beat, that the sufferer had no wound penetrating his breast, and that the blood at the corners of his mouth came from the nasal cavities, he had him laid flat upon the bed, without a pillow, his head on a level with his body, and even a little lower, with his chest bare, in order to facilitate respiration.

The body had not received any interior lesion; a ball, deadened by the pocket-book, had turned aside, and made the tour of the ribs with a hideous gash, but not deep, and consequently not dangerous. The long walk underground had completed the dislocation of the broken shoulder-blade, and there were serious difficulties there.

Basque and Nicolette tore up linen and made bandages; Nicolette sewed them, Basque folded them. There being no lint, the doctor stopped the flow of blood from the wounds temporarily with rolls of wadding. By the side of the bed, three candles were burning on a table upon which the surgical instruments were spread out. The doc-

134

tor washed Marius' face and hair with cold water. A bucketful was red in a moment. The porter, candle in hand, stood by.

At the moment the doctor was wiping the face and touching the still closed eyelids lightly with his finger, a door opened at the rear end of the parlor, and a long, pale figure approached.

It was the grandfather.

The revolt, for two days, had very much agitated, exasperated, and absorbed M. Gillenormand. He had not slept during the preceding night, and he had had a fever all day. At night, he had gone to bed very early, recommending that everything in the house be bolted, and, from fatigue, he had fallen asleep.

The slumbers of old men are easily broken; M. Gillenormand's room was next the parlor, and, in spite of the precautions they had taken, the noise had awakened him. Surprised by the light which he saw at the crack of his door, he had got out of bed, and groped his way along. He perceived the bed, and on the mattress that bleeding young man, white with a waxy whiteness, his eyes closed, his mouth open, his lips pallid, naked to the waist, gashed everywhere with red wounds, motionless, brightly lighted.

The grandfather had, from head to foot, as much of a shiver as ossified limbs can have; his eyes, the cornea of which had become yellow from his great age, were veiled with a sort of glassy haze; his whole face assumed in an instant the cadaverous angles of a skeleton head, his arms fell pendent as if a spring were broken in them, and his stupefied astonishment was expressed by the separation of the fingers of his aged, tremulous hands; his knees bent forward, showing through the opening of his nightgown his poor naked legs bristling with white hairs, and he murmured:

"Marius!"

"Monsieur," said Basque, "monsieur has just been brought home. He has been to the barricade, and——"

"He is dead!" cried the old man in a terrible voice. "Oh! the brigand."

Then a sort of sepulchral transfiguration made this centenarian as straight as a young man.

"Monsieur," said he, "you are the doctor. Come, tell me one thing. He is dead, isn't he?"

The physician, in the height of anxiety, kept silence.

M. Gillenormand went to a window, opened it wide as if he were stifling, and, standing before the shadow, he began to talk into the street to the night:

"Pierced, sabered, slaughtered, exterminated, slashed, cut in pieces! do you see that, the vagabond! He knew very well that I was waiting for him, and that I had had his room arranged for him, and that I had had his portrait of the time when he was a little boy hung at the head of my bed! He knew very well that he had only to come back, and that for years I had been calling him, and that I sat at night in my chimney corner, with my hands on my knees, not knowing what to do, and that I was a fool for his sake! You knew it very well, that you had only to come in and say: 'It is I,' and that you would be the master of the house, and that I would obey you, and that you would do whatever you liked with your old booby of a grandfather. You knew it very well, and you said: 'No, he is a royalist; I won't go!' And you went to the barricades, and you got yourself killed, out of spite!"

He approached Marius, who was still livid and motionless, and to whom the physician had returned, and he began to wring his hands. The old man's white lips moved as if mechanically, and made way for almost indistinct words, like whispers in a death-rattle, which could scarcely be heard: "Oh! heartless! Oh! clubbist! Oh! scoundrel! Oh! Septembrist! Yes, these times are infamous, infamous, infamous, and that is what I think of you, of your ideas, of your systems, of your masters, of your oracles, of your doctors, of your scamps of writers, of your beggars of philosophers, and of all the revolutions which for sixty years have frightened the flocks of crows in the Tuileries! And as you had no pity in getting yourself killed like that, I shall not have even any grief for your death, do you understand, assassin?"

At this moment, Marius slowly raised his lids, and his gaze, still veiled in the astonishment of lethargy, rested upon M. Gillenormand.

"Marius!" cried the old man. "Marius! my darling Marius! my child! my dear son! You are opening your eyes, you are looking at me, you are alive, thanks!"

And he fell fainting.

Javert made his way with slow steps from the Rue de l'Homme Armé. He walked with his head down, for the first time in his life, and, for the first time in his life as well, with his hands behind his back. Javert leaned both elbows on the parapet, with his chin in his hands, and while his fingers were clenched mechanically in the thickest of his whiskers, he reflected.

He saw before him two roads, both equally straight; but he saw two; and that terrified him—him, who had never in his life known but one straight line. And, bitter anguish, these two roads were contradictory. One of these two straight lines excluded the other. Which of the two was the true one?

To owe life to a malefactor, to accept that debt and to pay it, to be, in spite of himself, on a level with a fugitive from justice, and to pay him for one service with another service; to allow him to say: "Go away," and to say to him in turn: "Be free"; to sacrifice duty, that general obligation, to personal motives, and to feel in these personal motives something general also, and perhaps superior; to betray society in order to be true to his own conscience; that all these absurdities should be realized and that they should be accumulated upon himself, this it was by which he was prostrated.

Jean Valjean confounded him. All the axioms which had been the supports of his whole life crumbled away before this man. Jean Valjean's generosity towards him, Javert, overwhelmed him. Other acts, which he remembered and which he had hitherto treated as lies and follies, returned to him now as realities. M. Madeleine reappeared behind Jean Valjean, and the two figures overlaid each other so as to make but one, which was venerable. Javert felt that something horrible was penetrating his soul, admiration for a convict. Respect for a galley-slave, can that be possible? He shuddered at it, yet could not shake it off. It was useless to struggle, he was reduced to confess before his own inner tribunal the sublimity of this wretch. That was hateful.

Unnatural state, if ever there was one. There were only two ways to get out of it. One, to go resolutely to Jean Valjean, and to return the man of the galleys to the dungeon. The other—

Javert left the parapet.

The darkness was complete. It was the sepulchral moment which follows midnight. A ceiling of clouds concealed the stars. The sky was only an ominous depth. The houses in the city no longer showed a single light; nobody was passing; all that he could see of the streets and the quays was deserted; Notre Dame and the towers of the Palace of Justice seemed like features of the night. A lamp reddened the curb of the quay. The silhouettes of the bridges were distorted in the mist, one behind the other. The rains had swelled the river.

137

The place where Javert was leaning was situated exactly over the rapids of the Seine, perpendicularly over that formidable whirlpool which knots and unknots itself like an endless screw.

Javert bent his head and looked. All was black. He could distinguish nothing. He heard a frothing sound; but he did not see the river. At intervals, in that giddy depth, a gleam appeared in dim serpentine contortions, the water having this power, in the most complete night, of taking light, nobody knows whence, and changing it into an adder. The gleam vanished, and all became again indistinct. Immensity seemed open there. What was beneath was not water, it was chasm. The wall of the quay, abrupt, confused, mingled with vapor, suddenly lost to sight, seemed like an escarpment of the infinite.

He saw nothing, but he perceived the hostile chill of the water, and the insipid odor of the moist stones. A fierce breath rose from that abyss. The swollen river guessed at rather than perceived, the tragical whispering of the flood, the dismal vastness of the arches of the bridge, the imaginable fall into that gloomy void, all that shadow was full of horror.

Javert remained for some minutes motionless, gazing into that opening of darkness; he contemplated the invisible with a fixedness which resembled attention. The water gurgled. Suddenly he took off his hat and laid it on the edge of the quay. A moment afterwards, a tall and black form, which from the distance some belated passer might have taken for a phantom, appeared standing on the parapet, bent towards the Seine, then sprang up, and fell straight into the darkness; there was a dull splash; and the shadow alone was in the secret of the convulsions of that obscure form which had disappeared under the water.

[*For nearly four months, Marius hovers between life and death. Finally, he begins to recover and during his convalescence he becomes reconciled with his grandfather, M. Gillenormand, who, moreover, consents to his marriage with Cosette. Jean Valjean withdraws the money he had deposited under the name of M. Madeleine, tells Cosette that he is not her father, and invents a story to account for the 600,000 francs he gives as her dowry.*]

The enchantment, great as it was, did not efface other preoccupations from Marius' mind. During the preparations for the marriage, and while waiting for the time fixed upon, he had some difficult and careful retrospective researches made. He owed gratitude on several sides, he owed some on his father's account, he owed some on his own. There was Thénardier; there was the unknown man who had brought him, Marius, to M. Gillenormand's. He was lost in conjectures.

In the hope of deriving aid in his researches from them, Marius had preserved the bloody clothes which he wore when he was brought back to his grandfather's. On examining the coat, it was noticed that one skirt was oddly torn. A piece was missing.

One evening, Marius spoke, before Cosette and Jean Valjean, of all this singular adventure, of the numberless inquiries which he had made, and of the uselessness of his efforts. The cold countenance of "Monsieur Fauchelevent" made him impatient. He exclaimed with a vivacity which had almost the vibration of anger:

"Yes, that man, whoever he may be, was sublime. Do you know what he did, monsieur? He intervened like the archangel. He must have thrown himself into the midst of the combat, have snatched me out of it, have opened the sewer, have drawn me into it, have borne me through it! He must have made his way for more than four miles through hideous subterranean galleries, bent, stooping, in the darkness, in the cloaca, more than four miles, monsieur, with a corpse upon his back! And with what object? With the single object of saving that corpse. And that corpse was I. He said to himself: 'There is perhaps a glimmer of life still there; I will risk my own life for that miserable spark!' And his life, he did not risk it once, but twenty times! And each step was a danger. The proof is, that on coming out of the sewer he was arrested. Do you know, monsieur, that that man did all that? And he could expect no recompense. What was I? An insurgent. What was I? A vanquished man. Oh! if Cosette's six hundred thousand francs were mine—"

"They are yours," interrupted Jean Valjean.

"Well," resumed Marius, "I would give them to find that man!"

Jean Valjean kept silence.

Jean Valjean returned home. He lighted his candle and went upstairs. The apartment was empty. Toussaint herself was no longer there. Jean Valjean's step made more noise than usual in the rooms. All the closets were open. He went into Cosette's room. There were no sheets on the bed. The pillow, without a pillow-case and without laces, was laid upon the coverlets folded at the foot of the mattress of which the ticking was to be seen and on which nobody should sleep henceforth. All the little feminine objects to which Cosette clung had been carried away; there remained only the heavy furniture and the four walls. Toussaint's bed was also stripped. A single bed was made and seemed waiting for somebody, that was Jean Valjean's.

Then his venerable white head fell upon the bed, this old stoical heart broke, and anybody who had passed along the staircase at that moment, would have heard fearful sobs.

In what manner should Jean Valjean comport himself in regard to the happiness of Cosette and Marius? This happiness, it was he who had willed it, it was he who had made it; he had thrust it into his own heart, and at this hour, looking upon it, he might have the same satisfaction that an armorer would have, who should recognize his own mark upon a blade, on withdrawing it all reeking from his breast.

Cosette had Marius, Marius possessed Cosette. They had everything, even riches. And it was his work.

But this happiness, now that it existed, now that it was here, what was he to do with it, he, Jean Valjean? Should he impose himself upon this happiness? To impose his galleys upon these two dazzling children, or to consummate by himself his irremediable engulfment. On the one side the sacrifice of Cosette, on the other of himself.

He remained there until dawn, in the same attitude, doubled over on the bed, prostrated under the enormity of fate, crushed perhaps, alas! his fists clenched, his arms extended at a right angle, like one taken from the cross and thrown down with his face to the ground. He remained twelve hours, the twelve hours of a long winter night, chilled, without lifting his head, and without uttering a word. He was as motionless as a corpse.

[*Jean Valjean confesses to Marius that he is an ex-convict and Marius cannot help believing that he is also the murderer of Javert. He becomes more and more estranged from Valjean, who grows feebler as the days pass. Thénardier presents himself and, in an attempt to blackmail Marius, reveals that Javert was a suicide and claims to be able to prove that Jean Valjean murdered a man in the sewers.*]

Marius sat down, and made sign to him to sit down. Thénardier installed himself in a chair.

140

"Monsieur Baron, on the 6th of June, 1832, about a year ago, the day of the uprising, a man was in the Grand Sewer of Paris, near where the sewer empties into the Seine, between the Pont des Invalides and the Pont d'Iéna. The man heard a noise in the sewer. Very much surprised, he hid himself, and watched. It was a sound of steps, somebody was walking in the darkness; somebody was coming in his direction. Strange to say, there was another man in the sewer beside him. The grating of the outlet of the sewer was not far off. A little light which came from it enabled him to recognize the newcomer, and to see that this man was carrying something on his back. He walked bent over. The man who was walking bent over was an old convict, and what he was carrying upon his shoulders was a corpse. You understand now. He who was carrying the corpse was Jean Valjean; he who had the key is now speaking to you, and the piece of the coat—"

Thénardier finished the phrase by drawing from his pocket and holding up, on a level with his eyes, between his thumbs and his forefingers, a strip of ragged black cloth, covered with dark stains.

Marius had risen, pale, hardly breathing, his eye fixed upon the scrap of black cloth, and, without uttering a word, without losing sight of this rag, he retreated to the wall, and, with his right hand stretched behind him, groped about for a key which was in the lock of a closet near the chimney. He found this key, opened the closet, and thrust his arm into it without looking, and without removing his startled eyes from the fragment that Thénardier held up.

Meanwhile Thénardier continued:

"Monsieur Baron, I have the strongest reasons to believe that the assassinated young man was an opulent stranger drawn into a snare by Jean Valjean, and the bearer of an enormous sum."

"The young man was myself, and there is the coat!" cried Marius, and he threw an old black coat covered with blood upon the carpet.

Then, snatching the fragment from Thénardier's hands, he bent down over the coat, and applied the piece to the cut skirt. The edges fitted exactly, and the strip completed the coat.

Thénardier was petrified. He thought this: "I am floored."

Marius rose up, quivering, desperate, flashing.

He felt in his pocket, and walked, furious, towards Thénardier, offering him and almost pushing into his face his fist full of notes.

"You are a wretch! you are a liar, a slanderer, a scoundrel. You came to accuse this man, you have justified him; you wanted to destroy him, you have succeeded only in glorifying him. And it is you who are a robber! and it is you who are an assassin. I saw you, Thénardier, Jondrette, in that den on the Boulevard de l'Hôpital. I know enough about you to send you to the galleys, and further even, if I wished. Here, there are a thousand francs, braggart that you are!"

And he threw a bill for a thousand francs to Thénardier.

"Ah! Jondrette Thénardier, vile knave! let this be a lesson to you, peddler of secrets, trader in mysteries, fumbler in the dark, wretch! Take these five hundred francs, and leave this place! Waterloo protects you."

"Waterloo!" muttered Thénardier, pocketing the five hundred francs with the thousand francs.

"Yes, assassin! you saved the life of a colonel there—"

"Of a general," said Thénardier, raising his head.

"Of a colonel!" replied Marius with a burst of passion. "I would not give a farthing for a general. And you came here to act out your infamy! I tell you that you have committed every crime. Go! out of my sight! Be happy only, that is all that I desire. Ah! monster! there are three thousand francs more. Take them. You will start to-morrow for America, with your daughter, for your wife is dead, abominable liar. I will see to your departure, bandit, and I will count out to you then twenty thousand francs. Go and get hung elsewhere!"

"Monsieur Baron," answered Thénardier, bowing to the ground, "eternal gratitude."

And Thénardier went out, comprehending nothing, astounded and transported with this sweet crushing under sacks of gold and with this thunderbolt bursting upon his head in bank-notes.

Let us finish with this man at once. Two days after the events which we are now relating, he left, through Marius' care, for America, under a false name, with his daughter Azelma, provided with a draft upon New York for twenty thousand francs. Thénardier, the moral misery of Thénardier, the broken-down bourgeois, was irremediable; he was in America what he had been in Europe. The touch of a wicked man is often enough to corrupt a good deed and to make an evil result spring from it. With Marius' money, Thénardier became a slaver.

As soon as Thénardier was out of doors, Marius ran to the garden where Cosette was still walking:

"Cosette! Cosette!" cried he. "Come! come quick! Let us go.

142

Basque, a fiacre! Cosette, come. Oh! my God! It was he who saved my life! Let us not lose a minute! Put on your shawl."

Cosette thought him mad, and obeyed.

"Driver," said he, "Rue de l'Homme Armé, Number 7."

The fiacre started.

"Oh! what happiness!" said Cosette. "Rue de l'Homme Armé! I dared not speak to you of it again. We are going to see Monsieur Jean."

At the knock which he heard at his door, Jean Valjean turned his head.

"Come in," said he feebly.

The door opened. Cosette and Marius appeared.

Cosette rushed into the room.

Marius remained upon the threshold, leaning against the casing of the door.

"Cosette!" said Jean Valjean, and he rose in his chair, his arms stretched out and trembling, haggard, livid, terrible, with immense joy in his eyes.

Cosette, stifled with emotion, fell upon Jean Valjean's breast.

"Father!" said she.

Jean Valjean, beside himself, stammered:

"Cosette! she? you, madame? it is you, Cosette? Oh, my God!" And, clasped in Cosette's arms, he exclaimed:

"It is you, Cosette? you are here? You forgive me then!"

Marius, dropping his eyelids that the tears might not fall, stepped forward and murmured between his lips which were contracted convulsively to check the sobs:

"Father!"

"And you too, you forgive me!" said Jean Valjean.

Marius could not utter a word, and Jean Valjean added: "Thanks."

Cosette took off her shawl and threw her hat upon the bed.

"They are in my way," said she.

And, seating herself upon the old man's knees, she stroked away his white hair with an adorable grace, and kissed his forehead.

Jean Valjean, bewildered, offered no resistance.

Cosette, who had but a very confused understanding of all this, redoubled her caresses, as if she would pay Marius' debt.

Jean Valjean faltered:

"How foolish we are! I thought I should never see her again. Only

143

think, Monsieur Pontmercy, that at the moment you came in, I was saying to myself: It is over. There is her little dress, I am a miserable man, I shall never see Cosette again, I was saying that at the very moment you were coming up the stairs. Was I not silly? I was as silly as that! But we reckon without God."

For a moment he could not speak, then he continued:

"I really needed to see Cosette a little while from time to time. A heart does want a bone to gnaw. Still I felt plainly that I was in the way. I gave myself reasons: they have no need of you, stay in your corner, you have no right to continue for ever."

And Cosette replied:

"How naughty to have left us in this way! Where have you been? why were you away so long? Do you know that you are very much changed? Oh! the naughty father! he has been sick, and we did not know it! Here, Marius, feel his hand, how cold it is!"

"So you are here, Monsieur Pontmercy, you forgive me!" repeated Jean Valjean.

At these words, which Jean Valjean now said for the second time, all that was swelling in Marius' heart found an outlet, he broke forth:

"Cosette, do you hear? that is the way with him! he begs my pardon, and do you know what he has done for me, Cosette? he has saved my life. He has done more. He has given you to me. And, after having saved me, and after having given you to me, Cosette, what did he do with himself? he sacrificed himself. There is the man. And, to me the ungrateful, to me the forgetful, to me the pitiless, to me the guilty, he says: Thanks! Cosette, my whole life passed at the feet of this man would be too little. That barricade, that sewer, that furnace, that cloaca, he went through everything for me, for you, Cosette! He bore me through death in every form which he put aside from me, and which he accepted for himself. All courage, all virtue, all heroism, all sanctity, he has it all, Cosette, that man is an angel!"

"Hush! hush!" said Jean Valjean in a whisper. "Why tell all that?"

"But you!" exclaimed Marius, with a passion in which veneration was mingled, "why have not you told it? It is your fault, too. You save people's lives, and you hide it from them! You do more, under pretense of unmasking yourself, you calumniate yourself. It is frightful."

"I told the truth," answered Jean Valjean.

"No," replied Marius, "the truth is the whole truth; and you did not tell it. You were Monsieur Madeleine, why not have said so?

144

You had saved Javert, why not have said so? I owe my life to you, why not have said so?"

"Because I thought as you did. I felt that you were right. It was necessary that I should go away. If you had known that affair of the sewer, you would have made me stay with you. I should then have had to keep silent. If I had spoken, it would have embarrassed all."

"Embarrassed what? embarrassed whom?" replied Marius. "Do you suppose you are going to stay here? We are going to carry you back. Oh! my God! when I think it was by accident that I learned it all! We are going to carry you back. You are a part of us. You are her father and mine. You shall not spend another day in this horrid house. Do not imagine that you will be here to-morrow."

"To-morrow," said Jean Valjean, "I shall not be here, but I shall not be at your house."

"What do you mean?" replied Marius. "Ah now, we shall allow no more journeys. You shall never leave us again. You belong to us. We will not let you go."

"This time, it is for good," added Cosette. "We have a carriage below. I am going to carry you off. If necessary, I shall use force."

And laughing, she made as if she would lift the old man in her arms.

Jean Valjean listened to her without hearing her. He heard the music of her voice rather than the meaning of her words; one of those big tears which are the gloomy pearls of the soul, gathered slowly in his eye. He murmured:

"The proof that God is good is that she is here."

"Father!" cried Cosette.

Cosette took both the old man's hands in her own.

"My God!" said she, "your hands are colder yet. Are you sick? Are you suffering?"

"No," answered Jean Valjean. "I am very well. Only—"

He stopped.

"Only what?"

"I shall die in a few minutes."

Cosette and Marius shuddered.

"Die!" exclaimed Marius.

"Yes, but that is nothing," said Jean Valjean.

Cosette uttered a piercing cry:

"Father! my father! you shall live. You are going to live. I will have you live, do you hear!"

Jean Valjean raised his head towards her with adoration.

"Oh yes, forbid me to die. Who knows? I shall obey perhaps. I was just dying when you came. That stopped me, it seemed to me that I was born again."

"You are full of strength and life," exclaimed Marius. "Do you think people die like that? You have had trouble, you shall have no more. I ask your pardon now, and that on my knees! You shall live, and live with us, and live long. We will take you back. Both of us here will have but one thought henceforth, your happiness!"

"You see," added Cosette in tears, "that Marius says you will not die."

Jean Valjean continued to smile.

"If you should take me back, Monsieur Pontmercy, would that make me different from what I am? No; God thought as you and I did, and he has not changed his mind; it is best that I should go away. Death is a good arrangement. God knows better than we do what we need."

There was a noise at the door. It was the physician coming in.

"Good day and good-by, Doctor," said Jean Valjean. "Here are my poor children."

Marius approached the physician. He addressed this single word to him: "Monsieur?" but in the manner of pronouncing it, there was a complete question.

The physician felt his pulse.

"Ah! it was you he needed!" murmured he, looking at Cosette and Marius.

And, bending towards Marius' ear, he added very low:

"Too late."

Jean Valjean, almost without ceasing to gaze upon Cosette, turned upon Marius and the physician a look of serenity. They heard these almost inarticulate words come from his lips:

"It is nothing to die; it is frightful not to live."

Suddenly he arose. These returns of strength are sometimes a sign of the death-struggle. He walked with a firm step to the wall, put aside Marius and the physician, who offered to assist him, took down from the wall the little copper crucifix which hung there, came back, and sat down with all the freedom of motion of perfect health, and said in a loud voice, laying the crucifix on the table:

"Behold the great martyr."

146

Then his breast sank in, his head wavered, as if the dizziness of the tomb seized him.

The agony of death may be said to meander. It goes, comes, advances towards the grave, and returns towards life. There is some groping in the act of dying. Jean Valjean, after this swoon, gathered strength, shook his forehead as if to throw off the darkness, and became almost completely lucid once more. He took a fold of Cosette's sleeve, and kissed it.

"He is reviving! Doctor, he is reviving!" cried Marius.

The portress had come up, and was looking through the half-open door. The physician motioned her away, but he could not prevent that good, zealous woman from crying to the dying man before she went:

"Do you want a priest?"

"I have one," answered Jean Valjean.

And, with his finger, he seemed to designate a point above his head, where, you would have said, he saw someone.

It is probable that the Bishop was indeed a witness of this death-agony.

Cosette slipped a pillow under his back gently.

From moment to moment, Jean Valjean grew weaker. He was sinking; he was approaching the dark horizon. His breath had become intermittent; it was interrupted by a slight rattle. He had difficulty in moving his wrist, his feet had lost all motion, and, at the same time that the distress of the limbs and the exhaustion of the body increased, all the majesty of the soul rose and displayed itself upon his forehead. The light of the unknown world was already visible in his eye. He motioned to Cosette to approach, then to Marius; it was evidently the last minute of the last hour, and he began to speak to them in a voice so faint it seemed to come from afar, and you would have said that there was already a wall between them and him.

"Come closer, come closer, both of you. I love you dearly. Oh! it is good to die so! You too, you love me, my Cosette. I knew very well that you still had some affection for your old goodman. How kind you are to put this cushion under my back! You will weep for me a little, will you not? Not too much. I do not wish you to have any deep grief. You must amuse yourselves a great deal, my children. I was writing just now to Cosette. She will find my letter. To her I bequeath the two candlesticks which are on the mantel. They are silver; but to me they are gold, they are diamond; they change the candles which are put into them, into consecrated tapers. I do not know whether he who gave them to me is satisfied with me in heaven. I have done what I could. My children, you will not forget that I am a poor man, you will have me buried in the most convenient piece of ground under a stone to mark the spot. That is my wish. No name on the stone. If Cosette will come for a little while sometimes, it will give me a pleasure. You too, Monsieur Pontmercy. I must confess to you that I have not always loved you; I ask your pardon. Now, she and you are but one to me. I am very grateful to you. I feel that you make Cosette happy. If you knew, Monsieur Pontmercy, her beautiful rosy cheeks were my joy; when I saw her a little pale, I was sad. There is a five-hundred franc bill in the bureau. It is for the poor. Cosette, do you see your little dress, there on the bed? do you recognize it? Yet it was only ten years ago. How time passes! We have been very happy. It is over. My children, do not weep, I am not going very far, I shall see you from there. You will only have to look when it is night, you will see me smile. Cosette, do you remember Montfermeil? You were in the wood, you were very much frightened; do you remember when I took the handle of the water-bucket? That was the first time I touched your poor little hand. It was so cold! Ah! you had red hands in those days, mademoiselle, your hands are very white now. Those Thénardiers were wicked. We must forgive them. Cosette, the time has come to tell you the name of your mother. Her name was Fantine. Remember that name: Fantine. Fall on your knees whenever you pronounce it. She suffered much. And loved you much. Her measure of unhappiness was as full as yours of happiness. Such are the distributions of God. He is on high, he sees us all, and he knows what he does in the midst of his great stars. So I am going away, my children. Love each other dearly always. There is scarcely anything else in the world but that: to love one another. You will think sometimes of the poor old man who died here. O my Cosette! it is not my fault, indeed, if I have not seen you all this time, it broke my heart; I went as far as the corner of the street, I must have seemed strange to the people who saw me pass, I looked like a crazy man, once I went out with no hat. My children, I do not see very clearly now, I had some more things to say, but it makes no difference. Think of me a little. You are blessed creatures. I do not know what is the matter with me, I see a light. Come nearer. I die happy. Let me put my hands upon your dear beloved heads."

Cosette and Marius fell on their knees, overwhelmed, choked with tears, each grasping one of Jean Valjean's hands. Those august hands moved no more.

He had fallen backwards, the light from the candlesticks fell upon him; his white face looked up towards heaven, he let Cosette and Marius cover his hands with kisses; he was dead.

The night was starless and very dark. Without doubt, in the gloom some mighty angel was standing, with outstretched wings, awaiting the soul. . . .

There is, in the cemetery of Père Lachaise, in the neighborhood of the potter's field, far from the elegant quarter of that city of sepulchers, far from all those fantastic tombs which display in presence of eternity the hideous fashions of death, in a deserted corner, beside an old wall, beneath a great yew on which the bindweed climbs, among the dog-grass and the mosses, a stone. This stone is exempt no more than the rest from the leprosy of time, from the mold, the lichen, and the droppings of the birds. The air turns it black, the water green. It is near no path, and people do not like to go in that direction, because the grass is high, and they would wet their feet. When there is a little sunshine, the lizards come out. There is, all about, a rustling of wild oats. In the spring, the linnets sing in the tree.

This stone is entirely blank. The only thought in cutting it was of the essentials of the grave, and there was no other care than to make this stone long enough and narrow enough to cover a man.

No name can be read there.

Only many years ago, a hand wrote upon it in pencil these four lines which have become gradually illegible under the rain and the dust, and which are probably effaced:

> *Il dort. Quoique le sort fût pour lui bien étrange,*
> *Il vivait. Il mourut quand il n'eut plus son ange.*
> *La chose simplement d'elle-même arriva,*
> *Comme la nuit se fait lorsque le jour s'en va.**

* *He sleeps. Against the cruelest fate he lived,*
  Until his guardian angel showed the way.
  It was a thing that happened of itself;
  As night trails on the path of parting day.

THE
CELEBRATED
JUMPING FROG
OF CALAVERAS
COUNTY

by Mark Twain

HOME COURSE APPRECIATION

THE YEAR IS 1865. In one of the dismal taverns of a Far Rockies mining area known as Angel's Camp, a group of prospectors, miners, fortune hunters, and scalawags are gathered to while away a wintry afternoon. A man by the name of Ben Coon drawls his way through story after story—no one pays much attention—Ben is notorious for his inexhaustible stock of tales and his dreary, matter-of-fact way of telling them. He welcomes any ear, especially when there is the chance of a free drink, too.

One young man, however, is listening intently. He is a journalist on a Virginia City newspaper, and, on the side, a prospector without much luck. His name is Clemens, but recently he has been signing his humorous newspaper articles with the strange name of "Mark Twain."

He is a good listener. Nothing escapes him—no facial gesture, no intonation or drawl, and he relishes, in particular, every fresh turn of phrase. At night when he returns to the cabin shared with a friend, he jots down his experiences and the stories he has heard during the day. After listening to Ben Coon he writes: "Coleman with his jumping frog—bet a stranger $50—stranger had no frog—and C. got him one:—in the meantime stranger filled C.'s frog full of shot and he couldn't jump. The stranger's frog won."

The story built on that skeleton was to launch the young journalist

"... the smart Jim has been outwitted by the still smarter stranger."

on a career that would place him in the forefront of America's humorists and men of letters.

If Mark Twain was never fated to find real gold in California, he did indeed find another sort of ore—in the speech of the innumerable characters he encountered and in the stories he picked up—which he refined into the pure gold of literature.

The story of the jumping frog was already a part of American folklore when Mark Twain came across it. Where it originated no one could be certain. Like so much of the folk literature that went west with the pioneers, it had been enlarged and embellished, acquiring the flavor of each new region as it traveled from mouth to mouth. It was Mark Twain's particular genius to discover this truly native product of the American continent, to respond to the wit and wisdom of its unknown authors, and, by setting it down on paper, to ensure its permanence.

In reading *The Celebrated Jumping Frog of Calaveras County* we are actually watching Mark Twain at work. What was it he did in transforming the folk tale?

He "framed" the story, setting it against a background so vivid that we feel we are with him, ready to shake hands with his characters as he introduces them. He breathed real life into men and animals alike! Simon Wheeler, the old codger who *will* tell, in his deliberate, long-winded way, the story of venturesome Jim Smiley; Andrew Jackson, the sensitive bull-pup; and Daniel Webster, most intelligent, most modest of frogs. He preserved the very flavor of the frontier American speech, so that we hear these characters exactly as he heard them nearly a century ago. Through Simon Wheeler's eyes and words we catch Jim Smiley in action—Jim Smiley, the gambler who doesn't care which side of a wager he backs, so long as he has a bet going. With Simon we witness Jim meet his gambling match in the mysterious stranger.

Mark Twain defined the art of the humorist as the ability "to string incongruities and absurdities together in a wandering and sometimes purposeless way, and seem innocently unaware that they are absurdities." The story of the jumping frog perfectly exemplifies the definition. From the very first we are involved in an absurd situation: we have come to inquire after the Reverend *Leonidas* Smiley, and all old Simon wants to talk about is *Jim* Smiley. And what a fascinating figure Jim turns out to be! In no time at all the Reverend Leonidas is forgotten.

There had been great American humorists before Mark Twain. One of these, the celebrated "Artemus Ward," had in fact been responsible for making Mark Twain aware of the humorous possibilities of the American folk-tale. It was in answer to an invitation of the older man that Mark Twain sent *The Jumping Frog* to the editor of a volume of tall stories. It was rejected, however, and did not make its appearance until the November 18, 1865 edition of The Saturday Press. Success was immediate; two years later the story was re-issued in book form, along with some other sketches. "Mark Twain" had become a name.

The restlessness of his age was in the blood of Samuel Langhorne Clemens. The offspring of a Virginia family that had settled in Missouri, he was typical of the roving generation that was intent on pushing out the American frontier. He had tried his luck as a footloose journalist and a Mississippi River pilot before the success of the Jumping Frog determined him on a literary career. Thereafter book after book appeared, to poke fun at primness and hypocrisy, and affirm the dignity of human beings and the values of a democratic society. Easily the best are the two which seem to have grown directly out of the life he witnessed on the Mississippi, in the great days of the romantic paddle-wheelers. *Tom Sawyer* and *The Adventures of Huckleberry Finn* will live as long as books are read.

Mark Twain's love of adventure never died. At heart he remained the prospector, forever involved in ventures that promised limitless fortunes, and never paid off. He went bankrupt as a result of investing in unsound inventions, and a good portion of his later writing was done in an effort to liquidate his immense debts.

His fame was world-wide, and in his own lifetime he grew into a legend as he wandered up and down New York's Fifth Avenue, a tall figure in a white suit. Toward the end of his life the long shadows of industrialism and financial monopoly falling across the land dimmed the dream of America expressed in his early novels. As his pessimism deepened his writing grew somber and morose. When he died in 1910, he seemed an uneasy figure out of a distant, more generous past, unsympathetic with the century into which he had somehow lingered.

No one remembers the disenchanted old man now. He is lost in the larger figure, so curiously like Abraham Lincoln in his indifference to social taboos, his witty and idiomatic speech, and his faith in human beings. It is the spirit of that Mark Twain that lives forever in Huck Finn and Tom and the Connecticut Yankee—courageous, adventuresome, vigorous and free.

IN COMPLIANCE with the request of a friend of mine, who wrote me from the East, I called on good-natured, garrulous old Simon Wheeler, and inquired after my friend's friend, *Leonidas W.* Smiley, as requested to do, and I hereunto append the result. I have a lurking suspicion that *Leonidas W.* Smiley is a myth; that my friend never knew such a personage; and that he only conjectured that, if I asked old Wheeler about him, it would remind him of his infamous *Jim* Smiley, and he would go to work and bore me nearly to death with some infernal reminiscence of him as long and tedious as it should be useless to me. If that was the design, it certainly succeeded.

I found Simon Wheeler dozing comfortably by the barroom stove of the old, dilapidated tavern in the ancient mining camp of Angel's, and I noticed that he was fat and bald-headed, and had an expression of winning gentleness and simplicity upon his tranquil countenance. He roused up and gave me good-day. I told him a friend of mine had commissioned me to make some inquiries about a cherished companion of his boyhood named *Leonidas W.* Smiley—*Rev. Leonidas W.* Smiley—a young minister of the Gospel, who he had heard was at one time a resident of Angel's Camp. I added that, if Mr. Wheeler could tell me anything about this Rev. Leonidas W. Smiley, I would feel under many obligations to him.

Simon Wheeler backed me into a corner and blockaded me there with his chair, and then sat me down and reeled off the monotonous narrative which follows this paragraph. He never smiled, he never frowned, he never changed his voice from the gentle-flowing key to which he tuned the initial sentence, he never betrayed the slightest suspicion of enthusiasm; but all through the interminable narrative there ran a vein of impressive earnestness and sincerity, which showed me plainly that, so far from his imagining that there was anything ridiculous or funny about his story, he regarded it as a really important matter, and admitted its two heroes as men of transcendent genius in *finesse*. To me, the spectacle of a man drifting serenely along through such a queer yarn without ever smiling, was exquisitely absurd. As I said before, I asked him to tell me what he knew of Rev. Leonidas W. Smiley, and he replied as follows. I let him go on in his own way, and never interrupted him once:

There was a feller here once by the name of *Jim* Smiley, in the winter of '49—or maybe it was the spring of '50—I don't recollect exactly, somehow, though what makes me think it was one or the other is because I remember the big flume wasn't finished when he first came to the camp; but anyway, he was the curiousest man about always betting on anything that turned up you ever see, if he could get anybody to bet on the other side; and if he couldn't, he'd change sides. Any way what suited the other man would suit him—any way just so's he got a bet, *he* was satisfied. But still he was lucky, uncommon lucky; he most always come out winner. He was always ready and laying for a chance; there couldn't be no solit'ry thing mentioned but that feller'd offer to bet on it, and take any side you please, as I was just telling you. If there was a horse-race, you'd find him flush, or you'd find him busted at the end of it; if there was a dog-fight, he'd bet on it; if there was a cat-fight, he'd bet on it; if there was a chicken-fight, he'd bet on it; why, if there was two birds setting on a fence, he would bet you which one would fly first; or if there was a camp meeting, he would be there reg'lar, to bet on Parson Walker, which he judged to be the best exhorter about here, and so he was, too, and a good man. If he even seen a straddle-bug start to go anywheres, he would bet you how long it would take him to get wherever he was going to, and if you took him up, he would foller that straddle-bug to Mexico but what he would find out where he was bound for and how long he was on the road. Lots of the boys here had seen that Smiley, and can tell you about him. Why, it never made no difference to *him* —he would bet on *any*thing—the dangdest feller. Parson Walker's wife laid very sick once, for a good while, and it seemed as if they warn't going to save her; but one morning he came in, and Smiley asked how she was, and he said she was considerable better—thank the Lord for his inf'nit mercy—and coming on so smart that, with the blessing of Prov'dence, she'd get well yet; and Smiley, before he thought, says, "Well, I'll risk two-and-a-half that she don't, anyway."

Thish-yer Smiley had a mare—the boys called her the fifteen-minute nag, but that was only in fun, you know, because, of course, she was faster than that—and he used to win money on that horse, for all she was so slow and always had the asthma, or the distemper, or the consumption, or something of that kind. They used to give her two or three hundred yards start, and then pass her under way; but always at the fag-end of the race she'd get excited and desperate-like, and come cavorting and straddling up, and scattering her legs around limber, sometimes in the air, and sometimes out to one side amongst the fences, and kicking up m-o-r-e dust, and raising m-o-r-e racket with her coughing and sneezing and blowing her nose—and always fetch up at the stand just about a neck ahead, as near as you could cipher it down.

And he had a little small bull pup, that to look at him you'd think he wan't worth a cent but to set around and look ornery and lay for a chance to steal something. But as soon as money was up on him, he was a different dog; his under-jaw'd begin to stick out like the fo'castle of a steamboat, and his teeth would uncover, and shine savage like the furnaces. And a dog might tackle him, and bullyrag him, and bite him, and throw him over his shoulder two or three times, and Andrew Jackson—which was the name of the pup—Andrew Jackson would never let on but what *he* was satisfied, and hadn't expected nothing else—and the bets being doubled and doubled on the other side all the time, till the money was all up; and then all of a sudden he would grab that other dog jest by the j'int of his hind leg and freeze to it—not chaw, you understand, but only jest grip and hang on till they throwed up the sponge, if it was a year. Smiley always come out winner on that pup, till he harnessed a dog once that didn't have no hind legs, because they'd been sawed off by a circular saw, and when the thing had gone along far enough, and the money was all up, and he come to make a snatch for his pet holt, he saw in a minute how he'd been imposed on, and how the other dog had him in the door, so to speak, and he 'peared surprised, and then he looked sorter discouraged-like, and didn't try no more to win the fight, and so he got shucked out bad. He give Smiley a look, as much to say his heart was broke and it was *his* fault for putting up a dog that hadn't no hind legs for him to take holt of, which was his main dependence in a fight, and then he limped off a piece and laid down and died. It was a good pup, was that Andrew Jackson, and would have made a name for hisself if he'd lived, for the stuff was in him, and he had genius—I know it, because he hadn't no opportunities to speak of, and it don't stand to reason that a dog could make such a fight as he could under them circumstances, if he hadn't no talent. It always makes me feel sorry when I think of that last fight of his'n, and the way it turned out.

Well, thish-yer Smiley had rat-tarriers, and chicken-cocks, and tomcats, and all them kind of things, till you couldn't rest, and you couldn't fetch nothing for him to bet on but he'd match you. He ketched a frog one day, and took him home, and said he cal'klated to edercate him; and so he never done nothing for these three months but set in his back yard and learn that frog to jump. And you bet you he *did* learn him, too. He'd give him a little punch behind, and the next minute you'd see that frog whirling in the air like a doughnut— see him turn one summerset, or maybe a couple, if he got a good start, and come down flat-footed and all right, like a cat. He got him up so in the matter of catching flies, and kept him in practice so constant, that he'd nail a fly every time as far as he could see him. Smiley said all a frog wanted was education, and he could do most anything— and I believe him. Why, I've seen him set Dan'l Webster down here on this floor—Dan'l Webster was the name of the frog—and sing out, "Flies, Dan'l, flies!" and quicker'n you could wink, he'd spring straight up, and snake a fly off'n the counter there, and flop down on the floor again as solid as a gob of mud, and fall to scratching the side of his head with his hind foot as indifferent as if he hadn't no idea he's been doin' any more'n any frog might do. You never see a frog so modest and straight-for'ard as he was, for all he was so gifted. And when it come to fair and square jumping on the dead level, he could get over more ground at one straddle than any animal of his breed you ever see. Jumping on a dead level was his strong suit, you understand; and when it come to that, Smiley would ante up money on him as long as he had a red. Smiley was monstrous proud of his frog, and well he might be, for fellers that had traveled and been everywhere all said he laid over any frog that ever *they* see.

Well, Smiley kept the beast in a little lattice box, and he used to fetch him downtown sometimes and lay for a bet. One day a feller—

156

a stranger in the camp, he was—come across him with his box, and says:

"What might it be that you've got in the box?"

And Smiley says, sorter indifferent like, "It might be a parrot, or it might be a canary, maybe, but it ain't—it's only just a frog."

An' the feller took it, and looked at it careful, and turned it round this way and that, and says, "H'm—so 'tis. Well, what's *he* good for?"

"Well," Smiley says, easy and careless, "He's good enough for *one* thing, I should judge—he can outjump ary frog in Calaveras County."

The feller took the box again, and took another long, particular look, and gave it back to Smiley, and says, very deliberate, "Well, I don't see no p'ints about that frog that's any better'n any other frog."

"Maybe you don't," Smiley says. "Maybe you understand frogs, and maybe you don't understand 'em; maybe you've had experience, and maybe you ain't only a amature, as it were. Anyways, I've got *my* opinion, and I'll risk forty dollars that he can outjump any frog in Calaveras County."

And the feller studied a minute, and then says, kinder sad like, "Well, I'm only a stranger here, and I ain't got no frog; but if I had a frog, I'd bet you."

And then Smiley says, "That's all right—that's all right—if you'll hold my box a minute, I'll go and get you a frog." And so the feller took the box, and put up his forty dollars along with Smiley's, and set down to wait.

So he set there a good while thinking and thinking to hisself, and then he got the frog out and prized his mouth open and took a teaspoon and filled him full of quail shot—filled him pretty near up to his chin—and set him on the floor. Smiley he went to the swamp and slopped around in the mud for a long time, and finally he ketched a frog, and fetched him in, and give him to this feller, and says:

"Now, if you're ready, set him alongside of Dan'l, with his fore-paws just even with Dan'l, and I'll give the word." Then he says, "One—two—three—jump!" and him and the feller touched up the frogs from behind, and the new frog hopped off, but Dan'l give a heave, and hysted up his shoulders—so—like a Frenchman, but it wasn't no use—he couldn't budge; he was planted as solid as an anvil, and he couldn't no more stir than if he was anchored out. Smiley was a good deal surprised, and he was disgusted too, but he didn't have no idea what the matter was, of course.

The feller took the money and started away; and when he was

going out at the door, he sorter jerked his thumb over his shoulder—this way—at Dan'l, and says again, very deliberate, "Well, *I* don't see no p'ints about that frog that's any better'n any other frog."

Smiley he stood scratching his head and looking down at Dan'l a long time, and at last he says, "I do wonder what in the nation that frog throw'd off for—I wonder if there ain't something the matter with him—he 'pears to look mighty baggy, somehow." And he ketched Dan'l by the nap of the neck, and lifted him up and says, "Why, blame my cats, if he don't weigh five pounds!" and turned him upside down, and he belched out a double handful of shot. And then he see how it was, and he was the maddest man—he set the frog down and took out after that feller, but he never ketched him. And—

(Here Simon Wheeler heard his name called from the front yard, and got up to see what was wanted.) And turning to me as he moved away, he said: "Just set where you are, stranger, and rest easy—I ain't going to be gone a second."

But, by your leave, I did not think that a continuation of the history of the enterprising vagabond *Jim* Smiley would be likely to afford me much information concerning the Rev. *Leonidas W*. Smiley, and so I started away.

At the door I met the sociable Wheeler returning, and he button-holed me and recommenced:

"Well, thish-yer Smiley had a yeller one-eyed cow that didn't have no tail, only jest a short stump like a bannanner, and—"

"Oh, hang Smiley and his afflicted cow!" I muttered, good-naturedly, and bidding the old gentleman good-day, I departed.

THE
AUTOBIOGRAPHY
OF
BENJAMIN
FRANKLIN

A CONDENSATION

NOTE: *The editor's explanatory notes appear*
italicized and in brackets throughout the text.

NEITHER THE SMALL DETAILS of everyday living—bifocal spectacles, street lamps, and smoky chimneys—nor the grand affairs of political principle and international alliances were beyond the scope of Benjamin Franklin's mind. In appearance he was approximately five feet ten inches tall, good looking, with a large head, a round build (somewhat rounder in old age), light-brown hair, gray eyes, and a wide mouth. He had a normal share of small vanities and personal failings. But in a century that put a high premium on charm, he was among the most charming. In an age that set much store by reason, he was "the very incarnation of sanity." He was one of the greatest men of the eighteenth century, and the most human of the Founding Fathers of the United States.

Providence was especially generous to Franklin. It endowed him with a mind that was ever curious and alert, and a temperament that could abide neither injustice nor servitude. His restless mind sent him to books at an early age, and his free spirit led him on a career of self-improvement that went beyond his personal self to touch and influence the lives of untold millions.

JACK OF ALL TRADES AND MASTER OF MOST

Franklin was convinced that by constant application and steadfast adherence to the virtues, a man could improve his own lot and that of his fellow men. So successfully did he govern his own life by this belief that by the time he was forty-two he was able to retire from business to devote himself to his pleasures—public good and scientific experiment.

Devoting himself to the civic betterment of Philadelphia, he had the streets paved, improved their lighting, and evolved a prudent scheme for having them cleaned cheaply; he reformed the city watch, organized a fire brigade and a militia, and was instrumental in founding a library, a philosophical society, and an academy (now the University of Pennsylvania). He ran the post office (at a profit), invented a stove that consumed less wood and gave more heat than a fireplace, and devised an artificial arm for reaching high shelves and a lightning rod. He charted the Gulf Stream, traced the movement of northeastern storms, identified lightning with electricity, and investigated the causes of the common cold.

He conducted the affairs of state with honesty, integrity, industry, and thrift, achieving universal fame for himself and international respect for his country. He became the official agent to the British crown of the colonies of Pennsylvania, Georgia, New Jersey and Massachusetts. He was the first American minister to France, and three times President of Pennsylvania. His is the only name that appears on each of the four fundamental American documents: the Declaration of Independence, the treaty with France, the peace treaty with England, and the Constitution of the United States.

BIRTH AND GROWTH

FRANKLIN WAS BORN IN BOSTON of working people. He died an aristocrat—not as a member of the select Philadelphia upper classes, but as a member of that inclusive world aristocracy where citizenship is achieved by largeness of vision, broadness of intellect, and singularity of accomplishment. He was respected by nobles for his efficiency, admired by ladies for his wit, and welcomed by scholars for his learning. His name was known to kings and commoners, to citizens and peasants, to ladies of the court and kitchen maids. When he died, the city of Philadelphia gave him a magnificent funeral, and the French Assembly went into mourning for three days.

The years of his life, 1706–1790, cover almost all the years of the eighteenth century. The range of his interests—intellectual, spiritual, political—includes all the theories and principles of the eighteenth century. It may be said that Benjamin Franklin *is* the eighteenth century ideal of the universal man. Yet he was as American as the crackerbarrel.

By its interests, its aims, and its achievements, each period in history earns for itself some descriptive title. In the history books of the future, at least part of our twentieth century will probably be reviewed under the chapter-heading "The Atomic Age." The nineteenth century earned, among others, such titles as "The Romantic Period" or "The Age of Realism." The eighteenth century is called in American history "The Colonial Period" or "The Revolutionary Period"; in world history, it is alternately "The Enlightenment" or "The Age of Reason."

Now the Enlightenment earned its title not because it held a monopoly on reason, but because it relied exclusively on it. Its philosophers believed there were few problems that could not be solved by unaided human reason. They drew their inspiration from the work of the two great English thinkers of the late seventeenth century: John Locke and Sir Isaac Newton.

Locke's *Essay Concerning Human Understanding,* published in 1690, has been called "the inaugural address of the eighteenth century." It was the first formal declaration of the rights of man, in which it was maintained that man is not born evil, but pure and good, only to be sullied by experience. To reform man it is only necessary to reform the social institutions that surround him. All men are created equal, with certain inalienable rights. In America these rights were held to be life, liberty, property, and the pursuit of happiness.

RELIGION AND THE AGE OF REASON

THE IDEA OF HARMONIOUS social institutions which Locke propounded, is implicit in Newtonian science. In 1687, Newton published his *Principia,* which became the "bible" of the eighteenth century. Newton's importance to the Age of Reason is perhaps most succinctly expressed in Alexander Pope's couplet:

> *Nature and nature's laws lay hid in night:*
> *God said,* Let Newton be! *and all was light.*

Newton's law of gravitation and his laws of motion presented a universe of harmonious order. His findings so impressed the thinkers of the day that they began to use them as suitable formulas for every area of human activity. In religion they led to Deism.

To the Deists, God was not both creator and ruler of the universe, but only creator. His supreme intelligence had fashioned a universe of wonderful order and regularity, and once having done this, He did not intervene in the lives of men. God, as the Deists saw Him, was a benevolent father who had plowed the furrow and planted the seed, leaving it for His children to tend the plants and harvest the crop.

FRANKLIN AND THE AGE OF REASON

IN HIS RELIGIOUS BELIEFS, his practicality, and his high regard for the powers of the mind, Franklin was the embodiment of the Age of Reason. During the voyage home from his first trip to London, he recorded in his Journal a plan by which he would live in order to be a "rational creature." The Journal has come down to us, but the plan has not. However, it may very well be one that was printed many years later, for he states that "quite through to old age" he faithfully adhered to the code he had drawn up when he was only twenty. What were the qualities Franklin deemed imperative for the reasonable man?

"I have never fixed a regular design as to life. . . . I am now entering upon a new one; let me therefore make some resolutions . . . that henceforth I may live in all respects like a rational creature. 1. It is necessary for me to be extremely frugal for some time, till I have paid what I owe. 2. To endeavor to speak truth in every instance, to give nobody expectations that are not likely to be answered, but aim at sincerity in every word and action: the most amiable excellence in a rational being. 3. To apply myself industriously to whatever business I take in hand, and not to divert my mind from my business by any foolish project of growing suddenly rich; for industry and patience are the surest means of plenty. 4. I resolve to speak ill of no man whatever, not even in a matter of truth; but rather by some means excuse the faults I hear charged upon others, and upon proper occasions speak all the good I know of everybody."

But Franklin's moralizing is never objectionable. He tempered his rationalism with the typical American grain of salt. He recalls, for example, in the *Autobiography,* how he reasoned himself out of vegetarianism, and then observes: "So convenient a thing is it to be a *reasonable creature,* since it enables one to find or make a reason for everything one has a mind to do."

In religion he followed a form of scientific Deism. Born a Calvinist and reared in Puritan Boston, he arrived at his final religious beliefs by experience and reason, not through introspection and revelation. In the *Autobiography* he traces the development of his religious ideas, but this takes him only to his fifties. In a letter he wrote a month before he died, he stated the creed by which he had lived and served: "I believe in one God, Creator of the Universe. That he governs it by his Providence. That he ought to be worshipped. That the most acceptable Service we render to him is doing good to his other Children. That the soul of Man is immortal, and will be treated with Justice in another life respecting its Conduct in this. These I take to be the fundamental Principles of all sound Religion, and I regard them . . . in whatever Sect I meet with them."

Politically, Franklin was practical rather than theoretical. He never drew up a scheme of political philosophy; expediency and the public good were his guides. He believed in certain fundamental truths and acted to put these truths into practice. He believed with John Locke that man had natural rights—life, liberty, property, freedom of speech and religion—and that government was a social compact in which men surrendered only that amount of freedom which would allow the establishment of an organized authority.

His every political act was determined by these principles, and often they led him to support publicly measures of which he disapproved privately. He agitated against the Stamp Act—the British tax on commodities—but once it became law, he abided by it. He did not agree with every provision in the Constitution, but he recognized its greater good, and signed it. Reason and law—not political theory or rebellion against established authority—made him oppose the proprietors of Pennsylvania and, later, the British crown.

These, then, were his times—the century into which he was born, the atmosphere in which he grew to manhood, and the age which, in great measure, he helped to mold. Who was he, this Founding Father who met life with industry, ingenuity, practicality, morality, a twinkle in his eye?

PRINTER AND PUBLISHER

I, BENJAMIN FRANKLIN, PRINTER, late Minister Plenipotentiary from the United States of America to the Court of France, now President of Pennsylvania. . . ." Thus did Benjamin Franklin begin his will. This single sentence carries the key to the character of the man: handicraft came first, foreign ministries and presidencies afterward.

In the *Autobiography,* Franklin recalls his father's efforts to place him in a trade he would enjoy, and how his "bookish inclination"

Benjamin Franklin, Printer.

prompted his father to apprentice him to an elder brother who was a printer. Franklin is not accurate when he describes his brother's newspaper, the *New England Courant,* as the second newspaper in America. Actually, it was the fourth; but it was the first to print original contributions by the colonists instead of merely rehashing the London newspapers. Secretly and then openly, Franklin submitted little essays in the form of letters over the name "Silence Dogood," and became a published author by the time he was seventeen. He continued this way of expressing his observations of the customs and habits around him and was, at various times in his life, "Busy-body," "Anthony Afterwit," "Celia Single," and "Alice Addertongue."

It is difficult to separate Franklin the writer from Franklin the printer and Franklin the publisher, the man who accepts the financial risks and distributes the finished newspaper, magazine, or book. Sometimes he pursued each of these occupations singly; often they were merged. He was a conscientious citizen and a born "improver." He had a way with words and they came off his pen at the drop of an issue; by the use of his press, he was able to publicize his ideas. He himself has remarked that many of his plans were carried into execution because he had "prepared the minds of people for the change."

POOR RICHARD

Bᴜᴛ *Poor Richard's Almanac,* the most famous result of Franklin's three-roles-in-one, had nothing to do with civic improvement. True, anything he did had an element of utility in it and a touch of moral wisdom, but the *Almanac* was primarily entertaining.

Richard Saunders, the imaginary astrologer who supposedly wrote the *Almanac,* was a perfect extension of Franklin's homey, humorous character. In the preface of the first almanac he gave his reasons for going into this business: "Courteous Reader, I might in this place attempt to gain thy favor, by declaring that I write almanacs with no other view than that of the public good; but in this wise I should not be sincere. . . . The plain truth of the matter is, I am excessive poor, and . . . the printer has offered me some considerable share of the profits. . . ." The next year he expresses thanks for the profits; his wife Bridget has been able to buy new things which "have rendered her temper so much more pacific . . . that I may say I have slept more . . . within this last year than in the three foregoing years put together." This fictitious Richard and his equally fictitious wife tiffed through these prefaces for years; she had some sharp comments to make not only about the quality of his verse, but also about his remarks on the idleness of women, and she contributed her own views on the worthlessness of men.

Richard asked the reader's indulgence toward his weather forecasts: "We modestly desire only the favorable allowance of a day or two before and a day or two after the precise day against which the weather is set." Certainly the readers did not buy the almanacs for their weather forecasts. The preface and the proverbs with which Franklin "filled all the little spaces that occurred between the remarkable days in the calendar" were the attraction. "Early to bed and early to rise, makes a man healthy, wealthy, and wise." "God helps those that help themselves."

Franklin took his proverbs wherever he found them—from English and French authors or from the Latin classics. Some were original—"A used key is always bright"—and others he improved upon. "As poor Richard says" became a household saying and the almanac became an institution, selling 10,000 copies a year.

FRANKLIN THE WRITER

If you would not be forgotten,
As soon as you are dead and rotten,
Either write things worth reading,
Or do things worth writing.

Forty years as a printer and publisher greatly influenced Franklin's attitude toward the printed word. He was as concerned with the appearance of the printed page—the kind of print, the quality of paper and ink—as he was with the way the words were used to express ideas.

He disliked the system that was then coming into fashion, of eliminating italics and the long "s" which looked like an "f." He admitted that it created a uniform appearance on the page, but he compared the constant use of our short, round "s" to shortening all men's noses. Their faces might be rendered smoother, but they should also be less distinctive. He was impatient with printers who did not observe strictly "the emphasis of written discourses," to bring them as near as possible to the spoken word. He did not like his work to be tampered with, and wrote of an editor who had altered one of his pieces: "He has drawn the teeth and pared the nails of my paper, so that it can neither scratch nor bite. It seems only to paw and mumble."

But he was radical in other things. He wanted to reform spelling—

and wrote a charming essay, *The Petition of the Letter Z,* in which the last letter in our alphabet formally requests that he be moved to the beginning; and he proposed placing the question mark at the beginning of a sentence, as in Spanish, so that the reader does not have to wait until the end, but will know straight off that what he is reading will end as a question.

In spelling, Franklin was inconsistent but in choosing his words he used few Americanisms. His greatness as a writer rests on his versatility and on his style. He is famous for his concise and graceful style. He was conscious of style and worked hard to achieve his own.

In the *Autobiography,* he tells how he became conscious of style in writing. He had been corresponding with a friend, and his father pointed out that although Franklin's ideas were better, the friend expressed himself more fluently and thus made the better impression. Franklin set himself to learn to write. Fortunately he soon abandoned the elegant style of his first literary model, the London magazine called *The Spectator,* and developed the lucidity and freshness which were so perfect an expression of his own personality.

When he was older and a "master," he recommended to a friend that "before you sit down to write on any subject . . . spend some days in considering it, putting down at the same time, in short hints, every thought which occurs to you as proper to make a part of your intended piece." He himself made such an outline for his *Autobiography,* of which a copy is preserved. The first few thoughts which occurred to him as proper to his intended piece were: "My writing. Mrs. Dogood's letters. Differences arise between my brother and me (his temper and mine); their cause in general."

Despite some obscure sentences and occasional lapses—surely because it is essentially an unrevised, uncorrected work—the *Autobiography* fulfills Franklin's theory of literary style: "The words used should be the most expressive that the language affords, provided that they are the most generally understood. Nothing should be expressed in two words that can be well expressed in one; that is, no synonyms should be used, or very rarely, but the whole should be as short as possible . . . the words should be so placed as to be agreeable to the ear in reading; summarily, it should be *smooth, clear,* and *short,* for the contrary qualities are displeasing."

THE "AUTOBIOGRAPHY"

The *Autobiography* is Franklin's second masterpiece—if, in point of time, we count *Poor Richard's Almanac* his first. By way of the

"Thus I went up Market Street as far as Fourth Street."

pages of the "memoirs"—as Franklin always called them—he takes us from his ancestry in England to his birth in Boston, where, fortunately, he escaped the fate of an elder brother who was "drowned in a tub of suds," to his limited schooling, his apprenticeship, his self-education, and his flight to Philadelphia. He leaves us at the threshold of his greatness, at the time when he is becoming a world figure.

He begins modestly, almost apologetically, worried lest he seem a tiresome old man prattling on about himself, lest he appear vain. But humor and reason win out. He knows he is a person of importance in his world. He decides: "Most people dislike vanity in others . . . but I give it fair quarter wherever I meet with it, being persuaded that it is often productive of good to the possessor, and to others that are within his sphere of action."

It seems incredible that this greatest American autobiographical classic that has endeared itself to generation upon generation, was published in French, and translated from French into other languages, including English. Not until 1868—more than seventy years after Franklin's death—was the complete *Autobiography* published in English from the original manuscript.

If we consider the circumstances of its composition, we will be better able to appreciate this remarkable history and the different qualities of the work as a whole.

FRANKLIN BEGINS HIS "AUTOBIOGRAPHY" IN ENGLAND

FRANKLIN BEGAN TO WRITE his memoirs in 1771, at the age of sixty-five. He was then in England, in the seventh year of his mission as agent for Pennsylvania. During a two-week visit in July and August at the house of a friend some sixty-five miles from London, he wrote nearly eighty-six pages in the form of a letter to his son William. He used large sheets of paper, approximately thirteen by eight inches and wrote on only one half of the page, leaving the other half free for additions and corrections.

It was a story meant only for his son and immediate family, and not for the public. This intention, plus the haste in which he must have written so much in so short a time, undoubtedly account for the vigorous spontaneity of this first part. Nowhere else in the work does he again achieve this liveliness and zest.

When he stopped, Franklin had not covered much of his story, for he had reached only the year 1730.

THE "AUTOBIOGRAPHY" IS CONTINUED IN FRANCE

Four years later, in 1775, Franklin returned to America after an absence of eleven years. The very day after he arrived, he was appointed a delegate to the Second Continental Congress. The next year he was placed on the committee to draft the Declaration of Independence—with the actual composition of which he was not entrusted, it is said, for fear that he might not be able to refrain from inserting a joke. Later that same year, he was sent to France as an agent for the colonies.

It was on foreign soil, this time French, that he resumed the story of his life. More than ten years had passed since he had written those first eighty-six pages, and we can only conjecture whether he would have taken it up again at all had it not been for the insistence of his friends.

Even so, it was not until 1784 that Franklin began to write the second part. This second installment is completely different from the first. What follows is no longer a narrative for his son, but a sermon "intended for the public." Now he is consciously instructing youngsters who want to succeed and he is giving lessons in moral virtue. At this time, in Passy, outside Paris, he wrote only seventeen pages.

THE RETURN TO AMERICA AND MORE WORK

IN THE SUMMER of 1785, Franklin returned to America. He was elected President of Pennsylvania, re-elected the next year, and again the year after that. In November 1786, during his second term, he wrote a friend that having been persuaded that "such a *Life*, written by myself, may be useful to the rising Generation, I have made some progress in it, and hope to finish it in the Winter." But since there is no new installment to correspond with this statement, it has been assumed that his progress consisted of revisions and corrections in the two parts already written.

In April 1787, he wrote a friend that his third term as President of Pennsylvania would end in October, at which time he planned to retire to his grandson's home in New Jersey and take up the *Autobiography* once more, "and continue it daily till finished, which if my health permits, may be in the course of the ensuing year."

He began writing four months later, and noted in the margin: "I am now to write at home, August 1787." By this time Franklin was past eighty-two, and suffering agonizing pain that forced him to an occasional use of opium. His handwriting is shaky in some parts, and the work must have been difficult and slow. Yet he managed to write one hundred and seventeen pages during these months.

LAST ENTRIES IN THE BOOK

Shortly before his death he added seven and a half pages to the *Autobiography* under the heading: "We arrived in London the 27th of July, 1757." This addition starts: "As soon as I was settled in a lodging. . . ." These last pages do not appear in the two copies of the earlier parts which Franklin had his grandson make and send to friends in November 1789. In fact, this fourth part does not even appear in the first English edition that was published in 1818, because it was printed from one of these copies and not from Franklin's handwritten manuscript.

THE RICH LEGACY OF A GREAT MAN

THE EASY, FLOWING STYLE and the gentle matter-of-factness of the *Autobiography* are deceiving. The book would be delightful reading even if the author were unknown, because the cool logic, the common sense, the charm and wit are sufficient in themselves and need no "name" to sell them. But this dispassionate straight-forwardness can not conceal the pounding drama of man and history. The broad view, the varied activities are described with lively humor and charming fancy. Naive pride mingles with wry scepticism in the recounting of his presentation to five kings and of his dinner with one.

Here are his endearing qualities—ambition, passion for self-improvement, canny business sense, genius for self-advertisement, and devotion to common sense. In flashes and by casual references, his fantastic humor, his marvelous gift for parody, his genial playfulness, his gentle love of youngsters, and his interest in science disclose themselves.

Considered by itself, the book is the extraordinary success story of an engaging youngster grown into an intelligent and charming man who was of the heart and marrow of America.

Twyford, [*England*], *at the Bishop of St Asaph's,* 1771.

DEAR SON: I have ever had pleasure in obtaining any little anecdotes of my ancestors. You may remember the inquiries I made among the remains of my relations when you were with me in England, and the journey I undertook for that purpose. Imagining it may be equally agreeable to you to know the circumstances of my life, many of which you are yet unacquainted with, and expecting the enjoyment of a week's uninterrupted leisure in my present country retirement, I sit down to write them for you. To which I have besides some other inducements. Having emerged from the poverty and obscurity in which I was born and bred, to a state of affluence and some degree of reputation in the world, and having gone so far through life with a considerable share of felicity, the conducing means I made use of, which with the blessing of God so well succeeded, my posterity may like to know, as they may find some of them suitable to their own situations, and therefore fit to be imitated.

That felicity, when I reflected on it, has induced me sometimes to say that were it offered to my choice, I should have no objection to a repetition of the same life from its beginning, only asking the advantages authors have in a second edition to correct some faults of the first.

Hereby, too, I shall indulge the inclination so natural in old men [*he was then 65*], to be talking of themselves and their own past actions. Most people dislike vanity in others, whatever share they have of it themselves; but I give it fair quarter wherever I meet with it, being persuaded that it is often productive of good to the possessor, and to others that are within his sphere of action; and therefore, in many cases, it would not be altogether absurd if a man were to thank God for his vanity among the other comforts of life.

And now I speak of thanking God, I desire with all humility to acknowledge that I owe the mentioned happiness of my past life to His kind providence, which led me to the means I used and gave them success. My belief of this induces me to *hope,* though I must not *presume,* that the same goodness will still be exercised toward me, in continuing that happiness, or enabling me to bear a fatal reverse, which I may experience as others have done; the complexion of my future fortune being known to Him only in whose power it is to bless to us even our afflictions.

The notes one of my uncles (who had the same kind of curiosity in collecting family anecdotes) once put into my hands furnished me with several particulars relating to our ancestors. From these notes I learned that the family had lived in the same village, Ecton, in Northamptonshire, for three hundred years, and how much longer he knew not (perhaps from the time when the name of Franklin, that before was the name of an order of people [*free farmers owning land not subject to feudal obligations*], was assumed by them as a surname when others took surnames all over the kingdom), on a freehold of about thirty acres, aided by the smith's business, which had continued in the family till his time, the eldest son being always bred to that business; a custom which he and my father followed as to their eldest sons.

When I searched the registers at Ecton, I found an account of their births, marriages and burials from the year 1555 only, there being no registers kept in that parish at any time preceding. By that register I perceived that I was the youngest son of the youngest son for five generations back.

My grandfather Thomas, who was born in 1598, lived at Ecton till he grew too old to follow business longer, when he went to live with his son John, a dyer at Banbury, in Oxfordshire, with whom my father served an apprenticeship. My grandfather had four sons that grew up, viz.: Thomas, John, Benjamin and Josiah.

Thomas was bred a smith under his father; but, being ingenious, and encouraged in learning (as all my brothers were) by an Esquire

Palmer, then the principal gentleman in that parish, he qualified himself for the business of scrivener; became a considerable man in the county; was a chief mover of all public-spirited undertakings for the county or town of Northampton, and his own village, of which many instances were related of him; and much taken notice of and patronized by the then Lord Halifax. He died in 1702, January 6, old style, just four years to a day before I was born. The account we received of his life and character from some old people at Ecton, I remember, struck you as something extraordinary, from its similarity to what you knew of mine. "Had he died on the same day," you said, "one might have supposed a transmigration."

John was bred a dyer, I believe of woolens. Benjamin was bred a silk dyer, serving an apprenticeship at London. He was an ingenious man. I remember him well, for when I was a boy he came over to my father in Boston, and lived in the house with us some years. He lived to a great age. He left behind him two quarto volumes, MS., of his own poetry, consisting of little occasional pieces addressed to his friends and relations. He had formed a shorthand of his own, which he taught me, but, never practicing it, I have now forgot it. I was named after this uncle, there being a particular affection between him and my father. He was very pious, a great attender of sermons of the best preachers, which he took down in his shorthand, and had with him many volumes of them.

This obscure family of ours was early in the Reformation, and continued Protestants through the reign of Queen Mary, when they were sometimes in danger of trouble on account of their zeal against popery. They had got an English Bible, and to conceal and secure it, it was fastened open with tapes under and within the cover of a joint-stool. When my great-great-grandfather read it to his family, he turned up the joint-stool upon his knees, turning over the leaves then under the tapes. One of the children stood at the door to give notice if he saw the apparitor coming, who was an officer of the spiritual court. In that case the stool was turned down again upon its feet, when the Bible remained concealed under it as before.

Josiah, my father, married young, and carried his wife with three children into New England, about 1682. The conventicles having been forbidden by law, and frequently disturbed, induced some considerable men of his acquaintance to remove to that country, and he was prevailed with to accompany them thither, where they expected to enjoy their mode of religion with freedom. By the same wife he had four children more born there, and by a second wife ten more, in all seventeen; of which I remember thirteen sitting at one time at his table, who all grew up to be men and women, and married; I was the youngest son, and the youngest child but two, and was born in Boston, New England.

My mother, the second wife, was Abiah Folger, daughter of Peter Folger, one of the first settlers of New England, of whom honorable mention is made by Cotton Mather, in his church history of that country, entitled Magnalia Christi Americana, as *"a godly, learned Englishman,"* if I remember the words rightly. I have heard that he wrote sundry small occasional pieces, but only one of them was printed, which I saw now many years since. It was written in 1675, in the home-spun verse of that time and people, and addressed to those then concerned in the government there. It was in favor of liberty of conscience, and in behalf of the Baptists, Quakers, and other sectaries that had been under persecution. The whole appeared to me as written with a good deal of decent plainness and manly freedom. My elder brothers were all put apprentices to different trades. I was put to the grammar-school at eight years of age, my father intending to devote me, as the tithe of his sons, to the service of the Church. My early readiness in learning to read (which must have been very early, as I do not remember when I could not read), and the opinion of all his friends, that I should certainly make a good scholar, encouraged him in this purpose of his. I continued, however, at the grammar-school not quite one year, though in that time I had risen gradually from the middle of the class of that year to be the head of it, and farther was removed into the next class above it, in order to go with that into the third at the end of the year.

But my father, in the meantime, from a view of the expense of a college education, which having so large a family he could not well afford, and the mean living many so educated were afterwards able to obtain—reasons that he gave to his friends in my hearing—altered his first intention, took me from the grammar-school, and sent me to a school for writing and arithmetic, kept by a then famous man, Mr. George Brownell, very successful in his profession generally, and that by mild, encouraging methods. Under him I acquired fair writing pretty soon, but I failed in the arithmetic, and made no progress in it.

At ten years old I was taken home to assist my father in his business, which was that of a tallow-chandler and soap-boiler; a business he was not bred to, but had assumed on his arrival in New England,

and on finding his dyeing trade would not maintain his family, being in little request. Accordingly, I was employed in cutting wick for the candles, filling the dipping mold and the molds for cast candles, attending the shop, going of errands, etc.

I disliked the trade, and had a strong inclination for the sea, but my father declared against it. However, living near the water, I was much in and about it, learnt early to swim well, and to manage boats; and when in a boat or canoe with other boys, I was commonly allowed to govern, especially in any case of difficulty; and upon other occasions I was generally a leader among the boys, and sometimes led them into scrapes, of which I will mention one instance, as it shows an early projecting public spirit, tho' not then justly conducted.

There was a salt-marsh that bounded part of the millpond, on the edge of which, at high water, we used to stand to fish for minnows. By much trampling, we had made it a mere quagmire. My proposal was to build a wharf there fit for us to stand upon, and I showed my comrades a large heap of stones, which were intended for a new house near the marsh, and which would very well suit our purpose. Accordingly, in the evening, when the workmen were gone, I assembled a number of my play-fellows, and working with them diligently like so many emmets, sometimes two or three to a stone, we brought them all away and built our little wharf. The next morning the workmen were surprised at missing the stones, which were found in our wharf. Inquiry was made after the removers. We were discovered and complained of. Several of us were corrected by our fathers; and, though I pleaded the usefulness of the work, mine convinced me that nothing was useful which was not honest.

I think you may like to know something of his person and character. He had an excellent constitution of body, was of middle stature, but well set, and very strong. He was ingenious, could draw prettily, was skilled a little in music, and had a clear pleasing voice, so that when he played psalm tunes on his violin and sung withal, as he sometimes did in an evening after the business of the day was over, it was extremely agreeable to hear.

He had a mechanical genius too, and, on occasion, was very handy in the use of other tradesmen's tools; but his great excellence lay in a sound understanding and solid judgment in prudential matters, both in private and public affairs. In the latter, indeed, he was never employed, the numerous family he had to educate and the straitness of his circumstances keeping him close to his trade; but I remember well

165

his being frequently visited by leading people, who consulted him for his opinion in affairs of the town or of the church he belonged to, and showed a good deal of respect for his judgment and advice.

He was also much consulted by private persons about their affairs when any difficulty occurred, and frequently chosen an arbitrator between contending parties. At his table he liked to have, as often as he could, some sensible friend or neighbor to converse with, and always took care to start some ingenious or useful topic for discourse, which might tend to improve the minds of his children. By this means he turned our attention to what was good, just, and prudent in the conduct of life; and little or no notice was ever taken of what related to the victuals on the table, whether it was well or ill dressed, in or out of season, of good or bad flavor, preferable or inferior to this or that other thing of the kind, so that I was brought up in such a perfect inattention to those matters as to be quite indifferent what kind of food was set before me, and so unobservant of it, that to this day if I am asked I can scarce tell a few hours after dinner what I dined upon.

My mother had likewise an excellent constitution. She suckled all her ten children. I never knew either my father or mother to have any sickness but that of which they died, he at 89, and she at 85 years of age. They lie buried together at Boston, where I some years since placed a marble over their grave, with this inscription:

JOSIAH FRANKLIN,
and
ABIAH his wife,
lie here interred.
They lived lovingly together in wedlock
fifty-five years.
Without an estate, or any gainful employment,
By constant labor and industry,
with God's blessing,
They maintained a large family
comfortably,
and brought up thirteen children
and seven grandchildren
reputably.
From this instance, reader,
Be encouraged to diligence in thy calling,
And distrust not Providence.
He was a pious and prudent man;
She, a discreet and virtuous woman.
Their youngest son,

166

In filial regard to their memory,
Places this stone.
J. F. born 1655, died 1744, Ætat 89.
A. F. born 1667, died 1752, ——— 85.

By my rambling digressions I perceive myself to be grown old. I used to write more methodically. But one does not dress for private company as for a public ball. 'Tis perhaps only negligence.

To return: I continued thus employed in my father's business for two years, that is, till I was twelve years old; and my brother John, who was bred to that business, having left my father, married, and set up for himself at Rhode Island, there was all appearance that I was destined to supply his place, and become a tallow-chandler. But my dislike to the trade continuing, my father was under apprehensions that if he did not find one for me more agreeable, I should break away and get to sea, as his son Josiah had done, to his great vexation.

He therefore sometimes took me to walk with him, and see joiners, bricklayers, turners, braziers, etc., at their work, that he might observe my inclination, and endeavor to fix it on some trade or other on land. It has ever since been a pleasure to me to see good workmen handle their tools; and it has been useful to me, having learnt so much by it as to be able to do little jobs myself in my house when a workman could not readily be got, and to construct little machines for my experiments, while the intention of making the experiment was fresh and warm in my mind. My father at last fixed upon the cutler's trade, and my uncle Benjamin's son Samuel, who was bred to that business in London, being about that time established in Boston, I was sent to be with him some time on liking. But his expectations of a fee with me displeasing my father, I was taken home again.

From a child I was fond of reading, and all the little money that came into my hands was ever laid out in books. Pleased with the *Pilgrim's Progress,* my first collection was of John Bunyan's works in separate little volumes. I afterward sold them to enable me to buy R. Burton's *Historical Collections.* They were small chapmen's books, and cheap, 40 or 50 in all. My father's little library consisted chiefly of books in polemic divinity, most of which I read, and have since often regretted that, at a time when I had such a thirst for knowledge, more proper books had not fallen in my way, since it was now resolved I should not be a clergyman. Plutarch's *Lives* there was in which I read abundantly, and I still think that time spent to great advantage. There was also a book of De Foe's, called an *Essay on*

167

Projects, and another of Dr. Mather's called *Essays to do Good,* which perhaps gave me a turn of thinking that had an influence on some of the principal future events of my life.

This bookish inclination at length determined my father to make me a printer, though he had already one son (James) of that profession. In 1717 my brother James returned from England with a press and letters to set up his business in Boston. I liked it much better than that of my father, but still had a hankering for the sea. To prevent the apprehended effect of such an inclination, my father was impatient to have me bound to my brother. I stood out some time, but at last was persuaded, and signed the indentures when I was yet but twelve years old. I was to serve as an apprentice till I was twenty-one years of age, only I was to be allowed journeyman's wages during the last year.

In a little time I made great proficiency in the business, and became a useful hand to my brother. I now had access to better books. An acquaintance with the apprentices of booksellers enabled me sometimes to borrow a small one, which I was careful to return soon and clean. Often I sat up in my room reading the greatest part of the night, when the book was borrowed in the evening and to be returned early in the morning, lest it should be missed or wanted.

After some time an ingenious tradesman, Mr. Matthew Adams, who had a pretty collection of books, and who frequented our printing-house, took notice of me, invited me to his library, and very kindly lent me such books as I chose to read. I now took a fancy to poetry, and made some little pieces. My brother, thinking it might turn to account, encouraged me, and put me on composing occasional ballads. One was called *The Lighthouse Tragedy,* and contained an account of the drowning of Captain Worthilake, with his two daughters; the other was a sailor's song, on the taking of *Teach* (or Blackbeard) the pirate. They were wretched stuff, in the Grub-Street-ballad style; and when they were printed he sent me about the town to sell them. The first sold wonderfully, the event being recent, having made a great noise. This flattered my vanity; but my father discouraged me by ridiculing my performances, and telling me verse-makers were generally beggars. So I escaped being a poet, most probably a very bad one; but as prose writing has been of great use to me in the course of my life, and was a principal means of my advancement, I shall tell you how, in such a situation, I acquired what little ability I have in that way.

There was another bookish lad in the town, John Collins by name, with whom I was intimately acquainted. We sometimes disputed, and very fond we were of argument, and very desirous of confuting one another, which disputatious turn, by the way, is apt to become a very bad habit, making people often extremely disagreeable in company by the contradiction that is necessary to bring it into practice; and thence, besides souring and spoiling the conversation, is productive of disgusts and perhaps enmities where you may have occasion for friendship. I had caught it by reading my father's books of dispute about religion. Persons of good sense, I have since observed, seldom fall into it, except lawyers, university men, and men of all sorts that have been bred at Edinborough.

A question was once, somehow or other, started between Collins and me, of the propriety of educating the female sex in learning, and their abilities for study. He was of opinion that it was improper, and that they were naturally unequal to it. I took the contrary side, perhaps a little for dispute's sake. He was naturally more eloquent, had a ready plenty of words; and sometimes, as I thought, bore me down more by his fluency than by the strength of his reasons. As we parted without settling the point, and were not to see one another again for some time, I sat down to put my arguments in writing, which I copied fair and sent to him. He answered, and I replied. Three or four letters of a side had passed, when my father happened to find my papers and read them. Without entering into the discussion, he took occasion to talk to me about the manner of my writing; observed that, though I had the advantage of my antagonist in correct spelling and pointing (which I owed to the printing-house), I fell far short in elegance of expression, in method and in perspicuity, of which he convinced me by several instances. I saw the justice of his remarks, and thence grew more attentive to the manner in writing, and determined to endeavor an improvement.

About this time I met with an odd volume of the *Spectator*. It was the third. I had never before seen any of them. I bought it, read it over and over, and was much delighted with it. I thought the writing excellent, and wished, if possible, to imitate it. With this view I took some of the papers, and, making short hints of the sentiment in each sentence, laid them by a few days, and then, without looking at the book, tried to complete the papers again, by expressing each hinted sentiment at length, and as fully as it had been expressed before, in any suitable words that should come to hand. Then I compared my *Spectator* with the original, discovered some of my faults, and corrected them.

But I found I wanted a stock of words, or a readiness in recollecting and using them, which I thought I should have acquired before that time if I had gone on making verses; since the continual occasion for words of the same import, but of different length, to suit the measure, or of different sound for the rhyme, would have laid me under a constant necessity of searching for variety, and also have tended to fix that variety in my mind, and make me master of it. Therefore I took some of the tales and turned them into verse; and, after a time, when I had pretty well forgotten the prose, turned them back again.

I also sometimes jumbled my collections of hints into confusion, and after some weeks endeavored to reduce them into the best order, before I began to form the full sentences and complete the paper. This was to teach me method in the arrangement of thoughts. By comparing my work afterwards with the original, I discovered many faults and amended them; but I sometimes had the pleasure of fancying that, in certain particulars of small import, I had been lucky enough to improve the method or the language, and this encouraged me to think I might possibly in time come to be a tolerable English writer, of which I was extremely ambitious.

My time for these exercises and for reading was at night, after work or before it began in the morning, or on Sundays, when I contrived to be in the printing-house alone, evading as much as I could the common attendance on public worship which my father used to exact on me when I was under his care, and which indeed I still thought a duty, though I could not, as it seemed to me, afford time to practice it.

When about 16 years of age I happened to meet with a book, written by one Tryon, recommending a vegetable diet. I determined to go into it. My brother, being yet unmarried, did not keep house, but boarded himself and his apprentices in another family. My refusing to eat flesh occasioned an inconveniency, and I was frequently chid for my singularity. I made myself acquainted with Tryon's manner of preparing some of his dishes, such as boiling potatoes or rice, making hasty pudding, and a few others, and then proposed to my brother, that if he would give me, weekly, half the money he paid for my board, I would board myself. He instantly agreed to it, and I presently found that I could save half what he paid me.

This was an additional fund for buying books. But I had another advantage in it. My brother and the rest going from the printing-house to their meals, I remained there alone, and, dispatching presently my light repast, which often was no more than a biscuit or a slice of bread, a handful of raisins or a tart from the pastry-cook's, and a glass of water, had the rest of the time till their return for study, in which I made the greater progress, from that greater clearness of head and quicker apprehension which usually attend temperance in eating and drinking.

And now it was that, being on some occasion made ashamed of my ignorance in figures, which I had twice failed in learning when at school, I took Cocker's book of *Arithmetick,* and went through the whole by myself with great ease. I also read Seller's and Shermy's books of *Navigation,* and became acquainted with the little geometry they contain; but never proceeded far in that science. And I read about this time Locke *On Human Understanding,* and *The Art of Thinking,* by Messrs. du Port Royal.

While I was intent on improving my language, I met with an English grammar (I think it was Greenwood's), at the end of which there were two little sketches of the arts of rhetoric and logic, the latter finishing with a specimen of a dispute in the Socratic method; and soon after I procured Xenophon's *Memorable Things of Socrates,* wherein there are many instances of the same method. I was charmed with it, adopted it, dropped my abrupt contradiction and positive argumentation, and put on the humble inquirer and doubter.

And being then, from reading Shaftesbury and Collins, become a real doubter in many points of our religious doctrine, I found this method safest for myself and very embarrassing to those against whom I used it. Therefore I took a delight in it, practiced it continually, and grew very artful and expert in drawing people, even of superior knowledge, into concessions, the consequences of which they did not foresee, entangling them in difficulties out of which they could not extricate themselves, and so obtaining victories that neither myself nor my cause always deserved.

I continued this method some few years, but gradually left it, retaining only the habit of expressing myself in terms of modest diffidence; never using, when I advanced anything that may possibly be disputed, the words *certainly, undoubtedly,* or any others that give the air of positiveness to an opinion; but rather say, *I conceive, or apprehend, a thing to be so and so; It appears to me;* or *I should think it so or so,* for such and such reasons; or *I imagine it to be so;* or *it is so, if*

I am not mistaken. This habit, I believe, has been of great advantage to me when I have had occasion to inculcate my opinions, and persuade men into measures that I have been from time to time engaged in promoting. And, as the chief ends of conversation are to *inform* or to be *informed,* to *please* or to *persuade,* I wish well-meaning, sensible men would not lessen their power of doing good by a positive, assuming manner, that seldom fails to disgust, tends to create opposition, and to defeat everyone of those purposes for which speech was given to us, to wit, giving or receiving information or pleasure.

My brother had, in 1720 or 1721, begun to print a newspaper. It was the second that appeared in America, and was called the *New England Courant.* The only one before it was the *Boston News-Letter.* I remember his being dissuaded by some of his friends from the undertaking, as not likely to succeed, one newspaper being, in their judgment, enough for America. At this time (1771) there are not less than five-and-twenty. He went on, however, with the undertaking, and after having worked in composing the types and printing off the sheets, I was employed to carry the papers thro' the streets to the customers.

He had some ingenious men among his friends, who amused themselves by writing little pieces for this paper, which gained it credit and made it more in demand, and these gentlemen often visited us. Hearing their conversations, and their accounts of the approbation their papers were received with, I was excited to try my hand among them; but, being still a boy, and suspecting that my brother would object to printing anything of mine in his paper if he knew it to be mine, I contrived to disguise my hand, and, writing an anonymous paper, I put it in at night under the door of the printing-house. It was found in the morning, and communicated to his writing friends when they called in as usual. They read it, commented on it in my hearing, and I had the exquisite pleasure of finding it met with their approbation, and that, in their different guesses at the author, none were named but men of some character among us for learning and ingenuity. I suppose now that I was rather lucky in my judges, and that perhaps they were not really so very good ones as I then esteemed them.

Encouraged, however, by this, I wrote and conveyed in the same way to the press several more papers which were equally approved. [*These were sprightly satirical essays in the style of the* Spectator, *and were signed* Silence Dogood.] And I kept my secret till my small fund of sense for such performances was pretty well exhausted, and then I discovered it, when I began to be considered a little more by my brother's acquaintance, and in a manner that did not quite please him, as he thought, probably with reason, that it tended to make me too vain. And, perhaps, this might be one occasion of the differences that we began to have about this time.

Though a brother, he considered himself as my master, and me as his apprentice, and, accordingly, expected the same services from me as he would from another, while I thought he demeaned me too much in some he required of me, who from a brother expected more indulgence. Our disputes were often brought before our father, and I fancy I was either generally in the right, or else a better pleader, because the judgment was generally in my favor. But my brother was passionate, and had often beaten me, which I took extremely amiss; and, thinking my apprenticeship very tedious, I was continually wishing for some opportunity of shortening it, which at length offered in a manner unexpected. (I fancy his harsh and tyrannical treatment of me might be a means of impressing me with that aversion to arbitrary power that has stuck to me through my whole life.)

One of the pieces in our newspaper on some political point, which I have now forgotten, gave offense to the Assembly. He was taken up, censured, and imprisoned for a month, by the speaker's warrant, I suppose because he would not discover his author. I too was taken up and examined before the council; but, tho' I did not give them any satisfaction, they contented themselves with admonishing me, and dismissed me, considering me, perhaps, as an apprentice, who was bound to keep his master's secrets.

During my brother's confinement, which I resented a good deal, notwithstanding our private differences, I had the management of the paper; and I made bold to give our rulers some rubs in it, which my brother took very kindly, while others began to consider me in an unfavorable light, as a young genius that had a turn for libeling, and satire. My brother's discharge was accompanied with an order of the House (a very odd one), that *"James Franklin should no longer print the paper called the New England Courant."*

There was a consultation held in our printing-house among his friends, what he should do in this case. Some proposed to evade the order by changing the name of the paper; but my brother, seeing inconveniences in that, it was finally concluded on as a better way, to let it be printed for the future under the name of BENJAMIN FRANKLIN. And to avoid the censure of the Assembly, that might fall on him as still printing it by his apprentice, the contrivance was that my old indenture should be returned to me, with a full discharge on the back of it, to be shown on occasion, but to secure to him the benefit of my service, I was to sign new indentures for the remainder of the term, which were to be kept private. A very flimsy scheme it was; however, it was immediately executed, and the paper went on accordingly under my name for several months.

At length, a fresh difference arising between my brother and me, I took upon me to assert my freedom, presuming that he would not venture to produce the new indentures. It was not fair in me to take this advantage, and this I therefore reckon one of the first errata of my life. But the unfairness of it weighed little with me, when under the impressions of resentment for the blows his passion too often urged him to bestow upon me, though he was otherwise not an ill-natured man. Perhaps I was too saucy and provoking.

When he found I would leave him, he took care to prevent my getting employment in any other printing-house of the town, by going round and speaking to every master, who accordingly refused to give me work. I then thought of going to New York, as the nearest place where there was a printer; and I was rather inclined to leave Boston when I reflected that I had already made myself a little obnoxious to the governing party, and, from the arbitrary proceedings of the Assembly in my brother's case, it was likely I might, if I stayed, soon bring myself into scrapes; and farther, that my indiscreet disputations about religion began to make me pointed at with horror by good people as an infidel or atheist.

I determined on the point, but my father now siding with my brother, I was sensible that, if I attempted to go openly, means would be used to prevent me. My friend Collins, therefore, undertook to manage a little for me. He agreed with the captain of a New York sloop for my passage, under the notion of my being a young acquaintance of his that had got a naughty girl with child, whose friends would compel me to marry her, and therefore I could not appear or come away publicly. So I sold some of my books to raise a little money, was taken on board privately, and as we had a fair wind, in three days I found myself in New York, near 300 miles from home, a boy of but 17, without the least recommendation to, or knowledge of any person in the place, and with very little money in my pocket.

My inclinations for the sea were by this time worn out, or I might now have gratified them. But, having a trade, and supposing myself a pretty good workman, I offered my service to the printer in the place, old Mr. William Bradford, who had been the first printer in Pennsylvania, but removed from thence upon the quarrel of George Keith. He could give me no employment, having little to do, and help enough already; but says he, "My son at Philadelphia has lately lost his principal hand, Aquila Rose, by death. If you go thither, I believe he may employ you." Philadelphia was a hundred miles further. I set out, however, in a boat for Amboy, leaving my chest and things to follow me round by sea.

In crossing the bay, we met with a squall that tore our rotten sails to pieces, prevented our getting into the Kill, and drove us upon Long Island. In our way, a drunken Dutchman, who was a passenger too, fell overboard. When he was sinking, I reached through the water to his shock pate, and drew him up, so that we got him in again. His ducking sobered him a little, and he went to sleep, taking first out of his pocket a book, which he desired I would dry for him. It proved to be my old favorite author, Bunyan's *Pilgrim's Progress,* in Dutch, finely printed on good paper, with copper cuts, a dress better than I had ever seen it wear in its own language. I have since found that it has been translated into most of the languages of Europe, and suppose it has been more generally read than any other book, except perhaps the *Bible.*

When we drew near the island, we found it was at a place where there could be no landing, there being a great surf on the stony beach [*of Brooklyn*]. So we dropped anchor, and swung round towards the shore. Some people came down to the water edge and hallooed to us, as we did to them; but the wind was so high, and the surf so loud, that we could not hear so as to understand each other. There were canoes on the shore, and we made signs and hallooed that they should fetch us; but they either did not understand us, or thought it impracticable, so they went away, and night coming on, we had no remedy but to wait till the wind should abate. And, in the meantime, the boatman and I concluded to sleep, if we could; and so crowded into the scuttle, with the Dutchman, who was still wet, and the spray beating over the head of our boat, leaked thro' to us, so that we were soon almost as wet as he. In this manner we lay all night, with very little rest. But, the wind abating the next day, we made a shift to reach Amboy before night, having been thirty hours on the water, without victuals, or any drink but a bottle of filthy rum, and the water we sailed on being salt.

In the evening I found myself very feverish, and went into bed. But,

175

having read somewhere that cold water drank plentifully was good for a fever, I followed the prescription, sweat plentiful most of the night, my fever left me, and in the morning, crossing the ferry, I proceeded on my journey on foot, having fifty miles to Burlington, where I was told I should find boats that would carry me the rest of the way to Philadelphia.

It rained very hard all the day. I was thoroughly soaked, and by noon a good deal tired; so I stopped at a poor inn, where I stayed all night, beginning now to wish that I had never left home. I cut so miserable a figure, too, that I found, by the questions asked me, I was suspected to be some runaway servant, and in danger of being taken up on that suspicion. However, I proceeded the next day, and got in the evening to an inn within eight or ten miles of Burlington, kept by one Dr. Brown. He entered into conversation with me while I took some refreshment, and, finding I had read a little, became very sociable and friendly. Our acquaintance continued as long as he lived. He had been, I imagine, an itinerant doctor, for there was no town in England, or country in Europe, of which he could not give a very particular account.

At his house I lay that night, and the next morning reached Burlington, but had the mortification to find that the regular boats were gone a little before my coming, and no other expected to go before Tuesday, this being Saturday. Wherefore I returned to an old woman in the town, of whom I had bought gingerbread to eat on the water, and asked her advice. She invited me to lodge at her house till a passage by water should offer; and being tired with my foot traveling, I accepted the invitation. She understanding I was a printer, would have had me stay at that town and follow my business, being ignorant of the stock necessary to begin with. She was very hospitable, gave me a dinner of ox-cheek with great good will, accepting only of a pot of ale in return; and I thought myself fixed till Tuesday should come.

However, walking in the evening by the side of the river, a boat came by, which I found was going towards Philadelphia, with several people in her. They took me in, and, as there was no wind, we rowed all the way; and about midnight, not having yet seen the city, some of the company were confident we must have passed it, and would row no farther. The others knew not where we were; so we put toward the shore, got into a creek, landed near an old fence, with the rails of which we made a fire, the night being cold, in October, and there we remained till daylight. Then one of the company knew the place to be

Cooper's Creek, a little above Philadelphia, which we saw as soon as we got out of the creek, and arrived there about eight or nine o'clock on the Sunday morning, and landed at the Market Street wharf.

I have been the more particular in this description of my journey, and shall be so of my first entry into that city, that you may in your mind compare such unlikely beginnings with the figure I have since made there. I was in my working dress, my best clothes being to come round by sea. I was dirty from my journey; my pockets were stuffed out with shirts and stockings, and I knew no soul nor where to look for lodging. I was fatigued with traveling, rowing, and want of rest, I was very hungry; and my whole stock of cash consisted of a Dutch dollar, and about a shilling in copper. The latter I gave the people of the boat for my passage, who at first refused it, on account of my rowing; but I insisted on their taking it. A man being sometimes more generous when he has but a little money than when he has plenty, perhaps through fear of being thought to have but little.

Then I walked up the street, gazing about till near the market-house I met a boy with bread. I had many a meal on bread, and, inquiring where he got it, I went immediately to the baker's he directed me to, in Second Street, and asked for biscuits, intending such as we had in Boston; but they, it seems, were not made in Philadelphia. Then I asked for a three-penny loaf, and was told they had none such. So not considering or knowing the difference of money, and the greater cheapness nor the names of his bread, I bade him give me three-penny worth of any sort. He gave me, accordingly, three great puffy rolls. I was surprised at the quantity, but took it, and, having no room in my pockets, walked off with a roll under each arm, and eating the other. Thus I went up Market Street as far as Fourth Street, passing by the door of Mr. Read, my future wife's father; when she, standing at the door, saw me, and thought I made, as I certainly did, a most awkward, ridiculous appearance. Then I turned and went down Chestnut Street and part of Walnut Street, eating my roll all the way, and, coming round, found myself again at Market Street wharf, near the boat I came in, to which I went for a draught of the river water; and, being filled with one of my rolls, gave the other two to a woman and her child that came down the river in the boat with us, and were waiting to go farther.

Thus refreshed, I walked again up the street, which by this time had many clean-dressed people in it, who were all walking the same way. I joined them, and thereby was led into the great meeting-house of the

Quakers near the market. I sat down among them, and, after looking round awhile and hearing nothing said, being very drowsy through labor and want of rest the preceding night, I fell fast asleep, and continued so till the meeting broke up, when one was kind enough to rouse me. This was, therefore, the first house I was in, or slept in, in Philadelphia.

Walking down again toward the river, and, looking in the faces of people, I met a young Quaker man, whose countenance I liked, and, accosting him, requested he would tell me where a stranger could get lodging. We were then near the sign of the Three Mariners. "Here," says he, "is one place that entertains strangers, but it is not a reputable house; if thee wilt walk with me, I'll show thee a better." He brought me to the Crooked Billet in Water Street. Here I got a dinner; and, while I was eating it, several sly questions were asked me, as it seemed to be suspected from my youth and appearance that I might be some runaway.

After dinner, my sleepiness returned, and being shown to a bed, I lay down without undressing, and slept till six in the evening, was called to supper, went to bed again very early, and slept soundly till next morning. Then I made myself as tidy as I could, and went to Andrew Bradford the printer's. I found in the shop the old man his father, whom I had seen at New York, and who, traveling on horseback, had got to Philadelphia before me. He introduced me to his son, who received me civilly, gave me a breakfast, but told me he did not at present want a hand, being lately supplied with one; but there was another printer in town, lately set up, one Keimer, who, perhaps, might employ me. If not, I should be welcome to lodge at his house, and he would give me a little work to do now and then till fuller business should offer.

The old gentleman said he would go with me to the new printer; and when we found him, "Neighbor," says Bradford, "I have brought to see you a young man of your business. Perhaps you may want such a one." He asked me a few questions, put a composing stick in my hand to see how I worked, and then said he would employ me soon, though he had just then nothing for me to do; and, taking old Bradford, whom he had never seen before, to be of the town's people that had a good will for him, entered into a conversation on his present undertaking and prospects; while Bradford, not discovering that he was the other printer's father, on Keimer's saying he expected soon to get the greatest part of the business into his own hands, drew him on by artful questions, and starting little doubts, to explain all his views, what interest he relied on, and in what manner he intended to proceed. I, who stood by and heard all, saw immediately that one of them was a crafty old sophister, and the other a mere novice. Bradford left me with Keimer, who was greatly surprised when I told him who the old man was.

Keimer's printing-house, I found, consisted of an old shattered press, and one small, worn-out font of English, which he was then using himself, composing an Elegy on Aquila Rose, before mentioned, an ingenious young man, of excellent character, much respected in the town, clerk of the Assembly, and a pretty poet. Keimer made verses too, but very indifferently. He could not be said to write them, for his manner was to compose them in the types directly out of his head. So there being no copy, but one pair of cases, and the Elegy likely to require all the letters, no one could help him. I endeavored to put his press (which he had not yet used, and of which he understood nothing) into order fit to be worked with; and, promising to come and print off his Elegy as soon as he should have got it ready, I returned to Bradford's, who gave me a little job to do for the present, and there I lodged and dieted. A few days after, Keimer sent for me to print off the Elegy. And now he had got another pair of cases, and a pamphlet to reprint, on which he set me to work.

These two printers I found poorly qualified for their business, Bradford had not been bred to it, and was very illiterate; and Keimer, tho' something of a scholar, was a mere compositor, knowing nothing of presswork. He had been one of the French prophets, and could act their enthusiastic agitations. At this time he did not profess any particular religion, but something of all on occasion; was very ignorant of the world, and had, as I afterward found, a good deal of the knave in his composition. He did not like my lodging at Bradford's while I worked with him. He had a house, indeed, but without furniture, so he could not lodge me; but he got me a lodging at Mr. Read's, before mentioned, who was the owner of his house; and, my chest and clothes being come by this time, I made rather a more respectable appearance in the eyes of Miss Read than I had done when she first happened to see me eating my roll in the street.

I began now to have some acquaintance among the young people of the town that were lovers of reading, with whom I spent my evenings very pleasantly; and gaining money by my industry and frugality, I lived very agreeably, forgetting Boston as much as I could, and not desiring that any there should know where I resided, except my friend Collins, who was in my secret, and kept it when I wrote to him. At length, an incident happened that sent me back again much sooner than I had intended. I had a brother-in-law, Robert Holmes, master of a sloop that traded between Boston and Delaware. He being at Newcastle, forty miles below Philadelphia, heard there of me, and wrote me a letter mentioning the concern of my friends in Boston at my abrupt departure, assuring me of their good will to me, and that every thing would be accommodated to my mind if I would return, to which he exhorted me very earnestly. I wrote an answer to his letter, thanked him for his advice, but stated my reasons for quitting Boston fully and in such a light as to convince him I was not so wrong as he had apprehended.

Sir William Keith, governor of the province, was then at Newcastle, and Captain Holmes, happening to be in company with him when my letter came to hand, spoke to him of me, and showed him the letter. The governor read it, and seemed surprised when he was told of my age. He said I appeared a young man of promising parts, and therefore should be encouraged. The printers at Philadelphia were wretched ones; and, if I would set up there, he made no doubt I should succeed. For his part, he would procure me the public business, and do me every other service in his power. This my brother-in-law afterwards told me in Boston, but I knew as yet nothing of it, when one day, Keimer and I being at work together near the window, we saw the governor and another gentleman (which proved to be Colonel French, of Newcastle), finely dressed, come directly across the street to our house, and heard them at the door.

Keimer ran down immediately, thinking it a visit to him; but the governor inquired for me, came up, and with a condescension and politeness I had been quite unused to, made me many compliments, desired to be acquainted with me, blamed me kindly for not having made myself known to him when I first came to the place, and would have me away with him to the tavern, where he was going with Colonel French to taste, as he said, some excellent Madeira. I was not a little surprised, and Keimer stared like a pig poisoned.

I went, however, with the governor and Colonel French to a tavern, at the corner of Third Street, and over the Madeira he proposed my setting up my business, laid before me the probabilities of success, and both he and Colonel French assured me I should have their interest and influence in procuring the public business of both governments. On my doubting whether my father would assist me in it, Sir William said he would give me a letter to him, in which he would state the advantages, and he did not doubt of prevailing with him.

So it was concluded I should return to Boston in the first vessel, with the governor's letter recommending me to my father. In the mean time the intention was to be kept a secret, and I went on working with Keimer as usual, the governor sending for me now and then to dine with him, a very great honor I thought it, and conversing with me in the most affable, familiar, and friendly manner imaginable.

About the end of April, 1724, a little vessel offered for Boston. I took leave of Keimer as going to see my friends. The governor gave me an ample letter, saying many flattering things of me to my father, and strongly recommending the project of my setting up at Philadelphia as a thing that must make my fortune. We struck on a shoal in going down the bay, and sprung a leak. We had a blustering time at sea, and were obliged to pump almost continually, at which I took my turn.

We arrived safe, however, at Boston in about a fortnight. I had been absent seven months, and my friends had heard nothing of me; for my brother Holmes was not yet returned, and had not written about me. My unexpected appearance surprised the family. All were, however, very glad to see me, and made me welcome, except my brother. I went to see him at his printing-house. I was better dressed than ever while in his service, having a genteel new suit from head to foot, a watch, and my pockets lined with near five pounds sterling in silver. He received me not very frankly, looked me all over, and turned to his work again.

The journeymen were inquisitive where I had been, what sort of a country it was, and how I liked it. I praised it much, and the happy life I led in it, expressing strongly my intention of returning to it; and, one of them asking what kind of money we had there, I produced a handful of silver, and spread it before them, which was a kind of raree-show they had not been used to, paper being the money of Boston. Then I took an opportunity of letting them see my watch; and, lastly (my brother still glum and sullen), I gave them a piece of eight to drink, and took my leave. This visit of mine offended him extremely; for, when my mother some time after spoke to him of a reconciliation, and of her wishes to see us on good terms together,

181

and that we might live for the future as brothers, he said I had insulted him in such a manner before his people that he could never forget or forgive it. In this, however, he was mistaken.

My father received the governor's letter with some apparent surprise, but said little of it to me for some days, when Capt. Holmes returning he showed it to him; asked him if he knew Keith, and what kind of man he was; adding his opinion that he must be of small discretion to think of setting a boy up in business who wanted yet three years of being at man's estate. Holmes said what he could in favor of the project, but my father was clear in the impropriety of it, and at last gave a flat denial to it. Then he wrote a civil letter to Sir William, thanking him for the patronage he had so kindly offered me, but declining to assist me as yet in setting up, I being, in his opinion, too young to be trusted with the management of a business so important, and for which the preparation must be so expensive.

My friend and companion Collins, who was a clerk in the post-office, pleased with the account I gave him of my new country, determined to go thither also; and, while I waited for my father's determination, he set out before me by land to Rhode Island, leaving his books, which were a pretty collection of mathematics and natural philosophy, to come with mine and me to New York, where he proposed to wait for me.

My father, though he did not approve Sir William's proposition, was yet pleased that I had been able to obtain so advantageous a character from a person of such note where I had resided, and that I had been so industrious and careful as to equip myself so handsomely in so short a time. Therefore, seeing no prospect of an accommodation between my brother and me, he gave his consent to my returning again to Philadelphia, advised me to behave respectfully to the people there, endeavor to obtain the general esteem, and avoid lampooning and libeling, to which he thought I had too much inclination; telling me, that by steady industry and a prudent parsimony I might save enough by the time I was one-and-twenty to set me up; and that, if I came near the matter, he would help me out with the rest. This was all I could obtain, except some small gifts as tokens of his and my mother's love, when I embarked again for New York, now with their approbation and their blessing.

The sloop putting in at Newport, Rhode Island, I visited my brother John, who had been married and settled there some years. He received me very affectionately, for he always loved me. A friend of his, one

Vernon, having some money due to him in Pennsylvania, about thirty-five pounds currency, desired I would receive it for him, and keep it till I had his directions what to remit it in. Accordingly, he gave me an order. This afterwards occasioned me a good deal of uneasiness.

At Newport we took in a number of passengers for New York, among which were two young women, companions, and a grave, sensible, matron-like Quaker woman, with her attendants. I had shown an obliging readiness to do her some little services, which impressed her I suppose with a degree of good will toward me. Therefore, when she saw a daily growing familiarity between me and the two young women, which they appeared to encourage, she took me aside, and said, "Young man, I am concerned for thee, as thou has no friend with thee, and seems not to know much of the world, or of the snares youth is exposed to. Depend upon it, those are very bad women. I can see it in all their actions; and if thee are not upon thy guard, they will draw thee into some danger. They are strangers to thee, and I advise thee, in a friendly concern for thy welfare, to have no acquaintance with them." As I seemed at first not to think so ill of them as she did, she mentioned some things she had observed and heard that had escaped my notice, but now convinced me she was right. I thanked her for her kind advice, and promised to follow it.

When we arrived at New York, they told me where they lived, and invited me to come and see them; but I avoided it, and it was well I did; for the next day the captain missed a silver spoon and some other things, that had been taken out of his cabin, and, knowing that these were a couple of strumpets, he got a warrant to search their lodgings, found the stolen goods, and had the thieves punished. So, tho' we had escaped a sunken rock, which we scraped upon in the passage, I thought this escape of rather more importance to me.

At New York I found my friend Collins, who had arrived there some time before me. We had been intimate from children, and had read the same books together; but he had the advantage of more time for reading and studying, and a wonderful genius for mathematical learning, in which he far outstripped me. While I lived in Boston, most of my hours of leisure for conversation were spent with him, and he continued a sober as well as an industrious lad; was much respected for his learning by several of the clergy and other gentlemen, and seemed to promise making a good figure in life. But, during my absence, he had acquired a habit of sotting with brandy; and I found by his own account, and what I heard from others, that he had been drunk every day since his arrival at New York, and behaved very oddly. He had gamed, too, and lost his money, so that I was obliged to discharge his lodgings, and defray his expenses to and at Philadelphia, which proved extremely inconvenient to me.

The then governor of New York, Burnet (son of Bishop Burnet), hearing from the captain that a young man, one of his passengers, had a great many books, desired he would bring me to see him. I waited upon him accordingly, and should have taken Collins with me but that he was not sober. The governor treated me with great civility, showed me his library, which was a very large one, and we had a good deal of conversation about books and authors. This was the second governor who had done me the honor to take notice of me, which, to a poor boy like me, was very pleasing.

We proceeded to Philadelphia. I received on the way Vernon's money, without which we could hardly have finished our journey. Collins wished to be employed in some counting-house; but, whether they discovered his dramming by his breath, or by his behavior, though he had some recommendations, he met with no success in any application, and continued lodging and boarding at the same house with me, and at my expense. Knowing I had that money of Vernon's, he was continually borrowing of me, still promising repayment as soon as he should be in business. At length he had got so much of it that I was distressed to think what I should do in case of being called on to remit it.

The breaking into this money of Vernon's was one of the first great errata of my life; and this affair showed that my father was not much out in his judgment when he supposed me too young to manage business of importance. But Sir William, on reading his letter, said he was too prudent. There was great difference in persons; and discretion did not always accompany years, nor was youth always without it. "And since he will not set you up," says he, "I will do it myself. Give me an inventory of the things necessary to be had from England, and I will send for them. You shall repay me when you are able. I am resolved to have a good printer here, and I am sure you must succeed."

This was spoken with such an appearance of cordiality that I had not the least doubt of his meaning what he said. I had hitherto kept the proposition of my setting up a secret in Philadelphia, and I still kept it. Had it been known that I depended on the governor, probably some friend, that knew him better, would have advised me not to rely on him, as I afterwards heard it as his known character to be liberal of promises which he never meant to keep. Yet, unsolicited as he was by me, how could I think his generous offers insincere? I believed him one of the best men in the world.

I presented him an inventory of a little printing-house, amounting by my computation to about one hundred pounds sterling. He liked it, but asked me if my being on the spot in England to choose the types, and see that every thing was good of the kind, might not be of some advantage. "Then," says he, "when there, you may make acquaintances, and establish correspondences in the bookselling and stationery way." I agreed that this might be advantageous. "Then," says he, "get yourself ready to go with Annis"; which was the annual ship, and the only one at that time usually passing between London and Philadelphia. But it would be some months before Annis sailed, so I continued working with Keimer, fretting about the money Collins had got from me, and in daily apprehensions of being called upon by Vernon, which, however, did not happen for some years after.

I believe I have omitted mentioning that, in my first voyage from Boston, being becalmed off Block Island, our people set about catching cod, and hauled up a great many. Hitherto I had stuck to my resolution of not eating animal food, and on this occasion I considered, with my master Tryon, the taking every fish as a kind of unprovoked murder, since none of them had, or ever could do us any injury that might justify the slaughter. All this seemed very reasonable.

But I had formerly been a great lover of fish, and, when this came hot out of the frying-pan, it smelt admirably well. I balanced some time between principle and inclination, till I recollected that, when the fish were opened, I saw smaller fish taken out of their stomachs. Then thought I, "If you eat one another, I don't see why we mayn't eat you." So I dined upon cod very heartily, and continued to eat with other people, returning only now and then occasionally to a vegetable diet. So convenient a thing is it to be a *reasonable creature,* since it enables one to find or make a reason for everything one has a mind to do.

Keimer and I lived on a pretty good familiar footing, and agreed tolerably well, for he suspected nothing of my setting up. He retained a great deal of his old enthusiasms and loved argumentation. We therefore had many disputations. I used to work him so with my Socratic method, and had trepanned him so often by questions apparently so distant from any point we had in hand, and yet by degrees led to the point, and brought him into difficulties and contradictions, that at last he grew ridiculously cautious, and would hardly answer me the most common question, without asking first, *"What do you intend to infer from that?"* However, it gave him so high an opinion of my abilities in the confuting way that he seriously proposed my being his colleague in a project he had of setting up a new sect. He was to preach the doctrines, and I was to confound all opponents. When he came to explain with me upon the doctrines, I found several conundrums which I objected to, unless I might have my way a little too, and introduce some of mine.

Keimer wore his beard at full length, because somewhere in the Mosaic law it is said, *Thou shalt not mar the corners of thy beard.* He likewise kept the Seventh day, Sabbath; and these two points were essentials with him. I disliked both; but agreed to admit them upon condition of his adopting the doctrine of using no animal food. "I doubt," said he, "my constitution will not bear that." I assured him it would, and that he would be the better for it. He was usually a great glutton, and I promised myself some diversion in half starving him.

He agreed to try the practice, if I would keep him company. I did so, and we held it for three months. We had our victuals dressed and brought to us regularly by a woman in the neighborhood, who had from me a list of forty dishes, to be prepared for us at different times, in all which there was neither fish, flesh, nor fowl, and the whim suited me the better at this time from the cheapness of it, not costing us above eighteenpence sterling each per week. I went on pleasantly, but poor Keimer suffered grievously, tired of the project, longed for the flesh-pots of Egypt, and ordered a roast pig. He invited me and two women friends to dine with him; but, it being brought too soon upon table, he could not resist the temptation, and ate the whole before we came.

I had made some courtship during this time to Miss Read. I had a great respect and affection for her, and had some reason to believe she had the same for me; but, as I was about to take a long voyage, and we were both very young, only a little above eighteen, it was thought most prudent by her mother to prevent our going too far at present, as a marriage, if it was to take place, would be more convenient after my return, when I should be, as I expected, set up in my business. Perhaps, too, she thought my expectations not so well founded as I imagined them to be.

186

My chief acquaintances at this time were Charles Osborne, Joseph Watson, and James Ralph, all lovers of reading. The two first were clerks to an eminent scrivener or conveyancer in the town, Charles Brogden; the other was clerk to a merchant. Watson was a pious, sensible young man, of great integrity; the others rather more lax in their principles of religion, particularly Ralph, who, as well as Collins, had been unsettled by me, for which they both made me suffer. Osborne was sensible, candid, frank; sincere and affectionate to his friends; but, in literary matters, too fond of criticizing. Ralph was ingenious, genteel in his manners, and extremely eloquent. I think I never knew a prettier talker. Both of them great admirers of poetry, and began to try their hands in little pieces. Many pleasant walks we four had together on Sundays into the woods, near Schuylkill, where we read to one another, and conferred on what we read.

I shall just remark here, that Watson died in my arms a few years after, much lamented, being the best of our set. Osborne went to the West Indies, where he became an eminent lawyer and made money, but died young. He and I had made a serious agreement, that the one who happened first to die should, if possible, make a friendly visit to the other, and acquaint him how he found things in that separate state. But he never fulfilled his promise.

The governor, seeming to like my company, had me frequently to his house, and his setting me up was always mentioned as a fixed thing. I was to take with me letters recommendatory to a number of his friends, besides the letter of credit to furnish me with the necessary money for purchasing the press and types, paper, etc. For these letters I was appointed to call at different times, when they were to be ready; but a future time was still named. Thus he went on till the ship, whose departure too had been several times postponed, was on the point of sailing. Then, when I called to take my leave and receive the letters, his secretary, Dr. Bard, came out to me and said the governor was extremely busy in writing, but would be down at Newcastle before the ship, and there the letters would be delivered to me.

Ralph, though married, and having one child, had determined to accompany me in this voyage. It was thought he intended to establish a correspondence, and obtain goods to sell on commission. But I found afterwards, that, through some discontent with his wife's relations, he purposed to leave her on their hands, and never return again. Having taken leave of my friends, and interchanged some promises with Miss Read, I left Philadelphia in the ship, which anchored at

Newcastle. The governor was there; but when I went to his lodging, the secretary came to me from him with the civilest message in the world, that he could not then see me, being engaged in business of the utmost importance, but should send the letters to me on board, wished me heartily a good voyage and a speedy return, etc. I returned on board a little puzzled, but still not doubting.

Mr. Andrew Hamilton, a famous lawyer of Philadelphia, had taken passage in the same ship for himself and son, and with Mr. Denham, a Quaker merchant, and Messrs. Onion and Russel, masters of an iron work in Maryland, had engaged the great cabin; so that Ralph and I were forced to take up with a berth in the steerage, and none on board knowing us, were considered as ordinary persons. But Mr. Hamilton and his son (it was James, since governor) returned from Newcastle to Philadelphia, the father being recalled by a great fee to plead for a seized ship; and, just before we sailed, Colonel French coming on board, and showing me great respect, I was more taken notice of, and, with my friend Ralph, invited by the other gentlemen to come into the cabin, there being now room. Accordingly, we removed thither.

When we came into the Channel, the captain gave me an opportunity of examining the bag for the governor's letters. I found none upon which my name was put as under my care. I picked out six or seven, that, by the handwriting, I thought might be the promised letters, especially as one of them was directed to Basket, the king's printer, and another to some stationer.

We arrived in London the 24th of December, 1724. I waited upon the stationer, who came first in my way, delivering the letter as from Governor Keith. "I don't know such a person," says he; but, opening the letter, "O! this is from Riddlesden. I have lately found him to be a complete rascal, and I will have nothing to do with him, nor receive any letters from him." So, putting the letter into my hand, he turned on his heel and left me to serve some customer. I was surprised to find these were not the governor's letters; and, after recollecting and comparing circumstances, I began to doubt his sincerity.

I found my friend Denham, and opened the whole affair to him. He let me into Keith's character; told me there was not the least probability that he had written any letters for me; that no one, who knew him, had the smallest dependence on him; and he laughed at the notion of the governor's giving me a letter of credit, having, as he said, no credit to give. On my expressing some concern about what I should do, he advised me to endeavor getting some employment in the way of my business. "Among the printers here," said he, "you will improve yourself, and when you return to America, you will set up to greater advantage."

We both of us happened to know, as well as the stationer, that Riddlesden, the attorney, was a very knave. He had half ruined Miss Read's father by persuading him to be bound for him. By this letter it appeared there was a secret scheme on foot to the prejudice of Hamilton (supposed to be then coming over with us); and that Keith was concerned in it with Riddlesden. Denham, who was a friend of Hamilton's, thought he ought to be acquainted with it; so, when he arrived in England, which was soon after, partly from resentment and ill-will to Keith and Riddlesden, and partly from good-will to him, I waited on him, and gave him the letter. He thanked me cordially, the information being of importance to him; and from that time he became my friend, greatly to my advantage afterwards on many occasions.

Ralph and I were inseparable companions. We took lodgings together in Little Britain at three shillings and sixpence a week—as much as we could then afford. He found some relations, but they were poor, and unable to assist him. He now let me know his intentions of remaining in London, and that he never meant to return to Philadelphia. He had brought no money with him, the whole he could muster having been expended in paying his passage. I had fifteen pistoles; so he borrowed occasionally of me to subsist, while he was looking out for business. He first endeavored to get into the playhouse, believing himself qualified for an actor; but Wilkes, to whom he applied, advised him candidly not to think of that employment, as it was impossible he should succeed in it. Then he proposed to Roberts, a publisher in Paternoster Row, to write for him a weekly paper like the *Spectator,* on certain conditions, which Roberts did not approve. Then he endeavored to get employment as a hackney writer, to copy for the stationers and lawyers about the Temple, but could find no vacancy.

I immediately got into work at Palmer's, then a famous printing-house in Bartholomew Close, and here I continued near a year. I was pretty diligent, but spent with Ralph a good deal of my earnings in going to plays and other places of amusement. We had together consumed all my pistoles, and now just rubbed on from hand to mouth. He seemed quite to forget his wife and child, and I, by degrees, my engagements with Miss Read, to whom I never wrote more than one letter, and that was to let her know I was not likely soon to return. This was another of the great errata of my life, which I should wish to correct if I were to live it over again. In fact, by our expenses, I was constantly kept unable to pay my passage.

At Palmer's I was employed in composing for the second edition of Wollaston's *Religion of Nature*. Some of his reasonings not appearing to me well founded, I wrote a little metaphysical piece in which I made remarks on them. It was entitled *A Dissertation on Liberty and Necessity, Pleasure and Pain*. I inscribed it to my friend Ralph; I printed a small number. It occasioned my being more considered by Mr. Palmer as a young man of some ingenuity, though he seriously expostulated with me upon the principles of my pamphlet, which to him appeared abominable. My printing this pamphlet was another erratum. While I lodged in Little Britain, I made an acquaintance with one Wilcox, a book-seller, whose shop was at the next door. He had an immense collection of second-hand books. Circulating libraries were not then in use; but we agreed that, on certain reasonable terms, which I have now forgotten, I might take, read and return any of his books. This I esteemed a great advantage, and I made as much use of it as I could.

My pamphlet by some means falling into the hands of one Lyons, a surgeon, author of a book entitled *The Infallibility of Human Judgment,* it occasioned an acquaintance between us. He took great notice of me, called on me often to converse on those subjects, carried me to the Horns, a pale alehouse in ―― Lane, Cheapside, and introduced me to Dr. Mandeville, author of the *Fable of the Bees,* who had a club there, of which he was the soul, being a most facetious, entertaining companion. Lyons, too, introduced me to Dr. Pemberton, at Batson's Coffeehouse, who promised to give me an opportunity, some time or other, of seeing Sir Isaac Newton, of which I was extremely desirous; but this never happened.

I had brought over a few curiosities, among which the principal was a purse made of the asbestos, which purifies by fire. Sir Hans Sloane heard of it, came to see me, and invited me to his house in Bloomsbury Square, where he showed me all his curiosities, and persuaded me to let him add that to the number, for which he paid me handsomely.

In our house there lodged a young woman, a milliner, who, I think, had a shop in the Cloisters. She had been genteelly bred, was sensible and lively, and of most pleasing conversation. Ralph read plays to her in the evenings, they grew intimate, she took another lodging, and he followed her. They lived together some time; but, he being still out of business, and her income not sufficient to maintain them with her child, he took a resolution of going from London to try for a country school, which he thought himself well qualified to undertake, as he wrote an excellent hand, and was a master of arithmetic and accounts. This, however, he deemed a business below him, and confident of future better fortune, when he should be unwilling to have it known that he once was so meanly employed, he changed his name, and did me the honor to assume mine; for I soon after had a letter from him, acquainting me that he was settled in a small village (in Berkshire, I think it was, where he taught reading and writing to ten or a dozen boys, at sixpence each per week), recommending Mrs. T—— to my care, and desiring me to write to him, directing for Mr. Franklin, schoolmaster, at such a place.

He continued to write frequently, sending me large specimens of an epic poem which he was then composing, and desiring my remarks and corrections. These I gave him from time to time, but endeavored rather to discourage his proceeding. One of Young's *Satires* was then just published. I copied and sent him a great part of it, which set in a strong light the folly of pursuing the Muses with any hope of advancement by them. All was in vain; sheets of the poem continued to come by every post.

In the mean time, Mrs. T——, having on his account lost her friends and business, was often in distresses, and used to send for me, and borrow what I could spare to help her out of them. I grew fond of her company, and, being at that time under no religious restraint, and presuming upon my importance to her, I attempted familiarities (another erratum) which she repulsed with a proper resentment, and acquainted him with my behavior.

This made a breach between us; and, when he returned again to London, he let me know he thought I had canceled all the obligations he had been under to me. So I found I was never to expect his repaying me what I lent to him, or advanced for him. This, however, was not then of much consequence, as he was totally unable; and in the loss of his friendship I found myself relieved from a burden. I now began to think of getting a little money beforehand, and, expecting better work, I left Palmer's to work at Watts', near Lincoln's Inn Fields, a still greater printing-house. Here I continued all the rest of my stay in London.

At my first admission into this printing-house I took to working at press, imagining I felt a want of the bodily exercise I had been used to in America, where presswork is mixed with composing. I drank only water; the other workmen, near fifty in number, were great guzzlers of beer. On occasion, I carried up and down stairs a large form of types in each hand, when others carried but one in both hands. They wondered to see, from this and several instances, that the *Water-American,* as they called me, was *stronger* than themselves, who drank *strong* beer! We had an alehouse boy who attended always in the house to supply the workmen. My companion at the press drank every day a pint before breakfast, a pint at breakfast with his bread and cheese, a pint between breakfast and dinner, a pint at dinner, a pint in the afternoon about six o'clock, and another when he had done his day's work. I thought it a detestable custom; but it was necessary, he supposed, to drink *strong* beer, that he might be *strong* to labor. I endeavored to convince him that the bodily strength afforded by beer could only be in proportion to the grain or flour of the barley dissolved in the water of which it was made; that there was more flour in a pennyworth of bread; and therefore, if he would eat that with a pint of water, it would give him more strength than a quart of beer. He drank on, however, and had four or five shillings to pay out of his wages every Saturday night for that muddling liquor, an expense I was free from. And thus these poor devils keep themselves always under.

Watts, after some weeks, desiring to have me in the composing-room, I left the pressmen; a new sum for drink, being five shillings, was demanded of me by the compositors. I thought it an imposition, as I had paid below. The master thought so too, and forbade my paying it. I stood out two or three weeks, was accordingly considered as an excommunicate, and had so many little pieces of private mischief done me, by mixing my sorts, transposing my pages, breaking my matter, etc., etc., if I were ever so little out of the room, and all ascribed to the chapel ghost, which they said ever haunted those not regularly admitted, that, notwithstanding the master's protection, I found myself obliged to comply and pay the money, convinced of the folly of being on ill terms with those one is to live with continually.

I was now on a fair footing with them, and soon acquired considerable influence. I proposed some reasonable alterations in their chapel laws, and carried them against all opposition. From my example, a great part of them left their muddling breakfast of beer and bread and cheese, finding they could with me be supplied from a neighboring house with a large porringer of hot water-gruel, sprinkled with pepper, crumbed with bread, and a bit of butter in it, for the price of a pint of beer, viz., three half-pence. This was a more comfortable as well as cheaper breakfast, and kept their heads clearer.

Those who continued sotting with beer all day, were often, by not paying, out of credit at the alehouse, and used to make interest with me to get beer; their *light,* as they phrased it, *being out.* I watched the pay-table on Saturday night, and collected what I stood engaged for them, having to pay sometimes near thirty shillings a week on their accounts. This, and my being esteemed a pretty good *riggite,* that is, a jocular verbal satirist, supported my consequence in the society. My constant attendance (I never making a Saint Monday) recommended me to the master; and my uncommon quickness at composing occasioned my being put upon all work of dispatch, which was generally better paid. So I went on now very agreeably.

My lodging in Little Britain being too remote, I found another in Duke Street, opposite to the Romish Chapel. It was two pair of stairs backwards, at an Italian warehouse. A widow lady kept the house; she had a daughter, and a maid servant, and a journeyman who attended the warehouse, but lodged abroad. After sending to inquire my character at the house where I last lodged she agreed to take me in at the same rate, 3s. 6d. per week; cheaper, as she said, from the protection she expected in having a man lodge in the house.

She was a widow, an elderly woman; had been bred a Protestant, being a clergyman's daughter, but was converted to the Catholic religion by her husband, whose memory she much revered; had lived much among people of distinction, and knew a thousand anecdotes of them as far back as the times of Charles the Second. She was lame in her knees with the gout, and, therefore, seldom stirred out of her room, so sometimes wanted company; and hers was so highly amusing to me, that I was sure to spend an evening with her whenever she desired it. Our supper was only half an anchovy each, on a very little strip of bread and butter, and half a pint of ale between us; but the entertainment was in her conversation. My always keeping good hours, and giving little trouble in the family, made her unwilling to part with me; so that, when I talked of a lodging I had heard of, nearer my business, for two shillings a week, which, intent as I now was on saving money, made some difference, she bid me not think of it, for she would abate me two shillings a week for the future; so I remained with her at one shilling and sixpence as long as I stayed in London.

At Watts' printing-house I contracted an acquaintance with an ingenious young man, one Wygate, who, having wealthy relations, had been better educated than most printers; was a tolerable Latinist, spoke French, and loved reading. I taught him and a friend of his to swim at twice going into the river, and they soon became good swimmers. They introduced me to some gentlemen from the country, who went to Chelsea by water to see the College and Don Saltero's curiosities. In our return, at the request of the company, whose curiosity Wygate had excited, I stripped and leaped into the river, and swam from near Chelsea to Blackfriar's, performing on the way many feats of activity, both upon and under water, that surprised and pleased those to whom they were novelties.

I had from a child been ever delighted with this exercise, had studied and practised all Thevenot's motions and positions, added some of my own, aiming at the graceful and easy as well as the useful. All these I took this occasion of exhibiting to the company, and was much flattered by their admiration; and Wygate, who was desirous of becoming a master, grew more and more attached to me on that account, as well as from the similarity of our studies. He at length proposed to me traveling all over Europe together, supporting ourselves everywhere by working at our business. I was once inclined to it; but, mentioning it to my good friend Mr. Denham, with whom I often spent an hour when I had leisure, he dissuaded me from it, advising me to think only of returning to Pennsylvania, which he was now about to do.

He now told me he was about to return to Philadelphia, and should carry over a great quantity of goods in order to open a store there. He proposed to take me over as his clerk, to keep his books, in which he would instruct me, copy his letters, and attend the store. He added, that, as soon as I should be acquainted with mercantile business, he would promote me by sending me with a cargo of flour and bread, etc., to the West Indies, and procure me commissions from others which would be profitable; and, if I managed well, would establish me handsomely. The thing pleased me; for I was grown tired of London, remembered with pleasure the happy months I had spent in Pennsylvania, and wished again to see it; therefore I immediately agreed on the terms of fifty pounds a year, Pennsylvania money; less, indeed, than my present gettings as a compositor, but affording a better prospect.

I now took leave of printing, as I thought, for ever, and was daily employed in my new business, going about with Mr. Denham among the tradesmen to purchase various articles, and seeing them packed up, doing errands, calling upon workmen to dispatch, etc.; and, when all was on board, I had a few days' leisure. On one of these days, I was, to my surprise, sent for by a great man I knew only by name, a Sir William Wyndham, and I waited upon him. He had heard by some means or other of my swimming from Chelsea to Blackfriar's, and of my teaching Wygate and another young man to swim in a few hours. He had two sons, about to set out on their travels. He wished to have them first taught swimming, and proposed to gratify me handsomely if I would teach them. From this incident I thought it likely that, if I were to remain in England and open a swimming-school, I might get a good deal of money. Had the overture been sooner made me, probably I should not so soon have returned to America.

Thus I spent about eighteen months in London; most part of the time I worked hard at my business, and spent but little upon myself except in seeing plays and in books. My friend Ralph had kept me poor. He owed me about twenty-seven pounds, which I was now never likely to receive; a great sum out of my small earnings! I loved him, notwithstanding, for he had many amiable qualities.

I had by no means improved my fortune; but I had picked up some very ingenious acquaintance, whose conversation was of great advantage to me; and I had read considerably.

We sailed from Gravesend on the 23rd of July, 1726. We landed in Philadelphia on the 11th of October, where I found sundry alterations. Keith was no longer governor, being superseded by Major Gordon. I met him walking the streets as a common citizen. He seemed a little ashamed at seeing me, but passed without saying anything. I should have been as much ashamed at seeing Miss Read, had not her friends, despairing with reason of my return after the receipt of my letter, persuaded her to marry another, one Rogers, a potter, which was done in my absence. With him, however, she was never happy, and soon parted from him, refusing to cohabit with him or bear his name, it being now said that he had another wife. He was a worthless fellow, though an excellent workman, which was the temptation to her friends. He got into debt, ran away in 1727 or 1728, went to the West Indies, and died there. Keimer had got a better house, a shop well supplied with stationery, plenty of new types, a number of hands, though none good, and seemed to have a great deal of business.

Mr. Denham took a store in Water Street, where we opened our goods; I attended the business diligently, studied accounts, and grew, in a little time, expert at selling. We lodged and boarded together; he counseled me as a father, having a sincere regard for me. I respected and loved him, and we might have gone on together very happy; but, in the beginning of February, 1727, when I had just passed my twenty-first year, we were both taken ill.

My distemper was a pleurisy, which very nearly carried me off. I forget what his distemper was. It held him a long time, and at length carried him off. He left me a small legacy in a nuncupative will, as a token of his kindness for me, and he left me once more to the wild world; for the store was taken into the care of his executors, and my employment under him ended.

My brother-in-law, Holmes, being now at Philadelphia, advised my return to my business; and Keimer tempted me, with an offer of large wages by the year, to come and take the management of his printing-house, that he might better attend his stationer's shop. I had heard a bad character of him in London from his wife and her friends, and was not fond of having any more to do with him. I tried for farther employment as a merchant's clerk; but, not readily meeting with any, I closed again with Keimer.

I found in his house these hands: Hugh Meredith, a Welsh Pennsylvanian, thirty years of age, bred to country work; honest, sensible, had a great deal of solid observation, was something of a reader, but given to drink. Stephen Potts, a young countryman of full age, bred to the same, of uncommon natural parts, and great wit and humor, but a little idle. These he had agreed with an extreme low wages per week, to be raised a shilling every three months, as they would deserve by improving in their business; and the expectation of these high wages, to come on hereafter, was what he had drawn them in with. Meredith was to work at press, Potts at book-binding, which he, by agreement, was to teach them, though he knew neither one nor the other. John ——, a wild Irishman, brought up to no business, whose service, for four years, Keimer had purchased from the captain of a ship; he, too, was to be made a pressman. George Webb, an Oxford scholar, whose time for four years he had likewise bought, intending him for a compositor, of whom more presently; and David Harry, a country boy, whom he had taken apprentice.

I soon perceived that the intention of engaging me at wages so much higher than he had been used to give, was to have these raw, cheap hands formed thro' me; and, as soon as I had instructed them, then they being all articled to him, he should be able to do without me. I went on, however, very cheerfully, put his printing-house in order, which had been in great confusion, and brought his hands by degrees to mind their business and to do it better.

It was an odd thing to find an Oxford scholar in the situation of a bought servant. He was not more than eighteen years of age, and gave me this account of himself; that he was born in Gloucester, educated at a grammar-school there, had been distinguished among the scholars for some apparent superiority in performing his part, when they exhibited plays; belonged to the Witty Club there, and had written some pieces in prose and verse, which were printed in the Gloucester newspapers; thence he was sent to Oxford; where he continued about a year, but not well satisfied, wishing of all things to see London, and become a player.

At length, receiving his quarterly allowance of fifteen guineas, instead of discharging his debts he walked out of town, hid his gown in a furze bush, and footed it to London, where, having no friends to advise him, he fell into bad company, soon spent his guineas, found no means of being introduced among the players, grew necessitous, pawned his clothes, and wanted bread. Walking the street very hungry, and not knowing what to do with himself, a crimp's bill was put into his hand, offering immediate entertainment and encouragement to such as would bind themselves to service in America. He went directly, signed the indentures, was put into the ship, and came over, never writing a line to acquaint his friends what was become of him. He was lively, witty, good-natured, and a pleasant companion, but idle, thoughtless, and imprudent to the last degree.

John, the Irishman, soon ran away. With the rest I began to live very agreeably, for they all respected me the more, as they found Keimer incapable of instructing them, and that from me they learned something daily. We never worked on Saturday, that being Keimer's Sabbath, so I had two days for reading. My acquaintance with ingenious people in the town increased. Keimer himself treated me with great civility and apparent regard, and nothing now made me uneasy but my debt to Vernon, which I was yet unable to pay, being hitherto but a poor economist. He, however, kindly made no demand of it.

Our printing-house often wanted sorts, and there was no letter-founder in America. I had seen types cast at James' in London, but without much attention to the manner. However, I now contrived a mold, made use of the letters we had as puncheons, struck the matrices in lead, and thus supplied in a pretty tolerable way all deficiencies. I also engraved several things on occasion; I made the ink; I was warehouseman, and everything, and, in short, quite a factotum.

But, however serviceable I might be, I found that my services became every day of less importance as the other hands improved in the business; and, when Keimer paid my second quarter's wages, he let me know that he felt them too heavy, and thought I should make an abatement. He grew by degrees less civil, put on more of the master, frequently found fault, was captious, and seemed ready for an outbreaking. I went on, nevertheless, with a good deal of patience, thinking that his encumbered circumstances were partly the cause.

At length a trifle snapped our connections; for, a great noise happening near the court-house, I put my head out of the window to see what was the matter. Keimer, being in the street, looked up and saw me, called out to me in a loud voice and angry tone to mind my business, adding some reproachful words, that nettled me the more for their publicity, all the neighbors who were looking out on the same occasion being witnesses how I was treated. He came up immediately into the printing-house, continued the quarrel, high words passed on both sides, he gave me the quarter's warning we had stipulated, expressing a wish that he had not been obliged to so long a warning. I told him his wish was unnecessary, for I would leave him that instant; and so, taking my hat, walked out of doors, desiring Meredith, whom I saw below, to take care of some things I left, and bring them to my lodgings.

Meredith came accordingly in the evening, when we talked my affair over. He had conceived a great regard for me, and was very unwilling that I should leave the house while he remained in it. He dissuaded me from returning to my native country, which I began to think of. He reminded me that Keimer was in debt for all he possessed; that his creditors began to be uneasy; that he kept his shop miserably, sold often without profit for ready money, and often trusted without keeping accounts; that he must therefore fail, which would make a vacancy I might profit of. I objected my want of money. He then let me know that his father had a high opinion of me, and, from some discourse that had passed between them, he was sure would advance money to set us up, if I would enter into partnership with him. "My time," says he, "will be out with Keimer in the spring; by that time we may have our press and types in from London. I am sensible I am no workman. If you like it, your skill in the business shall be set against the stock I furnish, and we will share the profits equally."

The proposal was agreeable, and I consented. His father was in town and approved of it; the more as he saw I had great influence with his son, had prevailed on him to abstain long from dram-drinking, and he hoped might break him off that wretched habit entirely when we came to be so closely connected. I gave an inventory to the father, who carried it to a merchant. The things were sent for, the secret was to be kept till they should arrive, and in the meantime I was to get work, if I could, at the other printing-house. But I found no vacancy there, and so remained idle a few days, when Keimer, on a prospect of being employed to print some paper money in New Jersey, which would require cuts and various types that I only could supply, and apprehending Bradford might engage me and get the job from him, sent me a very civil message, that old friends should not part for a few words, the effect of sudden passion, and wishing me to return. Meredith persuaded me to comply, as it would give more opportunity for his improvement under my daily instructions. So I returned, and we went on more smoothly than for some time before. The New Jersey job was obtained; I contrived a copperplate press for it, the first that had been seen in the country; I cut several ornaments and checks for the bills. We went together to Burlington, where I executed the whole to satisfaction; and he received so large a sum for the work as to be able thereby to keep his head much longer above water.

At Burlington I made an acquaintance with many principal people of the province. Several of them had been appointed by the Assembly a committee to attend the press, and take care that no more bills were printed than the law directed. They were therefore, by turns, constantly with us, and generally he who attended brought with him a friend or two for company. My mind having been much more improved by reading than Keimer's, I suppose it was for that reason my conversation seemed to be more valued. They had me to their houses, introduced me to their friends, and showed me much civility; while he, though the master, was a little neglected. In truth, he was an odd fish: ignorant of common life, fond of rudely opposing received opinions, slovenly to extreme dirtiness, enthusiastic in some points of religion, and a little knavish withal.

We continued there near three months; and by that time I could reckon among my acquired friends Judge Allen, Samuel Bustill, the secretary of the Province, Isaac Pearson, Joseph Cooper, and several of the Smiths, members of Assembly, and Isaac Decow, the surveyor-general. The latter was a shrewd, sagacious old man, who told me that he began for himself, when young, by wheeling clay for the brick-makers, learned to write after he was of age, carried the chain for surveyors, who taught him surveying, and he had now, by his industry, acquired a good estate; and says he, "I foresee that you will soon work this man out of his business, and make a fortune in it at Philadelphia."

Before I enter upon my public appearance in business, it may be well to let you know the then state of my mind with regard to my principles and morals, that you may see how far those influenced the future events of my life. My parents had early given me religious impressions, and brought me through my childhood piously in the Dissenting way. But I was scarce fifteen, when, after doubting by turns of several points, as I found them disputed in the different books I read, I began to doubt of Revelation itself. Some books against Deism fell into my hands. They were said to be the substance of sermons preached at Boyle's Lectures. It happened that they wrought an effect on me quite contrary to what was intended by them; for the arguments of the Deists, which were quoted to be refuted, appeared to me much stronger than the refutations. In short, I soon became a thorough Deist.

[*Deism identifies God with the impersonal laws of Nature.*]

My arguments perverted some others, particularly Collins and Ralph; but, each of them having afterwards wronged me greatly without the least compunction, and recollecting Keith's conduct towards me (who was another freethinker), and my own towards Vernon and Miss Read, which at times gave me great trouble, I began to suspect that this doctrine, though it might be true, was not very useful. My London pamphlet, which had for its motto those lines of Dryden:

200

Whatever is, is right. Though purblind man
Sees but a part o' the chain, the nearest link:
His eyes not carrying to the equal beam,
That poises all above . . .

and from the attributes of God, his infinite wisdom, goodness and power, concluded that nothing could possibly be wrong in the world, and that vice and virtue were empty distinctions, no such things existing, appeared now not so clever a performance as I once thought it; and I doubted whether some error had not insinuated itself unperceived into my argument, so as to infect all that followed, as is common in metaphysical reasonings.

I grew convinced that *truth, sincerity* and *integrity* in dealings between man and man were of the utmost importance to the felicity of life; and I formed written resolutions, which still remain in my journal book, to practice them ever while I lived. Revelation had indeed no weight with me, as such; but I entertained an opinion that, though certain actions might not be bad *because* they were forbidden by it, or good *because* it commanded them, yet probably these actions might be forbidden *because* they were bad for us, or commanded *because* they were beneficial to us, in their own natures, all the circumstances of things considered.

And this persuasion, with the kind hand of Providence, or some guardian angel, or accidental favorable circumstances and situations, or all together, preserved me, through this dangerous time of youth, and the hazardous situations I was sometimes in among strangers, remote from the eye and advice of my father, without any willful gross immorality or injustice, that might have been expected from my want of religion. I say willful, because the instances I have mentioned had something of *necessity* in them, from my youth, inexperience, and the knavery of others. I had therefore a tolerable character to begin the world with. I valued it properly, and determined to preserve it.

We had not been long returned to Philadelphia before the new types arrived from London. We settled with Keimer, and left him by his consent before he heard of it. We found a house to hire near the market, and took it. To lessen the rent, which was then but twenty-four pounds a year, tho' I have since known it to let for seventy, we took in Thomas Godfrey, a glazier, and his family, who were to pay a considerable part of it to us, and we to board with them.

We had scarce opened our letters and put our press in order, before George House, an acquaintance of mine, brought a countryman to us, whom he had met in the street inquiring for a printer. All our cash was now expended in the variety of particulars we had been obliged to procure, and this countryman's five shillings, being our first-fruits, and coming so seasonably, gave me more pleasure than any crown I have since earned; and the gratitude I felt toward House has made me often more ready than perhaps I should otherwise have been to assist young beginners.

I should have mentioned before that, in the autumn of the preceding year, I had formed most of my ingenious acquaintance into a club of mutual improvements, which we called the Junto; we met on Friday evenings. The rules that I drew up required that every member, in turn, should produce one or more queries on any point of Morals, Politics, or Natural Philosophy, to be discussed by the company; and once in three months produce and read an essay of his own writing, on any subject he pleased. Our debates were to be under the direction of a president, and to be conducted in the sincere spirit of inquiry after truth, without fondness for dispute, or desire of victory; and, to prevent warmth, all expressions of positiveness in opinions, or direct contradiction, were after some time made contraband, and prohibited under small pecuniary penalties.

The first members were: Joseph Breintnal, a copier of deeds for the scriveners, a good-natured, friendly, middle-aged man, a great lover of poetry, reading all he could meet with, and writing some that was tolerable; very ingenious in many little nicknackeries, and of sensible conversation.

Thomas Godfrey, a self-taught mathematician, great in his way, and afterwards inventor of what is now called Hadley's Quadrant. But he knew little out of his way, and was not a pleasing companion; as, like most great mathematicians I have met with, he expected universal precision in everything said, or was forever denying or distinguishing upon trifles, to the disturbance of all conversation. He soon left us.

Nicholas Scull, a surveyor, afterwards surveyor-general, who loved books, and sometimes made a few verses.

William Parsons, bred a shoemaker, but, loving reading, had acquired a considerable share of mathematics, which he first studied with a view to astrology, that he afterwards laughed at. He also became surveyor-general.

William Maugridge, a joiner, a most exquisite mechanic, and a solid, sensible man.

Hugh Meredith, Stephen Potts, and George Webb I have characterized before.

Robert Grace, a young gentleman of some fortune, generous, lively, and witty; a lover of punning and of his friends.

And William Coleman, then a merchant's clerk, about my age, who had the coolest, clearest head, the best heart, and the exactest morals of almost any man I ever met with. He became afterwards a merchant of great note, and one of our provincial judges. Our friendship continued without interruption to his death, upward of forty years; and the club continued almost as long, and was the best school of philosophy, morality, and politics that then existed in the province. Here, too, we acquired better habits of conversation.

But my giving this account of it here is to show something of interest I had, every one of these exerting themselves in recommending business to us. Breintnal particularly procured us from the Quakers the printing of forty sheets of their history, the rest to be done by Keimer; and upon this we worked exceedingly hard, for the price was low. It was a folio, pro patria size, in pica, with long primer notes. I composed of it a sheet a day, and Meredith worked it off at press. It was often eleven at night, and sometimes later, before I had finished my distribution for the next day's work, for the little jobs sent in by our other friends now and then put us back.

But so determined I was to continue doing a sheet a day of the folio, that one night, when, having imposed my forms, I thought my day's work over, one of them by accident was broken, and two pages reduced to pi, I immediately distributed and composed it over again before I went to bed; and this industry, visible to our neighbors, began to give us character and credit. Particularly, I was told, that, mention being made of the new printing-office at the merchants' Every-night club, the general opinion was that it must fail, there being already two printers in the place, Keimer and Bradford; but Dr. Baird gave a contrary opinion: "For the industry of that Franklin," says he, "is superior to anything I ever saw of the kind. I see him still at work when I go home from club, and he is at work again before his neighbors are out of bed." This struck the rest, and we soon after had offers from one of them to supply us with stationery; but as yet we did not choose to engage in shop business.

I mention this industry the more particularly and the more freely, though it seems to be talking in my own praise, that those of my posterity who shall read it may know the use of that virtue, when they see its effects in my favor throughout this relation.

George Webb, who had found a female friend that lent him wherewith to purchase his time of Keimer, now came to offer himself as a journeyman to us. We could not then employ him, but I foolishly let him know as a secret that I soon intended to begin a newspaper, and might then have work for him. My hopes of success, as I told him, were founded on this, that the then only newspaper, printed by Bradford, was a paltry thing, wretchedly managed, no way entertaining, and yet profitable to him. I therefore thought a good paper would scarcely fail of good encouragement. I requested Webb not to mention it; but he told it to Keimer, who immediately, to be beforehand with me, published proposals for printing one himself, on which Webb was to be employed. I resented this; and, to counteract them, as I could not yet begin our paper, I wrote several pieces of entertainment for Bradford's paper, under the title of the BUSY BODY, which Breintnal continued some months. By this means the attention of the public was fixed on that paper, and Keimer's proposals, which we burlesqued and ridiculed, were disregarded. He began his paper, however, and, after carrying it on three-quarters of a year, with at most only ninety subscribers, he offered it to me for a trifle; and I, having been ready some time to go on with it, took it in hand directly; and it proved in a few years extremely profitable to me. [*This paper was the* Pennsylvania Gazette, *from which the* Saturday Evening Post *claims descent.*]

I perceive that I am apt to speak in the singular number, though our partnership still continued. The reason may be that, in fact, the whole management of the business lay upon me. Meredith was no compositor, a poor pressman, and seldom sober. My friends lamented my connection with him, but I was to make the best of it.

Our first papers made a quite different appearance from any before in the province; a better type, and better printed; but some spirited remarks of my writing, on the dispute then going on between Governor Burnet and the Massachusetts Assembly, struck the principal people, occasioned the paper and the manager of it to be much talked of, and in a few weeks brought them all to be our subscribers.

Their example was followed by many, and our number went on growing continually. This was one of the first good effects of my having learned a little to scribble. Another was, that the leading men, seeing a newspaper now in the hands of one who could also handle a pen, thought it convenient to oblige and encourage me. Bradford still printed the votes, and laws, and other public business. He had printed an address of the House to the governor, in a coarse, blundering manner. We reprinted it elegantly and correctly and sent one to every member. They were sensible of the difference. It strengthened the hands of our friends in the House, and they voted us their printers for the year ensuing.

Mr. Vernon, about this time, put me in mind of the debt I owed him, but did not press me. I wrote him an ingenuous letter of acknowledgment, craved his forbearance a little longer, which he allowed me, and as soon as I was able, I paid the principal with interest, and many thanks; so that erratum was in some degree corrected.

But now another difficulty came upon me which I had never the least reason to expect. Mr. Meredith's father, who was to have paid for our printing-house, according to the expectations given me, was able to advance only one hundred pounds currency, which had been paid; and a hundred more was due to the merchant, who grew impatient, and sued us all. We gave bail, but saw that, if the money could not be raised in time, the suit must soon come to a judgment and execution, and our hopeful prospects must, with us, be ruined, as the press and letters must be sold for payment, perhaps at half price.

In this distress two true friends, whose kindness I have never forgotten, nor ever shall forget while I can remember anything, came to me separately, unknown to each other, and, without any application from me, offering each of them to advance me all the money that should be necessary to enable me to take the whole business upon myself. These two friends were William Coleman and Robert Grace. I told them I could not propose a separation while any prospect remained of the Merediths' fulfilling their part of our agreement, because I thought myself under great obligations to them for what they had done, and would do if they could; but, if they finally failed in their performance, and our partnership must be dissolved, I should then think myself at liberty to accept the assistance of my friends.

Thus the matter rested for some time, when I said to my partner, "Perhaps your father is dissatisfied at the part you have undertaken in this affair of ours, and is unwilling to advance for you and me what he would for you alone. If that is the case, tell me, and I will resign the whole to you, and go about my business." "No," said he, "my father has really been disappointed, and is really unable; and I am unwilling to distress him farther. I see this is a business I am not fit for. I was bred a farmer, and it was a folly in me to come to town, and put myself, at thirty years of age, an apprentice to learn a new trade. Many of our Welsh people are going to settle in North Carolina, where land is cheap. I am inclined to go with them, and follow my old employment. You may find friends to assist you. If you will take the debts of the company upon you; return to my father the hundred pounds he has advanced; pay my little personal debts, and give me thirty pounds and a new saddle, I will relinquish the partnership, and leave the whole in your hands."

I agreed to this proposal: it was drawn up in writing, signed, and sealed immediately. I gave him what he demanded, and he went soon after to Carolina, from whence he sent me next year two long letters, containing the best account that had been given of that country, the climate, the soil, husbandry, etc., for in those matters he was very judicious. I printed them in the papers, and they gave great satisfaction to the public.

As soon as he was gone, I recurred to my two friends; and because I would not give an unkind preference to either, I took half of what each had offered and I wanted of one, and half of the other; paid off the company's debts, and went on with the business in my own name, advertising that the partnership was dissolved. I think this was in or about the year 1729.

About this time there was a cry among the people for more paper money, only fifteen thousand pounds being extant in the province, and that soon to be sunk. The wealthy inhabitants opposed any addition, being against all paper currency, from an apprehension that it would depreciate, as it had done in New England, to the prejudice of all creditors. We had discussed this point in our Junto, where I was on the side of an addition, being persuaded that the first small sum struck in 1723 had done much good by increasing the trade, employment, and number of inhabitants in the province.

Our debates possessed me so fully of the subject, that I wrote and printed an anonymous pamphlet on it, entitled *The Nature and Necessity of a Paper Currency*. It was well received by the common people in general; but the rich men disliked it, for it increased and strengthened the clamor for more money, and they happening to have no writers among them that were able to answer it, their opposition slackened, and the point was carried by a majority in the House. My friends there, who conceived I had been of some service, thought fit to reward me by employing me in printing the money; a very profitable job and a great help to me. This was another advantage gained by being able to write.

The utility of this currency became by time and experience so evident as never afterwards to be much disputed; so that it grew soon to fifty-five thousand pounds, and in 1739 to eighty thousand pounds, since which it arose during war to upwards of three hundred and fifty thousand pounds, trade, building, and inhabitants all the while increasing, though I now think there are limits beyond which the quantity may be hurtful.

I soon after obtained, thro' my friend Hamilton, the printing of the Newcastle [*Delaware Province*] paper money, another profitable job as I then thought it; small things appearing great to those in small circumstances; and these, to me, were really great advantages, as they were great encouragements. He procured for me, also, the printing of the laws and votes of that government, which continued in my hands as long as I followed the business.

I now opened a little stationer's shop. I had in it blanks of all sorts, the correctest that ever appeared among us, being assisted in that by my friend Breintnal. I had also paper, parchment, chapmen's books, etc. One Whitemash, a compositor I had known in London, an excellent workman, now came to me, and worked with me constantly and diligently; and I took an apprentice, the son of Aquila Rose.

I began now gradually to pay off the debt I was under for the printing-house. In order to secure my credit and character as a tradesman, I took care not only to be in *reality* industrious and frugal, but to avoid all appearances to the contrary. I dressed plainly. I was seen at no places of idle diversion. I never went out fishing or shooting. A book, indeed, sometimes debauched me from my work, but that was seldom, snug, and gave no scandal; and, to show that I was not above my business, I sometimes brought home the paper I purchased at the stores thro' the streets on a wheel-barrow. Thus being esteemed an industrious, thriving young man, and paying duly for what I bought, the merchants who imported stationery solicited my custom. Others proposed supplying me with books, and I went on swimmingly. In the meantime, Keimer's credit and business declining daily, he was at last forced to sell his printing-house to satisfy his creditors. He went to Barbados, and there lived some years in very poor circumstances.

There remained now no competitor with me at Philadelphia but the old one, Bradford; who was rich and easy, did a little printing now and then by straggling hands, but was not very anxious about the business. However, as he kept the post-office, it was imagined he had better opportunities of obtaining news. His paper was thought a better distributor of advertisements than mine, and therefore had many more, which was a profitable thing to him, and a disadvantage to me; for, though I did indeed receive and send papers by the post, yet the public opinion was otherwise, for what I did send was by bribing the riders, who took them privately, Bradford being unkind enough to forbid it, which occasioned some resentment on my part; and I thought so meanly of him for it, that, when I afterward came into his situation, I took care never to imitate it.

I had hitherto continued to board with Godfrey, who lived in part of my house with his wife and children, and had one side of the shop for his glazier's business, though he worked little, being always absorbed in his mathematics. Mrs. Godfrey projected a match for me with a relation's daughter, took opportunities of bringing us often together, till a serious courtship on my part ensued, the girl being in herself very deserving. The old folks encouraged me by continual invitations to supper, and by leaving us together, till at length it was time to explain. Mrs. Godfrey managed our little treaty. I let her know that I expected as much money with their daughter as would pay off my remaining debt for the printing-house, which I believe was not then above a hundred pounds. She brought me word they had no such sum to spare. I said they might mortgage their house in the loan-office. The answer to this, after some days, was, that they did not approve the match; that, on inquiry of Bradford, they had been informed the printing business was not a profitable one; the types would soon be worn out, and more wanted; that S. Keimer and D. Harry had failed one after the other, and I should probably soon follow them; and, therefore, I was forbidden the house, and the daughter shut up.

Whether this was a real change of sentiment or only artifice, on a supposition of our being too far engaged in affection to retract, and therefore that we should steal a marriage, which would leave them at liberty to give or withhold what they pleased, I know not; but I suspected the latter, resented it, and went no more. Mrs. Godfrey brought me afterward some more favorable accounts of their disposition, and would have drawn me on again; but I declared absolutely my resolution to have nothing more to do with that family. This was resented by the Godfreys. We differed, and they removed, leaving me the whole house, and I re-resolved to take no more inmates.

But this affair having turned my thoughts to marriage, I looked round me and made overtures of acquaintance in other places; but soon found that, the business of a printer being generally thought a poor one, I was not to expect money with a wife, unless with such a one as I should not otherwise think agreeable. In the meantime, that hard-to-be-governed passion of youth hurried me frequently into intrigues with low women that fell in my way, which were attended with some expense and great inconvenience, besides a continual risk to my health by a distemper which of all things I dreaded, though by great good luck I escaped it.

A friendly correspondence as neighbors and old acquaintances had continued between me and Mrs. Read's family, who all had a regard for me from the time of my first lodging in their house. I was often invited there and consulted in their affairs, wherein I sometimes was of service. I pitied poor Miss Read's unfortunate situation, who was generally dejected, seldom cheerful, and avoided company. I considered my giddiness and inconstancy when in London as in a great degree the cause of her unhappiness, though the mother was good enough to think the fault more her own than mine, as she had prevented our marrying before I went thither, and persuaded the other match in my absence.

Our mutual affection was revived, but there were now great objections to our union. The match was indeed looked upon as invalid, a preceding wife being said to be living in England; but this could not easily be proved, because of the distance; and, though there was a report of his death, it was not certain. Then, though it should be true, he had left many debts, which his successor might be called upon to pay. We ventured, however, over all these difficulties, and I took her to wife, September 1st, 1730. None of the inconveniences happened that we had apprehended. She proved a good and faithful helpmate, assisted me much by attending the shop. We throve together, and have ever mutually endeavored to make each other happy. Thus I corrected that great erratum as well as I could.

About this time, our club meeting, not at a tavern, but in a little room of Mr. Grace's, set apart for that purpose, a proposition was made by me that, since our books were often referred to in our disquisitions upon the queries, it might be convenient to us to have them altogether where we met, that upon occasion they might be consulted; and by thus clubbing our books to a common library, we should, while we liked to keep them together, have each of us the advantage of using the books of all the other members, which would be nearly as beneficial as if each owned the whole. It was liked and agreed to, and we filled one end of the room with such books as we could best spare. The number was not so great as we expected; and tho' they had been of great use, yet some inconveniences occurring for want of due care of them, the collection, after about a year, was separated, and each took his books home again.

And now I set on foot my first project of a public nature, that for a subscription library. I drew up the proposals, got them put into form by our great scrivener, Brockden, and, by the help of my friends in the Junto, procured fifty subscribers of forty shillings each to begin with, and ten shillings a year for fifty years, the term our company was to continue. We afterwards obtained a charter, the company being increased to one hundred. This was the mother of all the North American subscription libraries, now so numerous. It is become a great thing itself, and continually increasing.

Mem°. Thus far was written with the intention expressed in the beginning and therefore contains several little family anecdotes of no importance to others. What follows was written many years after, and intended for the public. The affairs of the Revolution occasioned the interruption.

Continuation of the Account of my Life, begun at
Passy, near Paris, 1784.

IT IS SOME TIME since I received these letters [*from Abel James and Benjamin Vaughan, urging him to complete his* Autobiography] but I have been too busy till now to think of complying with the request they contain. It might, too, be much better done if I were at home among my papers, which would aid my memory, and help to ascertain dates; but my return being uncertain, and having just now a little leisure, I will endeavor to recollect and write what I can. If I live to get home, it may there be corrected and improved.

At the time I established myself in Pennsylvania, there was not a good bookseller's shop in any of the colonies to the southward of Boston. In New York and Philadelphia the printers were indeed stationers. They sold only paper, almanacs, ballads, and a few common school-books. Those who loved reading were obliged to send for their books from England.

This library afforded me the means of improvement by constant study, for which I set apart an hour or two each day, and thus repaired in some degree the loss of the learned education my father once intended for me. Reading was the only amusement I allowed myself. I spent no time in taverns, games, or frolics of any kind; and my industry in my business continued as indefatigable as it was necessary. I was indebted for my printing-house, I had a young family coming on to be educated, and I had to contend with for business two printers who were established in the place before me.

My circumstances, however, grew daily easier. My original habits of frugality continuing, and my father having, among his instructions to me when a boy, frequently repeated a proverb of Solomon, "Seest thou a man diligent in his calling, he shall stand before kings, he shall not stand before mean men," I from thence considered industry as a means of obtaining wealth and distinction, which encouraged me, tho' I did not think that I should ever literally *stand before kings,* which, however, has since happened; for I have stood before *five,* and even had the honor of sitting down with one, the King of Denmark, to dinner.

We have an English proverb that says, *He that would thrive, must ask his wife.* It was lucky for me that I had one as much disposed to industry and frugality as myself. She assisted me cheerfully in my business, folding and stitching pamphlets, tending shop, purchasing old linen rags for the papermakers, etc., etc. We kept no idle servants, our table was plain and simple, our furniture of the cheapest. For instance, my breakfast was a long time bread and milk (no tea), and I ate it out of a twopenny earthen porringer, with a pewter spoon.

But mark how luxury will enter families, and make a progress, in spite of principle. Being called one morning to breakfast, I found it in a China bowl, with a spoon of silver! They had been bought for me without my knowledge by my wife, and had cost her the enormous sum of three-and-twenty shillings, for which she had no other excuse or apology to make, but that she thought *her* husband deserved a silver spoon and China bowl as well as any of his neighbors. This was the first appearance of plate and China in our house, which afterward, in a course of years, as our wealth increased, augmented gradually to several hundred pounds in value.

I had been religiously educated as a Presbyterian; and tho' some of the dogmas of that persuasion, such as *the eternal decrees of God, election, reprobation, etc.,* appeared to me unintelligible, others doubtful, and I early absented myself from the public assemblies of the sect,

Sunday being my studying day, I never was without some religious principles. I never doubted, for instance, the existence of the Deity; that he made the world, and governed it by his Providence; that the most acceptable service of God was the doing good to man; that our souls are immortal; and that all crime will be punished, and virtue rewarded, either here or hereafter.

These I esteemed the essentials of every religion; and, being found in all the religions we had in our country, I respected them all, though with different degrees of respect, as I found them more or less mixed with other articles, which, without any tendency to inspire, promote, or confirm morality, served principally to divide us, and make us unfriendly to one another. This respect to all, with an opinion that the worst had some good effects, induced me to avoid all discourse that might tend to lessen the good opinion another might have of his own religion; and as our province increased in people, and new places of worship were continually wanted, and generally erected by voluntary contribution, my mite for such purpose, whatever might be the sect, was never refused.

Though I seldom attended any public worship, I had still an opinion of its propriety, and of its utility when rightly conducted, and I regularly paid my annual subscription for the support of the only Presbyterian minister or meeting we had in Philadelphia. He used to visit me sometimes as a friend, and admonish me to attend his administrations, and I was now and then prevailed on to do so, once for five Sundays successively. Had he been in my opinion a good preacher, perhaps I might have continued, notwithstanding the occasion I had for the Sunday's leisure in my course of study. But his discourses were chiefly either polemic arguments, or explications of the peculiar doctrines of our sect, and were all to me very dry, uninteresting, and unedifying, since not a single moral principle was inculcated or enforced, their aim seeming to be rather to make us Presbyterians than good citizens.

I had some years before composed a little Liturgy, or form of prayer, for my own private use (viz., in 1728), entitled, *Articles of Belief and Acts of Religion.* I returned to the use of this, and went no more to the public assemblies. My conduct might be blameable, but I leave it, without attempting further to excuse it; my present purpose being to relate facts, and not to make apologies for them.

It was about this time I conceived the bold and arduous project of arriving at moral perfection. I wished to live without committing any fault at any time; I would conquer all that either natural inclination, custom, or company might lead me into. As I knew, or thought I knew, what was right and wrong, I did not see why I might not always do the one and avoid the other. But I soon found I had undertaken a task of more difficulty than I had imagined. While my care was employed in guarding against one fault, I was often surprised by another. Habit took the advantage of inattention. Inclination was sometimes too strong for reason. I concluded, at length, that the mere speculative conviction that it was our interest to be completely virtuous was not sufficient to prevent our slipping; and that the contrary habits must be broken, and good ones acquired and established, before we can have any dependence on a steady, uniform rectitude of conduct. For this purpose I therefore contrived the following method.

In the various enumerations of the moral virtues I had met with in my reading, I found the catalogue more or less numerous, as different writers included more or fewer ideas under the same name. I proposed to myself, for the sake of clearness, to use rather more names, with fewer ideas annexed to each, than a few names with more ideas; and I included under thirteen names of virtues all that at that time occurred to me as necessary or desirable, and annexed to each a short precept, which fully expressed the extent I gave to its meaning.

These names of virtues, with their precepts, were:

1. TEMPERANCE.— Eat not to dullness; drink not to elevation.

2. SILENCE.—Speak not but what may benefit others or yourself; avoid trifling conversation.

3. ORDER.—Let all your things have their places; let each part of your business have its time.

4. RESOLUTION.—Resolve to perform what you ought; perform without fail what you resolve.

5. FRUGALITY.—Make no expense but to do good to others or yourself; *i.e.,* waste nothing.

6. INDUSTRY.—Lose no time; be always employed in something useful; cut off all unnecessary actions.

7. SINCERITY.—Use no hurtful deceit; think innocently and justly, and, if you speak, speak accordingly.

8. JUSTICE.—Wrong none by doing injuries, or omitting the benefits that are your duty.

9. MODERATION.—Avoid extremes; forbear resenting injuries so much as you think they deserve.

10. CLEANLINESS.—Tolerate no uncleanliness in body, clothes, or habitation.

11. TRANQUILLITY.—Be not disturbed at trifles, or at accidents common or unavoidable.

12. CHASTITY.—Rarely use venery but for health or offspring, never to dullness, weakness, or the injury of your own or another's peace or reputation.

13. HUMILITY.—Imitate Jesus and Socrates.

My intention being to acquire the *habitude* of all these virtues, I judged it would be well not to distract my attention by attempting the whole at once, but to fix it on one of them at a time; and, when I should be master of that, then to proceed to another, and so on, till I should have gone thro' the thirteen; and, as the previous acquisition of some might facilitate the acquisition of certain others, I arranged them with that view, as they stand above.

Temperance first, as it tends to procure that coolness and clearness of head, which is so necessary where constant vigilance was to be kept up, and guard maintained against the unremitting attraction of ancient habits, and the force of perpetual temptations. This being acquired and established, *Silence* would be more easy; and my desire being to gain knowledge at the same time that I improved in virtue, and considering that in conversation it was obtained rather by the use of the ears than of the tongue, and therefore wishing to break a habit I was getting into of prattling, punning, and joking, which only made me acceptable to trifling company, I gave *Silence* the second place. This and the next, *Order,* I expected would allow me more time for attending to my project and my studies. *Resolution,* once become habitual, would keep me firm in my endeavors to obtain all the subsequent virtues; *Frugality* and *Industry* freeing me from my remaining debt, and producing affluence and independence, would make more easy the practice of *Sincerity* and *Justice,* etc., etc. Conceiving then, that, agreeably to the advice of Pythagoras in his Golden Verses, daily examination would be necessary, I contrived the following method for conducting that examination.

I made a little book, in which I allotted a page for each of the virtues. I ruled each page with red ink, so as to have seven columns, one for each day of the week, marking each column with a letter for the day. I crossed these columns with thirteen red lines, marking the beginning of each line with the first letter of one of the virtues, on which line, and in its proper column, I might mark, by a little black spot, every fault I found upon examination to have been committed respecting that virtue upon that day.

FORM OF THE PAGES

TEMPERANCE

Eat not to dullness; drink not to elevation

	Sun.	M.	T.	W.	Th.	F.	S.
Tem.							
Sil.	*	*		*		*	
Ord.	*	*			*	*	*
Res.		*				*	
Fru.		*				*	
Ind.			*				
Sinc.							
Jus.							
Mod.							
Clea.							
Tran.							
Chas.							
Hum.							

I determined to give a week's strict attention to each of the virtues successively. Thus, in the first week, my great guard was to avoid even the least offense against *Temperance,* leaving the other virtues to their ordinary chance, only marking every evening the faults of the day. Thus, if in the first week I could keep my first line, marked T, clear of spots, I supposed the habit of that virtue so much strengthened, and its opposite weakened, that I might venture extending my attention to include the next, and for the following week keep both lines clear of spots. Proceeding thus to the last, I could go through a course complete in thirteen weeks, and four courses in a year.

215

The precept of *Order* requiring that *every part of my business should have its allotted time,* one page in my little book contained the following scheme of employment for the twenty-four hours of a natural day.

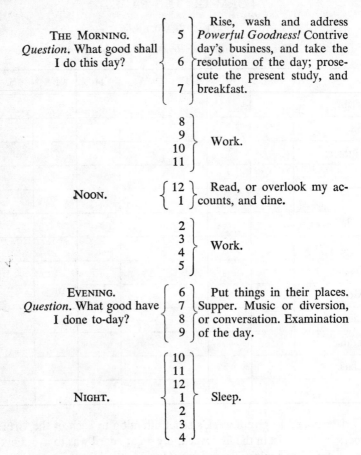

THE MORNING. Question. What good shall I do this day?	5 6 7	Rise, wash and address *Powerful Goodness!* Contrive day's business, and take the resolution of the day; prosecute the present study, and breakfast.
	8 9 10 11	Work.
NOON.	12 1	Read, or overlook my accounts, and dine.
	2 3 4 5	Work.
EVENING. Question. What good have I done to-day?	6 7 8 9	Put things in their places. Supper. Music or diversion, or conversation. Examination of the day.
NIGHT.	10 11 12 1 2 3 4	Sleep.

I entered upon the execution of this plan for self-examination, and continued it with occasional intermissions for some time. I was surprised to find myself so much fuller of faults than I had imagined; but I had the satisfaction of seeing them diminish. To avoid the trouble of renewing now and then my little book, which, by scraping out the marks on the paper of old faults to make room for new ones in a new course became full of holes, I transferred my tables and precepts to the ivory leaves of a memorandum book, on which the lines were drawn with red ink that made a durable stain, and on those lines I marked my faults with a black-lead pencil, which marks I could easily wipe out with a wet sponge. After a while I went through one course only in a year, and afterward only one in several years, till at length I omitted them entirely, being employed in voyages and business abroad, with a multiplicity of affairs that interfered; but I always carried my little book with me.

My scheme of *Order* gave me the most trouble; and I found that, though it might be practicable where a man's business was such as to leave him the disposition of his time, that of a journeyman printer, for instance, it was not possible to be exactly observed by a master, who must mix with the world, and often receive people of business at their own hours. *Order,* too, with regard to places for things, papers, etc., I found extremely difficult to acquire. I had not been early accustomed to it, and, having an exceeding good memory, I was not so sensible of the inconvenience attending want of method.

This article, therefore, cost me so much painful attention, and my faults in it vexed me so much, and I made so little progress in amendment, and had such frequent relapses, that I was almost ready to give up the attempt, and content myself with a faulty character in that respect, like the man who, in buying an ax of a smith, my neighbor, desired to have the whole of its surface as bright as the edge. The smith consented to grind it bright for him if he would turn the wheel; he turned, while the smith pressed the broad face of the ax hard and heavily on the stone, which made the turning of it very fatiguing. The man came every now and then from the wheel to see how the work went on, and at length would take his ax as it was, without further grinding. "No," said the smith, "turn on, turn on; we shall have it bright by-and-by; as yet, it is only speckled." "Yes," says the man, *"but I think I like a speckled ax best."*

In truth, I found myself incorrigible with respect to *Order;* and now I am grown old, and my memory bad, I feel very sensibly the want of it. But, on the whole, though I never arrived at the perfection I had been so ambitious of obtaining, but fell far short of it, yet I was, by the endeavor, a better and a happier man than I otherwise should have been if I had not attempted it; as those who aim at perfect writing by imitating the engraved copies, though they never reach the wished-for excellence of those copies, their hand is mended by the endeavor, and is tolerable while it continues fair and legible.

It may be well my posterity should be informed that to this little artifice, with the blessing of God, their ancestor owed the constant felicity of his life, down to his 79th year, in which this is written. What reverses may attend the remainder is in the hand of Providence; but, if they arrive, the reflection on past happiness enjoyed ought to help his bearing them with more resignation.

To *Temperance* he ascribes his long-continued health, and what is still left to him of a good constitution; to *Industry* and *Frugality,* the early easiness of his circumstances and acquisition of his fortune, with all that knowledge that enabled him to be a useful citizen, and obtained for him some degree of reputation among the learned; to *Sincerity* and *Justice,* the confidence of his country, and the honorable employs it conferred upon him; and to the joint influence of the whole mass of the virtues, even in the imperfect state he was able to acquire them, all that evenness of temper, and that cheerfulness in conversation, which makes his company still sought for, and agreeable even to his younger acquaintance. I hope, therefore, that some of my descendants may follow the example and reap the benefit.

It will be remarked that, though my scheme was not wholly without religion, there was in it no mark of any of the distinguishing tenets of any particular sect. I had purposely avoided them; for, being fully persuaded of the utility and excellency of my method, and that it might be serviceable to people in all religions, and intending some time or other to publish it, I would not have anything in it that should prejudice anyone, of any sect, against it. I purposed writing a little comment on each virtue, in which I would have shown the advantages of possessing it, and the mischiefs attending its opposite vice; and I should have called my book *The Art of Virtue,* because it would have shown the means and manner of obtaining virtue, which would have distinguished it from the mere exhortation to be good that does not instruct and indicate the means.

But it so happened that my intention of writing and publishing this comment was never fulfilled. I did, indeed, from time to time, put down short hints of the sentiments, reasonings, etc., to be made use of in it, some of which I have still by me; but the necessary close attention to private business in the earlier part of my life, and public business since, have occasioned my postponing it; for, it being connected in my mind with *a great and extensive project,* that required the whole man to execute, and which an unforeseen succession of employs prevented my attending to, it has hitherto remained unfinished.

218

In this piece it was my design to explain and enforce this doctrine, that vicious actions are not hurtful because they are forbidden, but forbidden because they are hurtful, the nature of man alone considered; that it was, therefore, every one's interest to be virtuous who wished to be happy even in this world; and I should, from this circumstance (there being always in the world a number of rich merchants, nobility, states, and princes, who have need of honest instruments for the management of their affairs, and such being so rare), have endeavored to convince young persons that no qualities were so likely to make a poor man's fortune as those of probity and integrity.

My list of virtues contained at first but twelve; but a Quaker friend having kindly informed me that I was generally thought proud; that my pride showed itself frequently in conversation; that I was not content with being in the right when discussing any point, but was overbearing, and rather insolent, of which he convinced me by mentioning several instances; I determined endeavoring to cure myself, if I could, of this vice or folly among the rest, and I added *Humility* to my list, giving an extensive meaning to the word.

I cannot boast of much success in acquiring the *reality* of this virtue, but I had a good deal with regard to the *appearance* of it. I made it a rule to forbear all direct contradiction to the sentiments of others, and all positive assertion of my own. I even forbid myself, agreeably to the old laws of our Junto, the use of every word or expression in the language that imported a fixed opinion, such as *certainly, undoubtedly,* etc., and I adopted, instead of them, *I conceive, I apprehend,* or *I imagine* a thing to be so or so; or *it so appears to me at present.*

When another asserted something that I thought an error, I denied myself the pleasure of contradicting him abruptly, and of showing immediately some absurdity in his proposition; and in answering I began by observing that in certain cases or circumstances his opinion would be right, but in the present case there *appeared* or *seemed* to me some difference, etc. I soon found the advantage of this change in my manner; the conversations I engaged in went on more pleasantly. The modest way in which I proposed my opinions procured them a readier reception and less contradiction; I had less mortification when I was found to be in the wrong; and I more easily prevailed with others to give up their mistakes and join with me when I happened to be in the right.

219

And this mode, which I at first put on with some violence to natural inclination, became at length so easy, and so habitual to me, that perhaps for these fifty years past no one has ever heard a dogmatical expression escape me. And to this habit (after my character of integrity) I think it principally owing that I had early so much weight with my fellow-citizens when I proposed new institutions, or alterations in the old, and so much influence in public councils when I became a member; for I was but a bad speaker, never eloquent, subject to much hesitation in my choice of words, hardly correct in language, and yet I generally carried my points.

In reality, there is, perhaps, no one of our natural passions so hard to subdue as *pride*. Disguise it, struggle with it, beat it down, stifle it, mortify it as much as one pleases, it is still alive, and will every now and then peep out and show itself; you will see it, perhaps, often in this history; for, even if I could conceive that I had completely overcome it, I should probably be proud of my humility.

[Thus far written at Passy, 1784.]

[*"I am now about to write at home, August, 1788, but can not have the help expected from my papers, many of them being lost in the war. I have, however, found the following."*]

HAVING mentioned a *great and extensive project* which I had conceived, it seems proper that some account should be here given of that project and its object. Its first rise in my mind appears in the following little paper, accidentally preserved, viz.:

Observations on my reading history, in Library, May 19th, 1731.

"That the great affairs of the world, the wars, revolutions, etc., are carried on and affected by parties.

"That the view of these parties is their present general interest, or what they take to be such.

"That the different views of these different parties occasion all confusion.

"That while a party is carrying on a general design, each man has his particular private interest in view.

"That as soon as a party has gained its general point, each member becomes intent upon his particular interest; which, thwarting others, breaks that party into divisions, and occasions more confusion.

"That few in public affairs act from a mere view of the good of their country, whatever they may pretend; and, though their actings bring real good to their country, yet men primarily considered that their own and their country's interest was united, and did not act from a principle of benevolence.

"That fewer still, in public affairs, act with a view to the good of mankind.

"There seems to me at present to be great occasion for raising a United Party for Virtue, by forming the virtuous and good men of all nations into a regular body, to be governed by suitable good and wise rules, which good and wise men may probably be more unanimous in their obedience to, than common people are to common laws.

"I at present think that whoever attempts this aright, and is well qualified, can not fail of pleasing God, and of meeting with success.

B.F."

Revolving this project in my mind, as to be undertaken hereafter, when my circumstances should afford me the necessary leisure, I put down from time to time, on pieces of paper, such thoughts as occurred to me respecting it. Most of these are lost; but I find one purporting to be the substance of an intended creed, containing, as I thought, the essentials of every known religion, and being free of everything that might shock the professors of any religion. It is expressed in these words, viz.:

"That there is one God, who made all things.

"That He governs the world by His providence.

"That He ought to be worshiped by adoration, prayer, and thanksgiving.

"But that the most acceptable service of God is doing good to man.

"That the soul is immortal.

"And that God will certainly reward virtue and punish vice, either here or hereafter."

My ideas at that time were that the sect should be begun and spread at first among young and single men only; that each person to be initiated should not only declare his assent to such creed, but should have exercised himself with the thirteen weeks' examination and practice of the virtues, as in the before-mentioned model; that the existence of such a society should be kept a secret, till it was become considerable, to prevent solicitations for the admission of improper persons, but that the members should each of them search among his acquaintance for ingenuous, well-disposed youths, to whom, with prudent caution, the scheme should be gradually communicated; that the members should engage to afford their advice, assistance, and support to each other in promoting one another's interests, business, and advancement in life; that, for distinction, we should be called *The Society of the Free and Easy:* free, as being, by the general practice and habit of the virtues, free from the dominion of vice; and particularly by the practice of industry and frugality, free from debt, which exposes a man to confinement, and a species of slavery to his creditors.

This is as much as I can now recollect of the project, except that I communicated it in part to two young men, who adopted it with some enthusiasm; but my then narrow circumstances, and the necessity I was under of sticking close to my business, occasioned my postponing the further prosecution of it at that time; and my multifarious occupations, public and private, induced me to continue postponing, so that it has been omitted till I have no longer strength or activity left sufficient for such an enterprise; though I am still of opinion that it was a practicable scheme, and might have been very useful, by forming a great number of good citizens; and I was not discouraged by the seeming magnitude of the undertaking, as I have always thought that one man of tolerable abilities may work great changes, and accomplish great affairs among mankind, if he first forms a good plan, and, cutting off all amusements or other employments that would divert his attention, makes the execution of that same plan his sole study and business.

In 1732 I first published my *Almanack,* under the name of *Richard Saunders;* it was continued by me about twenty-five years, commonly called *Poor Richard's Almanack.* I endeavored to make it both entertaining and useful, and it accordingly came to be in such demand, that I reaped considerable profit from it, vending annually near ten thousand. And observing that it was generally read, scarce any neighborhood in the province being without it, I considered it as a proper vehicle for conveying instruction among the common people, who bought scarcely any other books. I therefore filled all the little spaces that occurred between the remarkable days in the calendar with proverbial sentences, chiefly such as inculcated industry and frugality, as the means of procuring wealth, and thereby securing virtue; it being more difficult for a man in want to act always honestly, as, to use here one of those proverbs: *It is hard for an empty sack to stand upright.*

These proverbs, which contained the wisdom of many ages and nations, I assembled and formed into a connected discourse prefixed to the *Almanack* of 1757, as the harangue of a wise old man to the people attending an auction. The bringing all these scattered counsels thus into a focus enabled them to make greater impression. The piece, being universally approved, was copied in all the newspapers of the Continent; reprinted in Britain on a broad side, to be stuck up in houses. Two translations were made of it in French, and great numbers bought by the clergy and gentry, to distribute gratis among their poor parishioners and tenants. In Pennsylvania, as it discouraged useless expense in foreign superfluities, some thought it had its share of influence in producing that growing plenty of money which was observable for several years after its publication.

I considered my newspaper, also, as another means of communicating instruction, and in that view frequently reprinted in it extracts from the *Spectator,* and other moral writers; and sometimes published little pieces of my own, which had been first composed for reading in our Junto. Of these are a Socratic dialogue, tending to prove that, whatever might be his parts and abilities, a vicious man could not properly be called a man of sense; and a discourse on self-denial, showing that virtue was not secure till its practice became a habitude, and was free from the opposition of contrary inclinations. These may be found in the papers about the beginning of 1735.

In the conduct of my newspaper, I carefully excluded all libeling and personal abuse, which is of late years become so disgraceful to our country. Whenever I was solicited to insert anything of that kind, and the writers pleaded, as they generally did, the liberty of the press, and that a newspaper was like a stage-coach, in which anyone who would pay had a right to a place, my answer was, that I would print the piece separately if desired, and the author might have as many copies as he pleased to distribute himself, but that I would not take upon me to spread his detraction; and that, having contracted with my subscribers to furnish them with what might be either useful or entertaining, I could not fill their papers with private altercation, in which they had no concern, without doing them manifest injustice.

In 1733 I sent one of my journeymen to Charleston, South Carolina, where a printer was wanting. I furnished him with a press and letters, on an agreement of partnership, by which I was to receive one-third of the profits of the business, paying one-third of the expense. On his decease, the business was continued by his widow, who, being born and bred in Holland, where, as I have been informed, the knowledge of accounts makes a part of female education, she not only sent me as clear a state as she could find of the transactions past, but continued to account with the greatest regularity and exactness every quarter afterwards, and managed the business with such success, that she not only brought up reputably a family of children, but, at the expiration of the term, was able to purchase of me the printing-house, and establish her son in it.

I mention this affair chiefly for the sake of recommending that branch of education for our young females, as likely to be of more use to them and their children, in case of widowhood, than either music or dancing.

About the year 1734 there arrived among us from Ireland a young Presbyterian preacher, named Hemphill, who delivered with a good voice, and apparently extempore, most excellent discourses, which drew together considerable numbers of different persuasions, who joined in admiring them. Among the rest, I became one of his constant hearers, his sermons pleasing me, as they had little of the dogmatical kind, but inculcated strongly the practice of virtue, or what in the religious style are called good works.

Those, however, of our congregation, who considered themselves as orthodox Presbyterians, disapproved his doctrine, and were joined by most of the old clergy, who arraigned him of heterodoxy before the synod, in order to have him silenced. I became his zealous partisan, and contributed all I could to raise a party in his favor, and we combated for him a while with some hopes of success. There was much scribbling pro and con. I lent him my pen and wrote for him two or three pamphlets, and one piece in the *Gazette* of April, 1735.

During the contest an unlucky occurrence hurt his cause exceedingly. One of our adversaries having heard him preach a sermon that was much admired, thought he had somewhere read the sermon before, or at least a part of it. On search, he found that part quoted at length, in one of the British Reviews, from a discourse of Dr. Foster's. This detection gave many of our party disgust, who accordingly abandoned his cause. He afterward acknowledged to me that none of those he preached were his own; adding, that his memory was such as enabled him to retain and repeat any sermon after one reading only. On our defeat, he left us in search elsewhere of better fortune, and I quitted the congregation, never joining it after, though I continued many years my subscription for the support of its ministers.

I had begun in 1733 to study languages; I soon made myself so much a master of the French as to be able to read the books with ease. I then undertook the Italian. An acquaintance, who was also learning it, used often to tempt me to play chess with him. Finding this took up too much of the time I had to spare for study, I at length refused to play any more, unless on this condition, that the victor in every game should have a right to impose a task, either in parts of the grammar to be got by heart, or in translations, etc., which tasks the vanquished was to perform upon honor, before our next meeting. As we played pretty equally, we thus beat one another into that language. I afterwards with a little painstaking, acquired as much of the Spanish as to read their books also.

I have already mentioned that I had only one year's instruction in a Latin school, and that when very young, after which I neglected that language entirely. But, when I had attained an acquaintance with the French, Italian, and Spanish, I was surprised to find, on looking over a Latin Testament, that I understood so much more of that language than I had imagined, which encouraged me to apply myself again to the study of it, and I met with more success, as those preceding languages had greatly smoothed my way.

From these circumstances, I have thought that there is some inconsistency in our common mode of teaching languages. We are told that it is proper to begin first with the Latin, and, having acquired that, it will be more easy to attain those modern languages which are derived from it; and yet we do not begin with the Greek, in order more easily to acquire the Latin. I would therefore offer it to the consideration of those who superintend the education of our youth, whether it would not have been better to have begun with the French, proceeding to the Italian, etc.; for, though, after spending the same time, they should quit the study of languages and never arrive at the Latin, they would, however, have acquired another tongue or two, that, being in modern use, might be serviceable to them in common life.

After ten years' absence from Boston, and having become easy in my circumstances, I made a journey thither to visit my relations, which I could not sooner well afford. In returning, I called at Newport to see my brother, then settled there with his printing-house. Our former differences were forgotten, and our meeting was very cordial and affectionate. He was fast declining in his health, and requested of me that, in case of his death, which he apprehended not far distant, I would take home his son, then but ten years of age, and bring him up to the printing business. This I accordingly performed, sending him a few years to school before I took him into the office. His mother carried on the business till he was grown up, when I assisted him with an assortment of new types, those of his father being in a manner worn out. Thus it was that I made my brother ample amends for the service I had deprived him of by leaving him so early.

In 1736 I lost one of my sons, a fine boy of four years old, by the small-pox, taken in the common way. I long regretted bitterly, and still regret that I had not given it to him by inoculation. This I mention for the sake of parents who omit that operation, on the supposition that they should never forgive themselves if a child died under it; my example showing that the regret may be the same either way, and that, therefore, the safer should be chosen.

Our club, the Junto, was found so useful, and afforded such satisfaction to the members, that several were desirous of introducing their friends, which could not well be done without exceeding what we had settled as a convenient number, viz., twelve. We had from the beginning made it a rule to keep our institution a secret, which was pretty well observed; the intention was to avoid applications of improper persons for admittance, some of whom, perhaps, we might find it difficult to refuse.

I was one of those who were against any addition to our number, but, instead of it, made in writing a proposal, that every member separately should endeavor to form a subordinate club, with the same rules respecting queries, etc.

The project was approved, and every member undertook to form his club, but they did not all succeed. Five or six only were completed, which were called by different names, as the Vine, the Union, the Band, etc. They were useful to themselves, and afforded us a good deal of amusement, information, and instruction, besides answering, in some considerable degree, our views of influencing the public opinion on particular occasions.

My first promotion was my being chosen, in 1736, clerk of the General Assembly. The choice was made that year without opposition; but the year following, when I was again proposed (the choice, like that of the members, being annual), a new member made a long speech against me, in order to favor some other candidate. I was, however, chosen, which was the more agreeable to me, as, besides the pay for the immediate service as clerk, the place gave me a better opportunity of keeping up an interest among the members, which secured to me the business of printing the votes, laws, paper money, and other occasional jobs for the public, that, on the whole, were very profitable.

I therefore did not like the opposition of this new member, who was a gentleman of fortune and education, with talents that were likely to give him, in time, great influence in the House, which, indeed, afterwards happened. I did not, however, aim at gaining his favor by paying any servile respect to him, but, after some time, took this other method. Having heard that he had in his library a certain very scarce and curious book, I wrote a note to him, expressing my desire of perusing that book, and requesting he would do me the favor of lending it to me for a few days. He sent it immediately, and I returned it in about a week with another note, expressing strongly my sense of the favor. When we next met in the House, he spoke to me (which he had never done before), and with great civility; and he ever after manifested a readiness to serve me on all occasions, so that we became great friends, and our friendship continued to his death. This is another instance of the truth of an old maxim I had learned, which says, *He that has once done you a kindness will be more ready to do you another, than he whom you yourself have obliged.* And it shows how much more profitable it is prudently to remove, than to resent, return, and continue inimical proceedings.

In 1737, Colonel Spotswood, late governor of Virginia, and then postmaster-general, being dissatisfied with the conduct of his deputy at Philadelphia, respecting some negligence in rendering, and inexactitude of his accounts, took from him the commission and offered it to me. I accepted it readily, and found it of great advantage; for, though the salary was small, it facilitated the correspondence that improved my newspaper, increased the number demanded, as well as the advertisements to be inserted, so that it came to afford me a considerable income. My old competitor's newspaper declined proportionably, and I was satisfied without retaliating his refusal, while postmaster, to permit my papers being carried by the riders.

I began now to turn my thoughts a little to public affairs, beginning, however, with small matters. The city watch was one of the first things that I conceived to want regulation. It was managed by the constables of the respective wards in turn; the constable warned a number of housekeepers to attend him for the night. Those who chose never to attend paid him six shillings a year to be excused, which was supposed to be for hiring substitutes, but was, in reality, much more than was necessary for that purpose, and made the constableship a place of profit. And the constable, for a little drink, often got such ragamuffins about him as a watch, that respectable housekeepers did not choose to mix with. Walking the rounds, too, was often neglected, and most of the nights spent in tippling.

I thereupon wrote a paper to be read in Junto, representing these irregularities, but insisting more particularly on the inequality of this six-shilling tax of the constables, respecting the circumstances of those who paid it, since a poor widow housekeeper, all whose property to be guarded by the watch did not perhaps exceed the value of fifty pounds, paid as much as the wealthiest merchant, who had thousands of pounds' worth of goods in his stores. On the whole, I proposed as a more effectual watch, the hiring of proper men to serve constantly in that business; and as a more equitable way of supporting the charge, the levying a tax that should be proportioned to the property.

This idea, being approved by the Junto, was communicated to the other clubs, but as arising in each of them; and though the plan was not immediately carried into execution, yet, by preparing the minds of people for the change, it paved the way for the law obtained a few years after, when the members of our clubs were grown into more influence.

About this time I wrote a paper (first to be read in Junto, but it was afterward published) on the different accidents and carelessnesses by which houses were set on fire, with cautions against them, and means proposed of avoiding them. This was much spoken of as a useful piece, and gave rise to a project, which soon followed it, of forming a company for the more ready extinguishing of fires, and mutual assistance in removing and securing of goods when in danger. Associates in this scheme were presently found, amounting to thirty. Our articles of agreement obliged every member to keep always in good order, and fit for use, a certain number of leather buckets, with strong bags and baskets (for packing and transporting of goods), which were to be brought to every fire; and we agreed to meet once a month and spend a social evening together, in discoursing and communicating such ideas as occurred to us upon the subject of fires, as might be useful in our conduct on such occasions.

The utility of this institution soon appeared, and many more desiring to be admitted than we thought convenient for one company, they were advised to form another, which was accordingly done; and this went on, one new company being formed after another, till they became so numerous as to include most of the inhabitants who were men of property. And now, at the time of my writing this, though upward of fifty years since its establishment, that which I first formed, called the Union Fire Company, still subsists and flourishes, though the first members are all deceased but myself and one who is older by a year than I am. The small fines that have been paid by members for absence at the monthly meetings have been applied to the purchase of fire-engines, ladders, fire-hooks, and other useful implements for each company, so that I question whether there is a city in the world better provided with the means of putting a stop to beginning conflagrations; and, in fact, since these institutions, the city has never lost by fire more than one or two houses at a time, and the flames have often been extinguished before the house in which they began has been half consumed.

In 1739 arrived among us from Ireland the Reverend Mr. Whitefield, who had made himself remarkable there as an itinerant preacher. He was at first permitted to preach in some of our churches; but the clergy, taking a dislike to him, soon refused him their pulpits, and he was obliged to preach in the fields. The multitudes of all sects and denominations that attended his sermons were enormous, and it was matter of speculation to me, who was one of the number, to observe the extraordinary influence of his oratory on his hearers, and how much they admired and respected him, notwithstanding his common abuse of them, by assuring them they were naturally *half beasts and half devils*. It was wonderful to see the change soon made in the manners of our inhabitants. From being thoughtless or indifferent about religion, it seemed as if all the world were growing religious, so that one could not walk through the town in an evening without hearing psalms sung in different families of every street.

And it being found inconvenient to assemble in the open air, subject to its inclemencies, the building of a house to meet in was no sooner proposed, and persons appointed to receive contributions, but sufficient sums were soon received to procure the ground and erect the building, which was one hundred feet long and seventy broad, about the size of Westminster Hall; and the work was carried on with such spirit as to be finished in a much shorter time than could have been expected. Both house and ground were vested in trustees, expressly for the use of any preacher of any religious persuasion who might desire to say something to the people at Philadelphia; so that even if the Mufti of Constantinople were to send a missionary to preach Mohammedanism to us, he would find a pulpit at his service.

Mr. Whitefield, in leaving us, went preaching all the way through the colonies to Georgia. The settlement of that province had lately been begun, but, instead of being made with hardy, industrious husbandmen, accustomed to labor, the only people fit for such an enterprise, it was with families of broken shop-keepers and other insolvent debtors, many of indolent and idle habits, taken out of the jails, who, being set down in the woods, unqualified for clearing land, and unable to endure the hardships of a new settlement, perished in numbers, leaving many helpless children unprovided for. The sight of their miserable situation inspired the benevolent heart of Mr. Whitefield with the idea of building an Orphan House there, in which they might be supported and educated. Returning northward, he preached up this charity, and made large collections, for his eloquence had a wonderful power over the hearts and purses of his hearers, of which I myself was an instance.

The last time I saw Mr. Whitefield was in London, when he consulted me about his Orphan House concern, and his purpose of appropriating it to the establishment of a college.

He had a loud and clear voice, and articulated his words and sentences so perfectly that he might be heard and understood at a great distance, especially as his auditories, however numerous, observed the most exact silence. He preached one evening from the top of the Court-house steps, which are in the middle of Market Street, and on the west side of Second Street, which crosses it at right angles. Both streets were filled with his hearers to a considerable distance. Being among the hindmost in Market Street, I had the curiosity to learn how far he could be heard, by retiring backwards down the street towards the river; and I found his voice distinct till I came near Front Street, when some noise in that street obscured it. Imagining then a semi-circle, of which my distance should be the radius, and that it were filled with auditors, to each of whom I allowed two square feet, I computed that he might well be heard by more than thirty thousand. This reconciled me to the newspaper accounts of his having preached to twenty-five thousand people in the fields, and to the ancient histories of generals haranguing whole armies, of which I had sometimes doubted.

My business was now continually augmenting, and my circumstances growing daily easier, my newspaper having become very profitable, as being for a time almost the only one in this and the neighboring provinces. I experienced, too, the truth of the observation, *that after getting the first hundred pounds, it is more easy to get the second,* money itself being of a prolific nature.

The partnership at Carolina having succeeded, I was encouraged to engage in others, and to promote several of my workmen, who had behaved well, by establishing them with printing-houses in different colonies, on the same terms with that in Carolina. Most of them did well, being enabled at the end of our term, six years, to purchase the types of me and go on working for themselves, by which means several families were raised.

Partnerships often finish in quarrels; but I was happy in this, that mine were all carried on and ended amicably, owing, I think, a good deal to the precaution of having very explicitly settled, in our articles, everything to be done by or expected from each partner, so that there was nothing to dispute, which precaution I would therefore recommend to all who enter into partnerships; for, whatever esteem partners may have for, and confidence in each other at the time of the contract, little jealousies and disgusts may arise, with ideas of inequality in the care and burden of the business, etc., which are attended often with breach of friendship and of the connection, perhaps with lawsuits and other disagreeable consequences.

I had, on the whole, abundant reason to be satisfied with my being established in Pennsylvania. There were, however, two things that I regretted, there being no provision for defense, nor for a complete education of youth; no militia, nor any college. I therefore, in 1743, drew up a proposal for establishing an academy; and at that time, thinking the Reverend Mr. Peters, who was out of employ, a fit person to superintend such an institution, I communicated the project to him; but he, having more profitable views in the service of the proprietaries, which succeeded, declined the undertaking; and, not knowing another at that time suitable for such a trust, I let the scheme lie a while dormant. I succeeded better the next year, 1744, in proposing and establishing a Philosophical Society. The paper I wrote for that purpose will be found among my writings, when collected.

With respect to defense, Spain having been several years at war against Great Britain, and being at length joined by France, which brought us into great danger; and the labored and long-continued endeavor of our governor, Thomas, to prevail with our Quaker

Assembly to pass a militia law, and make other provisions for the security of the province, having proved abortive, I determined to try what might be done by a voluntary association of the people.

To promote this, I first wrote and published a pamphlet, entitled *Plain Truth,* in which I stated our defenseless situation in strong lights, with the necessity of union and discipline for our defense, and promised to propose in a few days an association, to be generally signed for that purpose. The pamphlet had a sudden and surprising effect. I was called upon for the instrument of association, and having settled the draft of it with a few friends, I appointed a meeting of the citizens in the large building before mentioned. The house was pretty full. I had prepared a number of printed copies, and provided pens and ink dispersed all over the room. I harangued them a little on the subject, read the paper, and explained it, and then distributed the copies, which were eagerly signed, not the least objection being made.

When the company separated, and the papers were collected, we found above twelve hundred hands; and, other copies being dispersed in the country, the subscribers amounted at length to upward of ten thousand. These all furnished themselves as soon as they could with arms, formed themselves into companies and regiments, chose their own officers, and met every week to be instructed in the manual exercise, and other parts of military discipline. The women, by subscriptions among themselves, provided silk colors, which they presented to the companies, painted with different devices and mottoes, which I supplied.

The officers of the companies composing the Philadelphia regiment, being met, chose me for their colonel; but, conceiving myself unfit, I declined that station, and recommended Mr. Lawrence, a fine person, and man of influence, who was accordingly appointed. I then proposed a lottery to defray the expense of building a battery below the town, and furnishing it with cannon. It filled expeditiously, and the battery was soon erected, the merlons being framed of logs and filled with earth. We bought some old cannon from Boston, but these not being sufficient, we wrote to England for more, soliciting, at the same time, our proprietaries for some assistance, though without much expectation of obtaining it.

Meanwhile, Colonel Lawrence, William Allen, Abram Taylor, Esqr., and myself were sent to New York by the associators, commissioned to borrow some cannon of Governor Clinton. He at first refused us peremptorily; but at dinner with his council, where there was great drinking of Madeira wine, as the custom of that place then was, he softened by degrees, and said he would lend us six. After a few more bumpers he advanced to ten; and at length he very good-naturedly conceded eighteen. They were fine cannon, eighteen-pounders, with their carriages, which we soon transported and mounted on our battery, where the associators kept a nightly guard while the war lasted, and among the rest I regularly took my turn of duty there as a common soldier.

My activity in these operations was agreeable to the governor and council. They took me into confidence, and I was consulted by them in every measure wherein their concurrence was thought useful to the association. Calling in the aid of religion, I proposed to them the proclaiming a fast, to promote reformation, and implore the blessing of Heaven on our undertaking. They embraced the motion; but, as it was the first fast ever thought of in the province, the secretary had no precedent from which to draw the proclamation. My education in New England, where a fast is proclaimed every year, was here of some advantage. I drew it in the accustomed style, it was translated into German, printed in both languages, and divulged through the province. This gave the clergy of the different sects an opportunity of influencing their congregations to join in the association, and it would probably have been general among all but Quakers if the peace had not soon intervened.

It was thought by some of my friends that, by my activity in these affairs, I should offend that sect, and thereby lose my interest in the Assembly of the province, where they formed a great majority. A young gentleman who had likewise some friends in the House, and wished to succeed me as their clerk, acquainted me that it was decided to displace me at the next election; and he, therefore, in good will, advised me to resign, as more consistent with my honor than being turned out. My answer to him was, that I had read or heard of some public man who made it a rule never to ask for an office, and never to refuse one when offered to him. "I approve," says I, "of his rule, and will practice it with a small addition; I shall never *ask,* never *refuse,* nor ever *resign* an office. If they will have my office of clerk to dispose of to another, they shall take it from me. I will not, by giving it up, lose my right of some time or other making reprisals on my adversaries." I heard, however, no more of this; I was chosen again unanimously as usual at the next election.

Indeed I had some cause to believe that the defense of the country

233

was not disagreeable to any of them, provided they were not required to assist in it. And I found that a much greater number of them than I could have imagined, tho' against offensive war, were clearly for the defensive. Many pamphlets *pro and con* were published on the subject, and some by good Quakers, in favor of defense, which I believe convinced most of their younger people.

My being many years in the Assembly, the majority of which were constantly Quakers, gave me frequent opportunities of seeing the embarrassment given them by their principle against war, whenever application was made to them, by order of the crown, to grant aids for military purposes. They were unwilling to offend government, on the one hand, by a direct refusal; and their friends, the body of the Quakers, on the other, by a compliance contrary to their principles; hence a variety of evasions to avoid complying, and modes of disguising the compliance when it became unavoidable. The common mode at last was to grant money under the phrase of its being *"for the king's use,"* and never to inquire how it was applied.

But, if the demand was not directly from the crown, that phrase was found not so proper, and some other was to be invented. As, when powder was wanting (I think it was for the garrison at Louisburg), and the government of New England solicited a grant of some from Pennsylvania, which was much urged on the House by Governor Thomas, they could not grant money to buy powder, because that was an ingredient of war; but they voted an aid to New England of three thousand pounds, to be put into the hands of the governor, and appropriated it for the purchasing of bread, flour, wheat, or *other grain.* Some of the council, desirous of giving the House still further embarrassment, advised the governor not to accept provision, as not being the thing he had demanded; but he replied, "I shall take the money, for I understand very well their meaning; other grain is gunpowder," which he accordingly bought, and they never objected to it.

It was in allusion to this fact that, when in our fire company we feared the success of our proposal in favor of the lottery, and I had said to my friend Mr. Syng, one of our members, "If we fail, let us move the purchase of a fire-engine with the money; the Quakers can have no objection to that; and then, if you nominate me and I you as a committee for that purpose, we will buy a great gun, which is certainly a *fire-engine.*" "I see," says he, "you have improved by being so long in the Assembly; your equivocal project would be just a match for their wheat or *other grain.*"

These embarrassments that the Quakers suffered from having established and published it as one of their principles that no kind of war was lawful, and which, being once published, they could not afterwards, however they might change their minds, easily get rid of, reminds me of what I think a more prudent conduct in another sect among us, that of the Dunkers. I was acquainted with one of its founders, Michael Welfare, soon after it appeared. He complained to me that they were grievously calumniated by the zealots of other persuasions, and charged with abominable principles and practices, to which they were utter strangers. I told him this had always been the case with new sects, and that, to put a stop to such abuse, I imagined it might be well to publish the articles of their belief, and the rules of their discipline. He said that it had been proposed among them, but not agreed to, for this reason: "When we were first drawn together as a society," says he, "it had pleased God to enlighten our minds so far as to see that some doctrines, which we once esteemed truths, were errors; and that others, which we had esteemed errors, were real truths. From time to time He has been pleased to afford us farther light, and our principles have been improving, and our errors diminishing. Now we are not sure that we are arrived at the end of this progression, and at the perfection of spiritual or theological knowledge; and we fear that, if we should once print our confession of faith, we should feel ourselves as if bound and confined by it, and perhaps be unwilling to receive further improvement, and our successors still more so, as conceiving what we their elders and founders had done, to be something sacred, never to be departed from."

This modesty in a sect is perhaps a singular instance in the history of mankind, every other sect supposing itself in possession of all truth, and that those who differ are so far in the wrong; like a man traveling in foggy weather, those at some distance before him on the road he sees wrapped up in the fog, as well as those behind him, and also the people in the fields on each side, but near him all appears clear, though in truth he is as much in the fog as any of them. To avoid this kind of embarrassment, the Quakers have of late years been gradually declining the public service in the Assembly and in the magistracy, choosing rather to quit their power than their principle.

In order of time, I should have mentioned before, that having, in 1742, invented an open stove for the better warming of rooms, and at the same time saving fuel, as the fresh air admitted was warmed in entering, I made a present of the model to Mr. Robert Grace, one of my early friends, who, having an iron-furnace, found the casting of the plates for these stoves a profitable thing, as they were growing in demand. To promote that demand, I wrote and published a pamphlet, entitled: *An Account of the New-Invented Pennsylvania Fireplaces; wherein their Construction and Manner of Operation is particularly explained; their Advantages above every other Method of warming Rooms demonstrated; and all Objections that have been raised against the Use of them answered and obviated,* etc. This pamphlet had a good effect. Governor Thomas was so pleased with the construction of this stove, as described in it, that he offered to give me a patent for the sole vending of them for a term of years; but I declined it from a principle which has ever weighed with me on such occasions, viz., *That, as we enjoy great advantages from the inventions of others, we should be glad of an opportunity to serve others by any invention of ours; and this we should do freely and generously.*

An ironmonger in London however, assuming a good deal of my pamphlet, and working it up into his own, and making some small changes in the machine, which rather hurt its operation, got a patent for it there, and made, as I was told, a little fortune by it. And this is not the only instance of patents taken out for my inventions by others, though not always with the same success, which I never contested, as having no desire of profiting by patents myself, and hating disputes. The use of these fireplaces in very many houses, both of this and the neighboring colonies, has been, and is, a great saving of wood to the inhabitants.

Peace being concluded, and the association business therefore at an end, I turned my thoughts again to the affair of establishing an academy. The first step I took was to associate in the design a number of active friends, of whom the Junto furnished a good part. The next was to write and publish a pamphlet, entitled *Proposals Relating to the Education of Youth in Pennsylvania.* This I distributed among the principal inhabitants gratis; and as soon as I could suppose their minds a little prepared by the perusal of it, I set on foot a subscription for opening and supporting an academy; it was to be paid in quotas yearly for five years; by so dividing it, I judged the subscription might be larger, and I believed it was so, amounting to no less, if I remember right, than five thousand pounds.

In the introduction to these proposals, I stated their publication, not as an act of mine, but of some *public-spirited gentlemen,* avoiding as much as I could, according to my usual rule, the presenting myself to the public as the author of any scheme for their benefit.

The subscribers, to carry the project into immediate execution, chose out of their number twenty-four trustees, and appointed Mr. Francis, then attorney-general, and myself to draw up constitutions for the government of the academy; which being done and signed, a house was hired, masters engaged, and the schools opened, I think, in the same year, 1749.

The scholars increasing fast, the house was soon found too small, and we were looking out for a piece of ground, properly situated, with intention to build, when Providence threw into our way a large house ready built, which, with a few alterations, might well serve our purpose. This was the building before mentioned, erected by the hearers of Mr. Whitefield, and was obtained for us in the following manner.

It is to be noted that the contributions to this building being made by people of different sects, care was taken in the nomination of trustees, in whom the building and ground was to be vested, that a predominancy should not be given to any sect, lest in time that predominancy might be a means of appropriating the whole to the use of such sect, contrary to the original intention. It was therefore that one of each sect was appointed, viz., one Church-of-England man, one Presbyterian, one Baptist, one Moravian, etc., those, in case of vacancy by death, were to fill it by election from among the contributors. The Moravian happened not to please his colleagues, and on his death they resolved to have no other of that sect. The difficulty then was, how to avoid having two of some other sect, by means of the new choice.

Several persons were named, and for that reason not agreed to. At length one mentioned me, with the observation that I was merely an honest man, and of no sect at all, which prevailed with them to choose me. The enthusiasm which existed when the house was built had long since abated, and its trustees had not been able to procure fresh contributions for paying the ground-rent, and discharging some other debts the building had occasioned, which embarrassed them greatly. Being now a member of both sets of trustees, that for the building and that for the academy, I had a good opportunity of negotiating with both, and brought them finally to an agreement, by which the trustees for the building were to cede it to those of the academy, the latter undertaking to discharge the debt, to keep forever open in the building a large hall for occasional preachers, according to the original intention, and maintain a free-school for the instruction of poor children.

Writings were accordingly drawn, and on paying the debts the trustees of the academy were put in possession of the premises; and by dividing the great and lofty hall into stories, and different rooms above and below for the several schools, and purchasing some additional ground, the whole was soon made fit for our purpose, and the scholars removed into the building. The care and trouble of agreeing with the workmen, purchasing materials, and superintending the work, fell upon me; and I went through it the more cheerfully as it did not then interfere with my private business, having the year before taken a very able, industrious, and honest partner, Mr. David Hall, with whose character I was well acquainted, as he had worked for me four years. He took off my hands all care of the printing-office, paying me punctually my share of the profits. The partnership continued eighteen years, successfully for us both.

The trustees of the academy, after a while, were incorporated by a charter from the governor. Their funds were increased by contributions in Britain and grants of land from the proprietaries, to which the Assembly has since made considerable addition; and thus was established the present University of Philadelphia [*now, University of Pennsylvania*]. I have been continued one of its trustees from the beginning, now near forty years, and have had the very great pleasure of seeing a number of the youth who have received their education in it distinguished by their improved abilities, serviceable in public stations, and ornaments to their country.

When I disengaged myself, as above mentioned, from private business, I flattered myself that, by the sufficient though moderate fortune I had acquired, I had secured leisure during the rest of my life for philosophical studies and amusements. I purchased all Dr. Spence's apparatus, who had come from England to lecture here, and I proceeded in my electrical experiments with great alacrity; but the public, now considering me as a man of leisure, laid hold of me for their purposes, every part of our civil government, and almost at the same time, imposing some duty upon me. The governor put me into the commission of the peace; the corporation of the city chose me of the common council, and soon after an alderman; and the citizens at large chose me a burgess to represent them in Assembly. This latter station was the more agreeable to me, as I was at length tired with sitting there to hear debates, in which, as clerk, I could take no part, and which were often so unentertaining that I was induced to amuse myself with making magic squares or circles, or anything to avoid weariness; and I conceived my becoming a member would enlarge my power of doing good. I would not, however, insinuate that my ambition was not flattered by all these promotions. It certainly was; for, considering my low beginning, they were great things to me; and they were still more pleasing, as being so many spontaneous testimonies of the public good opinion, and by me entirely unsolicited.

The office of justice of the peace I tried a little, by attending a few courts, and sitting on the bench to hear causes; but finding that more knowledge of the common law than I possessed was necessary to act in that station with credit, I gradually withdrew from it, excusing myself by my being obliged to attend the higher duties of a legislator in the Assembly. My election to this trust was repeated every year for ten years, without my ever asking any elector for his vote, or signifying, either directly or indirectly, any desire of being chosen. On taking my seat in the House, my son was appointed their clerk.

The year following, a treaty going to be held with the Indians at Carlisle, the governor sent a message to the House, proposing that they should nominate some of their members, to be joined with some members of council, as commissioners for that purpose. The House named the speaker (Mr. Norris) and myself; and, being commissioned, we went to Carlisle, and met the Indians accordingly.

As those people are extremely apt to get drunk, and, when so, are very quarrelsome and disorderly, we strictly forbade the selling any liquor to them; and when they complained of this restriction, we told them that if they would continue sober during the treaty, we would give them plenty of rum when business was over. They promised this, and they kept their promise, because they could get no liquor, and the treaty was conducted very orderly, and concluded to mutual satisfaction.

They then claimed and received the rum. This was in the afternoon. They were near one hundred men, women, and children, and were lodged in temporary cabins, built in the form of a square, just without the town. In the evening, hearing a great noise among them, the commissioners walked out to see what was the matter. We found they had made a great bonfire in the middle of the square. They were all drunk, men and women, quarreling and fighting. Their dark-colored bodies, half-naked, seen only by the gloomy light of the bonfire, running after and beating one another with firebrands, accompanied by their horrid yellings, formed a scene the most resembling our ideas of hell that could well be imagined. There was no appeasing the tumult, and we retired to our lodging. At midnight a number of them came thundering at our door, demanding more rum, of which we took no notice.

The next day, sensible they had misbehaved in giving us that disturbance, they sent three of their old counsellors to make their apology. The orator acknowledged the fault, but laid it upon the rum; and then endeavored to excuse the rum by saying, *"The Great Spirit, who made all things, made every thing for some use, and whatever use he designed anything for, that use it should always be put to. Now, when he made rum, he said, 'Let this be for the Indians to get drunk with,' and it must be so."* And, indeed, if it be the design of Providence to extirpate these savages in order to make room for cultivators of the earth, it seems not improbable that rum may be the appointed means. It has already annihilated all the tribes who formerly inhabited the sea-coast.

In 1751, Dr. Thomas Bond, a particular friend of mine, conceived the idea of establishing a hospital in Philadelphia (a very beneficent design, which has been ascribed to me, but was originally his), for the reception and cure of poor sick persons, whether inhabitants of the province or strangers. He was zealous and active in endeavoring to procure subscriptions for it, but the proposal being a novelty in America, and at first not well understood, he met with but small success.

At length he came to me with the compliment that he found there was no such thing as carrying a public-spirited project through without my being concerned in it. "For," says he, "I am often asked by those to whom I propose subscribing, 'Have you consulted Franklin upon this business? And what does he think of it?' And when I tell them that I have not (supposing it rather out of your line), they do not subscribe, but say they will consider of it." I inquired into the nature and probable utility of his scheme, and receiving from him a very satisfactory explanation, I not only subscribed to it myself, but engaged heartily in the design of procuring subscriptions from others. Previously, however, to the solicitation, I endeavored to prepare the minds of the people by writing on the subject in the newspapers, which was my usual custom in such cases, but which he had omitted.

The subscriptions afterwards were more free and generous; but, beginning to flag, I saw they would be insufficient without some assistance from the Assembly, and therefore proposed to petition for it, which was done. The country members did not at first relish the project. They objected that it could only be serviceable to the city, and therefore the citizens alone should be at the expense of it; and they doubted whether the citizens themselves generally approved of it. My allegation on the contrary, that it met with such approbation as to leave no doubt of our being able to raise two thousand pounds by voluntary donations, they considered as a most extravagant supposition, and utterly impossible.

On this I formed my plan; and, asking leave to bring in a bill for incorporating the contributors according to the prayer of their petition, and granting them a blank sum of money, which leave was obtained chiefly on the consideration that the House could throw the bill out if they did not like it, I drew it so as to make the important clause a conditional one, viz., "And be it enacted, by the authority aforesaid, that when the said contributors shall have met and chosen their managers and treasurer, *and shall have raised by their contributions a capital stock of* ————— *value* (the yearly interest of which is to be applied to the accommodating of the sick poor in the said hospital, free of charge for diet, attendance, advice, and medicines), *and shall make the same appear to the satisfaction of the speaker of the Assembly for the time being,* that *then* it shall and may be lawful for the said speaker, and he is hereby required, to sign an order on the provincial treasurer for the payment of two thousand pounds, in two yearly payments, to the treasurer of the said hospital, to be applied to the founding, building, and finishing of the same."

The condition carried the bill through; for the members, who had opposed the grant, and now conceived they might have the credit of being charitable without the expense, agreed to its passage; and then, in soliciting subscriptions among the people, we urged the conditional promise of the law as an additional motive to give, since every man's donation would be doubled; thus the clause worked both ways. The subscriptions accordingly soon exceeded the requisite sum, and we claimed and received the public gift, which enabled us to carry the design into execution. A convenient and handsome building was soon erected; the institution has by constant experience been found useful, and flourishes to this day; and I do not remember any of my political maneuvers, the success of which gave me at the time more pleasure, or wherein, after thinking of it, I more easily excused myself for having made some use of cunning.

It was about this time that another projector, the Rev. Gilbert Tennent, came to me with a request that I would assist him in procuring a subscription for erecting a new meeting-house. It was to be for the use of a congregation he had gathered among the Presbyterians, who were originally disciples of Mr. Whitefield. Unwilling to make myself disagreeable to my fellow-citizens by too frequently soliciting their contributions, I absolutely refused. He then desired I would furnish him with a list of the names of persons I knew by experience to be generous and public-spirited. I thought it would be unbecoming in me, after their kind compliance with my solicitations, to mark them out to be worried by other beggars, and therefore refused also to give such a list.

He then desired I would at least give him my advice. "That I will readily do," said I, "and, in the first place, I advise you to apply to all those whom you know will give something; next, to those whom you are uncertain whether they will give anything or not, and show them the list of those who have given; and, lastly, do not neglect those who you are sure will give nothing, for in some of them you may be mistaken." He laughed and thanked me, and said he would take my advice. He did so, for he asked of *everybody,* and he obtained a much larger sum than he expected, with which he erected the capacious and very elegant meeting-house that stands in Arch Street.

Our city, though laid out with a beautiful regularity, the streets large, straight, and crossing each other at right angles, had the disgrace of suffering those streets to remain long unpaved, and in wet weather the wheels of heavy carriages plowed them into a quagmire, so that it was difficult to cross them; and in dry weather the dust was offensive. I had lived near what was called the Jersey Market, and saw with pain the inhabitants wading in mud while purchasing their provisions. A strip of ground down the middle of that market was at length paved with brick, so that, being once in the market, they had firm footing, but were often over shoes in dirt to get there. By talking and writing on the subject, I was at length instrumental in getting the street paved with stone between the market and the bricked foot-pavement, that was on each side next the houses. This, for some time, gave an easy access to the market dry-shod; but, the rest of the street not being paved, whenever a carriage came out of the mud upon this pavement, it shook off and left its dirt upon it, and it was soon covered with mire, which was not removed, the city as yet having no scavengers.

242

After some inquiry, I found a poor, industrious man who was willing to undertake keeping the pavement clean, by sweeping it twice a week, carrying off the dirt from before all the neighbors' doors, for the sum of sixpence per month, to be paid by each house. I then wrote and printed a paper setting forth the advantages to the neighborhood that might be obtained by this small expense; the greater ease in keeping our houses clean, so much dirt not being brought in by people's feet; the benefit to the shops by more custom, etc., etc., as buyers could more easily get at them; and by not having, in windy weather, the dust blown in upon their goods, etc., etc. I sent one of these papers to each house, and in a day or two went round to see who would subscribe an agreement to pay these sixpences; it was unanimously signed, and for a time well executed. All the inhabitants of the city were delighted with the cleanliness of the pavement that surrounded the market, it being a convenience to all, and this raised a general desire to have all the streets paved, and made the people more willing to submit to a tax for that purpose.

After some time I drew a bill for paving the city, and brought it into the Assembly. It was just before I went to England, in 1757, and did not pass till I was gone, and then with an alteration in the mode of assessment which I thought not for the better, but with an additional provision for lighting as well as paving the streets, which was a great improvement. It was by a private person, the late Mr. John Clifton, his giving a sample of the utility of lamps, by placing one at his door, that the people were first impressed with the idea of enlighting all the city.

The honor of this public benefit has also been ascribed to me, but it belongs truly to that gentleman. I did but follow his example, and have only some merit to claim respecting the form of our lamps, as differing from the globe lamps we were at first supplied with from London. Those we found inconvenient in these respects: they admitted no air below; the smoke, therefore, did not readily go out above, but circulated in the globe, lodged on its inside, and soon obstructed the light they were intended to afford; giving, besides, the daily trouble of wiping them clean; and an accidental stroke on one of them would demolish it, and render it totally useless. I therefore suggested the composing them of four flat panes, with a long funnel above to draw up the smoke, and crevices admitting air below, to facilitate the ascent of the smoke. By this means they were kept clean, and did not grow dark in a few hours, as the London lamps do, but continued bright till morning, and an accidental stroke would generally break but a single pane, easily repaired.

Having been for some time employed by the postmaster-general of America as his comptroller in regulating several offices, and bringing the officers to account, I was, upon his death in 1753, appointed, jointly with Mr. William Hunter, to succeed him, by a commission from the postmaster-general in England. The American office never had hitherto paid anything to that of Britain. We were to have six hundred pounds a year between us, if we could make that sum out of the profits of the office. To do this, a variety of improvements were necessary. Some of these were inevitably at first expensive, so that in the first four years the office became above nine hundred pounds in debt to us. But it soon after began to repay us; and before I was displaced by a freak of the ministers, of which I shall speak hereafter, we had brought it to yield *three times* as much clear revenue to the crown as the postoffice of Ireland. Since that imprudent transaction, they have received from it—not one farthing!

The business of the postoffice occasioned my taking a journey this year to New England, where the College of Cambridge, of their own motion, presented me with the degree of Master of Arts. Yale College, in Connecticut, had before made me a similar compliment. Thus, without studying in any college, I came to partake of their honors. They were conferred in consideration of my improvements and discoveries in the electric branch of natural philosophy.

In 1754, war with France being again apprehended, a congress of commissioners from the different colonies was, by order of the Lord of Trade, to be assembled at Albany, there to confer with the chiefs of the Six Nations concerning the means of defending both their country and ours. Governor Hamilton, having received this order, acquainted the House with it, requesting they would furnish proper presents for the Indians, to be given on this occasion; and naming the speaker (Mr. Norris) and myself to join Mr. Thomas Penn and Mr. Secretary Peters as commissioners to act for Pennsylvania. The House approved the nomination, and provided the goods for the present, and though they did not much like treating out of the provinces; and we met the other commissioners at Albany about the middle of June.

In our way thither, I projected and drew a plan for the union of all the colonies under one government, so far as might be necessary for defense, and other important general purposes. As we passed thro' New York I had there shown my project to Mr. James Alexander and

Mr. Kennedy, two gentlemen of great knowledge in public affairs, and, being fortified by their approbation, I ventured to lay it before the Congress. It then appeared that several of the commissioners had formed plans of the same kind. A previous question was first taken, whether a union should be established, which passed in the affirmative unanimously. A committee was then appointed, one member from each colony, to consider the several plans and report. Mine happened to be preferred, and, with a few amendments, was accordingly reported.

By this plan the general government was to be administered by a president-general, appointed and supported by the crown, and a grand council was to be chosen by the representatives of the people of the several colonies, met in their respective assemblies. The debates upon it in Congress went on daily, hand in hand with the Indian business. Many objections and difficulties were started, but at length they were all overcome, and the plan was unanimously agreed to, and copies ordered to be transmitted to the Board of Trade and to the assemblies of the several provinces.

Its fate was singular. The assemblies did not adopt it, as they all thought there was too much *prerogative* in it, and in England it was judged to have too much of the *democratic*. The Board of Trade therefore did not approve of it, nor recommend it for the approbation of his majesty; but another scheme was formed, supposed to answer the same purpose better, whereby the governors of the provinces, with some members of their respective councils, were to meet and order the raising of troops, building of forts, etc., and to draw on the treasury of Great Britain for the expense, which was afterwards to be refunded by an act of Parliament laying a tax on America. My plan, with my reasons in support of it, is to be found among my political papers that are printed.

Being the winter following in Boston, I had much conversation with Governor Shirley upon both the plans. Part of what passed between us on the occasion may also be seen among those papers. The different and contrary reasons of dislike to my plan make me suspect that it was really the true medium; and I am still of the opinion it would have been happy for both sides of the water if it had been adopted. The colonies, so united, would have been sufficiently strong to have defended themselves. There would then have been no need of troops from England. Of course, the subsequent pretense for taxing America, and the bloody contest it occasioned, would have been avoided.

245

But such mistakes are not new. History is full of the errors of states and princes.

The Governor of Pennsylvania, in sending it down to the Assembly, expressed his approbation of the plan, "as appearing to him to be drawn up with great clearness and strength of judgment, and therefore recommended it as well worthy of their closest and most serious attention." The House, however, by the management of a certain member, took it up when I happened to be absent, which I thought not very fair, and reprobated it without paying any attention to it at all, to my no small mortification.

In my journey to Boston this year, I met at New York with our new governor, Mr. Morris, just arrived there from England, with whom I had been before intimately acquainted. He brought a commission to supersede Mr. Hamilton, who, tired with the disputes his proprietary instructions subjected him to, had resigned. Mr. Morris asked me if I thought he must expect as uncomfortable an administration. I said, "No; you may, on the contrary, have a very comfortable one, if you will only take care not to enter into any dispute with the Assembly." "My dear friend," says he, pleasantly, "how can you advise my avoiding disputes? You know I love disputing. It is one of my greatest pleasures. However, to show the regard I have for your counsel, I promise you I will, if possible, avoid them."

In returning, I met at New York with the votes of the Assembly, by which it appeared that, notwithstanding his promise to me, he and the House were already in high contention; and it was a continual battle between them as long as he retained the government. I had my share of it; for, as soon as I got back to my seat in the Assembly, I was put on every committee for answering his speeches and messages, and by the committees always desired to make the drafts. Our answers, as well as his messages, were often tart, and sometimes indecently abusive; and, as he knew I wrote for the Assembly, one might have imagined that, when we met, we could hardly avoid cutting throats; but he was so good-natured a man that no personal difference between him and me was occasioned by the contest, and we often dined together.

One afternoon, in the height of this public quarrel, we met in the street. "Franklin," says he, "you must go home with me and spend the evening. I am to have some company that you will like"; and, taking me by the arm, he led me to his house. In gay conversation over our wine, after supper, he told us, jokingly, that he much admired

246

the idea of Sancho Panza, who, when it was proposed to give him a government, requested it might be a government of *blacks,* as then, if he could not agree with his people, he might sell them. One of his friends, who sat next to me, says, "Franklin, why do you continue to side with these damned Quakers? Had not you better sell them? The proprietor would give you a good price." "The governor," says I, "has not yet *blacked* them enough." He, indeed, had labored hard to blacken the Assembly in all his messages, but they wiped off his coloring as fast as he laid it on, and placed it, in return, thick upon his own face; so that, finding he was likely to be negrofied himself, he, as well as Mr. Hamilton, grew tired of the contest, and quitted the government.

These public quarrels were all at bottom owing to the proprietaries, our hereditary governors [*the Penns*], who, when any expense was to be incurred for the defense of their province, with incredible meanness instructed their deputies to pass no act for levying the necessary taxes, unless their vast estates were in the same act expressly excused; and they had even taken bonds of these deputies to observe such instructions. The Assemblies for three years held out against this injustice, though constrained to bend at last. At length Captain Denny, who was Governor Morris' successor, ventured to disobey those instructions. How that was brought about I shall show hereafter.

War being in a manner commenced with France, the government of Massachusetts Bay projected an attack upon Crown Point, and sent Mr. Quincy to Pennsylvania, and Mr. Pownall, afterward Governor Pownall, to New York, to solicit assistance. As I was in the Assembly, knew its temper, and was Mr. Quincy's countryman, he applied to me for my influence and assistance. I dictated his address to them, which was well received. They voted an aid of ten thousand pounds, to be laid out in provisions. But the governor refusing his assent to their bill (which included this with other sums granted for the use of the crown), unless a clause were inserted exempting the proprietary estate from bearing any part of the tax that would be necessary, the Assembly, though very desirous of making their grant to New England effectual, were at a loss how to accomplish it. Mr. Quincy labored hard with the governor to obtain his assent, but he was obstinate.

I then suggested a method of doing the business without the governor, by orders on the trustees of the Loan Office, which, by law, the Assembly had the right of drawing. There was, indeed, little or no money at that time in the office, and therefore I proposed that the orders should be payable in a year, and to bear an interest of five per cent. With these orders I supposed the provisions might easily be purchased. The Assembly, with very little hesitation, adopted the proposal. The orders were immediately printed, and I was one of the committee directed to sign and dispose of them. Mr. Quincy returned thanks to the Assembly in a handsome memorial, went home highly pleased with the success of his embassy, and ever after bore for me the most cordial and affectionate friendship.

The British government, not choosing to permit the union of the colonies as proposed at Albany, and to trust that union with their defense, lest they should thereby grow too military, and feel their own strength, suspicions and jealousies at this time being entertained of them, sent over General Braddock with two regiments of regular English troops for that purpose. He landed at Alexandria, in Virginia, and thence marched to Fredericktown, in Maryland, where he halted for carriages. Our Assembly apprehending, from some information, that he had conceived violent prejudices against them, as averse to the service, wished me to wait upon him, not as from them, but as postmaster-general, under the guise of proposing to settle with him the mode of conducting with most celerity and certainty the dispatches between him and the governors of the several provinces, with whom he must necessarily have continual correspondence, and of which they proposed to pay the expense. My son accompanied me on this journey.

We found the general at Fredericktown, waiting impatiently for the return of those he had sent through the back parts of Maryland and Virginia to collect wagons. I stayed with him several days, dined with him daily, and had full opportunity of removing all his prejudices, by the information of what the Assembly had before his arrival actually done, and were still willing to do, to facilitate his operations. When I was about to depart, the returns of wagons to be obtained were brought in, by which it appeared that they amounted only to twenty-five, and not all of those were in serviceable condition. The general and all the officers were surprised, declared the expedition was then at an end, being impossible, and exclaimed against the ministers for ignorantly landing them in a country destitute of the means of conveying their stores, baggage, etc., not less than one hundred and fifty wagons being necessary.

I happened to say I thought it was a pity they had not been landed rather in Pennsylvania, as in that country almost every farmer had his wagon. The general eagerly laid hold of my words, and said, "Then you, sir, who are a man of interest there, can probably procure them for us; and I beg you will undertake it." I asked what terms were to be offered the owners of the wagons; and I was desired to put on paper the terms that appeared to me necessary. This I did, and they were agreed to, and a commission and instructions accordingly prepared immediately.

I received of the general about eight hundred pounds, to be disbursed in advance-money to the wagon owners, etc.; but that sum being insufficient, I advanced upward of two hundred pounds more, and in two weeks the one hundred and fifty wagons, with two hundred and fifty-nine carrying horses, were on their march for the camp. The advertisement promised payment according to the valuation, in case any wagon or horse should be lost. The owners, however, alleging they did not know General Braddock, or what dependence might be had on his promise, insisted on my bond for the performance, which I accordingly gave them.

While I was at the camp, supping one evening with the officers of Colonel Dunbar's regiment, he represented to me his concern for the subalterns, who, he said, were generally not in affluence, and could ill afford, in this dear country, to lay in the stores that might be necessary in so long a march, through a wilderness, where nothing was to be purchased. I commiserated their case, and resolved to endeavor procuring them some relief. I said nothing, however, to him of my intention, but wrote the next morning to the committee of the Assembly, who had the disposition of some public money, warmly recommending the case of these officers to their consideration, and proposing that a present should be sent them of necessaries and refreshments. My son, who had some experience of a camp life, and of its wants, drew up a list for me, which I enclosed in my letter. The committee approved, and used such diligence that, conducted by my son, the stores arrived at the camp as soon as the wagons. They consisted of twenty parcels, each containing:

6 lbs. loaf sugar	1 Gloucester cheese
6 lbs. good muscovado sugar	1 keg containing 20 lbs. good
1 lb. good green tea	butter
1 lb. good bohea tea	2 doz. old Madeira wine
6 lbs. good ground coffee	2 gallons Jamaica spirits
6 lbs. chocolate	1 bottle flour of mustard
1–2 cwt. best white biscuit	2 well-cured hams
1–2 lb. pepper	1–2 dozen dried tongues
1 quart best white wine vinegar	6 lbs. rice
6 lbs. raisins	

These twenty parcels, well packed, were placed on as many horses, each parcel, with the horse, being intended as a present for one officer. They were very thankfully received, and the kindness acknowledged by letters to me from the colonels of both regiments, in the most grateful terms. The general, too, was highly satisfied with my conduct in procuring him the wagons, etc., and readily paid my account of disbursements, thanking me repeatedly, and requesting my further assistance in sending provisions after him. I undertook this also, and was busily employed in it till we heard of his defeat, advancing for the service of my own money, upwards of one thousand pounds sterling, of which I sent him an account. It came to his hands, luckily for me, a few days before the battle, and he returned me immediately an order on the paymaster for the round sum of one thousand pounds, leaving the remainder to the next account. I consider this payment as good luck, having never been able to obtain that remainder, of which more hereafter.

This general was, I think, a brave man, and might probably have made a figure as a good officer in some European war. But he had too much self-confidence, too high an opinion of the validity of regular troops, and too mean a one of both Americans and Indians. George Croghan, our Indian interpreter, joined him on his march with one hundred of those people, who might have been of great use to his army as guides, scouts, etc., if he had treated them kindly; but he slighted and neglected them, and they gradually left him.

In conversation with him one day, he was giving me some account of his intended progress. "After taking Fort Duquesne," says he, "I am to proceed to Niagara; and, having taken that, to Frontenac, if the season will allow time; and I suppose it will, for Duquesne can hardly detain me above three or four days; and then I see nothing that can obstruct my march to Niagara." Having before revolved in my mind the long line his army must make in their march by a very narrow road, to be cut for them through the woods and bushes, and also what I had read of a former defeat of fifteen hundred French, who invaded the Iroquois country, I had conceived some doubts and some fears for the event of the campaign. But I ventured only to say, "To be sure, sir, if you arrive well before Duquesne, with these fine troops, so well provided with artillery, that place not yet completely fortified, and as we hear with no very strong garrison, can probably make but a short resistance. The only danger I apprehend of obstruction to your march is from ambuscades of Indians, who, by constant practice, are dexterous in laying and executing them; and the slender line, near four miles long, which your army must make, may expose it to be attacked by surprise in its flanks, and to be cut like a thread into several pieces, which, from their distance, can not come up in time to support each other."

He smiled at my ignorance, and replied, "These savages may, indeed, be a formidable enemy to your raw American militia, but upon the king's regular and disciplined troops, sir, it is impossible they should make any impression." I was conscious of an impropriety in my disputing with a military man in matters of his profession, and said no more.

The enemy, however, did not take the advantage of his army which I apprehended its long line of march exposed it to, but let it advance without interruption till within nine miles of the place; and then, when more in a body (for it had just passed a river, where the front had halted till all were come over), and in a more open part of the woods than any it had passed, attacked its advance guard by a heavy fire from behind trees and bushes, which was the first intelligence the general had of an enemy's being near him. This guard being disordered, the general hurried the troops up to their assistance, which was done in great confusion, through wagons, baggage, and cattle; and presently the fire came upon their flank: the officers, being on horseback, were more easily distinguished, picked out as marks, and fell very fast; and the soldiers were crowded together in a huddle, having or hearing no orders, and standing to be shot at till two-thirds of them were killed; and then, being seized with a panic, the whole fled with precipitation.

The wagoners took each a horse out of his team and scampered. Their example was immediately followed by others; so that all the wagons, provisions, artillery, and stores were left to the enemy. The general, being wounded, was brought off with difficulty. His secretary, Mr. Shirley, was killed by his side; and out of eighty-six officers, sixty-three were killed or wounded, and seven hundred and fourteen men killed out of eleven hundred. These eleven hundred had been picked men from the whole army. The rest had been left behind with Colonel Dunbar, who was to follow with the heavier part of the stores, provisions, and baggage.

The flyers, not being pursued, arrived at Dunbar's camp, and the panic they brought with them instantly seized him and all his people; and though he had now above one thousand men, and the enemy who had beaten Braddock did not at most exceed four hundred Indians and French together, instead of proceeding, and endeavoring to recover some of the lost honor, he ordered all the stores, ammunition, etc., to be destroyed, that he might have more horses to assist his flight towards the settlements, and less lumber to remove. He was there met with requests from the governors of Virginia, Maryland, and Pennsylvania, that he would post his troops on the frontier, so as to afford some protection to the inhabitants; but he continued his hasty march through all the country, not thinking himself safe till he arrived at Philadelphia, where the inhabitants could protect him. This whole transaction gave us Americans the first suspicion that our exalted ideas of the prowess of British regulars had not been well founded.

In their first march, too, from their landing till they got beyond the settlements, they had plundered and stripped the inhabitants, totally ruining some poor families, besides insulting, abusing, and confining the people if they remonstrated. This was enough to put us out of conceit of such defenders, if we had really wanted any. How different was the conduct of our French friends in 1781, who, during a march through the most inhabited part of our country from Rhode Island to Virginia, near seven hundred miles, occasioned not the smallest complaint for the loss of a pig, a chicken, or even an apple.

Captain Orme, who was one of the general's aids-de-camp, and, being grievously wounded, was brought off with him, and continued with him to his death, which happened in a few days, told me that he was totally silent all the first day, and at night only said, *"Who would have thought it?"* That he was silent again the following day, saying only at last, *"We shall better know how to deal with them another time";* and died in a few minutes after.

The secretary's papers, with all the general's orders, instructions, and correspondence, falling into the enemy's hands, they selected and translated into French a number of the articles, which they printed, to prove the hostile intentions of the British court before the declaration of war. Among these I saw some letters of the general to the ministry, speaking highly of the great service I had rendered the army, and recommending me to their notice. David Hume, too, who was some years after secretary to Lord Hertford, when minister in France, and afterward to General Conway, when secretary of state, told me he had seen among the papers in that office, letters from Braddock highly recommending me. But, the expedition having been unfortunate, my service, it seems, was not thought of much value, for those recommendations were never of any use to me.

As to rewards from himself, I asked only one, which was, that he would give orders to his officers not to enlist any more of our bought servants, and that he would discharge such as had been already enlisted. This he readily granted, and several were accordingly returned to their masters, on my application. Dunbar, when the command devolved on him, was not so generous. He being at Philadelphia, on his retreat, or rather flight, I applied to him for the discharge of the servants of three poor farmers of Lancaster County that he had enlisted, reminding him of the late general's orders on that head. He promised me that, if the masters would come to him at Trenton, where he should be in a few days on his march to New York, he would there deliver their men to them. They accordingly were at the expense and trouble of going to Trenton, and there he refused to perform his promise, to their great loss and disappointment.

As soon as the loss of the wagons and horses was generally known, all the owners came upon me for the valuation which I had given bond to pay. Their demands gave me a great deal of trouble, my acquainting them that the money was ready in the paymaster's hands, but that orders for paying it must first be obtained from General Shirley, and my assuring them that I had applied to that general by letter; but, he being at a distance, an answer could not soon be received, and they must have patience, all this was not sufficient to satisfy, and some began to sue me. General Shirley at length relieved me from this terrible situation by appointing commissioners to examine the claims, and ordering payment. They amounted to near twenty thousand pounds, which to pay would have ruined me.

Before we had the news of this defeat, the two Doctors Bond came to me with a subscription paper for raising money to defray the expense of a grand firework, which it was intended to exhibit at a rejoicing on receipt of the news of our taking Fort Duquesne. I looked grave, and said it would, I thought, be time enough to prepare for the rejoicing when we knew we should have occasion to rejoice. They seemed surprised that I did not immediately comply with their proposal. "Why the d—l!" says one of them, "you surely don't suppose that the fort will not be taken?" "I don't know that it will not be taken, but I know that the events of war are subject to great uncertainty." I gave them the reasons of my doubting; the subscription was dropped, and the projectors thereby missed the mortification they would have undergone if the firework had been prepared. Dr. Bond, on some other occasion afterward, said that he did not like Franklin's forebodings.

Governor Morris, who had continually worried the Assembly with message after message before the defeat of Braddock, to beat them into the making of acts to raise money for the defense of the province, without taxing, among others, the proprietary estates, and had rejected all their bills for not having such an exempting clause, now redoubled his attacks with more hope of success, the danger and necessity being greater. The Assembly, however, continued firm, believing they had justice on their side, and that it would be giving up an essential right if they suffered the governor to amend their money-bills. In one of the last, indeed, which was for granting fifty thousand pounds, his proposed amendment was only of a single word. The bill expressed "that all estates, real and personal, were to be taxed, those of the proprietaries *not* excepted." His amendment was, for *not* read *only:* a small, but very material alteration.

However, when the news of this disaster reached England, our friends there, whom we had taken care to furnish with all the Assembly's answers to the governor's messages, raised a clamor against the proprietaries for their meanness and injustice in giving their governor such instructions; some going so far as to say that, by obstructing the defense of their province, they forfeited their right to it. They were intimidated by this, and sent orders to their receiver-general to add five thousand pounds of their money to whatever sum might be given by the Assembly for such purpose.

This, being notified to the House, was accepted in lieu of their share of a general tax, and a new bill was formed, with an exempting clause, which passed accordingly. By this act I was appointed one of the commissioners for disposing of the money, sixty thousand pounds. I had been active in modeling the bill and procuring its passage, and had, at the same time, drawn a bill for establishing and disciplining a voluntary militia, which I carried through the House without much difficulty, as care was taken in it to leave the Quakers at their liberty. To promote the association necessary to form the militia, I wrote a dialogue, stating and answering all the objections I could think of to such a militia, which was printed, and had, as I thought, great effect.

While the several companies in the city and country were forming, and learning their exercise, the governor prevailed with me to take charge of our Northwestern frontier, which was infested by the enemy, and provide for the defense of the inhabitants by raising troops and building a line of forts. I undertook this military business, though I did not conceive myself well qualified for it. He gave me a commission with full powers, and a parcel of blank commissions for officers, to be given to whom I thought fit. I had but little difficulty in raising men, having soon five hundred and sixty under my command. My son, who had in the preceding war been an officer in the army raised against Canada, was my aid-de-camp, and of great use to me. The Indians had burned Gnadenhut, a village settled by the Moravians, and massacred the inhabitants; but the place was thought a good situation for one of the forts.

In order to march thither, I assembled the companies at Bethlehem, the chief establishment of those people. I was surprised to find it in so good a posture of defense; the destruction of Gnadenhut had made them apprehend danger. The principal buildings were defended by a stockade. They had purchased a quantity of arms and ammunition from New York, and had even placed quantities of small paving stones between the windows of their high stone houses, for their women to throw down upon the heads of any Indians that should attempt to force into them. The armed brethren, too, kept watch, and relieved as methodically as in any garrison town.

It was the beginning of January when we set out upon this business of building forts. I sent one detachment toward the Minisink, with instructions to erect one for the security of that upper part of the country, and another to the lower part, with similar instructions; and I concluded to go myself with the rest of my force to Gnadenhut, where a fort was thought more immediately necessary. The Moravians procured me five wagons for our tools, stores, baggage, etc.

Just before we left Bethlehem, eleven farmers, who had been driven from their plantations by the Indians, came to me requesting a supply of firearms, that they might go back and fetch off their cattle. I gave them each a gun with suitable ammunition. We had not marched many miles before it began to rain, and it continued raining all day; there were no habitations on the road to shelter us, till we arrived near night at the house of a German, where, in his barn, we were all huddled together, as wet as water could make us. It was well we were not attacked in our march, for our arms were of the most ordinary sort, and our men could not keep their gun locks dry. The Indians are dexterous in contrivances for that purpose, which we had not. They met that day the eleven poor farmers above mentioned, and killed ten of them. The one who escaped informed that his and his companions' guns would not go off, the priming being wet with the rain.

The next day being fair, we continued our march, and arrived at the desolated Gnadenhut. There was a saw-mill near, round which were left several piles of boards, with which we soon hutted ourselves; an operation the more necessary at that inclement season, as we had no tents. Our first work was to bury more effectually the dead we found there, who had been half interred by the country people.

The next morning our fort was planned and marked out, the circumference measuring four hundred and fifty-five feet, which would require as many palisades to be made of trees, one with another, of a foot diameter each. Our axes, of which we had seventy, were immediately set to work to cut down trees, and, our men being dexterous in the use of them, great dispatch was made. Seeing the trees fall so fast, I had the curiosity to look at my watch when two men began to cut at a pine; in six minutes they had it upon the ground, and I found it of fourteen inches diameter. Each pine made three palisades of eighteen feet long, pointed at one end.

While these were preparing, our other men dug a trench all round, of three feet deep, in which the palisades were to be planted; and, our wagons, the bodies being taken off, and the fore and hind wheels separated by taking out the pin which united the two parts of the perch, we had ten carriages, with two horses each, to bring the palisades from the woods to the spot. When they were set up, our carpenters built a stage of boards all round within, about six feet high, for the men to stand on when to fire through the loopholes. We had one swivel gun, which we mounted on one of the angles, and fired it as soon as fixed, to let the Indians know, if any were within hearing, that we had such pieces; and thus our fort, if such a magnificent name may be given to so miserable a stockade, was finished in a week, though it rained so hard every other day that the men could not work.

This gave me occasion to observe, that, when men are employed, they are best contented; for on the days they worked they were good-natured and cheerful, and, with the consciousness of having done a good day's work, they spent the evening jollily; but on our idle days they were mutinous and quarrelsome, finding fault with their pork, the bread, etc., and in continual ill-humor, which put me in mind of a sea-captain, whose rule it was to keep his men constantly at work; and, when his mate once told him that they had done everything, and there was nothing further to employ them about, *"Oh," says he, "make them scour the anchor."*

This kind of fort, however contemptible, is a sufficient defense against Indians, who have no cannon. Finding ourselves now posted securely, and having a place to retreat to on occasion, we ventured out in parties to scour the adjacent country. We met with no Indians, but we found the places on the neighboring hills where they had lain to watch our proceedings.

There was an art in their contrivance of those places that seems worth mention. It being winter, a fire was necessary for them; but a common fire on the surface of the ground would by its light have discovered their position at a distance. They had therefore dug holes in the ground about three feet in diameter, and somewhat deeper. We saw where they had with their hatchets cut off the charcoal from the sides of burnt logs lying in the woods. With these coals they had made small fires in the bottom of the holes, and we observed among the weeds and grass the prints of their bodies, made by their laying all round, with their legs hanging down in the holes to keep their feet warm, which, with them, is an essential point. This kind of fire, so managed, could not discover them, either by its light, flame, sparks, or even smoke: it appeared that their number was not great, and it seems they saw we were too many to be attacked by them with prospect of advantage.

We had for our chaplain a zealous Presbyterian minister, Mr. Beatty, who complained to me that the men did not generally attend his prayers and exhortations. When they enlisted, they were promised, besides pay and provisions, a gill of rum a day, which was punctually served out to them, half in the morning, and the other half in the evening; and I observed they were as punctual in attending to receive it; upon which I said to Mr. Beatty, "It is, perhaps, below the dignity of your profession to act as steward of the rum, but if you were to deal it out and only just after prayers, you would have them all about you." He liked the thought, undertook the office, and, with the help of a few hands to measure out the liquor, executed it to satisfaction, and never were prayers more generally and more punctually attended; so that I thought this method preferable to the punishment inflicted by some military laws for non-attendance on divine service.

I had hardly finished this business, and got my fort well stored with provisions, when I received a letter from the governor, acquainting me that he had called the Assembly, and wished my attendance there, if the posture of affairs on the frontiers were such that my remaining there was no longer necessary. My friends, too, of the Assembly, pressing me by their letters to be, if possible, at the meeting, and my three intended forts being now completed, and the inhabitants contented to remain on their farms under that protection, I resolved to return; the more willingly, as a New England officer, Colonel Clapham, experienced in Indian war, being on a visit to our establishment, consented to accept the command.

I gave him a commission, and, parading the garrison, had it read before them, and introduced him to them as an officer who, from his skill in military affairs, was much more fit to command them than myself; and, giving them a little exhortation, took my leave. I was escorted as far as Bethlehem, where I rested a few days to recover from the fatigue I had undergone. The first night, being in a good bed, I could hardly sleep, it was so different from my hard lodging on the floor of our hut at Gnadenhut, wrapped only in a blanket or two.

While at Bethlehem, I inquired a little into the practice of the Moravians: some of them had accompanied me, and all were very kind to me. I found they worked for a common stock, ate at common tables, and slept in common dormitories, great numbers together. In the dormitories I observed loopholes, at certain distances all along just under the ceiling, which I thought judiciously placed for change of air.

I was at their church, when I was entertained with good music, the organ being accompanied with violins, hautboys, flutes, clarinets, etc. I understood that their sermons were not usually preached to mixed congregations of men, women, and children, as is our common practice, but that they assembled sometimes the married men, at other times their wives, then the young men, the young women, and the little children, each division by itself. The sermon I heard was to the latter, who came in and were placed in rows on benches; the boys under the conduct of a young man, their tutor, and the girls conducted by a young woman. The discourse seemed well adapted to their capacities, and was delivered in a pleasing, familiar manner, coaxing them, as it were, to be good. They behaved very orderly, but looked pale and unhealthy, which made me suspect they were kept too much within doors, or not allowed sufficient exercise.

I inquired concerning the Moravian marriages, whether the report was true that they were by lot. I was told that lots were used only in particular cases; that generally, when a young man found himself disposed to marry, he informed the elders of his class, who consulted the elder ladies that governed the young women. As these elders of the different sexes were well acquainted with the tempers and dispositions of their respective pupils, they could best judge what matches were suitable, and their judgments were generally acquiesced in; but if, for example, it should happen that two or three young women were found to be equally proper for the young man, the lot was then recurred to. I objected, if the matches are not made by the mutual choice of the parties, some of them may chance to be very unhappy. "And so they may," answered my informer, "if you let the parties choose for themselves"; which, indeed, I could not deny.

Being returned to Philadelphia, I found the association went on swimmingly, the inhabitants that were not Quakers having pretty generally come into it, formed themselves into companies, and chose their captains, lieutenants, and ensigns, according to the new law. Dr. B. visited me, and gave an account of the pains he had taken to spread a general good liking to the law, and ascribed much to those endeavors. I had had the vanity to ascribe all to my *Dialogue;* however, not knowing but that he might be in the right, I let him enjoy his opinion, which I take to be generally the best way in such cases.

The officers, meeting, chose me to be a colonel of the regiment, which I this time accepted. I forgot how many companies we had, but we paraded about twelve hundred well-looking men, with a company of artillery, who had been furnished with six brass field-pieces, which they had become so expert in the use of as to fire twelve times in a minute. The first time I reviewed my regiment they accompanied me to my house, and would salute me with some rounds fired before my door, which shook down and broke several glasses of my electrical apparatus. And my new honor proved not much less brittle; for all our commissions were soon after broken by a repeal of the law in England.

During this short time of my colonelship, being about to set out on a journey to Virginia, the officers of my regiment took it into their heads that it would be proper for them to escort me out of town, as far as the Lower Ferry. Just as I was getting on horseback they came to my door, between thirty and forty, mounted, and all in their uniforms. I had not been previously acquainted with the project, or I should have prevented it, being naturally averse to the assuming of state on any occasion; and I was a good deal chagrined at their appearance, as I could not avoid their accompanying me. What made

259

it worse was, that, as soon as we began to move, they drew their swords and rode with them naked all the way. Somebody wrote an account of this to the proprietor, and it gave him great offense. No such honor had been paid him when in the province, nor to any of his governors; and he said it was only proper to princes of the blood royal, which may be true for aught I know, who was, and still am, ignorant of the etiquette in such cases.

This silly affair, however, greatly increased his rancor against me, which was before not a little, on account of my conduct in the Assembly respecting the exemption of his estate from taxation, which I had always opposed very warmly, and not without severe reflections on his meanness and injustice of contending for it. He accused me to the ministry as being the great obstacle to the king's service, preventing, by my influence in the House, the proper form of the bills for raising money, and he instanced this parade with my officers as a proof of my having an intention to take the government of the province out of his hands by force. He also applied to Sir Everard Fawkener, the postmaster-general, to deprive me of my office; but it had no other effect than to procure from Sir Everard a gentle admonition.

Notwithstanding the continual wrangle between the governor and the House, in which I, as a member, had so large a share, there still subsisted a civil intercourse between that gentleman and myself, and we never had any personal difference. I have sometimes since thought that his little or no resentment against me, for the answers it was known I drew up to his messages, might be the effect of professional habit, and that, being bred a lawyer, he might consider us both as merely advocates for contending clients in a suit, he for the proprietaries and I for the Assembly. He would, therefore, sometimes call in a friendly way to advise with me on difficult points, and sometimes, though not often, take my advice.

We acted in concert to supply Braddock's army with provisions; and, when the shocking news arrived of his defeat, the governor sent in haste for me, to consult with him on measures for preventing the desertion of the back counties. I forget now the advice I gave; but I think it was, that Dunbar should be written to, and prevailed with, if possible, to post his troops on the frontiers for their protection, till, by re-enforcements from the colonies, he might be able to proceed on the expedition.

And, after my return from the frontier, he would have had me undertake the conduct of such an expedition with provincial troops, for the reduction of Fort Duquesne, Dunbar and his men being otherwise employed; and he proposed to commission me as general. I had not so good an opinion of my military abilities as he professed to have, and I believe his professions must have exceeded his real sentiments. But probably he might think that my popularity would facilitate the raising of the men, and my influence in Assembly, the grant of money to pay them, and that, perhaps, without taxing the proprietary estate. Finding me not so forward to engage as he expected, the project was dropped, and he soon after left the government, being superseded by Captain Denny.

Before I proceed in relating the part I had in public affairs under this new governor's administration, it may not be amiss here to give some account of the rise and progress of my philosophical reputation.

In 1746, being at Boston, I met there with a Dr. Spence, who was lately arrived from Scotland, and showed me some electric experiments. They were imperfectly performed, as he was not very expert; but, being on a subject quite new to me, they equally surprised and pleased me. Soon after my return to Philadelphia, our library company received from Mr. P. Collinson, Fellow of the Royal Society of London, a present of a glass tube, with some account of the use of it in making such experiments. I eagerly seized the opportunity of repeating what I had seen at Boston; and, by much practice, acquired great readiness in performing those, also, which we had an account of from England, adding a number of new ones. I say much practice, for my house was continually full, for some time, with people who came to see these new wonders.

To divide a little this incumbrance among my friends, I caused a number of similar tubes to be blown at our glasshouse, with which they furnished themselves, so that we had at length several performers. Among these, the principal was Mr. Kinnersley, an ingenious neighbor, who, being out of business, I encouraged to undertake showing the experiments for money, and drew up for him two lectures, in which the experiments were ranged in such order, and accompanied with such explanations in such method, as that the foregoing should assist in comprehending the following. He procured an elegant apparatus for the purpose, in which all the little machines that I had roughly made for myself were nicely formed by instrument-makers. His lectures were well attended, and gave great satisfaction; and after some time he went through the colonies, exhibiting them in every capital town, and picked up some money. In the West India islands, indeed, it was with difficulty the experiments could be made, from the general moisture of the air.

Obliged as we were to Mr. Collinson for his present of the tube, etc., I thought it right he should be informed of our success in using it, and wrote him several letters containing accounts of our experiments. He got them read in the Royal Society, where they were not at first thought worth so much notice as to be printed in their Transactions.

One paper, which I wrote for Mr. Kinnersley, on the sameness of lightning with electricity, I sent Dr. Mitchel, an acquaintance of mine, and one of the members also of that society, who wrote me word that it had been read, but was laughed at by the connoisseurs. The papers, however, being shown to Dr. Fothergill, he thought them of too much value to be stifled, and advised the printing of them. Mr. Collinson then gave them to Cave for publication in his *Gentleman's Magazine;* but he chose to print them separately in a pamphlet, and Dr. Fothergill wrote the preface. Cave, it seems, judged rightly for his profit, for by the additions that arrived afterward they swelled, to a quarto volume, which has had five editions, and cost him nothing for copy-money.

It was, however, some time before those papers were much taken notice of in England. A copy of them happening to fall into the hands of the Count de Buffon, a philosopher deservedly of great reputation in France, and, indeed, all over Europe, he prevailed with M. Dalibard to translate them into French, and they were printed at Paris. The publication offended the Abbé Nollet, preceptor in Natural Philosophy to the royal family, and an able experimenter, who had formed and published a theory of electricity, which then had the general vogue. He could not at first believe that such a work came from America, and said it must have been fabricated by his enemies at Paris, to decry his system. Afterwards, having been assured that there really existed such a person as Franklin at Philadelphia, which he had doubted, he wrote and published a volume of *Letters,* chiefly addressed to me, defending his theory, and denying the verity of my experiments, and of the positions deduced from them.

I once purposed answering the abbé, and actually began the answer; but, on consideration that my writings contained a description of experiments which anyone might repeat and verify, and if not to be verified, could not be defended; or of observations offered as conjectures, and not delivered dogmatically, therefore not laying me under any obligation to defend them; and reflecting that a dispute between two persons, writing in different languages, might be lengthened greatly by mistranslations, and thence misconceptions of one another's meaning, much of one of the abbé's letters being founded on an error in the translation, I concluded to let my papers shift for themselves, believing it was better to spend what time I could spare from public business in making new experiments, than in disputing about those already made.

I therefore never answered M. Nollet, and the event gave me no cause to repent my silence; for my friend M. le Roy, of the Royal Academy of Sciences, took up my cause and refuted him; my book was translated into the Italian, German, and Latin languages; and the doctrine it contained was by degrees universally adopted by the philosophers of Europe, in preference to that of the abbé; so that he lived to see himself the last of his sect, except Monsieur B——, of Paris, his immediate disciple.

What gave my book the more sudden and general celebrity was the success of one of its proposed experiments, made by Messrs. Dalibard and De Lor at Marly, for drawing lightning from the clouds. This engaged the public attention everywhere. M. de Lor, who had an apparatus for experimental philosophy, and lectured in that branch of science, undertook to repeat what he called the *Philadelphia Experiments;* and, after they were performed before the king and court, all the curious of Paris flocked to see them. I will not swell this narrative with an account of that capital experiment, nor of the infinite pleasure I received in the success of a similar one I made soon after with a kite at Philadelphia, as both are to be found in the histories of electricity.

Dr. Wright, an English physician, when at Paris, wrote to a friend, who was of the Royal Society, an account of the high esteem my experiments were in among the learned abroad, and of their wonder that my writings had been so little noticed in England. The society, on this, resumed the consideration of the letters that had been read to them; and the celebrated Dr. Watson drew up a summary account of them, and of all I had afterwards sent to England on the subject, which he accompanied with some praise of the writer. This summary was then printed in their *Transactions;* and some members of the society in London, particularly the very ingenious Mr. Canton, having verified the experiment of procuring lightning from the clouds by a pointed rod, and acquainting them with the success, they soon made me more than amends for the slight with which they had before treated me. Without my having made any application for that honor, they chose me a member, and voted that I should be excused the customary payments, which would have amounted to twenty-five guineas; and ever since have given me their *Transactions* gratis. They also presented me with the gold medal of Sir Godfrey Copley for the year 1753, the delivery of which was accompanied by a very handsome speech of the president, Lord Macclesfield, wherein I was highly honored.

Our new governor, Captain Denny, brought over for me the beforementioned medal from the Royal Society, which he presented to me at an entertainment given him by the city. He accompanied it with very polite expressions of his esteem for me, having, as he said, been long acquainted with my character. After dinner, when the company, as was customary at that time, were engaged in drinking, he took me aside into another room, and acquainted me that he had been advised by his friends in England to cultivate a friendship with me, as one who was capable of giving him the best advice, and of contributing most effectually to the making his administration easy; that he therefore desired of all things to have a good understanding with me, and he begged me to be assured of his readiness on all occasions to render me every service that might be in his power.

He said much to me, also, of the proprietor's good disposition towards the province, and of the advantage it might be to us all, and to me in particular, if the opposition that had been so long continued to his measures was dropped, and harmony restored between him and the people; in effecting which, it was thought no one could be more serviceable than myself; and I might depend on adequate acknowledgments and recompenses, etc., etc. The drinkers, finding we did not return immediately to the table, sent us a decanter of Madeira, which the governor made liberal use of, and in proportion became more profuse of his solicitations and promises.

My answers were to this purpose: that my circumstances, thanks to God, were such as to make proprietary favors unnecessary to me; and that, being a member of the Assembly, I could not possibly accept of any; that, however, I had no personal enmity to the proprietary, and that, whenever the public measures he proposed should appear to be for the good of the people, no one should espouse and forward them more zealously than myself; my past opposition having been founded on this, that the measures which had been urged were evidently intended to serve the proprietary interest, with great prejudice to that of the people; that I was much obliged to him (the governor) for his professions of regard to me and that he might rely on everything in my power to make his administration as easy as possible, hoping at the same time that he had not brought with him the same unfortunate instruction his predecessor had been hampered with.

On this he did not then explain himself; but when he afterwards came to do business with the Assembly, they appeared again, the disputes were renewed, and I was as active as ever in the opposition, being the penman, first, of the request to have a communication of the instructions, and then of the remarks upon them, which may be found in the votes of the time, and in the Historical Review I afterward published. But between us personally no enmity arose. We were often together. He was a man of letters, had seen much of the world, and was very entertaining and pleasing in conversation.

He gave me the first information that my old friend James Ralph was still alive; that he was esteemed one of the best political writers in England; had been employed in the dispute between Prince Frederic and the king, and had obtained a pension of three hundred a year; that his reputation was indeed small as a poet, Pope having damned his poetry in the Dunciad; but his prose was thought as good as any man's.

The Assembly finally finding the proprietary obstinately persisted in manacling their deputies with instructions inconsistent not only with the privileges of the people, but with the service of the crown, resolved to petition the king against them, and appointed me their agent to go over to England, to present and support the petition. The House had sent up a bill to the governor, granting a sum of sixty thousand pounds for the king's use (ten thousand pounds of which was subjected to the orders of the then general, Lord Loudoun), which the governor absolutely refused to pass, in compliance with his instructions.

I had agreed with Captain Morris, of the packet at New York, for my passage, and my stores were put on board, when Lord Loudoun arrived at Philadelphia, expressly, as he told me, to endeavor an accommodation between the governor and Assembly, that his majesty's service might not be obstructed by their dissensions. Accordingly, he desired the governor and myself to meet him, that he might hear what was to be said on both sides. We met and discussed the business. In behalf of the Assembly, I urged all the various arguments that may be found in the public papers of that time, which were of my writing, and are printed with the minutes of the Assembly; and the governor pleaded his instructions; the bond he had given to observe them, and his ruin if he disobeyed, yet seemed not unwilling to hazard himself if Lord Loudoun would advise it. This his lordship did not choose to do, though I once thought I had nearly prevailed with him to do it; but finally he rather chose to urge the compliance of the Assembly; and he entreated me to use my endeavors with them for that purpose, declaring that he would spare none of the king's troops for the defense of our frontiers, and that, if we did not continue to provide for that defense ourselves, they must remain exposed to the enemy.

I acquainted the House with what had passed, and, presenting them with a set of resolutions I had drawn up, declaring our rights, and that we did not relinquish our claim to those rights, but only suspended the exercise of them on this occasion through *force,* against which we protested, they at length agreed to drop that bill, and frame another conformable to the proprietary instructions. This of course the governor passed, and I was then at liberty to proceed on my voyage. But, in the meantime, the packet had sailed with my sea-stores, which was some loss to me, and my only recompense was his lordship's thanks for my service, all the credit of obtaining the accommodation falling to his share.

He set out for New York before me; and, as the time for dispatching the packet-boats was at his disposition, and there were two then remaining there, one of which, he said, was to sail very soon, I requested to know the precise time, that I might not miss her by any delay of mine. His answer was, "I have given out that she is to sail on Saturday next; but I may let you know that if you are there by Monday morning, you will be in time, but do not delay longer."

By some accidental hindrance at a ferry, it was Monday noon before I arrived, and I was much afraid she might have sailed, as the wind was fair; but I was soon made easy by the information that she was still in the harbor, and would not move till the next day. One would imagine that I was now on the very point of departing for Europe. I thought so; but I was not then so well acquainted with his lordship's character, of which *indecision* was one of the strongest features. I shall give some instances.

It was about the beginning of April that I came to New York, and I think it was near the end of June before we sailed. There were then two of the packet-boats, which had been long in port, but were detained for the general's letters, which were always to be ready to-morrow. Another packet arrived; she too was detained; and, before we sailed, a fourth was expected. Ours was the first to be dispatched, as having been there longest. Passengers were engaged in all, and some extremely impatient to be gone, and the merchants uneasy about their letters, and the orders they had given for insurance (it being war time) for fall goods; but their anxiety availed nothing; his lordship's letters were not ready; and yet whoever waited on him found him always at his desk, pen in hand, and concluded he must needs write abundantly.

This daily expectation of sailing, and all the three packets going down to Sand Hook, to join the fleet there, the passengers thought it best to be on board, lest by a sudden order the ships should sail, and they be left behind. There, if I remember right, we were about six weeks, consuming our sea-stores, and obliged to procure more. At length the fleet sailed, the General and all his army on board, bound to Louisburg, with intent to besiege and take that fortress; all the packet-boats in company ordered to attend the General's ship, ready to receive his dispatches when they should be ready. We were out five days before we got a letter with leave to part, and then our ship quitted the fleet and steered for England. The other two packets he still detained, carried them with him to Halifax, where he stayed some time to exercise the men in sham attacks upon sham forts, then altered his mind as to besieging Louisburg, and returned to New York, with all his troops, together with the two packets above mentioned, and all their passengers! During his absence the French and savages had taken Fort George, on the frontier of that province, and the savages had massacred many of the garrison after capitulation.

On the whole, I wondered much how such a man came to be entrusted with so important a business as the conduct of a great army; but, having since seen more of the great world, and the means of obtaining, and motives for giving places, my wonder is diminished. General Shirley, on whom the command of the army devolved upon the death of Braddock, would, in my opinion, if continued in place, have made a much better campaign than that of Loudoun in 1757, which was frivolous, expensive, and disgraceful to our nation beyond conception; for, though Shirley was not a bred soldier, he was sensible and sagacious in himself, and attentive to good advice from others, capable of forming judicious plans, and quick and active in carrying them into execution.

Loudoun, instead of defending the colonies with his great army, left

267

them totally exposed while he paraded idly at Halifax, by which means Fort George was lost, besides, he deranged all our mercantile operations, and distressed our trade, by a long embargo on the exportation of provisions, on pretense of keeping supplies from being obtained by the enemy, but in reality for beating down their price in favor of the contractors, in whose profits, it was said, perhaps from suspicion only, he had a share. And, when at length the embargo was taken off, by neglecting to send notice of it to Charlestown, the Carolina fleet was detained near three months longer, whereby their bottoms were so much damaged by the worm that a great part of them foundered in their passage home.

While I was, as aforementioned, detained at New York, I received all the accounts of the provisions, etc., that I had furnished to Braddock, some of which accounts could not sooner be obtained from the different persons I had employed to assist in the business. I presented them to Lord Loudoun, desiring to be paid the balance. He caused them to be regularly examined by the proper officer, who, after comparing every article with its voucher, certified them to be right; and the balance due for which his lordship promised to give me an order on the paymaster. This was, however, put off from time to time; and, though I called often for it by appointment, I did not get it. At length, just before my departure, he told me he had, on better consideration, concluded not to mix his accounts with those of his predecessors. "And you," says he, "when in England, have only to exhibit your accounts at the treasury, and you will be paid immediately." I am not paid it to this day, of which more hereafter.

Our captain of the packet had boasted much, before we sailed, of the swiftness of his ship. Unfortunately, when we came to sea, she proved the dullest of ninety-six sail, to his no small mortification. After many conjectures respecting the cause, when we were near another ship almost as dull as ours, which, however, gained upon us, the captain ordered all hands to come aft, and stand as near the ensign staff as possible. We were, passengers included, about forty persons. While we stood there, the ship mended her pace, and soon left her neighbor far behind, which proved clearly what our captain suspected, that she was loaded too much by the head. The casks of water, it seems, had been all placed forward. These he therefore ordered to be moved further aft, on which the ship recovered her character, and proved the sailer in the fleet.

The captain said she had once gone at the rate of thirteen knots, which is accounted thirteen miles per hour. We had on board, as a passenger, Captain Kennedy, of the Navy, who contended that it was impossible, and that no ship ever sailed so fast, and that there must have been some error in the division of the log-line, or some mistake in heaving the log. A wager ensued between the two captains, to be decided when there should be sufficient wind. Kennedy thereupon examined rigorously the log-line, and, being satisfied with that, he determined to throw the log himself. Accordingly some days after, when the wind blew very fair and fresh, and the captain of the packet, Lutwidge, said he believed she then went at the rate of thirteen knots, Kennedy made the experiment, and owned his wager lost.

We were several times chased in our passage, but outsailed everything, and in thirty days had soundings. We had a good observation, and the captain judged himself so near our port, Falmouth, that, if we made a good run in the night, we might be off the mouth of that harbor in the morning, and by running in the night might escape the notice of the enemy's privateers, who often cruised near the entrance of the channel. Accordingly, all the sail was set that we could possibly make, and the wind being very fresh and fair, we went right before it, and made great way. The captain, after his observation, shaped his course, as he thought, so as to pass wide of the Scilly Isles; but it seems there is sometimes a strong indraft setting up St. George's Channel, which deceives seamen and caused the loss of Sir Cloudesley Shovel's squadron. This indraft was probably the cause of what happened to us.

We had a watchman placed in the bow, to whom they often called, *"Look well out before there,"* and he as often answered, *"Ay, ay";* but perhaps had his eyes shut, and was half-asleep at the time, they sometimes answering, as is said, mechanically; for he did not see a light just before us, which had been hid by the studding-sails from the man at the helm, and from the rest of the watch, but by an accidental yaw of the ship was discovered, and occasioned great alarm, we being very near it, the light appearing to me as big as a cart-wheel. It was midnight, and our captain fast asleep; but Captain Kennedy, jumping upon deck, and seeing the danger, ordered the ship to wear round, all sails standing; an operation dangerous to the masts, but it carried us clear, and we escaped shipwreck, for we were running right upon the rocks on which the light-house was erected.

In the morning it was found by the soundings, etc., that we were near our port, but a thick fog hid the land from our sight. About nine

269

o'clock the fog began to rise, and seemed to be lifted up from the water like the curtain at a play-house, discovering underneath, the town of Falmouth, the vessels in its harbor, and the fields that surrounded it.

I set out immediately, with my son, for London, and we only stopped a little by the way to view Stonehenge on Salisbury Plain, and Lord Pembroke's house and gardens, with his very curious antiques at Wilton. We arrived in London the 27th of July, 1757. As soon as I was settled in a lodging Mr. Charles had provided for me, I went to visit Dr. Fothergill, to whom I was strongly recommended, and whose counsel respecting my proceedings I was advised to obtain. He was against an immediate complaint to government, and thought the proprietaries should first be personally applied to, who might possibly be induced by the interposition and persuasion of some private friends, to accommodate matters amicably.

I then waited on my old friend and correspondent, Mr. Peter Collinson, who told me that John Hanbury, the great Virginia merchant, had requested to be informed when I should arrive, that he might carry me to Lord Granville's, who was then President of the Council and wished to see me as soon as possible. I agreed to go with him the next morning.

Accordingly Mr. Hanbury called for me and took me in his carriage to that nobleman's, who received me with great civility; and after some questions respecting the present state of affairs in America and discourse thereupon, he said to me: "You Americans have wrong ideas of the nature of your constitution; you contend that the king's instructions to his governors are not laws, and think yourselves at liberty to regard or disregard them at your own discretion. But those instructions are not like the pocket instructions given to a minister going abroad, for regulating his conduct in some trifling point of ceremony. They are first drawn up by judges learned in the laws; they are then considered, debated, and perhaps amended in Council, after which they are signed by the king. They are then, so far as they relate to you, the *law of the land,* for the king is the *Legislator of the Colonies."*

I told his lordship this was new doctrine to me. I had always understood from our charters that our laws were to be made by our Assemblies, to be presented indeed to the king for his royal assent, but that being once given the king could not repeal or alter them. And as the Assemblies could not make permanent laws without his assent, so neither could he make a law for them without theirs. He assured me I was totally mistaken. I did not think so, however, and his lordship's conversation having a little alarmed me as to what might be the sentiments of the court concerning us, I wrote it down as soon as I returned to my lodgings.

After some days, Dr. Fothergill having spoken to the proprietaries, they agreed to a meeting with me at Mr. T. Penn's house in Spring Garden. The conversation at first consisted of mutual declarations of disposition to reasonable accommodations, but I suppose each party had its own ideas of what should be meant by *reasonable*. We then went into consideration of our several points of complaint, which I enumerated. The proprietaries justified their conduct as well as they could, and I the Assembly's. We now appeared very wide, and so far from each other in our opinions as to discourage all hope of agreement. However, it was concluded that I should give them the heads of our complaints in writing, and they promised then to consider them.

I did so soon after, but they put the paper into the hands of their solicitor, Ferdinand John Paris, who managed for them all their law business in their great suit with the neighboring proprietary of Maryland, Lord Baltimore, which had subsisted 70 years, and wrote for them all their papers and messages in their dispute with the Assembly. He was a proud, angry man, and as I had occasionally in the answers of the Assembly treated his papers with some severity, they being really weak in point of argument and haughty in expression, he had conceived a mortal enmity to me, which discovering itself whenever we met, I declined the proprietary's proposal that he and I should discuss the heads of complaint between our two selves, and refused treating with anyone but them.

They then by his advice put the paper into the hands of the Attorney and Solicitor-General for their opinion and counsel upon it, where it lay unanswered a year wanting eight days, during which time I made frequent demands of an answer from the proprietaries, but without obtaining any other than that they had not yet received the opinion of the Attorney and Solicitor-General. What it was when they did receive it I never learnt.

But during this delay, the Assembly having prevailed with Governor Denny to pass an act taxing the proprietary estate in common with the estates of the people, which was the grand point in dispute, they omitted answering the message.

When this act however came over, the proprietaries, counseled by

Paris, determined to oppose its receiving the royal assent. Accordingly they petitioned the king in Council, and a hearing was appointed in which two lawyers were employed by them against the act, and two by me in support of it. They alleged that the act was intended to load the proprietary estate in order to spare those of the people, and that if it were suffered to continue in force, and the proprietaries who were in odium with the people, left to their mercy in proportioning the taxes, they would inevitably be ruined.

We replied that the act had no such intention, and would have no such effect. That the assessors were honest and discreet men under an oath to assess fairly and equitably, and that any advantage each of them might expect in lessening his own tax by augmenting that of the proprietaries was too trifling to induce them to perjure themselves. This is the purport of what I remember as urged by both sides, except that we insisted strongly on the mischievous consequences that must attend a repeal, for that the money, £100,000, being printed and given to the king's use, expended in his service, and now spread among the people, the repeal would strike it dead in their hands to the ruin of many; and the total discouragement of future grants, and the selfishness of the proprietors in soliciting such a general catastrophe, merely from a groundless fear of their estate being taxed too highly, was insisted on in the strongest terms.

On this, Lord Mansfield, one of the counsel, rose, and beckoning me took me into the clerk's chamber, while the lawyers were pleading, and asked me if I was really of opinion that no injury would be done the proprietary estate in the execution of the act. I said certainly. "Then," says he, "you can have little objection to enter into an engagement to assure that point." I answered, "None at all." He then called in Paris, and after some discourse, his lordship's proposition was accepted on both sides. A paper to the purpose was drawn up by the Clerk of the Council, which I signed with Mr. Charles, who was also an Agent of the Province for their ordinary affairs, when Lord Mansfield returned to the Council Chamber, where finally the law was allowed to pass.

Some changes were however recommended and we also engaged they should be made by a subsequent law, but the Assembly did not think them necessary; for one year's tax having been levied by the act before the order of Council arrived, they appointed a committee to examine the proceedings of the assessors, and on this committee they put several particular friends of the proprietaries. After a full inquiry, they unanimously signed a report that they found the tax had been assessed with perfect equity.

The Assembly looked into my entering into the first part of the engagement, as an essential service to the Province, since it secured the credit of the paper money then spread over all the country. They gave me their thanks in form when I returned. But the proprietaries were enraged at Governor Denny for having passed the act, and turned him out with threats of suing him for breach of instructions which he had given bond to observe. He, however, having done it at the instance of the General, and for His Majesty's service, and having some powerful interest at court, despised the threats and they were never put in execution. . . . [Unfinished].

THE

FRENCH

REVOLUTION

by Thomas Carlyle

A CONDENSATION

THE
FRENCH
REVOLUTION

by Thomas Carlyle

A CONDENSATION

HOME COURSE APPRECIATION

LIKE JEREMIAH OF OLD, calling down the wrath of heaven upon a sinful and unheeding Israel, Thomas Carlyle looked out upon his own world through eyes of fierce and uncompromising righteousness. For more than forty years, he poured his volcanic fury over the quackeries, the complacencies, and the materialism of his age.

"God's Angry Man," a phrase applied to the fanatic abolitionist John Brown, seems fitting for this embodiment of the Puritan conscience of England. Out of sympathy with the leading trends of his period, eccentric and pessimistic in a society which held conformity and optimism as cardinal virtues, Carlyle's genius shattered itself against "the huge black precipice of British Philistinism."

He once declared that the world seemed "a vast, solitary Golgotha and mill of death," and at the end of his life he was convinced that only disaster and ruin lay ahead. "Torpid, gluttonous, sooty, swollen, and squalid England is grown a phenomenon which fills me with disgust and apprehension, almost desperate, as far as it is concerned. What a base, pot-bellied blockhead this our heroic nation is become; sunk in its own dirty fat and offal, and of a stupidity defying the very gods."

CHRONIC DISCONTENT AND CREATIVE WRITING

A man of such violent and embittered temperament is predestined to a life of discontent if not of wretchedness, and in Carlyle's case, the original gloomy cast of his mind was aggravated by chronic illness. He seldom enjoyed a good meal. The worst hell he could imagine was "to be compelled to digest to all eternity with this stomach." As he grew older he became morbidly sensitive and insomnia was a curse. The annoyance caused by the loud crowing of a neighbor's rooster almost drove him to a frenzy, and forced Mrs. Carlyle to buy the offending fowl at a high price for the sake of family peace.

This and many other true anecdotes faithfully preserved by his biographer James Anthony Froude demonstrate that in the ordinary business of living Carlyle was one of the most difficult people who ever tried the patience of wife and friends. In the psychology-conscious twentieth century he would unquestionably be thought a fit subject for psychiatric treatment.

It is perhaps fortunate for literature that the treatment of emotional disorder was not advanced in Carlyle's day. A normal Carlyle is unthinkable. If ever a man channeled the miseries of a neurotic personality into creative achievement, it was Thomas Carlyle.

Had he been personally fortunate in the possession of health and emotional stability, he might still have accomplished memorable and worthy things; but he might not have made his unique contribution to the thought and literature of nineteenth-century England.

CARLYLE BEGINS HIS LITERARY CAREER

CARLYLE WAS BORN IN 1795 in a village in Dumfriesshire, the border county of southwest Scotland. The influence of his mother, a woman who inherited the granite character of her Scottish Calvinist forebears, was strong upon his childhood. It remained a powerful formative force throughout his life. In 1809 he entered the University of Edinburgh, where he took his degree in 1814. For four years he taught school; curiously enough for one of literary tastes, his subject was mathematics. In 1818 he returned to Edinburgh to study law and theology.

He began very early to write for magazines and for the popular *Brewster's Encyclopedia*. His first work of repute was a translation of Goethe's *Wilhelm Meister,* which appeared in 1824. This book, and a *Life of Schiller* written a year earlier, were the first fruits of his life-long interest in German literature. He became the great English interpreter and apostle of that country's culture.

In 1826 he married Jane Welsh, a witty young woman who matched Carlyle in literary perception. Money was scarce, and the young couple was forced for several years to live at the home of the bride's parents at Craigenputtock, Scotland. Here Carlyle wrote his first great essay, on Robert Burns, which appeared in the famous *Edinburgh Review*. Though the financial rewards were small, Carlyle was slowly acquiring a reputation and was finding his abilities as a writer.

CARLYLE WRITES A CLASSIC IN LONDON

IN 1834, THE CARLYLES MOVED to London, taking the famous Cheyne Row house in Chelsea that remained their home until his death. At the center of British intellectual life, Carlyle began to know the leading figures of letters and politics, and felt himself a part of the busy life around him. Among others, he met the philosopher John Stuart Mill, whom he called "the newest approach to a real man that I find here." He had earlier met Ralph Waldo Emerson, who visited England in 1832, and with whom he maintained a correspondence for the rest of his life. Before long the brightest names in English literature were on the cards left at Cheyne Row.

The great work of his first years in London was *The French Revolution,* in which all the major elements of his genius appeared in fully developed form. The success of this book assured Carlyle of a place among the first British writers of his century. The judgment of later ages has shared the opinion of his contemporaries, and the book has taken its place with the classics of historical philosophy. Although it has been criticized by scholars of what Carlyle used to call the "dry-as-dust" school, it is a lasting monument of historical imagination. Even those who have spoken most harshly of its defects have not denied its inspiration and have often conceded its great vigor and insight.

A BITTER LOSS AND A PAINFUL RECOVERY

The writing of *The French Revolution* was the great turning point in Carlyle's personal history. It had been an arduous task for a man who was never fluent, made even more arduous by a lamentable accident. The manuscript of the first volume, painfully written in longhand, was lent to John Stuart Mill for reading. Mill read it in bed, and put the sheets on a table before going to sleep. A maid, tidying up the room, mistook the work for waste paper and threw it into the fire. On March 6, 1835, Mill appeared at the Carlyle house "deadly pale, and at first unable to speak." When Mill finally told him about the disaster, Carlyle comforted his disconsolate friend. His words to Mrs. Carlyle after Mill had left show the true mettle of his character:

"Well, Mill, poor fellow, is terribly cut up; we must endeavor to hide from him how very serious this business is to us."

The burned volume was rewritten after months of labor. It is, of course, impossible to know what changes were made in this revised version, but by unanimous consent, the first volume as it now stands, containing the graphic picture of the last days of Louis XV, is perhaps the most powerful and noble portion of the whole work.

OUR PICTURE OF THE FRENCH REVOLUTION

THE FRENCH REVOLUTION, which gave the death-blow to the old feudal system not only in France but in all of Europe, is one of the greatest events of modern history. For English-speaking readers, aside from a handful of professional scholars, Carlyle's picture of the Revolution dominates all others. Those who have not read Carlyle directly may have read him through Dickens' dramatic novel *A Tale of Two Cities,* which uses Carlyle for its vivid background.

The tremendous rise of the French people against their oppressive masters, the storming of the Bastille, the reaction and counter-revolution that called forth the terrible events of the massacre of September, the trial and execution of Louis XVI, and the Reign of Terror with its tumbrils moving daily to the guillotine, are fixed forever in the minds of English readers everywhere by the genius of Carlyle and Dickens. Modern research added certain details to Carlyle's account, shifting its emphasis from the dramatic interplay of personalities to a less exciting analysis of economic forces and day-to-day political affairs; but the works of Carlyle and Dickens persist, not only because they are works of genius, but because they give true, if highly personal, accounts.

SCORN FOR ENGLAND AND FRANCE

WITH THE PUBLICATION IN 1837 of *The French Revolution,* Carlyle arrived as a literary personality; throughout the remainder of his life, he enjoyed steadily increasing fame. He continued to labor heroically, producing book after book, and developing more of those cantankerous traits which reflected his frustration and deep pessimism.

Beyond all things, Carlyle valued sincerity and strength. The great man, the hero, was in his eyes the true justification of the human race. A man possessed of an overpowering idea, who realized a mission and drove to its accomplishment over all obstacles, was the only object

"The Bastille's took!" . . . "Go, then, all Frenchmen,
And have hearts in your bodies!"

"The Bastille is besieged! . . . On, then, all Frenchmen, that have hearts in your bodies!"

worthy of his admiration and study. Oliver Cromwell and Frederick the Great were examples of this dedicated will and energy, and to them Carlyle devoted two of his greatest and most characteristic books.

The skeptical man of thought, whom France has produced in great numbers, was, on the other hand, unsympathetic for Carlyle; he was never able to do justice to him. As Carlyle looked about him searching for a hero, he found mostly compromisers and critics, men who were essentially small, preoccupied by ideas that were essentially unimportant. Of Gladstone, the celebrated chancellor of the exchequer and Prime Minister he said, "Gladstone appears to me one of the contemptiblest men I ever looked on. A poor Ritualist; almost spectral kind of phantasm of a man—nothing in him but forms and ceremonies and outside wrappages; incapable of seeing veritably any fact whatever, but seeing, crediting, and laying to heart the mere clothes of the fact, and fancying that all the rest does not exist. Let him fight his battle, in the name of Beelzebub the god of Ekron, who seems to be his god. Poor phantasm!"

If this seems a harsh judgment, Gladstone was at least in excellent company in the gallery of Carlyle's hates. Few of Carlyle's contemporaries escaped his lash. Coleridge, the great critic and poet, was "a weak, diffusive, weltering, ineffectual man. . . . Never did I see such apparatus got ready for thinking, and so little thought. He mounts scaffolding, pulleys, and tackle, gathers all the tools in the neighborhood with labor, with noise, demonstration, precept, abuse, and sets—three bricks." Thomas Babington Macaulay, another historian and empire builder, was "essentially a poor creature . . . with his dictionary learning" whose *History of England,* which reached a fourth edition in 1849, was a "book to which four hundred editions could not lend any permanent value, there being no depth of sense in it at all, and a very great quantity of rhetorical wind and other temporary ingredients, which are the reverse of sense."

ADMIRATION FOR GERMANY

IF CARLYLE WAS IMMODERATELY CRITICAL in his judgments of men, he was harsher still in his judgments of the institutions and ideals of his time. A fanatic hater of materialism and the measurement of "progress" by material standards, he raged against many nineteenth-century movements. Democracy, industrialization, the British Liberal Party, the theories of political economy (it was he who dubbed economics "the dismal science"), and above all the easy optimism and respectability that are loosely termed "Victorianism" were the whipping-boys of his indignation.

Deeply conscious of human frailty, as strongly sensible of original sin as any New England Puritan, Carlyle never for a moment believed that social reform in the ordinary sense could effect any significant improvement in the human condition unless it were accompanied by a profound moral regeneration—a regeneration for which he looked in vain.

In Germany he found the depth and the seriousness that he felt were lacking in the French spirit and in the English culture of his day. At the very end of his life he braved a tempest of public opinion to express his approval of the German victory in the Franco-Prussian War of 1870–71. His excessive admiration of German culture and the "Germanism" of his style and thought have made him second to Shakespeare as the English writer most widely read in Germany. It is characteristic that at the close of his life he refused to accept a baronetcy and the Grand Cross of the Order of the Bath, but accepted the Prussian Order of Merit from the German Emperor. He also declined the offer of a tomb in Westminster Abbey.

"MERCIFUL AND INDISPENSABLE REFUGE"

Despite his many pecularities, Carlyle was respected not only by men of letters, but by workingmen as well, who admired his strength of character. An anecdote of his old age reported by Froude is worth repeating:

"In an omnibus his arbitrary ways were very amusing. He always craved for fresh air, took his seat by the door when he could get it, and sat obliquely in the corner to avoid being squeezed. The conductor knew him, and his appearance was so marked that the passengers generally knew him also, and treated him with high respect. A stranger on the box one day, seeing Carlyle get in, observed that the 'old fellow 'ad a queer 'at!' 'Queer 'at!' answered the driver. 'Ay, 'e may wear a queer 'at, but what would you give for the 'eadpiece that's inside of it?' "

In 1877 Carlyle's rugged health, weakened by long suffering from nervous dyspepsia, began to fail, and he gradually declined to his death in 1881. It was a welcome relief for him, almost longed for after the death of Mrs. Carlyle in 1866, who took with her his greatest spiritual support. "For a long time back I have been accustomed to

Louis XVI being led to his execution.

look at the *ernster Freund* (i.e., death) as the most merciful and indispensable refuge appointed by the Great Creator for his wearied children whose work is done. Alas, alas! the final mercy of God, it in late years always appears to me is, that he delivers us from life which has become a task too hard for us."

"CARLYLESE"

OF ALL THE GREAT WRITERS of the nineteenth century, Carlyle is the most individual and lonely. Every paragraph of his writing bears his personal stamp, and it has been maliciously suggested that he wrote not English, but "Carlylese." His unconventional punctuation and capitalization, his tormented inversions, his Biblical phraseology, and his strange word coinage all make for difficult reading—at first. But the reader who persists will find himself rewarded by contact with Carlyle's strong personality and moral fiber. He was a man of passionate seriousness, intent on carrying his message to his reader's heart. Of *The French Revolution* he said: "I know not whether this book is worth anything, nor what the world will do with it, or misdo, or entirely forbear to do, as is likeliest; but this I could tell the world: You have not had for a hundred years any book which comes more direct and flamingly from the heart of a living man."

Foreword

[Carlyle's style is highly individual—so much so, indeed, that it has been unkindly suggested that he wrote "Carlylese" rather than English. His biblical phraseology, his often strange and tormented word-order, his peculiarities of spelling and capitalization (derived in part from his deep familiarity with German), his farfetched allusions, and his occasionally grotesque metaphors all make for difficult reading—at first. But the reader who persists will find himself rewarded by contact with Carlyle's fierce earnestness and energy, and by flashes of insight which at their best can only be compared with the higher passages of poetry.

In preparing the present abridgment the editor has not felt justified in modernizing Carlyle's peculiarities of punctuation, spelling, and capitalization, since so much of the flavor of his writing depends precisely on these devices. Even the British "-our" in such words as "honour," "splendour," and "neighbour" has been allowed to stand. The only changes that have been made in the text are omissions, which in the most important cases have been summarized by parenthetical italics. Footnotes, in which Carlyle indicated his sources, are of interest only to specialists, and have been expunged throughout.]

277

Death of Louis XV

LOUIS THE WELL-BELOVED

PRESIDENT HÉNAULT, remarking on royal Surnames of Honour how difficult it often is to ascertain not only why, but even when, they were conferred, takes occasion in his sleek official way to make a philosophical reflection. 'The Surname of *Bien-aimé* (Well-beloved)', says he, 'which Louis XV bears, will not leave posterity in the same doubt. This Prince, in the year 1744, while hastening from one end of his kingdom to the other, and suspending his conquests in Flanders that he might fly to the assistance of Alsace, was arrested at Metz by a malady which threatened to cut short his days. At the news of this, Paris, all in terror, seemed a city taken by storm: the churches resounded with supplications and groans; the prayers of priests and people were every moment interrupted by their sobs: and it was from an interest so dear and tender that this Surname of *Bien-aimé* fashioned itself—a title higher still than all the rest which this great Prince has earned'.

So stands it written; in lasting memorial of that year 1744. Thirty other years have come and gone; and 'this great Prince' again lies sick; but in how altered circumstances now! Churches resound not with excessive groanings; Paris is stoically calm: sobs interrupt no prayers, for indeed none are offered. . . . This shepherd of the people has been carried home from Little Trianon, heavy of heart, and been put to bed in his own Château of Versailles: the flock knows it, and heeds it not. At most, in the immeasurable tide of French Speech (which ceases not day after day, and only ebbs towards the short hours of night), may this of the royal sickness emerge from time to time as an article of news. Bets are doubtless depending; nay, some people 'express themselves loudly in the streets.' But for the rest, on green field and steepled city, the May sun shines out, the May evening fades; and men ply their useful or useless business as if no Louis lay in danger.

Dame Dubarry, indeed, might pray, if she had a talent for it; Duke

278

d'Aiguillon too, Maupeou and the Parlement Maupeou: these, as they sit in their high places, with France harnessed under their feet, know well on what basis they continue there. Look to it, D'Aiguillon; sharply as thou didst, from the Mill of St. Cast, on Quiberon and the invading English; thou 'covered if not with glory yet with meal!' Fortune was ever accounted inconstant: and each dog has but his day.

Beautiful Armida-Palace, where the inmates live enchanted lives; lapped in soft music of adulation; waited on by the splendours of the world; which nevertheless hangs wondrously as by a single hair. Should the Most Christian King die; or even get seriously afraid of dying! For, alas, had not the fair haughty Chateauroux to fly, with wet cheeks and flaming heart, from that Fever-scene at Metz, long since; driven forth by sour shavelings? She hardly returned, when fever and shavelings were both swept into the background. Pompadour too, when Damiens wounded Royalty 'slightly, under the fifth rib,' and our drive to Trianon went off futile, in shrieks and madly shaken torches, had to pack, and be in readiness: yet did not go, the wound not proving poisoned. For his Majesty has religious faith; believes, at least in a Devil. And now a third peril; and who knows what may be in it! For the Doctors look grave; ask privily, If his Majesty had not the small-pox long ago?—and doubt it may have been a false kind. Yes, Maupeou, pucker those sinister brows of thine, and peer out on it with thy malign rat-eyes: it is a questionable case. Sure only that man is mortal; that with the life of one mortal snaps irrevocably the wonderfullest talisman, and all Dubarrydom rushes off, with tumult, into infinite Space; and ye, as subterranean Apparitions are wont, vanish utterly, leaving only a smell of sulphur!

These, and what holds of these may pray, to Beelzebub, or whoever will hear them. But from the rest of France there comes, as was said, no prayer; or one of an *opposite* character, 'expressed openly in the streets.' Château or Hôtel, where an enlightened Philosophism scrutinizes many things, is not given to prayer: neither are Rossbach victories, Terray Finances, nor, say only 'sixty thousand *Lettres de Cachet*' (which is Maupeou's share), persuasives towards that. O Hénault! Prayers? From a France smitten (by black-art) with plague after plague; and lying now, in shame and pain, with a Harlot's foot on its neck, what prayer can come? Those lank scarecrows, that prowl hunger-stricken through all highways and byways of French Existence, will they pray? The dull millions that, in the workshop or furrowfield, grind foredone at the wheel of Labour, like haltered gin-horses, if blind so much the quieter? Or they that in the Bicêtre Hospital, 'eight to a bed,' lie waiting their manumission? Dim are those heads of theirs, dull stagnant those hearts: to them the great Sovereign is known mainly as the great Regrater of Bread. If they hear of his sickness, they will answer with a dull *Tant pis pour lui;* or with the question, Will he die?

Yes, will he die? that is now, for all France, the grand question, and hope; whereby alone the King's sickness has still some interest.

REALIZED IDEALS

SUCH A CHANGED FRANCE have we; and a changed Louis. Changed, truly; and further than thou yet seest!—To the eye of History many things, in that sick-room of Louis, are now visible, which to the Courtiers there present were invisible. For indeed it is well said, 'in every object there is inexhaustible meaning; the eye sees in it what the eye brings means of seeing.' To Newton and to Newton's Dog Diamond, what a different pair of Universes; while the painting on the optical retina of both was, most likely, the same! Let the Reader here, in this sick-room of Louis, endeavour to look with the mind too.

Time was when men could (so to speak) of a given man, by nourishing and decorating him with fit appliances, to the due pitch, *make* themselves a King, almost as the Bees do; and, what was still more to the purpose, loyally obey him when made. The man so nourished and decorated, thenceforth named royal, does verily bear rule; and is said, and even thought, to be, for example, 'prosecuting conquests in Flanders', when he lets himself like luggage be carried thither: and no light luggage; covering miles of road. For he has his unblushing Chateauroux, with her bandboxes and rouge-pots, at his side; so that, at every new station, a wooden gallery must be run up between their lodgings. He has not only his *Maison-Bouche,* and *Valetaille* without end, but his very Troop of Players, with their pasteboard coulisses, thunder-barrels, their kettles, fiddles, stage-wardrobes, portable larders (and chaffering and quarrelling enough); all mounted in wagons, tumbrils, second-hand chaises—sufficient not to conquer Flanders, but the patience of the world. With such a flood of loud jingling appurtenances does he lumber along, prosecuting his conquests in Flanders: wonderful to behold. So nevertheless it was and had been: to some solitary thinker it might seem strange; but even to him, inevitable, not unnatural.

For ours is a most fictile world; and man is the most fingent plastic of creatures. A world not fixable; not fathomable! An unfathomable Somewhat, which is *Not we;* which we can work with, and live amidst,—and model, miraculously in our miraculous Being, and name World.—But if the very Rocks and Rivers (as Metaphysic teaches) are, in strict language, *made* by those Outward Senses of ours, how much more, by the Inward Sense, are all Phenomena of the spiritual kind: Dignities, Authorities, Holies, Unholies! Which inward sense, moreover, is not permanent like the outward ones, but for ever growing and changing. Does not the Black African take of Sticks and Old Clothes (say, exported Monmouth-Street cast-clothes) what will suffice; and of these, cunningly combining them, fabricate for himself an Eidolon (Idol, or *Thing Seen*), and name it *Mumbo-Jumbo;* which he can thenceforth pray to, with upturned awestruck eye, not without hope? The white European mocks; but ought rather to consider; and see whether he, at home, could not do the like a little more wisely.

So it *was,* we say, in those conquests of Flanders, thirty years ago: but so it no longer is. Alas, much more lies sick than poor Louis: not the French King only, but the French Kingship; this too, after long rough tear and wear, is breaking down. The world is all so changed; so much that seemed vigorous has sunk decrepit, so much that was not is beginning to be!—Borne over the Atlantic, to the closing ear of Louis, King by the Grace of God, what sounds are these; muffled-ominous, new in our centuries? Boston Harbour is black with unexpected Tea: behold a Pennsylvanian Congress gather; and ere long, on Bunker Hill, DEMOCRACY announcing, in rifle-volleys death-winged, under her Star Banner, to the tune of Yankee-doodle-doo, that she is born, and, whirlwind-like, will envelop the whole world!

Sovereigns die and Sovereignties; how all dies, and is for a Time only; is a 'Time-phantasm, yet reckons itself real'! The Merovingian Kings, slowly wending on their bullock-carts through the streets of Paris, with their long hair flowing, have all wended slowly on—into

281

Eternity. Charlemagne sleeps at Salzburg, with truncheon grounded; only Fable expecting that he will awaken. Charles the Hammer, Pepin Bow-legged, where now is their eye of menace, their voice of command? Rollo and his shaggy Northmen cover not the Seine with ships; but have sailed off on a longer voyage. The hair of Towhead (*Tête d'étoupes*) now needs no combing; Iron-cutter (*Taillefer*) cannot cut a cobweb; shrill Fredegonda, shrill Brunhilda have had their hot life-scold, and lie silent, their hot life-frenzy cooled. Neither from that black Tower de Nesle descends now darkling the doomed gallant, in his sack, to the Seine waters; plunging into Night; for Dame de Nesle now cares not for this world's gallantry, heeds not this world's scandal; Dame de Nesle is herself gone into Night. They are all gone; sunk down, down, with the tumult they made; and the rolling and the trampling of ever new generations passes over them; and they hear it not any more for ever.

And yet withal has there not been realized somewhat? Consider (to go no further) these strong Stone-edifices, and what they hold! Mud-Town of the Borderers (*Lutetia Parisiorum* or *Barisiorum*) has paved itself, has spread over all the Seine Islands, and far and wide on each bank, and become City of Paris, sometimes boasting to be 'Athens of Europe', and even 'Capital of the Universe.' Stone towers frown aloft; long-lasting, grim with a thousand years. Cathedrals are there, and a Creed (or memory of a Creed) in them; Palaces, and a State and Law. Thou seest the Smoke-vapour; *un*extinguished Breath as of a thing living. Labour's thousand hammers ring on her anvils: also a more miraculous Labour works noiselessly, not with the Hand but with the Thought. How have cunning workmen in all crafts, with their cunning head and right-hand, tamed the Four Elements to be their ministers; yoking the Winds to their Sea-chariot, making the very Stars their Nautical Timepiece;—and written and collected a *Bibliothèque du Roi;* among whose Books is the Hebrew Book! A wondrous race of creatures: *these* have been realized, and what of Skill is in these: call not the Past Time, with all its confused wretchednesses, a lost one.

Observe, however, that of man's whole terrestrial possessions and attainments, unspeakably the noblest are his Symbols, divine or divine-seeming; under which he marches and fights, with victorious assurance, in this life-battle; what we can call his Realized Ideals. Of which realized Ideals, omitting the rest, consider only these two: his Church, or spiritual Guidance; his Kingship, or temporal one. The

Church: what a word was there; richer than Golconda and the treasures of the world! In the heart of the remotest mountains rises the little Kirk; the Dead all slumbering round it, under their white memorial-stones, 'in hope of a happy resurrection':—dull wert thou, O Reader, if never in any hour (say of moaning midnight, when such Kirk hung spectral in the sky, and Being was as if swallowed up of Darkness) it spoke to thee—things unspeakable, that went to thy soul's soul. Strong was he that had a Church, what we can call a Church: he stood thereby, though 'in the centre of Immensities, in the conflux of Eternities', yet manlike towards God and man; the vague shoreless Universe had become for him a firm city, and dwelling which he knew. Such virtue was in Belief; in these words, well spoken: *I believe.* Well might men prize their *Credo,* and raise stateliest Temples for it, and reverend Hierarchies, and give it the tithe of their substance; it was worth living for and dying for.

Neither was that an inconsiderable moment when wild armed men first raised their Strongest aloft on the buckler-throne; and, with clanging armour and hearts, said solemnly: Be thou our Acknowledged Strongest! In such Acknowledged Strongest (well named King, *Könning,* Can-ning, or Man that was Able) what a Symbol shone now for them—significant with the destinies of the world! A Symbol of true Guidance in return for loving Obedience; properly, if he knew it, the prime want of man. A Symbol which might be called sacred; for is there not, in reverence for what is better than we, an indestructible sacredness? On which ground, too, it was well said there lay in the Acknowledged Strongest a divine right; as surely there might in the Strongest, whether Acknowledged or not—considering *who* it was that made him strong. And so, in the midst of confusions and unutterable incongruities (as all growth is confused), did this of Royalty, with Loyalty environing it, spring up; and grow mysteriously, subduing and assimilating (for a principle of Life was in it); till it also had grown world-great, and was among the main Facts of our modern existence. Such a Fact, that Louis XIV, for example, could answer the expostulatory Magistrate with his *'L'Etat c'est moi* (The State? I am the State)'; and be replied to by silence and abashed looks. So far had accident and forethought; had your Louis Elevenths, with the leaden Virgin in their hatband, and torture-wheels and conical *oubliettes* (man-eating!) under their feet; your Henri Fourths, with their prophesied social millennium, 'when every peasant should have his fowl in the pot;' and on the whole, the fertility of this most fertile Existence, named of Good and Evil—brought it, in the matter of the Kingship. Wondrous! Concerning which may we not again say, that in the huge mass of Evil, as it rolls and swells, there is ever some Good working imprisoned; working towards deliverance and triumph?

How such Ideals do realize themselves; and grow, wondrously, from amid the incongruous ever-fluctuating chaos of the Actual: this is what World-History, if it teach any thing, has to teach us. How they grow; and, after long stormy growth, bloom out mature, supreme; then quickly (for the blossom is brief) fall into decay; sorrowfully dwindle; and crumble down, or rush down, noisily or noiselessly disappearing. The blossom is so brief; as of some centennial Cactus-flower, which after a century of waiting shines out for hours! Thus from the day when rough Clovis, in the Champ de Mars, in sight of his whole army, had to cleave retributively the head of that rough Frank, with sudden battle-axe, and the fierce words, 'It was thus thou clavest the vase' (St. Remi's and mine) 'at Soissons', forward to Louis the Grand and his *L'Etat c'est moi,* we count some twelve hundred years: and now this the very next Louis is dying, and so much dying with him! . . .

But of those decadent ages in which no Ideal either grows or blossoms? When Belief and Loyalty have passed away, and only the cant and false echo of them remains; and all Solemnity has become Pageantry; and the Creed of persons in authority has become one of two things: an Imbecility or a Machiavelism? Alas, of these ages World-History can take no notice; they have to become compressed more and more, and finally suppressed in the Annals of Mankind; blotted out as spurious—which indeed they are. Hapless ages: wherein, if ever in any, it is an unhappiness to be born. To be born, and to learn only, by every tradition and example, that God's Universe is Belial's and a Lie; and 'the Supreme Quack' the hierarch of men! In which mournfullest faith, nevertheless, do we not see whole generations (two, and sometimes even three successively) live, what they call living; and vanish—without chance of reappearance?

In such a decadent age, or one fast verging that way, had our poor Louis been born. Grant also that if the French Kingship had not, by course of Nature, long to live, he of all men was the man to accelerate Nature. The blossom of French Royalty, cactus-like, has accordingly made an astonishing progress. In those Metz days, it was still standing with all its petals, though bedimmed by Orleans Regents and *Roué* Ministers and Cardinals; but now, in 1774, we behold it bald, and the virtue nigh gone out of it.

Disastrous indeed does it look with those same 'realized Ideals', one and all! The Church, which in its palmy season, seven hundred years ago, could make an Emperor wait barefoot, in penance-shirt, three days, in the snow, has for centuries seen itself decaying; reduced even to forget old purposes and enmities, and join interest with the Kingship: on this younger strength it would fain stay its decrepitude; and these two will henceforth stand and fall together. Alas, the Sorbonne still sits there, in its old mansion; but mumbles only jargon of dotage, and no longer leads the consciences of men: not the Sorbonne; it is *Encyclopédies, Philosophie,* and who knows what nameless innumerable multitude of ready Writers, profane Singers, Romancers, Players, Disputators, and Pamphleteers, that now form the Spiritual Guidance of the world. The world's Practical Guidance too is lost, or has glided into the same miscellaneous hands. Who is it that the King (*Able-man,* named also *Roi, Rex,* or Director) now guides? His own huntsmen and prickers: when there is to be no hunt, it is well said, '*Le Roi ne fera rien* (To-day his Majesty will do *nothing*).' He lives and lingers there, because he is living there, and none has yet laid hands on him.

The Nobles, in like manner, have nearly ceased either to guide or misguide; and are now, as their master is, little more than ornamental figures. It is long since they have done with butchering one another or their king: the Workers, protected, encouraged by Majesty, have ages ago built walled towns, and there ply their crafts; will permit no Robber Baron to 'live by the saddle,' but maintain a gallows to prevent it. Ever since that period of the *Fronde,* the Noble has changed his fighting sword into a court rapier; and now loyally attends his King as ministering satellite; divides the spoil, not now by violence and murder, but by soliciting and finesse. These men call themselves supports of the throne: singular gilt-pasteboard *caryatides* in that singular edifice! For the rest, their privileges every way are now much curtailed. That Law authorizing a Seigneur, as he returned from hunting, to kill not more than two Serfs, and refresh his feet in their warm blood and bowels, has fallen into perfect desuetude, and even into incredibility; for if Deputy Lapoule can believe in it, and call for the abrogation of it, so cannot we. No Charolois, for these last fifty years, though never so fond of shooting, has been in use to bring down slaters and plumbers, and see them roll from their roofs; but contents himself with partridges and grouse. Close-viewed, their industry and function is that of dressing gracefully and eating sumptuously. As for their debauchery and depravity, it is perhaps unexampled since the era of Tiberius and Commodus. Nevertheless, one has still partly a feeling with the lady Maréchale. 'Depend upon it, Sir, God thinks twice before damning a man of that quality.' These people, of old, surely had virtues, uses; or they could not have been there. Nay, one virtue they are still required to have (for mortal man cannot live without a conscience): the virtue of perfect readiness to fight duels.

Such are the shepherds of the people: and now how fares it with the flock? With the flock, as is inevitable, it fares ill, and ever worse. They are not tended, they are only regularly shorn. They are sent for, to do statute-labour, to pay statute-taxes; to fatten battlefields (named 'bed of honour') with their bodies, in quarrels which are not theirs; their hand and toil is in every possession of man; but for themselves they have little or no possession. Untaught, uncomforted, unfed; to pine stagnantly in thick obscuration, in squalid destitution and obstruction: this is the lot of the millions; *peuple taillable et corvéable à merci et miséricorde*. In Brittany they once rose in revolt at the first introduction of Pendulum Clocks; thinking it had something to do with the *Gabelle*. Paris requires to be cleared out periodically by the Police; and the horde of hunger-stricken vagabonds to be sent wandering again over space—for a time. 'During one such periodical clearance,' says Lacretelle, 'in May, 1750, the Police had presumed withal to carry off some reputable people's children, in the hope of extorting ransoms for them. The mothers fill the public places with cries of despair; crowds gather, get excited; so many women in distraction run about exaggerating the alarm: an absurd and horrid fable rises among the people; it is said that the Doctors have ordered a Great Person to take baths of young human blood for the restoration of his own, all spoiled by debaucheries. Some of the rioters,' adds Lacretelle, quite coolly, 'were hanged on the following days': the Police went on. O ye poor naked wretches! and this then is your inarticulate cry to Heaven, as of a dumb tortured animal, crying from uttermost depths of pain and debasement? Do these azure skies, like a dead crystalline vault, only reverberate the echo of it on you? Respond to it only by 'hanging on the following days?'—Not so: not for ever! Ye are heard in Heaven. And the answer too will come—in a horror of great darkness, and shakings of the world, and a cup of trembling which all the nations shall drink.

Remark, meanwhile, how from amid the wrecks and dust of this universal Decay new Powers are fashioning themselves, adapted to the new time, and its destinies. Besides the old Noblesse, originally of Fighters, there is a new recognized Noblesse of Lawyers; whose gala-day and proud battle-day even now is. An unrecognized Noblesse of Commerce; powerful enough, with money in its pocket. Lastly, powerfullest of all, least recognized of all, a Noblesse of Literature; without steel on their thigh, without gold in their purse, but with the 'grand thaumaturgic faculty of Thought' in their head. French Philosophism has arisen; in which little word how much do we include! Here, indeed, lies properly the cardinal symptom of the whole wide-spread malady. Faith is gone out; Scepticism is come in. Evil abounds and accumulates; no man has Faith to withstand it, to amend it, to begin by amending himself; it must even go on accumulating. While hollow languor and vacuity is the lot of the Upper, and want and stagnation of the Lower, and universal misery is very certain, what other thing is certain? That a Lie cannot be believed! Philosophism knows only this: her other Belief is mainly, that in spiritual supersensual matters no Belief is possible. Unhappy! Nay, as yet the Contradiction of a Lie is some kind of Belief; but the Lie with its Contradiction once swept away, what will remain? The five unsatiated Senses will remain, the sixth insatiable Sense (of Vanity); the whole *daemonic* nature of man will remain—hurled forth to rage blindly without rule or rein; savage itself, yet with all the tools and weapons of civilization: a spectacle new in History.

In such a France, as in a Powder-tower, where fire unquenched and now unquenchable is smoking and smouldering all around, has Louis XV lain down to die. With Pompadourism and Dubarryism, his Fleur-de-lis has been shamefully struck down in all lands and on all seas; Poverty invades even the Royal Exchequer, and Tax-farming can squeeze out no more; there is a quarrel of twenty-five years' standing with the Parlement; everywhere Want, Dishonesty, Unbelief, and hot-brained Sciolists for state-physicians: it is a portentous hour.

Such things can the eye of History see in this sick-room of King Louis, which were invisible to the Courtiers there. It is twenty years, gone Christmas-day, since Lord Chesterfield, summing up what he

287

had noted of this same France, wrote, and sent off by post, the following words, that have become memorable: 'In short, all the symptoms which I have ever met with in History, previous to great Changes and Revolutions in Governments, now exist and daily increase in France.'

LOUIS THE UNFORGOTTEN

FOR THE PRESENT, HOWEVER, the grand question with the Governors of France is: Shall extreme unction, or other ghostly viaticum (to Louis, not to France), be administered?

It is a deep question. For, if administered, if so much as spoken of, must not, on the very threshold of the business, Witch Dubarry vanish; hardly to return should Louis even recover? With her vanishes Duke d'Aiguillon and Company, and all their Armida-Palace, as was said; Chaos swallows the whole again, and there is left nothing but a smell of brimstone. But then, on the other hand, what will the Dauphinists and Choiseulists say? Nay, what may the royal martyr himself say, should he happen to get deadly-worse, without getting delirious? For the present, he still kisses the Dubarry hand; so we, from the anteroom, can note: but afterwards? Doctors' Bulletins may run as they are ordered, but it is 'confluent small-pox'—of which, as is whispered too, the Gatekeeper's once so buxom Daughter lies ill: and Louis XV is not a man to be trifled with in his viaticum. Was he not wont to catechize his very girls in the *Parc-aux-cerfs,* and pray with and for them, that they might preserve their—orthodoxy? A strange fact, not an unexampled one; for there is no animal so strange as man.

Poor Louis! With these it is a hollow phantasmagory, where like mimes they mope and mowl, and utter false sounds for hire; but with thee it is frightful earnest.

Frightful to all men is Death; from of old named King of Terrors. Our little compact home of an Existence, where we dwelt complaining, yet as in a home, is passing, in dark agonies, into an Unknown of Separation, Foreignness, unconditioned Possibility. The Heathen Emperor asks his soul: Into what places art thou now departing? The Catholic King must answer: To the Judgement-bar of the Most High God! Yes, it is a summing up of Life; a final settling, and giving-in the 'account of the deeds done in the body': they are done now; and lie there unalterable, and do bear their fruits, long as Eternity shall last.

Louis XV had always the kingliest abhorrence of Death. Unlike that praying Duke of Orleans, *Egalité's* grandfather—for indeed several of them had a touch of madness—who honestly believed that there was no Death! He, if the Court Newsmen can be believed, started up once on a time, glowing with sulphurous contempt and indignation on his poor Secretary, who had stumbled on the words, *feu roi d'Espagne* (the late King of Spain): *'Feu roi, Monsieur?'*—'Monseigneur,' hastily answered the trembling but adroit man of business, *'c'est une titre qu'ils prennent'* ('tis a title they take).' Louis, we say, was not so happy: but he did what he could. He would not suffer Death to be spoken of; avoided the sight of churchyards, funereal monuments, and whatsoever could bring it to mind. It is the resource of the Ostrich; who, hard hunted, sticks his foolish head in the ground, and would fain forget that his foolish unseeing body is not unseen too. Or sometimes, with a spasmodic antagonism, significant of the same thing, and of more, he *would* go; or stopping his court carriages, would send into churchyards, and ask 'how many new graves there were to-day', though it gave his poor Pompadour the disagreeablest qualms. We can figure the thought of Louis that day, when, all royally caparisoned for hunting, he met, at some sudden turning in the Wood of Senart, a ragged Peasant with a coffin: 'For whom?'—It was for a poor brother slave, whom Majesty had sometimes noticed slaving in those quarters: 'What did he die of?'—'Of hunger':—the King gave his steed the spur.

But figure his thought, when Death is now clutching at his own heart-strings; unlooked for, inexorable! Yes, poor Louis, Death has found thee. No palace walls or life-guards, gorgeous tapestries or gilt buckram of stiffest ceremonial could keep him out; but he is here, here at thy very life-breath, and will extinguish it. Thou, whose whole existence hitherto was a chimera and scenic show, at length becomest a reality: sumptuous Versailles bursts asunder, like a Dream, into void Immensity; Time is done, and all the scaffolding of Time falls wrecked with hideous clangour round thy soul: the pale Kingdoms yawn open; there must thou enter, naked, all unking'd, and await what is appointed thee! Unhappy man, there as thou turnest, in dull agony, on thy bed of weariness, what a thought is thine! Purgatory and Hellfire, now all too possible, in the prospect: in the retrospect—alas, what thing didst thou do that were not better un-done; what mortal didst thou generously help; what sorrow hadst thou mercy on? Do the 'five hundred thousand' ghosts, who sank shamefully on so many battle-fields from Rossbach to Quebec, that thy Harlot might take revenge for an epigram—crowd round thee in this hour? Thy foul Harem; the curses of mothers, the tears and in-famy of daughters? Miserable man! thou 'hast done evil as thou couldst': thy whole existence seems one hideous abortion and mis-take of Nature; the use and meaning of thee not yet known. Wert thou a fabulous Griffin, *devouring* the works of men; daily dragging virgins to thy cave; clad also in scales that no spear would pierce: no spear but Death's? A Griffin not fabulous but real! Frightful, O Louis, seem these moments for thee.—We will pry no further into the horrors of a sinner's deathbed.

And yet let no meanest man lay flattering unction to his soul. Louis was a Ruler; but art not thou also one? His wide France, look at it from the Fixed Stars (themselves not yet Infinitude), is no wider than thy narrow brickfield, where thou too didst faithfully, or didst unfaithfully. Man, 'Symbol of Eternity imprisoned into Time!' it is not thy works, which are all mortal, infinitely little, and the greatest no greater than the least, but only the Spirit thou workest in, that can have worth or continuance.

But reflect, in any case, what a life-problem this of poor Louis, when he rose as *Bien-aimé* from that Metz sick-bed, really was! What son of Adam could have swayed such incoherences into co-herence? Could he? Blindest Fortune alone has cast *him* on the top of it: he swims there; can as little sway it as the drift-log sways the wind-tossed moon-stirred Atlantic. 'What have I done to be so loved?' he said then. He may say now: What have I done to be so hated? Thou hast done nothing, poor Louis! Thy fault is properly even this, that thou didst *nothing*. What could poor Louis do? Ab-dicate, and wash his hands of it—in favour of the first that would accept! Other clear wisdom there was none for him. As it was, he stood gazing dubiously, the absurdest mortal extant (a very Solecism Incarnate) into the absurdest confused world; wherein at last noth-ing seemed so certain as this, That he, the incarnate Solecism, had five senses; that there were Flying Tables (*Tables Volantes,* which vanish through the floor, to come back reloaded), and a *Parc-aux-cerfs.*

290

Doomed mortal—for is it not a doom to be Solecism incarnate! A new *Roi Fainéant,* King Do-nothing; but with the strangest new *Mayor of the Palace:* no bow-legged Pepin now for *Mayor,* but that same cloud-capt, fire-breathing Spectre of DEMOCRACY; incalculable, which is enveloping the world!—Was Louis, then, no wickeder than this or the other private Do-nothing and Eat-all; such as we often enough see, under the name of Man of Pleasure, cumbering God's diligent Creation, for a time? Say, wretcheder! His Life-solecism was seen and felt of a whole scandalized world; him endless Oblivion cannot engulf, and swallow to endless depths—not yet for a generation or two.

However, be this as it will, we remark, not without interest, that 'on the evening of the 4th,' Dame Dubarry issues from the sick-room, with perceptible 'trouble in her visage.' It is the fourth evening of May, year of Grace 1774. Such a whispering in the Œil-de-Bœuf! Is he dying then? What can be said is that Dubarry seems making up her packages; she sails weeping through her gilt boudoirs, as if taking leave. D'Aiguillon and Company are near their last card; nevertheless they will not yet throw up the game. But as for the sacramental controversy, it is as good as settled without being mentioned; Louis sends for his Abbé Moudon in the course of next night; is confessed by him, some say for the space of 'seventeen minutes,' and demands the sacraments of his own accord.

Nay already, in the afternoon, behold is not this your Sorceress Dubarry with the handkerchief at her eyes, mounting D'Aiguillon's chariot; rolling off in his Duchess's consolatory arms? She is gone: and her place knows her no more. Vanish, false Sorceress; into Space! Needless to hover at neighbouring Ruel; for thy day is done. Shut are the royal palace-gates for evermore; hardly in coming years shalt thou, under cloud of night, descend once, in black domino, like a black night-bird, and disturb the fair Antoinette's music-party in the Park; all Birds of Paradise flying from thee, and musical wind-pipes growing mute. Thou unclean, yet unmalignant, not unpitiable thing! What a course was thine from that first trucklebed (in Joan of Arc's country) where thy mother bore thee, with tears, to an un-named father; forward, through lowest subterranean depths, and over highest sunlit heights, of Harlotdom and Rascaldom—to the guillotine-axe, which sheers away thy vainly whimpering head! Rest there uncursed; only buried and abolished; what else befitted thee?

Louis, meanwhile, is in considerable impatience for his sacraments; sends more than once to the window, to see whether they are not coming. Be of comfort, Louis, what comfort thou canst: they are under way, these sacraments. Towards six in the morning, they arrive. . . .

Alas, the Chapel organs may keep going; the Shrine of Sainte Genevieve be let down, and pulled up again—without effect. In the evening the whole Court, with Dauphin and Dauphiness, assist at the Chapel: priests are hoarse with chanting their 'Prayers of Forty Hours;' and the heaving bellows blow. Almost frightful! For the very heaven blackens; battering rain-torrents dash, with thunder; almost drowning the organ's voice: and electric fire-flashes make the very flambeaux on the altar pale. So that the most, as we are told, retired, when it was over, with hurried steps 'in a state of meditation (*recueillement*)' and said little or nothing.

So it has lasted for the better half of a fortnight; the Dubarry gone almost a week. Besenval says, all the world was getting impatient *que cela finît;* that poor Louis would have done with it. It is now the 10th of May, 1774. He will soon have done now.

This tenth May day falls into the loathsome sick-bed; but dull, unnoticed there: for they that look out of the windows are quite darkened; the cistern-wheel moves discordant on its axis; Life, like a spent steed, is panting towards the goal. In their remote apartments, Dauphin and Dauphiness stand road-ready; all grooms and equerries booted and spurred: waiting for some signal to escape the house of pestilence. And, hark! across the Œil-de-Bœuf, what sound is that; sound 'terrible and absolutely like thunder'? It is the rush of the whole Court, rushing as in wager, to salute the new Sovereigns: Hail to your Majesties! The Dauphin and Dauphiness are King and Queen! Overpowered with many emotions, they two fall on their knees together, and, with streaming tears, exclaim: 'O God, guide us, protect us; we are too young to reign!'—Too young indeed.

But thus, in any case, 'with a sound absolutely like thunder', has the Horologe of Time struck, and an old Era passed away. The Louis that was, lies forsaken, a mass of abhorred clay; abandoned 'to some poor persons, and priests of the *Chapelle Ardente*'—who make haste to put him 'in two lead coffins, pouring in abundant spirits of wine.' The new Louis with his Court is rolling towards Choisy, through the summer afternoon: the royal tears still flow; but a word

292

mispronounced by Monseigneur d'Artois sets them all laughing, and they weep no more. Light mortals, how ye walk your life-minuet, over bottomless abysses, divided from you by a film!

SECTION II

States-General

[*Louis XV died in 1774, and for some fifteen years the outworn system creaked along through constantly increasing difficulties. Two able ministers, Turgot (1774–1776) and Necker (1777–1781) attempted to reform the tax structure and to set the nation on a sounder financial basis, but their efforts were blocked by the intrigues of corrupt court favorites and by the supine attitude of the king. Much discontent was aroused by the revelations of corruption and waste made public by Necker's "Comte rendu," and by scandals involving the queen which circulated in common talk. One of these last was the notorious "Affair of the Diamond Necklace," which demonstrated an almost incredible laxity in the handling of court accounts, though the queen appears to have been entirely innocent. Under the ministers Calonne (1783–1787) and Loménie de Brienne (1783–1788) the government deficit continued to mount, while piecemeal and partial solutions to the problem became daily more glaringly inadequate. At length, in 1788, the king yielded to demands for the summoning of the "States-General," the medieval representative body of the kingdom, which had not met since 1614. Necker was recalled to power as Minister of Finance, and elections were held in the winter of 1788–89. On May 4, 1789, the States-General met at Versailles.*]

THE PROCESSION

O N THE FIRST Saturday of May, it is gala at Versailles; and Monday, fourth of the month, is to be a still greater day. The Deputies have mostly got thither, and sought out lodgings; and are now successively, in long well-ushered files, kissing the hand of Majesty in the Château. Supreme Usher de Brézé does not give the highest satisfaction: we cannot but observe that in ushering Noblesse or Clergy into the anointed Presence, he liberally opens *both* his folding-doors; and on the other hand, for members of the Third Estate, opens only one! However, there is room to enter; Majesty has smiles for all.

The good Louis welcomes his Honourable Members, with smiles of hope. He has prepared for them the Hall of *Menus,* the largest near him; and often surveyed the workmen as they went on. A spacious Hall: with raised platform for Throne, Court and Blood-royal; space for six hundred Commons Deputies in front; for half as many Clergy on this hand, and half as many Noblesse on that. It has lofty galleries; wherefrom dames of honour, splendent in *gaze d'or;* foreign Diplomacies, and other gilt-edged white-frilled individuals, to the number of two thousand—may sit and look. Broad passages flow through it; and, outside the inner wall, all round it. There are committee-rooms, guard-rooms, robing-rooms: really a noble Hall; where upholstery, aided by the subject fine-arts, has done its best; and crimson tasselled cloths, and emblematic *fleurs-de-lys* are not wanting.

The Hall is ready: the very costume, as we said, has been settled; and the Commons are *not* to wear that hated slouch-hat (*chapeau clabaud*), but one not quite so slouched (*chapeau rabattu*). As for their manner of *working,* when all dressed; for their 'voting by head or by order' and the rest—this, which it were perhaps still time to settle, and in few hours will be no longer time, remains unsettled; hangs dubious in the breast of Twelve Hundred men.

But now finally the Sun, on Monday the 4th of May, has risen; unconcerned, as if it were no special day. And yet, as his first rays could strike music from the Memnon's Statue on the Nile, what tones were these, so thrilling, tremulous, of preparation and foreboding, which he awoke in every bosom at Versailles! Huge Paris, in all conceivable and inconceivable vehicles, is pouring itself forth; from each Town and Village come subsidiary rills: Versailles is a very sea of men. But above all, from the Church of St. Louis to the Church of Notre-Dame: one vast suspended-billow of Life—with *spray* scattered even to the chimney-tops! For on chimney-tops too, as over the roofs, and up thitherwards on every lamp-iron, signpost, breakneck coign of vantage, sits patriotic Courage; and every window bursts with patriotic Beauty: for the Deputies are gathering at

St. Louis Church; to march in procession to Notre-Dame, and hear sermon.

Yes, friends, ye may sit and look: bodily or in thought, all France, and all Europe, may sit and look; for it is a day like few others. Oh, one might weep like Xerxes:—So many serried rows sit perched there; like winged creatures, alighted out of Heaven: all these, and so many more that follow them, shall have wholly fled aloft again, vanishing into the blue Deep; and the memory of this day still be fresh. It is the baptism day of Democracy; sick Time has given it birth, the numbered months being run. The extreme-unction day of Feudalism! A super-annuated System of Society, decrepit with toils (for has it not done much; produced *you,* and what ye have and know!)—and with thefts and brawls, named glorious-victories; and with profligacies, sensualities, and on the whole with dotage and se- nility—is now to die: and so, with death-throes and birth-throes, a new one is to be born. What a work, O Earth and Heavens, what a work! Battles and bloodshed, September Massacres, Bridges of Lodi, retreats of Moscow, Waterloos, Peterloos, Tenpound Franchises, Tarbarrels and Guillotines—and from this present date, if one might prophesy, some two centuries of it still to fight! Two centuries; hardly less; before Democracy go through its due, most baleful, stages of *Quack*ocracy; and a pestilential World be burnt up, and have begun to grow green and young again.

Rejoice nevertheless, ye Versailles multitudes; to you, from whom all this is hid, the glorious end of it is visible. This day, sentence of death is pronounced on Shams; judgement of resuscitation, were it but afar off, is pronounced on Realities. This day, it is declared aloud, as with a Doom-trumpet, that *a Lie is unbelievable.* Believe that, stand by that, if more there be not; and let what thing or things soever will follow it follow. 'Ye can no other; God be your help!' So spake a greater than any of you; opening *his* Chapter of World-His- tory.

Behold, however! The doors of St. Louis Church flung wide; and the Procession of Processions advancing towards Notre-Dame! Shouts rend the air; one shout, at which Grecian birds might drop dead. It is indeed a stately, solemn sight. The Elected of France, and then the Court of France; they are marshalled and march there, all in prescribed place and costume. Our Commons 'in plain black man- tle and white cravat'; Noblesse, in gold-worked, bright-dyed cloaks

295

of velvet, resplendent, rustling with laces, waving with plumes; the Clergy in rochet, alb, or other best *pontificalibus:* lastly comes the King himself, and King's Household, also in their brightest blaze of pomp—their brightest and final one. Some Fourteen Hundred Men blown together from all winds, on the deepest errand.

Yes, in that silent marching mass there lies Futurity enough. No symbolic Ark, like the old Hebrews, do these men bear: yet with them too is a Covenant; they too preside at a new Era in the History of Men. The whole Future is there, and Destiny dim-brooding over it; in the hearts and unshaped thoughts of these men, it lies illegible, inevitable. Singular to think: *they* have it in them; yet not they, not mortal, only the Eye above can read it—as it shall unfold itself, in fire and thunder, of siege, and field artillery; in the rustling of battle-banners, the tramp of hosts, in the glow of burning cities, the shriek of strangled nations! Such things lie hidden, safe-wrapt in this Fourth day of May;—say rather, had lain in some other unknown day, of which this latter is the public fruit and outcome. As indeed what wonders lie in every Day—had we the sight, as happily we have not, to decipher it: for is not every meanest Day 'the conflux of two Eternities'!

Meanwhile, suppose we too, good Reader, should, as now without miracle Muse Clio enables us, take *our* station also on some coign of vantage; and glance momentarily over this Procession, and this Life-sea; with far other eyes than the rest do, namely with prophetic? We can mount, and stand there, without fear of falling.

As for the Life-sea, or onlooking unnumbered Multitude, it is unfortunately all too dim. Yet as we gaze fixedly, do not nameless Figures not a few, which shall not always be nameless, disclose themselves; visible or presumable there! Young Baroness de Staël—she evidently looks from a window; among older honourable women. Her father is Minister, and one of the gala personages; to his own eyes the chief one. Young spiritual Amazon, thy rest is not there; nor thy loved Father's: 'as Malebranche saw all things in God, so M. Necker sees all things in Necker'—a theorem that will not hold.

But where is the brown-locked, light-behaved, fire-hearted Demoiselle Théroigne? Brown eloquent Beauty; who, with thy winged words and glances, shall thrill rough bosoms, whole steel battalions, and persuade an Austrian Kaiser—pike and helm lie provided for thee in due season; and, alas, also strait-waistcoat and long lodging in the Salpêtrière! Better hadst thou stayed in native Luxemburg, and been the mother of some brave man's children: but it was not thy task, it was not thy lot.

Of the rougher sex how, without tongue, or hundred tongues of iron, enumerate the notabilities! Has not Marquis Valadi hastily quitted his Quaker broadbrim; his Pythagorean Greek in Wapping, and the city of Glasgow? De Morande from his *Courrier de l'Europe;* Linguet from his *Annales,* they looked eager through the London fog, and became Ex-Editors, that they might feed the guillotine, and have their due. Does Louvet (of *Faublas*) stand a-tiptoe? And Brissot, hight De Warville, friend of the Blacks? He, with Marquis Condorcet, and Clavière the Genevese 'have created the *Moniteur* Newspaper', or are about creating it. Able Editors must give account of such a day.

Or seest thou with any distinctness, low down probably, not in places of honour, a Stanislas Maillard, riding-tipstaff (*huissier à cheval*) of the Châtelet; one of the shiftiest of men? A Captain Hulin of Geneva, Captain Elie of the Queen's Regiment; both with an air of half-pay? Jourdan, with tile-coloured whiskers, not yet with tile-beard; an unjust dealer in mules? He shall be, in few months, Jourdan the Headsman, and have other work.

Surely also, in some place not of honour, stands or sprawls up querulous, that he too, though short, may see, one squalidest bleared mortal, redolent of soot and horse-drugs: Jean Paul Marat of Neuchâtel! O Marat, Renovator of Human Science, Lecturer on Optics; O thou remarkablest Horseleech, once in D'Artois' Stables, as thy bleared soul looks forth, through thy bleared, dull-acrid, woe-stricken face, what sees it in all this? Any faintest light of hope; like dayspring after Nova-Zembla night? Or is it but *blue* sulphur-light, and spectres; woe, suspicion, revenge without end?

Of Draper Lecointre, how he shut his cloth-shop hard by, and stepped forth, one need hardly speak. Nor of Santerre, the sonorous Brewer from the Faubourg Saint Antoine. Two other Figures, and only two, we signalize there. The huge, brawny Figure; through whose black brows, and rude flattened face (*figure écrasée*), there looks a waste energy as of Hercules not yet furibund—he is an esurient, unprovided Advocate; Danton by name: him mark. Then that other, his slight-built comrade, and craft-brother; he with the long curling locks; with the face of dingy blackguardism, wondrously irradiated with genius, as if a naphtha-lamp burnt within it: that Fig-

297

ure is Camille Desmoulins. A fellow of infinite shrewdness, wit, nay humour; one of the sprightliest, clearest souls in all these millions. Thou poor Camille, say of thee what they may, it were but falsehood to pretend one did not almost love thee, thou headlong lightly sparkling man! But the brawny, not yet furibund Figure, we say, is Jacques Danton; a name that shall be 'tolerably known in the Revolution'. He is President of the electoral Cordeliers District at Paris, or about to be it; and shall open his lungs of brass.

We dwell no longer on the mixed shouting Multitude: for now, behold, the Commons Deputies are at hand!

Which of these Six Hundred individuals, in plain white cravat, that have come up to regenerate France, might one guess would become their *king?* For a king or leader they, as all bodies of men, must have; be their work what it may, there is one man there who, by character, faculty, position, is fittest of all to do it; that man, as future not yet elected king, walks there among the rest. He with the thick black locks, will it be? With the *hure,* as himself calls it, or black *boar's-head,* fit to be 'shaken' as a senatorial portent? Through whose shaggy beetle-brows, and rough-hewn, seamed, carbuncled face, there look natural ugliness, small-pox, incontinence, bankruptcy—and burning fire of genius; like comet-fire glaring fuliginous through murkiest confusions? It is *Gabriel Honoré Riquetti de Mirabeau,* the world-compeller; man-ruling Deputy of Aix! According to the Baroness de Staël, he steps proudly along, though looked at askance here; and shakes his black *chevelure,* or lion's-mane; as if prophetic of great deeds.

Yes, Reader, that is the Type-Frenchman of this epoch; as Voltaire was of the last. He is French in his aspirations, acquisitions, in his virtues, in his vices; perhaps more French than any other man— and intrinsically such a mass of manhood too. Mark him well. The National Assembly were all different without that one; nay, he might say with the old Despot: 'The National Assembly? I am that.'

Of a southern climate, of wild southern blood: for the Riquettis, or Arrighettis, had to fly from Florence and the Guelfs, long centuries ago, and settled in Provence; where from generation to generation they have ever approved themselves a peculiar kindred: irascible, indomitable, sharp-cutting, true, like the steel they wore; of an intensity and activity that sometimes verged towards madness, yet did not reach it. One ancient Riquetti, in mad fulfillment of a mad

298

vow, chains two Mountains together; and the chain, with its 'iron star of five rays', is still to be seen. May not a modern Riquetti *un*-chain so much, and set it drifting—which also shall be seen?

Destiny has work for that swart burly-headed Mirabeau: Destiny has watched over him, prepared him from afar. Did not his Grandfather, stout *Col-d'Argent* (Silver-Stock, so they named him), shattered and slashed by seven-and-twenty wounds in one fell day, lie sunk together on the Bridge at Casano; while Prince Eugene's cavalry galloped and regalloped over him—only the flying sergeant had thrown a camp-kettle over that loved head; and Vendôme, dropping his spyglass, moaned out, 'Mirabeau is *dead,* then!' Nevertheless he was not dead: he awoke to breath, and miraculous surgery—for Gabriel was yet to be. With his *silver stock* he kept his scarred head erect, through long years; and wedded; and produced tough Marquis Victor, the *Friend of Men.* Whereby at last in the appointed year 1749, this long-expected rough-hewn Gabriel Honoré did likewise see the light: roughest lion's whelp ever littered of that rough breed. How the old lion (for our old Marquis too was lionlike, most unconquerable, kingly-genial, most perverse) gazed wondering on his offspring; and determined to train him as no lion had yet been! It is in vain, O Marquis! This cub, though thou slay him and flay him, will not learn to draw in dogcart of Political Economy, and be a *Friend of Men;* he will not be Thou, but must and will be Himself, another than Thou. Divorce lawsuits, 'whole family save one in prison, and three-score *Lettres-de-Cachet*' for thy own sole use, do but astonish the world.

Our luckless Gabriel, sinned against and sinning, has been in the Isle of Rhé, and heard the Atlantic from his tower; in the Castle of If, and heard the Mediterranean at Marseilles. He has been in the Fortress of Joux; and forty-two months, with hardly clothing to his back, in the Dungeon of Vincennes;—all by *Lettre-de-Cachet,* from his lion father. He has been in Pontarlier Jails (self-constituted prisoner); was noticed fording estuaries of the sea (at low water), in flight from the face of men. He has pleaded before Aix Parlements (to get back his wife); the public gathering on roofs, to see since they could not hear: 'the clatter-teeth (*claque-dents*)!' snarls singular old Mirabeau; discerning in such admired forensic eloquence nothing but two chattering jaw-bones, and a head vacant, sonorous, of the drum species.

But as for Gabriel Honoré, in these strange wayfarings, what has he not seen and tried! From drill-sergeants, to prime ministers, to foreign and domestic booksellers, all manner of men he has seen. All manner of men he has gained; for at bottom it is a social, loving heart, that wild unconquerable one:—more especially all manner of women. From the Archer's Daughter at Saintes to that fair young Sophie Madame Monnier, whom he could not but 'steal', and be beheaded for—in effigy! For indeed hardly since the Arabian Prophet lay dead to Ali's admiration, was there seen such a Love-hero. In War, again, he has helped to conquer Corsica; fought duels, irregular brawls; horsewhipped calumnious barons. In Literature, he has written on *Despotism,* on *Lettres-de-Cachet;* Erotics Sapphic-Werterean, Obscenities, Profanities; Books on the *Prussian Monarchy,* on *Cagliostro,* on *Calonne,* on *the Water Companies of Paris:*—each Book comparable, we will say, to a bituminous alarum-fire; huge, smoky, sudden! The firepan, the kindling, the bitumen were his own; but the lumber, of rags, old wood and nameless combustible rubbish (for all is fuel to him), was gathered from hucksters of every description under heaven. Whereby, indeed, hucksters enough have been heard to exclaim: Out upon it, the fire is *mine!*

But now if Mirabeau is the greatest, who of these Six Hundred may be the meanest? Shall we say, that anxious, slight, ineffectual-looking man, under thirty, in spectacles; his eyes (were the glasses off) troubled, careful; with upturned face, snuffing dimly the uncertain future times; complexion of a multiplex atrabiliar colour, the final shade of which may be the pale sea-green. That greenish-coloured (*verdâtre*) individual is an Advocate of Arras; his name is *Maximilien Robespierre.* The son of an Advocate; his father founded mason-lodges under Charles Edward, the English Prince or Pretender. Maximilien the first-born was thriftily educated; he had brisk Camille Desmoulins for schoolmate in the College of Louis le Grand, at Paris. But he begged our famed Necklace-Cardinal, Rohan, the patron, to let him depart thence, and resign in favour of a younger brother. The strict-minded Max departed; home to paternal Arras; and even had a Law-case there and pleaded, not unsuccessfully, 'in favour of the first Franklin thunder-rod.' With a strict painful mind, an understanding small but clear and ready, he grew in favour with official persons, who could foresee in him an excellent man of business, happily quite free from genius. The Bishop, therefore, taking counsel, appoints him Judge of his diocese; and he faithfully does justice to the people: till behold, one day, a culprit comes whose

300

crime merits hanging; and the strict-minded Max must abdicate, for his conscience will not permit the dooming of any son of Adam to die. A strict-minded, strait-laced man! A man unfit for Revolutions? Whose small soul, transparent wholesome-looking as small-ale, could by no chance ferment into virulent *alegar*—the mother of ever new alegar; till all France were grown acetous virulent? We shall see.

Between which two extremes of grandest and meanest, so many grand and mean roll on, towards their several destinies, in that Procession! There is *Cazalès,* the learned young soldier; who shall become the eloquent orator of Royalism, and earn the shadow of a name. Experienced *Mounier,* experienced *Malouet;* whose Presidential Parlementary experience the stream of things shall soon leave stranded. A *Pétion* has left his gown and briefs at Chartres for a stormier sort of pleading; has not forgotten his violin, being fond of music. His hair is grizzled, though he is still young: convictions, beliefs placid-unalterable are in that man; not hindmost of them, belief in himself. A Protestant-clerical *Rabaut-St.-Etienne,* a slender young eloquent and vehement *Barnave,* will help to regenerate France. There are so many of them young. Till thirty the Spartans did not suffer a man to marry: but how many men here under thirty; coming to produce not one sufficient citizen, but a nation and a world of such! The old to heal up rents; the young to remove rubbish—which latter, is it not, indeed, the task here?

Dim, formless from this distance, yet authentically there, thou noticest the Deputies from Nantes? To us mere clothes-screens, with slouch-hat and cloak, but bearing in their pocket a *Cahier* of *doléances* with this singular clause, and more such, in it: 'That the master wigmakers of Nantes be not troubled with new guild-brethren, the actually existing number of ninety-two being more than sufficient!' The Rennes people have elected Farmer *Gérard,* 'a man of natural sense and rectitude, without any learning.' He walks there, with solid step; unique, 'in his rustic farmer-clothes;' which he will wear always; careless of short-cloaks and costumes. The name Gérard, or *'Père Gérard,* Father Gérard', as they please to call him, will fly far; borne about in endless banter; in Royalist satires, in Republican didactic Almanacs. As for the man Gérard, being asked once, what he did, after trial of it, candidly think of this Parlementary work,—'I think,' answered he, 'that there are a good many scoundrels among us.' So walks Father Gérard; solid in his thick shoes, whithersoever bound.

And worthy *Doctor Guillotin,* whom we hoped to behold one other time? If not here, the Doctor should be here, and we see him with the eye of prophecy: for indeed the Parisian Deputies are all a little late. Singular Guillotin, respectable practitioner; doomed by a satiric destiny to the strangest immortal glory that ever kept obscure mortal from his resting-place, the bosom of oblivion! Guillotin can improve the ventilation of the Hall; in all cases of medical police and *hygiène* be a present aid: but, greater far, he can produce his 'Report on the Penal Code'; and reveal therein a cunningly devised Beheading Machine, which shall become famous and world-famous. This is the product of Guillotin's endeavours, gained not without meditation and reading; which product popular gratitude or levity christens by a feminine derivative name, as if it were his daughter: *La Guillotine!* 'With my machine, Messieurs, I whisk off your head (*vous fais sauter la tête*) in a twinkling, and you have no pain;'— whereat they all laugh. Unfortunate Doctor! For two-and-twenty years he, unguillotined, shall hear nothing but guillotine, see nothing but guillotine; then dying, shall through long centuries wander, as it were, a disconsolate ghost, on the wrong side of Styx and Lethe; his name like to outlive Caesar's.

See *Bailly,* likewise of Paris, time-honoured Historian of Astronomy Ancient and Modern. Poor Bailly, how thy serenely beautiful Philosophizing, with its soft moonshiny clearness and thinness, ends in foul thick confusion—of Presidency, Mayorship, diplomatic Officiality, rabid Triviality, and the throat of everlasting Darkness! Far was it to descend from the heavenly Galaxy to the *Drapeau Rouge:* beside that fatal dung-heap, on that last hell-day, thou must 'tremble', though only with cold, *'de froid'*. Speculation is not practice: to be weak is not so miserable; but to be weaker than our task. Wo the day when they mounted thee, a peaceable pedestrian, on that wild Hippogryff of a Democracy; which, spurning the firm earth, nay lashing at the very *stars,* no yet known Astolpho could have ridden!

In the Commons Deputies there are Merchants, Artists, Men of Letters; three hundred and seventy-four Lawyers; and at least one Clergyman: the *Abbé Siéyès.* Him also Paris sends, among its twenty. Behold him, the light thin man; cold, but elastic, wiry; instinct with the pride of Logic; passionless, or with but one passion, that of self-conceit. If indeed that can be called a passion, which, in its independent concentrated greatness, seems to have soared into transcendentalism; and to sit there with a kind of god-like indifference, and look down on passion! He is the man, and wisdom shall die with him. This is the Siéyès who shall be System-builder, Constitution-builder General; and build Constitutions (as many as wanted) sky-high—which shall all unfortunately fall before he get the scaffolding away. '*La Politique*', said he to Dumont, 'Polity is a science I think I have completed (*achevée*).' What things, O Siéyès, with thy clear assiduous eyes, art thou to see! But were it not curious to know how Siéyès, now in these days (for he is said to be still alive), looks out on all that Constitution masonry, through the rheumy soberness of extreme age? Might we hope, still with the old irrefragable transcen-dentalism? The victorious cause pleased the gods, the vanquished one pleased Siéyès (*victa Catoni*).

Thus, however, amid skyrending *vivats,* and blessings from every heart, has the Procession of the Commons Deputies rolled by.

Next follow the Noblesse, and next the Clergy; concerning both of whom it might be asked, What they specially have come for? Spe-cially, little as they dream of it, to answer this question, put in a voice of thunder: What are you doing in God's fair Earth and Task-garden; where whosoever is not working is begging or stealing? Wo, wo to themselves and to all, if they can only answer: Collecting tithes, Preserving game!—Remark, meanwhile, how *D'Orléans* affects to step before his own Order, and mingle with the Commons. For him are *vivats:* few for the rest, though all wave in plumed 'hats of a feudal cut', and have sword on thigh; though among them is *D'An-traigues,* the young Languedocian gentleman, and indeed many a Peer more or less noteworthy.

There are *Liancourt,* and *La Rochefoucault;* the liberal Anglo-maniac Dukes. There is a filially pious *Lally;* a couple of liberal *Lameths.* Above all, there is a *Lafayette;* whose name shall be Cromwell-Grandison, and fill the world. Many a 'formula' has this Lafayette too made away with; yet not *all* formulas. He sticks by the Washington-formula; and by that he will stick;—and hang by it, as by sure bower-anchor hangs and swings the tight warship, which, after all changes of wildest weather and water, is found still hanging. Happy for him; be it glorious or not! Alone of all Frenchmen he has a theory of the world, and right mind to conform thereto; he can be-come a hero and perfect character, were it but the hero of one idea. Note further our old Parlementary friend, *Crispin-Catiline d'Espré-ménil.* He is returned from the Mediterranean Islands, a redhot

303

royalist, repentant to the finger ends; unsettled-looking; whose light, dusky-glowing at best, now flickers foul in the socket; whom the National Assembly will by and by, to save time, 'regard as in a state of distraction'. Note lastly that globular *Younger* Mirabeau; indignant that his elder Brother is among the Commons: it is *Viscomte* Mirabeau; named oftener Mirabeau *Tonneau* (Barrel Mirabeau), on account of his rotundity, and the quantities of strong liquor he contains.

There then walks our French Noblesse. All in the old pomp of chivalry: and yet, alas, how changed from the old position; drifted far down from their native latitude, like Arctic icebergs got into the Equatorial sea, and fast thawing there! Once these Chivalry *Duces* (Dukes, as they are still named) did actually *lead* the world—were it only towards battle-spoil, where lay the world's best wages then: moreover, being the ablest Leaders going, they had their lion's share, those *Duces;* which none could grudge them. But now, when so many Looms, improved Ploughshares, Steam-Engines and Bills of Exchange have been invented; and, for battle-brawling itself, men hire Drill-Sergeants at eighteen-pence a-day—what means these goldmantled Chivalry Figures, walking there 'in black velvet cloaks,' in high-plumed 'hats of a feudal cut'? Reeds shaken in the wind!

The Clergy have got up; with *Cahiers* for abolishing pluralities, enforcing residence of bishops, better payment of tithes. The Dignitaries, we can observe, walk stately, apart from the numerous Undignified—who indeed are properly little other than Commons disguised in Curate-frocks. Here, however, though by strange ways, shall the Precept be fulfilled, and they that are greatest (much to their astonishment) become least. For one example, out of many, mark that plausible *Grégoire:* one day Curé Grégoire shall be a Bishop, when the now stately are wandering distracted, as Bishops *in partibus.* With other thought, mark also the *Abbé Maury:* his broad bold face; mouth accurately primmed; full eyes, that ray out intelligence, falsehood—the sort of sophistry which is astonished you should find it sophistical. Skilfullest vamper up of old rotten leather, to make it look like new; always a rising man; he used to tell Mercier, 'You will see; I shall be in the Academy before you.' Likely indeed, thou skilfullest Maury; nay thou shalt have a Cardinal's Hat, and plush and glory; but alas, also, in the long run—mere oblivion, like the rest of us; and six feet of earth! What boots it, vamping rotten leather on these terms? Glorious in comparison is the livelihood thy good old Father earns, by making shoes—one may hope, in a sufficient manner. Maury does not want for audacity. He shall wear pistols, by and by; and, at death-cries of 'La Lanterne, the Lamp-iron!'—answer coolly, 'Friends, will you see better there?'

But yonder, halting lamely along, thou noticest next Bishop Talley-rand-Perigord, his Reverence of Autun. A sardonic grimness lies in that irreverend Reverence of Autun. He will do and suffer strange things; and will become surely one of the strangest things ever seen, or like to be seen. A man living in falsehood, and on falsehood; yet not what you can call a false man: there is the specialty! It will be an enigma for future ages, one may hope: hitherto such a product of Nature and Art was possible only for this age of ours—Age of Paper, and of the Burning of Paper. Consider Bishop Talleyrand and Mar-quis Lafayette as the topmost of their two kinds; and say once more, looking at what they did and what they were, O Tempus ferax rerum!

On the whole, however, has not this unfortunate Clergy also drifted in the Time-stream, far from its native latitude? An anomalous mass of men; of whom the whole world has already a dim understanding that it can understand nothing. They were once a Priesthood, inter-preters of Wisdom, revealers of the Holy that is in Man; a true Clerus (or Inheritance of God on Earth): but now?—They pass silently, with such Cahiers as they have been able to redact. . . .

King Louis with his Court brings up the rear: he cheerful, in this day of hope, is saluted with plaudits; still more Necker his Minister. Not so the Queen; on whom hope shines not steadily any more. Ill-fated Queen! Her hair is already grey with many cares and crosses; her first-born son is dying in these weeks; black falsehood has in-effaceably soiled her name; ineffaceably while this generation lasts. Instead of Vive la Reine, voices insult her with Vive d'Orléans. Of her queenly beauty little remains except its stateliness; not now gracious, but haughty, rigid, silently enduring. With a most mixed feeling, wherein joy has no part, she resigns herself to a day she hoped never to have seen. Poor Marie Antoinette; with thy quick noble instincts; vehement glancings, vision all-too fitful narrow for the work thou hast to do! O there are tears in store for thee; bitterest wailings, soft womanly meltings, though thou hast the heart of an imperial Theresa's Daughter. Thou doomed one, shut thy eyes on the future!—

And so, in stately Procession, have passed the Elected of France. Some towards honour and quick fire-consummation; most towards dishonour; not a few towards massacre, confusion, emigration, desperation: all towards Eternity!—So many heterogeneities cast together into the fermenting-vat; there, with incalculable action, counteraction, elective affinities, explosive developments, to work out healing for a sick moribund System of Society! Probably the strangest Body of Men, if we consider well, that ever met together on our Planet on such an errand. So thousandfold complex a Society, ready to burst up from its infinite depths; and these men, its rulers and healers, without life-rule for themselves—other life-rule than a Gospel according to Jean Jacques! To [him] . . . man is properly an Accident under the sky. Man is without Duty round him; except it be 'to make the Constitution.' He is without Heaven above him, or Hell beneath him; he has no God in the world.

What further or better belief can be said to exist in these Twelve Hundred? Belief in high-plumed hats of a feudal cut; in heraldic scutcheons; in the divine right of Kings, in the divine right of Game-destroyers. Belief, or what is still worse, canting half-belief, or worst of all, mere Machiavelic pretence-of-belief. . . . Nevertheless in that immeasurable Confusion and Corruption, which struggles there so blindly to become less confused and corrupt, there is, as we said, this one salient-point of a New Life discernible: the deep fixed Determination to have done with Shams. A determination, which, consciously or unconsciously, is *fixed;* which waxes ever more fixed, into very madness and fixed-idea; which in such embodiment as lies provided there, shall now unfold itself rapidly: monstrous, stupendous, unspeakable; new for long thousands of years!—How has the Heaven's *light,* oftentimes in this Earth, to clothe itself in thunder and electric murkiness; and descend as molten *lightning,* blasting, if purifying! Nay is it not rather the very murkiness, and atmospheric suffocation, that *brings* the lightning and the light? The new Evangel, as the old had been, was it to be born in the Destruction of a World?

But how the Deputies assisted at High Mass, and heard sermon, and applauded the preacher, church as it was, when he preached politics; how, next day, with sustained pomp, they are, for the first time, installed in their *Salle des Menus* (Hall no longer of *Amusements*), and become a States-General—readers can fancy for themselves. The King from his *estrade,* gorgeous as Solomon in all his glory, runs his eye over that majestic Hall; many-plumed, many-glancing;

306

bright-tinted as rainbow, in the galleries and near side-spaces, where Beauty sits raining bright influence. Satisfaction, as of one that after long voyaging had got to port, plays over his broad simple face: the innocent King! He rises and speaks, with sonorous tone, a conceivable speech. With which, still more with the succeeding one-hour and two-hour speeches of Garde-des-Sceaux and M. Necker, full of nothing but patriotism, hope, faith, and deficiency of the revenue—no reader of these pages shall be tried.

We remark only that, as his Majesty, on finishing the speech, put on his plumed hat, and the Noblesse according to custom imitated him, our Tiers-État Deputies did mostly, not without a shade of fierceness, in like manner clap on, and even crush on their slouched hats; and stand there awaiting the issue. Thick buzz among them, between majority and minority of *Couvrez-vous, Découvrez-vous* (Hats off, Hats on)! To which his Majesty puts end, by taking *off* his own royal hat again.

The session terminates without further accident or omen than this; with which, significantly enough, France has opened her States-General.

SECTION III

The Bastille

[*The States-General opened formal sittings on May 5, and an immediate dispute arose over the question whether it should sit and vote as a single body or separately by orders. Since the Third Estate (commoners) had a double representation, it would have a controlling voice if the vote were to be by head in a single body, but would be outvoted if the organization were by separate orders. This dispute was eventually resolved by the first distinctly revolutionary act of the Third Estate, which under the leadership of Mirabeau and Abbé Siéyès, defying the express command of the King, boldly declared itself the "National Assembly" (also called "Constituent Assembly"), and took the famous "Oath of the Tennis Court" (June 20) not to disband until they had made a new constitution for France. In this action the Third Estate was joined by the more liberal nobles and clergy, and the King, after a feeble*

307

resistance, abandoned his attempt to force the Assembly to sit and vote by separate orders. But in July rumors began to circulate that the King intended to dissolve the National Assembly and was concentrating troops for that purpose near Paris.]

TO ARMS!

So HANGS IT, dubious, fateful, in the sultry days of July. It is the passionate printed *advice* of M. Marat, to abstain, of all things, from violence. Nevertheless the hungry poor are already burning Town Barriers, where Tribute on eatables is levied; getting clamorous for food.

The twelfth July morning is Sunday: the streets are all placarded with an enormous-sized *De par le Roi,* 'inviting peaceable citizens to remain within doors,' to feel no alarm, to gather in no crowd. Why so? What mean these 'placards of enormous size?' Above all, what means this clatter of military; dragoons, hussars, rattling in from all points of the compass towards the Place Louis Quinze; with a staid gravity of face, though saluted with mere nicknames, hootings and even missiles? Besenval is with them. Swiss Guards of his are already in the Champs Elysées, with four pieces of artillery.

Have the destroyers descended on us, then? From the Bridge of Sèvres to utmost Vincennes, from Saint-Denis to the Champ-de-Mars, we are begirt! Alarm, of the vague unknown, is in every heart. The Palais Royal has become a place of awestruck interjections, silent shakings of the head: one can fancy with what dolorous sound the noontide cannon (which the Sun fires at crossing of his meridian) went off there; bodeful, like an inarticulate voice of doom. Are these troops verily come out 'against Brigands?' Where are the Brigands? What mystery is in the wind?—Hark! a human voice reporting articulately the Job's-news: *Necker, People's Minister, Saviour of France, is dismissed.* Impossible; incredible! Treasonous to the public peace! Such a voice ought to be choked in the water-works;—had not the news-bringer quickly fled. Nevertheless, friends make of it what ye will, the news is true. Necker is gone. Necker hies northward incessantly, in obedient secrecy, since yesternight. We have a new Ministry: Broglie the War-god; Aristocrat Breteuil; Foulon who said the people might eat grass!

Rumour, therefore, shall arise; in the Palais Royal, and in broad France. Paleness sits on every face; confused tremor and fremescence; waxing into thunder-peals, of Fury stirred on by Fear.

But see Camille Desmoulins, from the Café de Foy, rushing out, sibylline in face; his hair streaming, in each hand a pistol! He springs to a table: the Police satellites are eyeing him; alive they shall not take him, not they alive him alive. This time, he speaks without stammering:—Friends! shall we die like hunted hares? Like sheep hounded into their pinfold; bleating for mercy, where is no mercy, but only a whetted knife? The hour is come; the supreme hour of Frenchman and Man; when Oppressors are to try conclusions with Oppressed; and the word is, swift Death, or Deliverance for ever. Let such hour be *well*-come! Us, meseems, one cry only befits: To Arms! Let universal Paris, universal France, as with the throat of the whirlwind, sound only: To arms!—'To arms!' yell responsive the innumerable voices; like one great voice, as of a Demon yelling from the air: for all faces wax fire-eyed, all hearts burn up into madness. In such, or fitter words, does Camille evoke the Elemental Powers, in this great moment.—Friends, continues Camille, some rallying-sign! Cockades; green ones—the colour of Hope!—As with the flight of locusts, these green tree-leaves; green ribands from the neighbouring shops; all green things are snatched, and made cockades of. Camille descends from his table; 'stifled with embraces, wetted with tears'; has a bit of green riband handed him; sticks it in his hat. And now to Curtius' Image-shop there; to the Boulevards; to the four winds, and rest not till France be on fire!

France, so long shaken and wind-parched, is probably at the right inflammable point.—As for poor Curtius, who, one grieves to think, might be but imperfectly paid, he cannot make two words about his Images. The Wax-bust of Necker, the Wax-bust of D'Orléans, helpers of France: these, covered with crape, as in funeral procession, or after the manner of suppliants appealing to Heaven, to Earth, and Tartarus itself, a mixed multitude bears off. For a sign! As indeed man, with his singular imaginative faculties, can do little or nothing without signs: thus Turks look to their Prophet's Banner; also Osier *Mannikins* have been burnt, and Necker's Portrait has erewhile figured, aloft on its perch.

In this manner march they, a mixed, continually increasing multitude; armed with axes, staves and miscellanea; grim, many-sounding, through the streets. Be all Theatres shut; let all dancing, on planked floor, or on the natural greensward, cease! Instead of a Christian Sabbath, and feast of *guinguette* tabernacles, it shall be a Sorcerer's Sabbath; and Paris, gone rabid, dance—with the Fiend for piper!

On Monday, the huge City has awoke, not to its week-day industry: to what a different one! The working man has become a fighting man; has one want only: that of arms. The industry of all crafts has paused; except it be the smith's, fiercely hammering pikes; and, in a faint degree, the kitchener's, cooking offhand victuals, for *bouche va toujours.* Women too are sewing cockades—not now, of *green,* which being D'Artois colour, the Hôtel-de-Ville has had to interfere in it; but of *red* and *blue,* our old Paris colours: these, once based on a ground of constitutional *white,* are the famed TRICOLOR—which (if Prophecy err not) 'will go round the world'.

All shops, unless it be the Bakers' and Vintners', are shut: Paris is in the streets—rushing, foaming like some Venice wine-glass into which you had dropped poison. The tocsin, by order, is pealing madly from all steeples. Arms, ye Elector Municipals; thou Flesselles with thy Echevins, give us arms! Flesselles gives what he can: fallacious, perhaps insidious promises of arms from Charleville; order to seek arms here, order to seek them there. The new Municipals give what they can; some three hundred and sixty indifferent firelocks, the equipment of the City-Watch: 'a man in wooden shoes, and without coat, directly clutches one of them, and mounts guard.' Also as hinted, an order to all Smiths to make pikes with their whole soul.

But to the living and the struggling, a new, Fourteenth morning dawns. Under all roofs of this distracted City is the nodus of a drama, not untragical, crowding towards solution. The bustlings and preparings, the tremors and menaces; the tears that fell from old eyes! This day, my sons, ye shall quit you like men. By the memory of your fathers' wrongs, by the hope of your children's rights! Tyranny impends in red wrath: help for you is none, if not in your own right hands. This day ye must do or die.

From earliest light, a sleepless Permanent Committee has heard the old cry, now waxing almost frantic, mutinous: Arms! Arms! Provost Flesselles, or what traitors there are among you, may think of those Charleville Boxes. A hundred-and-fifty thousand of us; and but the third man furnished with so much as a pike! Arms are the one thing needful: with arms we are an unconquerable man-defying National Guard; without arms, a rabble to be whiffed with grapeshot.

Happily the word has arisen, for no secret can be kept—that there lie muskets at the *Hôtel des Invalides.* Thither will we: King's Procureur M. Ethys de Corny, and whatsoever of authority a Permanent Committee can lend, shall go with us. Besenval's Camp is there; perhaps he will not fire on us; if he kill us, we shall but die.

Alas, poor Besenval, with his troops melting away in that manner, has not the smallest humour to fire! At five o'clock, this morning, as he lay dreaming, oblivious in the *École Militaire,* a 'figure' stood suddenly at his bedside; 'with face rather handsome; eyes inflamed, speech rapid and curt, air audacious': such a figure drew Priam's curtains! The message and monition of the figure was, that resistance would be hopeless; that if blood flowed, woe to him who shed it. Thus spoke the figure: and vanished. 'Withal there was a kind of eloquence that struck one.' Besenval admits that he should have arrested him, but did not. Who this figure with inflamed eyes, with speech rapid and curt, might be? Besenval knows, but mentions not. Camille Desmoulins? Pythagorean Marquis Valadi, inflamed with 'violent motions all night at the Palais Royal'? Fame names him. 'Young M. Meillar;' then shuts her lips about him for ever.

In any case, behold about nine in the morning, our National Volunteers rolling in long wide flood, southwestward to the *Hôtel des Invalides;* in search of the one thing needful. King's Procureur M. Ethys de Corny and officials are there; the Curé of Saint-Etienne du Mont marches unpacific, at the head of his militant Parish; the Clerks of the Basoche in red coats we see marching, now Volunteers of the Basoche; the Volunteers of the Palais Royal—National Volunteers, numerable by tens of thousands; of one heart and mind. The King's muskets are the Nation's; think, old M. de Sombreuil, how, in this extremity, thou wilt refuse them! Old M. de Sombreuil would fain hold parley, send couriers; but it skills not: the walls are scaled, no Invalide firing a shot; the gates must be flung open. Patriotism rushes in, tumultuous, from grunsel up to ridge-tile, through all rooms and passages; rummaging distractedly for arms. What cellar, or what cranny can escape it? The arms are found; all safe there; lying packed in straw, apparently with a view to being burnt! More ravenous than famishing lions over dead prey, the multitude, with clangour and vociferation, pounces on them; struggling, dashing, clutching:—to the jamming-up, to the pressure, fracture and probable extinction of the weaker Patriot. And so, with such protracted crash of deafening, most discordant Orchestra-music, the Scene is changed; and eight-and-twenty thousand sufficient firelocks are on the shoulders of as many National Guards, lifted thereby out of darkness into fiery light.

Let Besenval look at the glitter of these muskets, as they flash by! Gardes Françaises, it is said, have cannon levelled on him; ready to open, if need were, from the other side of the River. Motionless sits he; 'astonished,' one may flatter oneself, 'at the proud bearing (*fière contenance*) of the Parisians.'—And now, to the Bastille, ye intrepid Parisians! There grapeshot still threatens: thither all men's thoughts and steps are now tending.

Old De Launay, as we hinted, withdrew 'into his interior' soon after midnight of Sunday. He remains there ever since hampered, as all military gentlemen now are, in the saddest conflict of uncertainties. The Hôtel-de-Ville 'invites' him to admit National Soldiers, which is a soft name for surrendering. On the other hand, His Majesty's orders were precise. His garrison is but eighty-two old Invalides, reinforced by thirty-two young Swiss; his walls indeed are nine feet thick, he has cannon and powder; but, alas, only one day's provision of victuals. The city too is French, the poor garrison mostly French. Rigorous old De Launay, think what thou wilt do!

All morning, since nine, there has been a cry everywhere: To the Bastille! Repeated 'deputations of citizens' have been here, passionate for arms; whom De Launay has got dismissed by soft speeches through port-holes. Towards noon, Elector Thuriot de la Rosière gains admittance; finds De Launay indisposed for surrender; nay, disposed for blowing up the place rather. Thuriot mounts with him to the battlements: heaps of paving-stones, old iron and missiles lie piled; cannon all duly levelled; in every embrasure a cannon, only drawn back a little! But outwards, behold, O Thuriot, how the multitude flows on, welling through every street: tocsin furiously pealing, all drums beating the *générale:* the Suburb Saint-Antoine rolling hitherward wholly, as one man! Such vision (spectral yet real) thou, O Thuriot, as from thy Mount of Vision, beholdest in this moment: prophetic of what other Phantasmagories, and loud-gibbering Spectral Realities, which thou yet beholdest not, but shalt! *'Que voulez-vous?'* said De Launay, turning pale at the sight, with an air of reproach, almost of menace. 'Monsieur', said Thuriot, rising into the moral-sublime, 'what mean

312

you? Consider if I could not precipitate *both* of us from this height'—
say only a hundred feet, exclusive of the walled ditch! Whereupon
De Launay fell silent. Thuriot shows himself from some pinnacle, to
comfort the multitude becoming suspicious, fremescent: then descends; departs with protest; with warning addressed also to the Invalides—on whom, however, it produces but a mixed indistinct impression. The old heads are none of the clearest; besides, it is said,
De Launay has been profuse of beverages (*prodigua des buissons*).
They think, they will not fire—if not fired on, if they can help it; but
must, on the whole, be ruled considerably by circumstances.

Woe to thee, De Launay, in such an hour, if thou canst not, taking
some one firm decision, *rule* circumstances! Soft speeches will not
serve; hard grapeshot is questionable; but hovering between the two
is *un*questionable. Even wilder swells the tide of men; their infinite
hum waxing ever louder, into imprecations, perhaps into crackle of
stray musketry—which latter, on walls nine feet thick, cannot do
execution. The Outer Drawbridge has been lowered for Thuriot; new
deputation of citizens (it is the third, and noisiest of all) penetrates
that way into the Outer Court: soft speeches producing no clearance
of these, De Launay gives fire; pulls up his Drawbridge. A slight
sputter; which has *kindled* the too combustible chaos; made it a
roaring fire-chaos! Bursts forth Insurrection, at sight of its own blood
(for there were deaths by that sputter of fire), into endless rolling
explosion of musketry, distraction, execration—and overhead, from
the Fortress, let one great gun, with its grapeshot, go booming, to
show what we *could* do. The Bastille is besieged!

STORM AND VICTORY

O N, THEN, ALL FRENCHMEN, that have hearts in your bodies! Roar
with all your throats, of cartilage and metal, ye Sons of Liberty;
stir spasmodically whatsoever of utmost faculty is in you, soul, body,
or spirit; for it is the hour! Smite, thou Louis Tournay, cartwright of
the Marais, old-soldier of the Regiment Dauphiné; smite at that Outer
Drawbridge chain, though the fiery hail whistles round thee! Never,
over nave or felloe, did thy axe strike such a stroke. Down with it,
man; down with it to Orcus: let the whole accursed Edifice sink
thither, and Tyranny be swallowed up for ever! Mounted, some say,
on the roof of the guard-room, some 'on bayonets stuck into joints of

the wall,' Louis Tournay smites, brave Aubin Bonnemère (also an old soldier) seconding him: the chain yields, breaks; the huge Draw-bridge slams down, thundering (*avec fracas*). Glorious: and yet, alas, it is still but the outworks. The Eight grim Towers, with their Invalide musketry, their paving stones and cannon-mouths, still soar aloft in-tact—Ditch yawning impassable, stone-faced; the inner Drawbridge with its *back* towards us: the Bastille is still to take!

To describe this Siege of the Bastille (thought to be one of the most important in History) perhaps transcends the talent of mortals. Could one but, after infinite reading, get to understand so much as the plan of the building! But there is open Esplanade, at the end of the Rue Saint-Antoine; there are such Forecourts, *Cour Avancé, Cour de l'Orme,* arched Gateway (where Louis Tournay now fights); then new drawbridges, dormant-bridges, rampart-bastions, and the grim Eight Towers: a labyrinthic Mass, high-frowning there, of all ages from twenty years to four hundred and twenty—beleaguered, in this its last hour, as we said, by mere Chaos come again! Ordnance of all calibres; throats of all capacities; men of all plans, every man his own engineer: seldom since the war of Pygmies and Cranes was there seen so anomalous a thing. Half-pay Elie is home for a suit of regimentals; no one would heed him in coloured clothes: half-pay Hulin is harangu-ing Gardes Françaises in the Place de Grève. Frantic Patriots pick up the grapeshots; bear them, still hot (or seemingly so), to the Hôtel-de-Ville. Paris, you perceive, is to be burnt! Flesselles is 'pale to the very lips', for the roar of the multitude grows deep. Paris wholly has got to the acme of its frenzy; whirled, all ways, by panic madness. At every street-barricade, there whirls simmering a minor whirlpool, strengthen-ing the barricade, since God knows what is coming; and all minor whirlpools play distractedly into that grand Fire-Maelstrom which is lashing round the Bastille.

And so it lashes and it roars. Cholat the wine-merchant has become an impromptu cannoneer. See Georget, of the Marine Service, fresh from Brest, ply the King of Siam's cannon. Singular (if we were not used to the like): Georget lay, last night, taking his ease at his inn; the King of Siam's cannon also lay, knowing nothing of *him,* for a hundred years. Yet now, at the right instant, they have got together, and discourse eloquent music. For, hearing what was toward, Georget sprang from the Brest Diligence, and ran. Gardes Françaises also will be here, with real artillery: were not the walls so thick! Upwards from the Esplanade, horizontally from all neighbouring roofs and windows, flashes one irregular deluge of musketry, without effect. The Invalides lie flat, firing comparatively at their ease from behind stone; hardly through portholes, show the tip of a nose. We fall, shot; and make no impression!

Let conflagration rage; of whatsoever is combustible! Guard-rooms are burnt, Invalides mess-rooms. A distracted 'perukemaker with two fiery torches' is for burning 'the saltpetres of the Arsenal;' had not a woman run screaming; had not a Patriot, with some tincture of Natural Philosophy, instantly struck the wind out of him (butt of musket on pit of stomach), overturned barrels, and stayed the devouring element. A young beautiful lady, seized escaping in these Outer Courts, and thought falsely to be De Launay's daughter, shall be burnt in De Launay's sight; she lies swooned on a paillasse: but again a Patriot, it is brave Aubin Bonnemère the old soldier, dashes in, and rescues her. Straw is burnt; three cartloads of it, hauled thither, go up in white smoke: almost to the choking of Patriotism itself; so that Elie had, with singed brows, to drag back one cart; and Réole the 'gigantic haberdasher' another. Smoke as of Tophet; confusion as of Babel; noise as of the Crack of Doom!

Blood flows; the aliment of new madness. The wounded are carried into houses of the Rue Cerisaie; the dying leave their last mandate not to yield till the accursed Stronghold fall. And yet, alas, how fall? The walls are so thick! Deputations, three in number, arrive from the Hôtel-de-Ville; Abbé Fauchet (who was of one) can say, with what almost superhuman courage of benevolence. These wave their Town-flag in the arched Gateway; and stand, rolling their drum; but to no purpose. In such Crack of Doom, De Launay cannot hear them, dare not believe them: they return, with justified rage, the whew of lead still singing in their ears. What to do? The Firemen are here, squirting with their fire-pumps on the Invalides cannon, to wet the touchholes; they unfortunately cannot squirt so high; but produce only clouds of spray. Individuals of classical knowledge propose *catapults*. Santerre, the sonorous Brewer of the Suburb Saint-Antoine, advises rather that the place be fired, by a 'mixture of phosphorus and oil-of-turpentine spouted up through forcing pumps': O Spinola-Santerre, hast thou the mixture *ready*? Every man his own engineer! And still the fire-deluge abates not: even women are firing, and Turks; at least one woman

315

(with her sweetheart), and one Turk. Gardes Françaises have come: real cannon, real cannoneers. Usher Maillard is busy; half-pay Elie, half-pay Hulin rage in the midst of thousands.

How the great Bastille Clock ticks (inaudible) in its Inner Court there, at its ease, hour after hour; as if nothing special, for it or the world, were passing! It tolled One when the firing began; and is now pointing towards Five, and still the firing slakes not.—Far down, in their vaults, the seven Prisoners hear muffled din as of earthquakes; their Turnkeys answer vaguely.

Woe to thee, De Launay, with thy poor hundred Invalides! Broglie is distant, and his ears heavy: Besenval hears, but can send no help. One poor troop of Hussars has crept, reconnoitring, cautiously along the Quais, as far as the Pont Neuf. 'We are come to join you', said the Captain; for the crowd seems shoreless. A large-headed dwarfish individual, of smoke-bleared aspect, shambles forward, opening his blue lips, for there is sense in him; and croaks: 'alight then, and give up your arms!' The Hussar-Captain is too happy to be escorted to the Barriers, and dismissed on parole. Who the squat individual was? Men answer, It is M. Marat, author of the excellent pacific *Avis au Peuple!* Great truly, O thou remarkable Dogleech, is this thy day of emergence and new-birth: and yet this same day come four years—!—But let the curtains of the Future hang.

What shall De Launay do? One thing only De Launay could have done: what he said he would do. Fancy him sitting, from the first, with lighted taper, within arm's length of the Powder-Magazine; motionless, like old Roman Senator, or Bronze Lamp-holder; coldly apprising Thuriot, and all men, by a slight motion of his eye, what his resolution was:—Harmless he sat there, while unharmed; but the King's Fortress, meanwhile, could, might, would, or should, in nowise be surrendered, save to the King's Messenger: one old man's life is worthless, so it be lost with honour; but think, ye brawling *canaille,* how will it be when a whole Bastille springs skyward!—In such statuesque, taper-holding attitude, one fancies De Launay might have left Thuriot, the red Clerks of the Basoche, Curé of Saint-Stephen and all the tag-rag-and-bobtail of the world, to work their will.

And yet, withal, he could not do it. Hast thou considered how each man's heart is so tremulously responsive to the hearts of all men; hast thou noted how omnipotent is the very sound of many men? How their shriek of indignation palsies the strong soul; their howl of contumely withers with unfelt pangs? The Ritter Glück confessed that

316

the ground-tone of the noblest passage, in one of his noblest Operas, was the voice of the Populace he had heard at Vienna, crying to their Kaiser: Bread! Bread! Great is the combined voice of men; the utterance of their *instincts,* which are truer than their *thoughts:* it is the greatest a man encounters, among the sounds and shadows which make up this World of Time. He who can resist that, has his footing somewhere *beyond* Time. De Launay could not do it. Distracted, he hovers between two; hopes in the middle of despair; surrenders not his Fortress; declares that he will blow it up, seizes torches to blow it up, and does not blow it. Unhappy old De Launay, it is the death-agony of thy Bastille and thee! Jail, Jailoring and Jailor, all three, such as they may have been, must finish.

For four hours now has the World-Bedlam roared: call it the World-Chimera, blowing fire! The poor Invalides have sunk under their battlements, or rise only with reversed muskets: they have made a white flag of napkins: go beating the *chamade,* or seeming to beat, for one can hear nothing. The very Swiss at the portcullis look weary of firing; disheartened in the fire-deluge: a porthole at the drawbridge is opened, as by one that would speak. See Huissier Maillard, the shifty man! On his plank, swinging over the abyss of that stone Ditch; plank resting on parapet, balanced by weight of Patriots, he hovers perilous: such a Dove towards such an Ark! Deftly, thou shifty Usher: one man already fell; and lies smashed, far down there, against the masonry! Usher Maillard falls not: deftly, unerring he walks, with outspread palm. The Swiss holds a paper through his porthole; the shifty Usher snatches it, and returns. Terms of surrender: Pardon, immunity to all! Are they accepted?—'*Foi d'officier,* On the word of an officer,' answers half-pay Hulin,—or half-pay Elie, for men do not agree on it, 'they are!' Sinks the drawbridge—Usher Maillard bolting it when down; rushes-in the living deluge: the Bastille is fallen! *Victoire! La Bastille est prise!*

NOT A REVOLT

WHY DWELL ON WHAT FOLLOWS? Hulin's *foi d'officier* should have been kept, but could not. The Swiss stand drawn up, disguised in white canvas smocks; the Invalides without disguise; their arms all piled against the wall. The first rush of victors, in ecstasy that the death-peril is passed, 'leaps joyfully on their necks;' but new victors rush, and ever new, also in ecstasy not wholly of joy. As we said, it was a living deluge, plunging headlong: had not the Gardes Françaises, in their cool military way, 'wheeled round with arms levelled', it would have plunged suicidally, by the hundred or the thousand, into the Bastille-ditch.

And so it goes plunging through court and corridor; billowing uncontrollable, firing from windows—on itself; in hot frenzy of triumph, of grief and vengeance for its slain. The poor Invalides will fare ill; one Swiss, running off in his white smock, is driven back, with a death-thrust. Let all Prisoners be marched to the Townhall, to be judged!— Alas, already one poor Invalide has his right hand slashed off him; his maimed body dragged to the Place de Grève, and hanged there. This same right hand, it is said, turned back De Launay from the Powder-Magazine, and saved Paris.

De Launay, 'discovered in grey frock with poppy-coloured riband,' is for killing himself with the sword of his cane. He shall to the Hôtel-de-Ville; Hulin, Maillard and others escorting him; Elie marching foremost 'with the capitulation-paper on his sword's point'. Through roarings and cursings; through hustlings, clutchings, and at last through strokes! Your escort is hustled aside, felled down; Hulin sinks exhausted on a heap of stones. Miserable De Launay! He shall never enter the Hôtel-de-Ville: only his 'bloody hair-queue, held up in a bloody hand;' that shall enter, for a sign. The bleeding trunk lies on the steps there; the head is off through the streets; ghastly, aloft on a pike.

Rigorous De Launay has died; crying out, 'O friends, kill me fast!' Merciful De Losme must die; though Gratitude embraces him, in this fearful hour, and will die for him; it avails not. Brothers, your wrath is cruel! Your Place de Grève is become a Throat of the Tiger; full of mere fierce bellowings, and thirst of blood. One other officer is massacred; one other Invalide is hanged on the Lamp-iron; with difficulty, with generous perseverance, the Gardes Françaises will save the rest. Provost Flesselles, stricken long since with the paleness of death, must descend from his seat, 'to be judged at the Palais Royal'—alas, to be shot dead, by an unknown hand, at the turning of the first street!

O evening sun of July, how, at this hour, thy beams fall slant on reapers amid peaceful woody fields; on old women spinning in cottages; on ships far out in the silent main; on Balls at the Orangerie of Versailles, where high-rouged Dames of the Palace are even now dancing with double-jacketed Hussar-Officers—and also on this roaring Hell-porch of a Hôtel-de-Ville! Babel Tower, with the confusion of tongues, were not Bedlam added with the conflagration of thoughts, was no type of it. One forest of distracted steel bristles, endless, in front of an Electoral Committee; points itself, in horrid radii, against this and the other accused breast. It was the Titans warring with Olympus; and they, scarcely crediting it, have *conquered:* prodigy of prodigies; delirious—as it could not but be. Denunciation, vengeance; blaze of triumph on a dark ground of terror: all outward, all inward things fallen into one general wreck of madness!

Electoral Committee? Had it a thousand throats of brass, it would not suffice. Abbé Lefevre, in the Vaults down below, is black as Vulcan, distributing that 'five thousand-weight of Powder'; with what perils, these eight-and-forty hours! Last night, a Patriot, in liquor, insisted on sitting to smoke on the edge of one of the Powder-barrels: there smoked he, independent of the world—till the Abbé 'purchased his pipe for three francs', and pitched it far.

Elie, in the grand Hall, Electoral Committee looking on, sits 'with drawn sword bent in three places'; with battered helm, for he was of the Queen's Regiment, Cavalry; with torn regimentals, face singed and soiled; comparable, some think, to 'an antique warrior'—judging the people; forming a list of Bastille Heroes. O Friends, stain not with blood the greenest laurels ever gained in this world: such is the burden of Elie's song: could it but be listened to. Courage, Elie! Courage, ye Municipal Electors! A declining sun; the need of victuals, and of telling news, will bring assuagement, dispersion: all earthly things must end.

Along the streets of Paris circulate Seven Bastille Prisoners, borne shoulder-high; seven Heads on pikes; the Keys of the Bastille; and much else. See also the Gardes Françaises, in their steadfast military way, marching home to their barracks, with the Invalides and Swiss kindly enclosed in hollow square. It is one year and two months since these same men stood unparticipating, with Brennus d'Agoust at the Palais de Justice, when Fate overtook D'Espréménil; and now they have participated; and will participate. Not Gardes Françaises henceforth, but *Centre Grenadiers of the National Guard:* men of iron discipline and humour—not without a kind of thought in them!

Likewise ashlar stones of the Bastille continue thundering through the dusk; its paper archives shall fly white. Old secrets come to view;

and long-buried Despair finds voice. Read this portion of an old Letter: 'If for my consolation Monseigneur would grant me, for the sake of God and the Most Blessed Trinity, that I could have news of my dear wife; were it only her name on a card, to show that she is alive! It were the greatest consolation I could receive; and I should for ever bless the greatness of Monseigneur.' Poor Prisoner, who namest thyself *Quéret-Démery,* and has no other history—she is *dead,* that dear wife of thine, and thou art dead! 'Tis fifty years since thy breaking heart put this question; to be heard now first, and long heard, in the hearts of men.

But so does the July twilight thicken; so must Paris, as sick children, and all distracted creatures do, brawl itself finally into a kind of sleep. Municipal Electors, astonished to find their heads still uppermost, are home: only Moreau de Saint-Méry of tropical birth and heart, of coolest judgement; he, with two others, shall sit permanent at the Townhall. Paris sleeps; gleams upward the illuminated City: patrols go clashing, without common watchword; there go rumours; alarms of war, to the extent of 'fifteen thousand men marching through the Suburb Saint-Antoine'—who never got it marched through. Of the day's distraction judge by this of the night: Moreau de Saint-Méry, 'before rising from his seat, gave upwards of three thousand orders.' What a head; comparable to Friar Bacon's Brass Head! Within it lies all Paris. Prompt must the answer be, right or wrong; in Paris is no other authority extant. Seriously, a most cool clear head—for which also thou, O brave Saint-Méry, in many capacities, from august Senator to Merchant's-Clerk, Book-dealer, Vice-King; in many places, from Virginia to Sardinia, shalt, ever as a brave man, find employment.

Besenval has decamped, under cloud of dusk, 'amid a great affluence of people', who did not harm him; he marches, with faint-growing tread, down the left bank of the Seine, all night—towards infinite space. Re-summoned shall Besenval himself be; for trial, for difficult acquittal. His King's-troops, his Royal-Allemand, are gone hence for ever.

The Versailles Ball and lemonade is done; the Orangerie is silent except for nightbirds. Over in the Salle des Menus, Vice-president Lafayette, with unsnuffed lights, 'with some Hundred or so of Members, stretched on tables round him', sits erect; outwatching the Bear. This day, a second solemn Deputation went to his Majesty; a second and then a third: with no effect. What will the end of these things be?

In the Court, all is mystery, not without whisperings of terror; though ye dream of lemonade and epaulettes, ye foolish women! His Majesty, kept in happy ignorance, perhaps dreams of double-barrels and the Woods of Meudon. Late at night, the Duke de Liancourt, having official right of entrance, gains access to the Royal Apartments; unfolds with earnest clearness, in his constitutional way, the Job's-news. *'Mais,'* said poor Louis, *'c'est une révolte,* Why, that is a revolt!' —'Sire,' answered Liancourt, 'it is not a revolt,—it is a revolution.'

THE LANTERNE

THE FALL OF THE BASTILLE may be said to have shaken all France to the deepest foundations of its existence. The rumour of these wonders flies everywhere: with the natural speed of Rumour; with an effect thought to be preternatural, produced by plots. Did D'Orléans or Laclos, nay did Mirabeau (not overburdened with money at this time) send riding Couriers out from Paris; to gallop 'on all radii', or high-ways, towards all points of France? It is a miracle, which no penetrating man will call in question.

Already in most Towns, Electoral Committees were met; to regret Necker, in harangue and resolution. In many a Town, as Rennes, Caen, Lyons, an ebullient people was already regretting him in brick-bats and musketry. But now, at every Town's-end in France, there do arrive, in these days of terror—'men', as men will arrive; nay 'men on horseback', since Rumour oftenest travels riding. These men declare, with alarmed countenance, *The* BRIGANDS to be coming, to be just at hand; and do then—ride on, about their further business, be what it might! Whereupon the whole population of such Town defensively flies to arms. Petition is soon thereafter forwarded to National Assembly; in such peril and terror of peril, leave to organize yourself cannot be withheld: the armed population becomes everywhere an enrolled National Guard. Thus rides Rumour, careering along all radii, from Paris outwards, to such purpose: in few days, some say in not many hours, all France to the utmost borders bristles with bayonets. Singular, but undeniable—miraculous or not!—But thus may any chemical liquid, though cooled to the freezing-point, or far lower, still continue liquid; and then, on the slightest stroke or shake, it at once rushes wholly into ice. Thus has France, for long months and even years, been chemically dealt with; brought below zero; and now, shaken by the Fall of a Bastille, it instantaneously congeals: into one crystallized mass, of sharp-cutting steel! *Guai a chi la tocca,* 'Ware who touches it!

In Paris, an Electoral Committee, with a new Mayor and General, is urgent with belligerent workmen to resume their handicrafts. Strong Dames of the Market (*Dames de la Halle*) deliver congratulatory harangues; present 'bouquets to the Shrine of Sainte Geneviève.' Unenrolled men deposit their arms—not so readily as could be wished: and receive 'nine francs.' With *Te Deums,* Royal Visits, and sanctioned Revolution, there is halcyon weather; weather even of preternatural brightness; the hurricane being overblown.

Nevertheless, as is natural, the waves still run high, hollow rocks retaining their murmur. We are but at the 22nd of the month, hardly above a week since the Bastille fell, when it suddenly appears that old Foulon is alive; nay, that he is here, in early morning, in the streets of Paris: the extortioner, the plotter, who would make the people eat grass, and was a liar from the beginning!—It is even so. The deceptive 'sumptuous funeral' (of some domestic that died); the hiding-place at Vitry towards Fountainebleau, have not availed that wretched old man. Some living domestic or dependant, for none loves Foulon, has betrayed him to the Village. Merciless boors of Vitry unearth him; pounce on him, like hell-hounds: Westward, old Infamy; to Paris, to be judged at the Hôtel-de-Ville! His old head, which seventy-four years have bleached, is bare; they have tied an emblematic bundle of grass on his back; a garland of nettles and thistles is round his neck: in this manner; led with ropes; goaded on with curses and menaces, must he, with his old limbs, sprawl forward; the pitiablest, most unpitied of all old men.

Sooty Saint-Antoine, and every street, musters its crowds as he passes—the Hall of the Hôtel-de-Ville, the Place de Grève itself, will scarcely hold his escort and him. Foulon must not only be judged righteously, but judged there where he stands, without any delay. Appoint seven judges, ye Municipals, or seventy-and-seven; name them yourselves, or we will name them: but judge him! Electoral rhetoric, eloquence of Mayor Bailly, is wasted, for hours, explaining the beauty of the Law's delay. Delay, and still delay! Behold, O Mayor of the People, the morning has worn itself into noon: and he is still unjudged!—Lafayette, pressingly sent for, arrives; gives voice: This Foulon, a known man, is guilty almost beyond doubt; but may he not have accomplices? Ought not the truth to be cunningly pumped out of him—in the Abbaye Prison? It is a new light! Sansculottism claps hands—at which handclapping, Foulon (in his faintness, as his Destiny would have it) also claps. 'See! they understand one another!' cries dark Sansculottism, blazing into fury of suspicion.—'Friends,' said 'a person in good clothes,' stepping forward, 'what is the use of judging this man? Has he not been judged these thirty years?' With wild yells, Sansculottism clutches him, in its hundred hands: he is whirled across the Place de Grève, to the *'Lanterne'*, Lamp-iron which there is at the corner of the *Rue de la Vannerie;* pleading bitterly for life—to the deaf winds. Only with the third rope (for two ropes broke, and the quavering voice still pleaded) can he be so much as got hanged! His Body is dragged through the streets; his Head goes aloft on a pike, the mouth filled with grass: amid sounds as of Tophet, from a grass-eating people.

Surely if Revenge is a 'kind of Justice,' it is a 'wild' kind! O mad Sansculottism, hast thou risen, in thy mad darkness, in thy soot and rags; unexpectedly, like an Enceladus, living-buried, from under his Trinacria? They that would make grass be eaten do now eat grass, in *this* manner? After long dumb-groaning generations, has the turn suddenly become thine?—To such abysmal overturns, and frightful instantaneous inversions of the centre-of-gravity, are human Solecisms all liable, if they but knew it; the more liable, the falser (and top-heavier) they are!—

To add to the horror of Mayor Bailly and his Municipals, word comes that Berthier has also been arrested; that he is on his way hither from Compiègne. Berthier, Intendant (say *Tax-levier*) of Paris; syco-phant and tyrant; forestaller of Corn; contriver of Camps against the people; accused of many things: is he not Foulon's son-in-law; and, in that one point, guilty of all? In these hours too, when Sansculottism has its blood up! The shuddering Municipals send one of their number to escort him, with mounted National Guards.

At the fall of day, the wretched Berthier, still wearing a face of courage, arrives at the Barrier; in an open carriage; with the Munici-pal beside him; five hundred horsemen with drawn sabres; unarmed footmen enough: not without noise! Placards go brandished round him; bearing legibly his indictment, as Sansculottism, with unlegal

323

brevity, 'in huge letters', draws it up. *'Il a volé le Roi et la France* (He robbed the King and France).' 'He devoured the substance of the People.' 'He was the slave of the rich, and the tyrant of the poor.' 'He drank the blood of the widow and orphan.' 'He betrayed his country'. Paris is come forth to meet him: with hand-clappings, with windows flung up; with dances, triumph-songs, as of the Furies. Lastly, the Head of Foulon; this also meets him on a pike. Well might his 'look become glazed', and sense fail him, at such sight!—Nevertheless, be the man's conscience what it may, his nerves are of iron. At the Hôtel-de-Ville, he will answer nothing. He says he obeyed superior orders; they have his papers; they may judge and determine: as for himself, not having closed an eye these two nights, he demands, before all things, to have sleep. Leaden sleep, thou miserable Berthier! Guards rise with him, in motion towards the Abbaye. At the very door of the Hôtel-de-Ville, they are clutched; flung asunder, as by a vortex of mad arms; Berthier whirls towards the Lanterne. He snatches a musket; fells and strikes, defending himself like a mad lion: he is borne down, trampled, hanged, mangled: his Head too, and even his Heart, flies over the City on a pike.

Horrible, in Lands that had known equal justice! Not so unnatural in Lands that had never known it, *'Le sang qui coule, est-il donc si pur?'* asks Barnave; intimating that the Gallows, though by irregular methods, has its own.—Thou thyself, O Reader, when thou turnest the corner of the Rue de la Vannerie, and discernest still that same grim Bracket of old Iron, wilt not want for reflections. 'Over a grocer's shop', or otherwise; with 'a bust of Louis XIV in the niche under it', now no longer in the niche,—*it* still sticks there; still holding out an ineffectual light, of fish-oil; and has seen worlds wrecked, and says nothing.

But to the eye of enlightened Patriotism, what a thunder-cloud was this; suddenly shaping itself in the radiance of the halcyon weather! Cloud of Erebus blackness; betokening latent electricity without limit. Mayor Bailly, General Lafayette throw up their commissions, in an indignant manner; need to be flattered back again. The cloud disappears, as thunder-clouds do. The halcyon weather returns, though of a greyer complexion; of a character more and more evidently *not* supernatural.

Thus, in any case, with what rubs soever, shall the Bastille be abolished from our Earth; and with it, Feudalism, Despotism; and, one hopes, Scoundrelism generally, and all hard usage of man by his brother man. Alas, the Scoundrelism and hard usage are not so easy of abolition! But as for the Bastille, it sinks day after day, and month after month; its ashlars and boulders tumbling down continually, by express order of our Municipals. Crowds of the curious roam through its caverns; gaze on the skeletons found walled-up, on the *oubliettes,* iron cages, monstrous stone-blocks with padlock chains. One day we discern Mirabeau there; along with the Genevese Dumont. Workers and onlookers make reverent way for him; fling verses, flowers on his path, Bastille-papers and curiosities into his carriage, with *vivats.*

Able Editors compile Books from the *Bastille Archives;* from what of them remain unburnt. The Key of that Robber-Den shall cross the Atlantic; shall lie on Washington's hall-table. The great Clock ticks now in a private patriotic Clockmaker's apartment; no longer measuring hours of mere heaviness. Vanished is the Bastille, what we call vanished: the *body,* or sandstones, of it hanging, in benign metamorphosis, for centuries to come, over the Seine waters, as *Pont Louis Seize;* the soul of it living, perhaps still longer, in the memories of men.

So far, ye august Senators, with your Tennis-Court Oaths, your inertia and impetus, your sagacity and pertinacity, have ye brought us. 'And yet think, Messieurs,' as the Petitioners justly urged, 'you who were saviours did yourselves need saviours'—the brave Bastillers, namely; workmen of Paris; many of them in straitened pecuniary circumstances! Subscriptions are opened; Lists are formed, more accurate than Elie's; harangues are delivered. A Body of *Bastille Heroes,* tolerably complete, did get together; comparable to the Argonauts; hoping to endure like them. But in little more than a year, the whirlpool of things threw them asunder again, and they sank. So many highest superlatives achieved by man are followed by new higher; and dwindle into comparatives and positives! The Siege of the Bastille, weighed with which, in the Historical balance, most other sieges, including that of Troy Town, are gossamer, cost, as we find, in killed and mortally wounded, on the part of the Besiegers, some Eighty-three persons: on the part of the Besieged, after all that straw-burning, fire-pumping, and deluge of musketry, One poor solitary Invalid, shot stone-dead (*roide-mort*) on the battlements! The Bastille Fortress, like the City of Jericho, was overturned by miraculous *sound.*

After the Bastille

MAKE THE CONSTITUTION

HERE PERHAPS IS the place to fix, a little more precisely, what these two words, *French Revolution,* shall mean; for, strictly considered, they may have as many meanings as there are speakers of them. All things are in revolution; in change from moment to moment, which becomes sensible from epoch to epoch: in this Time-World of ours there is properly nothing else but revolution and mutation, and even nothing else conceivable. Revolution, you answer, means *speedier* change. Whereupon one has still to ask: How speedy? At what degree of speed; in what particular points of this variable course, which varies in velocity, but can never stop till Time itself stops, does revolution begin and end; cease to be ordinary mutation, and again become such? It is a thing that will depend on definition more or less arbitrary.

For ourselves, we answer that French Revolution means here the open violent Rebellion, and Victory, of disimprisoned Anarchy against corrupt worn-out Authority: how Anarchy breaks prison; bursts up from the infinite Deep, and rages uncontrollable, immeasurable, enveloping a world; in phasis after phasis of fever-frenzy;—till the frenzy burning itself out, and what elements of new Order it held (since all Force holds such) developing themselves, the Uncontrollable be got, if not reimprisoned, yet harnessed, and its mad forces made to work towards their object as sane regulated ones. For as Hierarchies and Dynasties of all kinds, Theocracies, Aristocracies, Autocracies, Strumpetocracies, have ruled over the world; so it was appointed, in the decrees of Providence, that this same Victorious Anarchy, Jacobinism, Sansculottism, French Revolution, Horrors of French Revolution, or what else mortals name it, should have its turn. The 'destructive wrath' of Sansculottism: this is what we speak, having unhappily no voice for singing.

Surely a great Phenomenon: nay it is a *transcendental* one, overstepping all rules and experience; the crowning Phenomenon of our

326

Modern Time. For here again, most unexpectedly, comes antique Fanaticism in new and newest vesture; miraculous, as all Fanaticism is. Call it the Fanaticism of 'making away with formulas, *de humer les formules.*' The world of formulas, the *formed* regulated world, which all habitable world is—must needs hate such Fanaticism like death; and be at deadly variance with it. The world of formulas must conquer it; or failing that, must die execrating it, anathematizing it—can nevertheless in nowise prevent its being and its having been. The Anathemas are there, and the miraculous Thing is there.

Whence it cometh? Whither it goeth? These are questions! When the age of Miracles lay faded into the distance as an incredible tradition, and even the age of Conventionalities was now old; and Man's Existence had for long generations rested on mere formulas which were grown hollow by course of time; and it seemed as if no Reality any longer existed, but only Phantasms of realities, and God's Universe were the work of the Tailor and Upholsterer mainly, and men were buckram masks that went about becking and grimacing there— on a sudden, the Earth yawns asunder, and amid Tartarean smoke, and glare of fierce brightness, rises SANSCULOTTISM, many-headed, fire-breathing, and asks: What think ye of *me?* Well may the buckram masks start together, terror-struck; 'into expressive well-concerted groups!' It is indeed, Friends, a most singular, most fatal thing. Let whosoever is but buckram and a phantasm look to it: ill verily may it fare with him; here methinks he cannot much longer be. Woe also to many a one who is not wholly buckram, but partly real and human! The age of Miracles has come back! 'Behold the World-Phoenix, in fire-consummation and fire-creation: wide are her fanning wings; loud is her death-melody, of battle-thunders and falling towns; skyward lashes the funeral flame, enveloping all things: it is the Death-Birth of a World!'

Whereby, however, as we often say, shall one unspeakable blessing seem attainable. This, namely: that Man and his Life rest no more on hollowness and a Lie, but on solidity and some kind of Truth. Welcome the beggarliest truth, so it *be* one, in exchange for the royallest sham! Truth of any kind breeds ever new and better truth; thus hard granite rock will crumble down into soil, under the blessed skyey influences; and cover itself with verdure, with fruitage and umbrage. But as for Falsehood, which, in like contrary manner grows ever falser—what can it, or what should it do but decease, being

327

ripe; decompose itself, gently or even violently, and return to the Father of it—too probably in flames of fire?

Sansculottism will burn much; but what is incombustible it will not burn. Fear not Sansculottism; recognize it for what it is, the portentous inevitable end of much, the miraculous beginning of much. One other thing thou mayst understand of it: that it too came from God; for has it not *been?* From of old, as it is written, are His goings forth; in the great Deep of things; fearful and wonderful now as in the beginning: in the whirlwind also He speaks; and the wrath of men is made to praise Him. But to gauge and measure this immeasurable Thing, and what is called *account for it,* and reduce it to a dead logic-formula, attempt not! Much less shalt thou shriek thyself hoarse, cursing it; for that, to all needful lengths, has been already done. As an actually existing Son of Time, *look,* with unspeakable manifold interest, oftenest in silence, at what the Time did bring: therewith edify, instruct, nourish thyself, or were it but to amuse and gratify thyself, as it is given thee.

Another question which at every new turn will rise on us, requiring ever new reply, is this: Where the French Revolution specially *is?* In the King's Palace, in his Majesty's or her Majesty's managements, and maltreatments, cabals, imbecilities and woes, answer some few. In the National Assembly, answer a large mixed multitude: who accordingly seat themselves in the Reporter's Chair; and therefrom noting what Proclamations, Acts, Reports, passages of logic-fence, bursts of parliamentary eloquence seem notable within doors, and what tumults and rumours of tumult become audible from without, produce volume on volume; and, naming it History of the French Revolution, contentedly publish the same. To do the like, to almost any extent, with so many Filed Newspapers, *Choix des Rapports, Histoires Parlementaires* as there are, amounting to many horseloads, were easy for us. Easy but unprofitable. The National Assembly, named now Constituent Assembly, goes its course; making the Constitution; but the French Revolution also goes *its* course.

In general, may we not say that the French Revolution lies in the heart and head of every violent-speaking, of every violent-thinking French Man? How the Twenty-five Millions of such, in their perplexed combination, acting and counter-acting may give birth to events; which event successively is the cardinal one; and from what point of vision it may best be surveyed: this is a problem. Which problem the best insight, seeking light from all possible sources, shifting its point of vision whithersoever vision or glimpse of vision can be had, may employ itself in solving; and be well content to solve in some tolerably approximate way.

As to the National Assembly, in so far as it still towers eminent over France, after the manner of a car-borne *Carroccio,* though now no longer in the van; and ring signals for retreat or advance—it is and continues a reality among other realities. But in so far as it sits making the Constitution, on the other hand, it is a fatuity and chimera mainly. Alas, in the never so heroic building of Montesquieu-Mably card-castles, though shouted over by the world, what interest is there? Occupied in that way, an august National Assembly becomes for us little other than a Sanhedrim of Pedants, not of the gerund-grinding, yet of no fruitfuller sort; and its loud debatings and recriminations about Rights of Man, Right of Peace and War, *Veto suspensif, Veto absolu,* what are they but so many Pedant's-curses, 'May God confound you for your *Theory of Irregular Verbs!*'

Or is it the nature of National Assemblies generally to do, with endless labour and clangour, Nothing? Are Representative Governments mostly at bottom Tyrannies too? Shall we say, the *Tyrants,* the ambitious contentious Persons, from all corners of the country do, in this manner, get gathered into one place; and there, with motion and counter-motion, with jargon and hubbub, *cancel* one another, like the fabulous Kilkenny Cats; and produce, for net-result, *zero*—the country meanwhile *governing* or guiding *itself,* by such wisdom, recognized, or for most part unrecognized, as may exist in individual heads here and there?—Nay, even that were a great improvement: for of old, with their Guelf Factions and Ghibelline Factions, with their Red Roses and White Roses, they were wont to cancel the whole country as well. Besides they do it now in a much narrower cockpit; within the four walls of their Assembly House, and here and there an outpost of Hustings and Barrel-heads; do it with tongues too, not with swords: all which improvements, in the art of producing zero, are they not great? Nay, best of all, some happy Continents (as the Western one, with its Savannahs, where whosoever has four willing limbs finds food under his feet, and an infinite sky over his head) can do without governing.—What Sphinx-questions; which the distracted world, in these very generations, must answer or die!

One thing an elected Assembly of Twelve Hundred is fit for: Destroying. Which indeed is but a more decided exercise of its natural

329

talent for Doing Nothing. Do nothing, only keep agitating, debating; and things will destroy themselves.

So and not otherwise proved it with an august National Assembly. It took the name Constituent, as if its mission and function had been to construct or build; which also, with its whole soul, it endeavoured to do: yet, in the fates, in the nature of things, there lay for it precisely of all functions the most opposite to that. Singular, what Gospels men will believe; even Gospels according to Jean Jacques! It was the fixed Faith of these National Deputies, as of all thinking Frenchmen, that the Constitution could be *made;* that they, there and then, were called to make it. How, with the toughness of old Hebrews or Ishmaelite Moslem, did the otherwise light unbelieving People persist in this their *Credo quia impossibile;* and front the armed world with it; and grow fanatic, and even heroic, and do exploits by it! The Constituent Assembly's Constitution, and several others, will, being printed and not manuscript, survive to future generations, as an instructive well-nigh incredible document of the Time: the most significant Picture of the then existing France; or at lowest, Picture of these men's Picture of it.

But in truth and seriousness, what could the National Assembly have done? The thing to *be* done was, actually as they said, to regenerate France; to abolish the old France, and make a new one, quietly or forcibly, by concession or by violence: this by the Law of Nature has become inevitable. With what degree of violence, depends on the wisdom of those that preside over it. With perfect wisdom on the part of the National Assembly, it had all been otherwise; but whether, in any wise, it could have been pacific, nay other than bloody and convulsive, may still be a question.

Grant, meanwhile, that this Constituent Assembly does to the last continue to be something. With a sigh, it sees itself incessantly forced away from its infinite divine task of perfecting 'the Theory of Irregular Verbs'—to finite terrestrial tasks, which latter have still a significance for us. It is the cynosure of revolutionary France, this National Assembly. All work of Government has fallen into its hands, or under its control; all men look to it for guidance. In the middle of that huge Revolt of Twenty-five millions, it hovers always aloft as Carrocio or Battle-Standard, impelling and impelled, in the most confused way: if it cannot give much guidance, it will still seem to give some. It emits pacificatory Proclamations, not a few; with more or with less result. It authorizes the enrolment of National Guards—lest Brigands come to devour us, and reap the unripe crops. It sends missions to quell 'effervescences'; to deliver men from the Lanterne. It can listen to congratulatory Addresses, which arrive daily by the sackful; mostly in King Cambyses' vein: also to Petitions and complaints from all mortals; so that every mortal's complaint, if it cannot get redressed, may at least hear itself complain. For the rest, an august National Assembly can produce Parliamentary Eloquence; and appoint Committees. Committees of the Constitution, of Reports, of Researches; and of much else: which again yield mountains of Printed Paper; the theme of new Parliamentary Eloquence, in bursts, or in plenteous smooth-flowing floods. And so, from the waste vortex whereon all things go whirling and grinding, Organic Laws, or the similitude of such, slowly emerge.

With endless debating, we get the *Rights of Man* written down and promulgated: true paper basis of all paper Constitutions. Neglecting, cry the opponents, to declare the Duties of Man! Forgetting, answer we, to ascertain the *Mights* of Man—one of the fatallest omissions! Nay, sometimes, as on the Fourth of August, our National Assembly, fired suddenly by an almost preternatural enthusiasm, will get through whole masses of work in one night. A memorable night, this Fourth of August: Dignitaries temporal and spiritual; Peers, Archbishops, Parlement-Presidents, each outdoing the other in patriotic devotedness, come successively to throw their now untenable possessions on the 'altar of the fatherland.' With louder and louder vivats—for indeed it is 'after dinner' too—they abolish Tithes, Seignorial Dues, Gabelle, excessive preservation of Game; nay Privilege, Immunity, Feudalism root and branch; then appoint a *Te Deum* for it; and so, finally, disperse about three in the morning, striking the stars with their sublime heads. Such night, unforeseen but for ever memorable, was this of the Fourth of August 1789. Miraculous, or semi-miraculous, some seem to think it. A new Night of Pentecost, shall we say, shaped according to the new Time, and new Church of Jean Jacques Rousseau? It had its causes; also its effects.

In such manner labour the National Deputies; perfecting their Theory of Irregular Verbs; governing France, and being governed by it; with toil and noise—cutting asunder ancient intolerable bonds; and, for new ones, assiduously spinning ropes of sand. Were their labours a nothing or a something, yet the eyes of all France being reverently fixed on them, History can never very long leave them altogether out of sight.

For the present, if we glance into that Assembly Hall of theirs, it will be found, as is natural, 'most irregular'. As many as 'a hundred members are on their feet at once;' no rule in making motions, or only commencements of a rule; Spectators' Gallery allowed to applaud, and even to hiss; President, appointed once a fortnight, raising many times no serene head above the waves. Nevertheless, as in all human Assemblages, like does begin arranging itself to like; the perennial rule, *Ubi homines sunt modi sunt,* proves valid. Rudiments of Methods disclose themselves; rudiments of Parties. There is a Right Side (*Côté Droit*) a Left Side (*Côté Gauche*); sitting on M. le President's right hand, or on his left: the *Côté Droit* conservative; the *Côté Gauche* destructive. Intermediate is Anglomaniac Constitutionalism, or Two-Chamber Royalism; with its Mouniers, its Lallys—fast verging towards nonentity. Pre-eminent, on the Right Side, pleads and perorates Cazalès the Dragoon-captain, eloquent, mildly fervent; earning for himself the shadow of a name. There also blusters Barrel-Mirabeau, the Younger Mirabeau, not without wit: dusky D'Éspréménil does nothing but sniff and ejaculate; *might,* it is fondly thought, lay prostrate the Elder Mirabeau himself, would he but try—which he does not. Last and greatest, see, for one moment, the Abbé Maury; with his jesuitic eyes, his impassive brass face, 'image of all the cardinal sins'. Indomitable, unquenchable, he fights jesuitico-rhetorically; with toughest lungs and heart; for Throne, especially for Altar and Tithes. So that a shrill voice exclaims once, from the Gallery: 'Messieurs of the Clergy, you *have* to be shaved; if you wriggle too much, you will get cut.'

The Left side is also called the D'Orléans side; and sometimes, derisively, the Palais Royal. And yet, so confused, real-imaginary seems everything, 'it is doubtful,' as Mirabeau said, 'whether D'Orléans himself belong to that same D'Orléans party.' What can be known and seen is, that his moon-visage does beam forth from that point of space. There likewise sits seagreen Robespierre; throwing in his light weight, with decision, not yet with effect. A thin lean Puritan and Precisian, he would make away with formulas; yet lives, moves and has his being wholly in formulas, of another sort. *Peuple,* such, according to Robespierre, ought to be the Royal method of promulgating Laws, '*Peuple,* this is the Law I have framed for thee; dost thou accept it?'—answered, from Right Side, from Centre and Left, by inextinguishable laughter. Yet men of insight discern that the Seagreen may by chance go far: 'This man,' observes Mirabeau, 'will do somewhat; he believes every word he says.'

Abbé Siéyès is busy with mere Constitutional work; wherein, unluckily, fellow-workmen are less pliable than, with one who has completed the Science of Polity, they ought to be. Courage, Siéyès, nevertheless! Some twenty months of heroic travail, of contradiction from the stupid, and the Constitution shall be built; the top-stone of it brought out with shouting—say rather, the top-paper, for it is all Paper; and *thou* hast done in it what the Earth or the Heaven could require, thy utmost. Note likewise this Trio; memorable for several things; memorable were it only that their history is written in an epigram: 'whatsoever these Three have in hand,' it is said, 'Duport thinks it, Barnave speaks it, Lameth does it.'

But royal Mirabeau? Conspicuous among all parties, raised above and beyond them all, this man rises more and more. As we often say, he has an *eye,* he is a reality; while others are formulas and eyeglasses. In the Transient he will detect the Perennial; find some firm footing even among Paper-vortexes. His fame is gone forth to all lands; it gladdened the heart of the crabbed old Friend of Men himself before he died. The very Postilions of inns have heard of Mirabeau: when an impatient Traveller complains that the team is insufficient, his Postilion answers, 'Yes, Monsieur, the wheelers are weak; but my *mirabeau* (main horse), you see, is a right one *mais mon mirabeau est excellent.'*

And now, Reader, thou shalt quit this noisy Discrepancy of a National Assembly; not (if thou be of humane mind) without pity. Twelve hundred brother men are there, in the centre of Twenty-five Millions; fighting so fiercely with Fate and with one another; struggling their lives out, as most sons of Adam do, for that which profiteth not. Nay, on the whole, it is admitted further to be very *dull.* 'Dull as this day's Assembly', said some one. 'Why date, *Pourquoi dater?'* answered Mirabeau.

Consider that they are Twelve Hundred; that they not only speak, but *read* their speeches; and even borrow and steal speeches to read! With Twelve Hundred fluent speakers, and their Noah's Deluge of vociferous commonplace, silence unattainable may well seem the one blessing of Life. But figure Twelve Hundred pamphleteers; droning forth perpetual pamphlets: and no man to gag them! Neither, as in the American Congress, do the arrangements seem perfect. A Senator has not his own Desk and Newspaper here; of Tobacco (much less of Pipes) there is not the slightest provision. Conversation itself must be transacted in a low tone, with continual interruption: only 'pencil Notes' circulate freely; 'in incredible numbers, to the foot of the very tribune.'—Such work is it, regenerating a Nation; perfecting one's Theory of Irregular Verbs!

THE GENERAL OVERTURN

O F THE KING'S COURT, for the present, there is almost nothing whatever to be said. Silent, deserted are these halls; Royalty languishes forsaken of its war-god and all its hopes, till once the Œil-de-Bœuf rally again. The sceptre is departed from King Louis; is gone over to the *Salle des Menus,* to the Paris Townhall, or one knows not whither. In the July days, while all ears were yet deafened by the crash of the Bastille, and Ministers and Princes were scattered to the four winds, it seemed as if the very Valets had grown heavy of hearing. Besenval, also in flight towards Infinite Space, but hovering a little at Versailles, was addressing his Majesty personally for an Order about post-horses; when, lo, 'the Valet-in-waiting places himself familiarly between his Majesty and me', stretching out his rascal neck to learn what it was! His Majesty, in sudden choler, whirled round; made a clutch at the tongs: 'I gently prevented him; he grasped my hand in thankfulness; and I noticed tears in his eyes.'

Poor King; for French Kings also are men! Louis Fourteenth himself once clutched the tongs, and even smote with them; but then it was at Louvois, and Dame Maintenon ran up.—The Queen sits weeping in her inner apartments, surrounded by weak women: she is 'at the height of unpopularity;' universally regarded as the evil genius of France. Her friends and familiar counsellors have all fled; and fled, surely, on the foolishest errand. The Château Polignac still frowns aloft, on its 'bold and enormous cubical rock,' amid the blooming champaigns, amid the blue girdling mountains of Auvergne: but no Duke and Duchess Polignac look forth from it; they have fled, they have 'met Necker at Bâle;' they shall not return. That France should see her Nobles resist the Irresistible, Inevitable, with the face of angry men, was unhappy, not unexpected; but with the face and sense of pettish children? This was her peculiarity. They understood nothing; would understand nothing. Does not, at this hour, a new Polignac, first-born of these Two, sit reflective in the Castle of Ham; in an astonishment he will never recover from; the most confused of existing mortals?

King Louis has his new Ministry: mere Popularities; Old-President Pompignan; Necker, coming back in triumph; and other such. But what will it avail him? As was said, the sceptre, all but the wooden gilt sceptre, has departed elsewhither. Volition, determination is not in this man: only innocence, indolence; dependence on all persons but himself, on all circumstances but the circumstances he were lord of. So troublous internally is our Versailles and its work. Beautiful, if seen from afar, resplendent like a Sun; seen near at hand, a mere Sun's-Atmosphere, hiding darkness, confused ferment of ruin!

But over France, there goes on the indisputablest 'destruction of formulas;' transaction of realities that follow therefrom. So many millions of persons, all gyved, and nigh strangled, with formulas; whose Life nevertheless, at least the digestion and hunger of it, was real enough! Heaven has at length sent an abundant harvest: but what profits it the poor man, when Earth with her formulas interposes? Industry, in these times of insurrection, must needs lie dormant; capital, as usual, not circulating, but stagnating timorously in nooks. The poor man is short of work, is therefore short of money; nay even had he money, bread is not to be bought for it. Were it plotting of Aristocrats, plotting of D'Orléans; were it Brigands, preternatural terror, and the clang of Phoebus Apollo's silver bow—enough, the markets are scarce of grain, plentiful only in tumult. Farmers seem lazy to thresh; being either 'bribed;' or needing no bribe, with prices ever rising, with perhaps rent itself no longer so pressing. Neither, what is singular, do municipal enactments, 'That along with so many measures of wheat you shall sell so many of rye,' and other the like, much mend the matter. Dragoons with drawn swords stand ranked among the corn-sacks, often more dragoons than sacks. Meal-mobs abound; growing into mobs of a still darker quality.

Starvation has been known among the French Commonalty before this; known and familiar. Did we not see them, in the year 1775, presenting, in sallow faces, in wretchedness and raggedness, their Petition of Grievances; and, for answer, getting a brand-new Gallows forty feet high? Hunger and Darkness, through long years! For look back on that earlier Paris Riot, when a Great Personage, worn out by debauchery, was believed to be in want of Blood-baths; and Mothers,

335

in worn raiment, yet with living hearts under it, 'filled the public places' with their wild Rachel-cries—stilled also by the Gallows. Twenty years ago, the Friend of Men (preaching to the deaf) described the Limousin Peasants as wearing a pain-stricken (*souffre-douleur*) look, a look *past* complaint, 'as if the oppression of the great were like the hail and the thunder, a thing irremediable, the ordinance of Nature'. And now if in some great hour, the shock of a falling Bastille should awaken you; and it were found to be the ordinance of Art merely; and remediable, reversible!

Or has the Reader forgotten that 'flood of savages,' which, in sight of the same Friend of Men, descended from the mountains at Mont d'Or? Lank-haired haggard faces; shapes rawboned, in high sabots; in woollen jupes, with leather girdles studded with copper nails! They rocked from foot to foot, and beat time with their elbows too, as the quarrel and battle, which was not long in beginning, went on; shouting fiercely; the lank faces distorted into the similitude of a cruel laugh. For they were darkened and hardened: long had they been the prey of excise-men and tax-men; of 'clerks with the cold spurt of their pen.' It was the fixed prophecy of our old Marquis, which no man would listen to, that 'such Government by Blind-man's-buff, stumbling along too far, would end by the General Overturn, the *Culbute Générale!'*

No man would listen, each went his thoughtless way—and Time and Destiny also travelled on. The Government by Blind-man's-buff, stumbling along, has reached the precipice inevitable for it. Dull Drudgery, driven on, by clerks with the cold dastard spurt of their pen, has been driven—into a Communion of Drudges! For now, moreover, there have come the strangest confused tidings; by Paris Journals with their paper wings; or still more portentous, where no Journals are, by rumour and conjecture: Oppression *not* inevitable; a Bastille prostrate, and the Constitution fast getting ready! Which Constitution, if it be something and not nothing, what can it be but bread to eat?

The Traveller, 'walking up hill bridle in hand', overtakes 'a poor woman;' the image, as such commonly are, of drudgery and scarcity; 'looking sixty years of age, though she is not yet twenty-eight.' They have seven children, her poor drudge and she: a farm, with one cow, which helps to make the children soup; also one little horse, or garron. They have rents and quit-rents, Hens to pay to this Seigneur, Oatsacks to that; King's taxes, Statute-labour, Church-taxes, taxes enough—and think the times inexpressible. She has heard that some*where,* in some

336

manner, some*thing* is to be done for the poor: 'God send it soon; for the dues and taxes crush us down (*nous écrasent*)!'

Fair prophecies are spoken, but they are not fulfilled. There have been Notables, Assemblages, turnings out and comings in. Intriguing and manœuvring; Parlementary eloquence and arguing, Greek meeting Greek in high places, has long gone on; yet still bread comes not. The harvest is reaped and garnered; yet still we have no bread. Urged by despair and by hope, what can Drudgery do, but rise, as predicted, and produce the General Overturn?

Fancy, then, some Five full-grown Millions of such gaunt figures, with their haggard faces (*figures hâves*); in woollen jupes, with copper-studded leather girths, and high sabots, starting up to ask, as in forest-roarings, their washed Upper-Classes, after long unreviewed centuries, virtually this question: How have ye treated us; how have ye taught us, fed us, and led us, while we toiled for you? The answer can be read in flames, over the nightly summer-sky. *This* is the feeding and leading we have had of you: EMPTINESS—of pocket, of stomach, of head and of heart. Behold there is *nothing in us;* nothing but what Nature gives her wild children of the desert: Ferocity and Appetite; Strength grounded on Hunger. Did ye mark among your Rights of Man, that man was not to die of starvation, while there was bread reaped by him? It is among the Mights of Man.

Seventy-two Châteaus have flamed aloft in the Mâconnais and Beaujolais alone: this seems the centre of the conflagration; but it has spread over Dauphiné, Alsace, the Lyonnais; the whole South-East is in a blaze. All over the North, from Rouen to Metz, disorder is abroad: smugglers of salt go openly in armed bands: the barriers of towns are burnt; toll-gatherers, tax-gatherers, official persons put to flight. 'It was thought,' says Young, 'the people, from hunger, would revolt;' and we see they have done it. Desperate Lack-alls, long prowling aimless, now finding hope in desperation itself, everywhere form a nucleus. They ring the Church-bell by way of tocsin: and the Parish turns out to the work. Ferocity, atrocity; hunger and revenge: such work as we can imagine!

Ill stands it now with the Seigneur, who, for example, 'has walled up the only Fountain of the Township;' who has ridden high on his *chartier* and parchments; who has preserved Game not wisely but too well. Churches also, and Canonries, are sacked, without mercy; which have shorn the flock too close, forgetting to feed it. Woe to the land over which Sansculottism, in its day of vengeance, tramps rough-shod,

337

—shod in sabots! Highbred Seigneurs, with their delicate women and little ones, had to 'fly half-naked,' under cloud of night: glad to escape the flames, and even worse. You meet them at the *tables-d'hôte* of inns; making wise reflections or foolish, that 'rank is destroyed'; uncertain whither they shall now wend. The *métayer* will find it convenient to be slack in paying rent. As for the Tax-gatherer, he, long hunting as a biped of prey, may now find himself hunted as one; his Majesty's Exchequer will not 'fill up the Deficit,' this season: it is the notion of many that a Patriot Majesty, being the Restorer of French Liberty, has abolished most taxes, though, for their private ends, some men make a secret of it.

Where will this end? In the Abyss, one may prophesy; whither all Delusions are, at all moments, travelling; where this Delusion has now arrived. For if there be a Faith, from of old, it is this, as we often repeat, that no Lie can live for ever. The very Truth has to change its vesture, from time to time; and be born again. But all Lies have sentence of death written down against them, in Heaven's Chancery itself; and, slowly or fast, advance incessantly towards their hour. 'The signs of a Grand Seigneur being landlord', says the vehement plainspoken Arthur Young, 'are wastes, *landes,* deserts, ling: go to his residence, you will find it in the middle of a forest, peopled with deer, wild boars and wolves. The fields are scenes of pitiable management, as the houses are of misery. To see so many millions of hands, that would be industrious, all idle and starving: Oh, if I were legislator of France for one day, I would make these great lords skip again!' O Arthur, thou now actually beholdest them *skip*—wilt thou grow to grumble at that too?

For long years and generations it lasted; but the time came. Featherbrain, whom no reasoning and no pleading could touch, the glare of the firebrand had to illuminate: there remained but that method. Consider it, look at it! The widow is gathering nettles for her children's dinner; a perfumed Seigneur, delicately lounging in the Œil-de-Bœuf, has an alchemy whereby he will extract from her the third nettle, and name it Rent and Law: such an arrangement must end. Ought it not? But, O most fearful is *such* an ending! Let those, to whom God, in his great mercy, has granted time and space, prepare another and milder one.

To some it is a matter of wonder that the Seigneurs did not do something to help themselves; say, combine and arm: for there were a 'hundred and fifty thousand of them', all valiant enough. Unhappily, a hundred and fifty thousand, scattered over wide Provinces, divided by mutual ill-will, cannot combine. The highest Seigneurs, as we have seen, had already emigrated—with a view of putting France to the blush. Neither are arms now the peculiar property of Seigneurs; but of every mortal who has ten shillings, wherewith to buy a secondhand firelock.

Besides, those starving Peasants, after all, have not four feet and claws, that you could keep them down permanently in that manner. They are not even of black colour: they are mere Unwashed Seigneurs; and a Seigneur too has human bowels!—The Seigneurs did what they could; enrolled in National Guards; fled, with shrieks, complaining to Heaven and Earth. One Seigneur, famed Memmay of Quincey, near Vesoul, invited all the rustics of his neighbourhood to a banquet; blew up his Château and them with gunpowder; and instantaneously vanished, no man yet knows whither. Some half-dozen years after, he came back; and demonstrated that it was by accident.

Nor are the Authorities idle; though unluckily, all Authorities, Municipalities and such like, are in the uncertain transitionary state; getting regenerated from old Monarchic to new Democratic; no Official yet knows clearly what he is. Nevertheless, Mayors old or new do gather *Marechaussées,* National Guards, Troops of the line; justice, of the most summary sort, is not wanting. The Electoral Committee of Mâcon, though but a Committee, goes the length of hanging, for its own behoof, as many as twenty. The Prévôt of Dauphiné traverses the country 'with a movable column', with tipstaves, gallows-ropes; for gallows any tree will serve, and suspend its culprit, or 'thirteen' culprits.

Unhappy country! How is the fair gold-and-green of the ripe bright Year defaced with horrid blackness; black ashes of Châteaus, black bodies of gibbeted Men! Industry has ceased in it; not sounds of the hammer and saw, but of the tocsin and alarm-drum. The sceptre has departed, *whither* one knows not—breaking itself in pieces: here impotent, there tyrannous. National Guards are unskilful, and of doubtful purpose; Soldiers are inclined to mutiny: there is danger that they too may quarrel, danger that they may *agree.* Strasbourg has seen riots: a Townhall torn to shreds, its archives scattered white on the winds; drunk soldiers embracing drunk citizens for three days, and Mayor Dietrich and Marshal Rochambeau reduced nigh to desperation.

339

Through the middle of all which phenomena is seen, on his triumphant transit, 'escorted,' through Béfort for instance, 'by fifty National Horsemen and all the military music of the place'—M. Necker, returning from Bâle! Glorious as the meridian; though poor Necker himself partly guesses whither it is leading. One highest culminating day, at the Paris Townhall; with immortal vivats, with wife and daughter kneeling publicly to kiss his hand; with Besenval's pardon granted—but indeed revoked before sunset: one highest day, but then lower days, and ever lower, down even to lowest! Such magic is in a name; and in the want of name. Like some enchanted Mambrino's Helmet, essential to victory, comes this 'Saviour of France'; beshouted, becymballed by the world: alas, so soon to be *dis*enchanted, to be pitched shamefully over the lists as a Barber's Bason! Gibbon 'could wish to show him' (in this ejected, Barber's-Bason state) to any man of solidity, who were minded to have the soul burnt out of him, and become a *caput mortuum,* by Ambition, unsuccessful or successful.

Another small phasis we add, and no more: how, in the Autumn months, our sharp-tempered Arthur has been 'pestered for some days past', by shot, lead-drops and slugs, 'rattling five or six times into my chaise and about my ears'; all the mob of the country gone out to kill Game! It is even so. On the Cliffs of Dover, over all the Marches of France, there appear, this autumn, two signs on the Earth: emigrant flights of French Seigneurs; emigrant winged flights of French Game! Finished, one may say, or as good as finished, is the Preservation of Game on this Earth; completed for endless Time. What part *it* had to play in the History of Civilization is played: *plaudite; exeat!*

In this manner does Sansculottism blaze up, illustrating many things —producing, among the rest, as we saw, on the Fourth of August, that semi-miraculous Night of Pentecost in the National Assembly; semi-miraculous, which had its causes, and its effects. Feudalism is struck dead; not on parchment only, and by ink; but in very fact, by fire; say, by self-combustion. This conflagration of the South-East will abate; will be got scattered, to the West, or elsewhither: extinguish it will not, till the *fuel* be all done.

IN QUEUE

IF WE LOOK NOW AT PARIS, one thing is too evident: that the Bakers' shops have got their *Queues,* or Tails; their long strings of purchasers, arranged *in tail,* so that the first come be the first served—were the shop once open! This waiting in tail, not seen since the early days of July, again makes its appearance in August. In time, we shall see it perfected by practice to the rank almost of an art; and the art, or quasi-art, of standing in tail become one of the characteristics of the Parisian People, distinguishing them from all other Peoples whatsoever.

But consider, while work itself is so scarce, how a man must not only realize money, but stand waiting (if his wife is too weak to wait and struggle) for half-days in the Tail, till he get it changed for dear bad bread! Controversies, to the length sometimes of blood and battery, must arise in these exasperated Queues. Or if no controversy, then it is but one accordant *Pange Lingua* of complaint against the Powers that be. France has begun her long Curriculum of Hungering, instructive and productive beyond Academic Curriculums; which extends over some seven most strenuous years. As Jean Paul says of his own Life, 'to a great height shall the business of Hungering go.'

Or consider, in strange contrast, the jubilee Ceremonies; for, in general, the aspect of Paris presents these two features: jubilee ceremonials and scarcity of victual. Processions enough walk in jubilee; of Young Women, decked and dizened, their ribands all tricolor; moving with song and tabor, to the Shrine of Sainte Geneviève, to thank her that the Bastille is down. The Strong Men of the Market, and the Strong Women, fail not with their bouquets and speeches. Abbé Fauchet, famed in such work (for Abbé Lefevre could only distribute powder) blesses tricolor cloth for the National Guard; and makes it a National Tricolor Flag; victorious, or to be victorious, in the cause of civil and religious liberty all over the world. Fauchet, we say, is the man for *Te-Deums,* and public Consecrations—to which, as in this instance of the Flag, our National Guard will 'reply with volleys of musketry', Church and Cathedral though it be; filling Notre Dame with such noisiest fuliginous *Amen,* significant of several things.

On the whole, we will say our new Mayor Bailly, our new Commander Lafayette named also 'Scipio-Americanus', have bought their preferment dear. Bailly rides in gilt state-coach, with beef-eaters and sumptuosity; Camille Desmoulins, and others, sniffing at him for it:

341

Scipio bestrides the 'white charger,' and waves with civic plumes in sight of all France. Neither of them, however, does it for nothing; but, in truth, at an exorbitant rate. At this rate, namely: of feeding Paris, and keeping it from fighting. Out of the City-funds, some seventeen thousand of the utterly destitute are employed digging on Montmartre, at ten pence a day, which buys them, at market price, almost two pounds of bad bread: they look very yellow, when Lafayette goes to harangue them. The Townhall is in travail, night and day; it must bring forth Bread, a Municipal Constitution, regulations of all kinds, curbs on the Sansculottic Press; above all, Bread, Bread.

Purveyors prowl the country far and wide, with the appetite of lions; detect hidden grain, purchase open grain; by gentle means or forcible, must and will find grain. A most thankless task; and so difficult, so dangerous—even if a man did gain some trifle by it! On the 19th of August, there is food for one day. Complaints there are that the food is spoiled, and produces an effect on the intestines: not corn but plaster-of-Paris! Which effect on the intestines, as well as that 'smarting in the throat and palate', a Townhall Proclamation warns you to disregard, or even to consider as drastic-beneficial. The Mayor of Saint-Denis, so black was his bread, has, by a dyspeptic populace, been hanged on the Lanterne there. National Guards protect the Paris Corn-Market: first ten suffice; then six hundred. Busy are ye, Bailly, Brissot de Warville, Condorcet, and ye others!

For, as just hinted, there is a Municipal Constitution to be made too. The old Bastille Electors, after some ten days of psalmodying over their glorious victory, began to hear it asked, in a splenetic tone, Who put *you* there? They accordingly had to give place, not without moanings, and audible growlings on both sides, to a new larger Body, specially elected for that post. Which new Body, augmented, altered, then fixed finally at the number of Three Hundred, with the title of Town Representatives (*Représentants de la Commune*), now sits there; rightly portioned into Committees; assiduous making a Constitution; at all moments when not seeking flour.

And such a Constitution; little short of miraculous: one that shall 'consolidate the Revolution!' The Revolution is finished then? Mayor Bailly and all respectable friends of Freedom would fain think so. Your Revolution, like jelly sufficiently *boiled,* needs only to be poured into *shapes,* of Constitution, and 'consolidated' therein? Could it, indeed, contrive to *cool;* which last, however, is precisely the doubtful thing, or even the not doubtful!

342

Unhappy Friends of Freedom; consolidating a Revolution! They must sit at work there, their pavilion spread on very Chaos; between two hostile worlds, the Upper Court-world, the nether Sansculottic one; and, beaten on by both, toil painfully, perilously—doing, in sad literal earnest, 'the impossible.'

SECTION V

The Legislative Assembly and European War

[The National Assembly continued to sit until the end of September 1791. It accomplished its great task of making a new constitution, of which the preliminary draft was accepted by the King on July 14, 1790 (the anniversary of the fall of the Bastille), and the final draft on September 14, 1791. The constitution established a limited monarchy with the principal power in the hands of a "Legislative Assembly" of 745 members. It included also the famous "Declaration of the Rights of Man," composed from English and American precedents and embodying the political theories of the "philosophes." All the old feudal rights and privileges were legally abolished (the "August Days," 1789). Unfortunately many forces and events were working to drive the revolution from peaceful reform to violent overturn. The King and court never wholeheartedly co-operated with the Assembly, and accepted reforms only under duress. A popular uprising of the Paris mob (October 5–6, 1789), known as the "Insurrection of Women," forced the King and Assembly to leave Versailles and establish themselves in Paris. Through the year 1790 the influence of the Parisian populace continued to increase. On April 2, 1791, Mirabeau, who had taken the side of conservative monarchy, died, breaking the last strong link uniting the King with the Assembly. Many nobles had fled the country (émigrés) and were organizing counter-revolution in London, Coblenz, and other foreign centers. In June the King himself attempted to flee Paris with his family, but was intercepted at Varennes and brought back virtually a prisoner. When the National Assembly dissolved to make way for the newly elected Legislative Assembly, the King was generally unpopular and distrusted. The

new constitution was thus launched under very unfavorable auspices. Elements of discord were the opposition of the clergy, the dissatisfaction of the radicals, the increasing agitation of the Paris clubs (Jacobins, Cordeliers), and the failure of the Legislative Assembly to deal with the continuing high prices and profiteering. The personnel of the Legislative Assembly were lacking in experience, since by a gesture of disinterestedness the National Assembly had passed the "self-denying ordinance" making its own members ineligible for re-election to the Legislative.]

KINGS AND EMIGRANTS

EXTREMELY RHEUMATIC Constitutions have been known to march, and keep on their feet, though in a staggering sprawling manner, for long periods, in virtue of one thing only: that the *Head* were healthy. But this Head of the French Constitution! What King Louis is and cannot help being, Readers already know. A King who cannot take the Constitution, nor reject the Constitution: nor do anything at all, but miserably ask, What shall I do? A King environed with endless confusions; in whose own mind is no germ of order. Haughty implacable remnants of Noblesse struggling with humiliated repentant Barnave-Lameths; struggling in that obscure element of fetchers and carriers, of Half-pay braggarts from the Café Valois, of Chambermaids, whisperers, and subaltern officious persons: fierce Patriotism looking on all the while, more and more suspicious, from without: what, in such struggle, can they do? At best, *cancel* one another, and produce *zero.* Poor King! Barnave and your Senatorial Jaucourts speak earnestly into this ear; Bertrand-Moleville, and Messengers from Coblentz, speak earnestly into that: the poor Royal head turns to the one side and to the other side; can turn itself fixedly to no side. Let Decency drop a veil over it: sorrier misery was seldom enacted in the world. This one small fact, does it not throw the saddest light on much? The Queen is lamenting to Madame Campan: 'What am I to do? When they, these Barnaves, get us advised to any step which the Noblesse do not like, then I am pouted at; nobody comes to my card-table; the King's Couchee is solitary.' In such a case of dubiety, what *is* one to do? Go inevitably to the ground!

The King has accepted this Constitution, knowing beforehand that it will not serve: he studies it, and executes it in the hope mainly that it will be found inexecutable. King's Ships lie rotting in harbour, their officers gone; the Armies disorganized; robbers scour the Highways, which wear down unrepaired; all Public Service lies slack and waste: the Executive makes no effort, or an effort only to throw the blame on the Constitution. Shamming death, '*faisant la mort!*' What Constitution, use it in this manner, can march? 'Grow to disgust the Nation,' it will truly—unless *you* first grow to disgust the Nation! It is Bertrand de Moleville's plan, and his Majesty's; the best they can form.

Or if, after all, this best-plan proved too slow; proved a failure? Provident of that too, the Queen, shrouded in deepest mystery, 'writes all day, in cipher, day after day, to Coblentz;' Engineer Goguelat, he of the *Night of Spurs,* whom the Lafayette Amnesty has delivered from Prison, rides and runs. Now and then, on fit occasion, a Royal familiar visit can be paid to that Salle de Manége, an affecting encouraging Royal Speech (sincere, doubt it not, for the moment) can be delivered there, and the Senators all cheer and almost weep—at the same time Mallet du Pan has visibly ceased editing, and invisibly bears abroad a King's Autograph, soliciting help from the Foreign Potentates. Unhappy Louis, *do* this thing or else that other—if thou couldst!

The thing which the King's Government did do was to stagger distractedly from contradiction to contradiction; and wedding Fire to Water, envelop itself in hissing, and ashy steam. Danton and needy corruptible Patriots are sopped with presents of cash: they accept the sop; they rise refreshed by it and—travel their own way. Nay, the King's Government did likewise hire Hand-clappers, or *claqueurs,* persons to applaud. Subterranean Rivarol has Fifteen Hundred Men in King's pay, at the rate of some £10,000 sterling per month; what he calls 'a staff of genius': Paragraph-writers, Placard Journalists; 'two hundred and eighty Applauders, at three shillings a day': one of the strangest Staffs ever commanded by man. The muster-rolls and account-books of which still exist. Bertrand-Moleville himself, in a way he thinks very dexterous, contrives to pack the Galleries of the Legislative; gets Sansculottes hired to go thither, and applaud at a signal given, they fancying it was Pétion that bade them: a device which was not detected for almost a week. Dexterous enough; as if a man, finding the Day fast decline, should determine on altering the Clock-hands: *that* is a thing possible for him.

Here too let us note an unexpected apparition of Philippe d'Orléans at Court: his last at the Levée of any King. D'Orléans, sometime in the

345

winter months seemingly, has been appointed to that old first-coveted rank of admiral—though only over ships rotting in port. The wished-for comes too late! However, he waits on Bertrand-Moleville to give thanks: nay to state that he would willingly thank his Majesty in person; that, in spite of all the horrible things men have said and sung, he is far from being his Majesty's enemy; at bottom, how far! Bertrand delivers the message, brings about the royal Interview, which does pass to the satisfaction of his Majesty; D'Orléans seeming clearly repentant, determined to turn over a new leaf. And yet, next Sunday, what do we see? 'Next Sunday,' says Bertrand, 'he came to the King's Levée; but the Courtiers, ignorant of what had passed, the Crowd of Royalists who were accustomed to resort thither on that day specially to pay their court, gave him the most humiliating reception. They came pressing round him; managing, as if by mistake, to tread on his toes, to elbow him towards the door, and not let him enter again. He went downstairs to her Majesty's Apartments, where cover was laid; so soon as he showed face, sounds rose on all sides, *"Messieurs, take care of the dishes,"* as if he had carried poison in his pockets. The insults, which his presence everywhere excited, forced him to retire without having seen the Royal Family: the crowd followed him to the Queen's staircase; in descending, he received a spitting (*crachat*) on the head, and some others on his clothes. Rage and spite were seen visibly painted on his face': as indeed how could they miss to be? He imputes it all to the King and Queen, who know nothing of it, who are even much grieved at it; and so descends to his Chaos again. Bertrand was there at the Château that day himself, and an eye-witness to these things.

For the rest, Non-jurant Priests, and the repression of them, will distract the King's conscience; Emigrant Princes and Noblesse will force him to double-dealing: there must be *veto* on *veto;* amid the ever-waxing indignation of men. For Patriotism, as we said, looks on from without, more and more suspicious. Waxing tempest, blast after blast, of Patriotic indignation, from without; dim inorganic whirl of Intrigues, Fatuities, within! Inorganic, fatuous; from which the eye turns away. De Staël intrigues for her so gallant Narbonne, to get him made War-Minister; and ceases not, having got him made. The King shall fly to Rouen; shall there, with the gallant Narbonne, properly 'modify the Constitution.' This is the same brisk Narbonne, who, last year, cut out from their entanglement, by force of dragoons, those poor fugitive Royal Aunts. He drives now, with his De Staël, rapidly to the Armies, to the Frontier Towns; produces rose-coloured Reports, not too credible; perorates, gesticulates; wavers poising himself on the top, for a moment, seen of men; then tumbles, dismissed, washed away by the Time-flood.

Also the fair Princess de Lamballe intrigues, bosom-friend of her Majesty: to the angering of Patriotism. Beautiful Unfortunate, why did she ever return from England? Her small silver-voice, what can it profit in that piping of the black World-tornado? Which will whirl *her,* poor fragile Bird of Paradise, against grim rocks. Lamballe and De Staël intrigue visibly, apart or together: but who shall reckon how many others, and in what infinite ways, invisibly! Is there not what one may call an 'Austrian Committee,' sitting invisible in the Tuileries; centre of an invisible Anti-National Spiderweb, which, for we sleep among mysteries, stretches its threads to the ends of the Earth? Journalist Carra has now the clearest certainty of it: to Brissotin Patriotism, and France generally, it is growing more and more probable.

O Reader, hast thou no pity for this Constitution? Rheumatic shooting pains in its members; pressure of hydrocephale and hysteric vapours on its Brain: a Constitution divided against itself; which will never march, hardly even stagger! Why were not Drouet and Procureur Sausse in their beds, that unblessed Varennes Night! Why did they not, in the name of Heaven, let the Korff Berline go whither it listed! Nameless incoherency, incompatibility, perhaps prodigies at which the world still shudders, had been spared.

But now comes the third thing that bodes ill for the marching of this French Constitution: besides the French People, and the French King, there is thirdly—the assembled European World. It has become necessary now to look at that also. Fair France is so luminous: and round and round it, is troublous Cimmerian Night. Calonnes, Breteuils hover dim, far-flown; overnetting Europe with intrigues. From Turin to Vienna; to Berlin, and utmost Petersburg in the frozen North! Great Burke has raised his great voice long ago; eloquently demonstrating that the end of an Epoch is come, to all appearance the end of Civilized Time. Him many answer: Camille Desmoulins, Clootz Speaker of Mankind, Paine the rebellious Needleman, and honourable Gaelic Vindicators in that country and in this: but the great Burke remains unanswerable; 'the Age of Chivalry *is* gone', and could not but go, having now produced the still more indomitable Age of Hunger. Altars enough, of the Dubois-Rohan sort, changing to the Gobel-and-Talleyrand sort, are faring by rapid transmutations to—shall we say,

347

the right Proprietor of them? French Game and French Game-Preservers did alight on the Cliffs of Dover, with cries of distress. Who will say that the end of much is not come? A set of mortals has risen, who believe that Truth is not a printed Speculation, but a practical Fact; that Freedom and Brotherhood are possible in this Earth, supposed always to be Belial's, which 'the Supreme Quack' was to inherit! Who will say that Church, State, Throne, Altar are not in danger: that the sacred Strongbox itself, last Palladium of effete Humanity, may not be blasphemously blown upon, and its padlocks undone?

The poor Constituent Assembly might act with what delicacy and diplomacy it would; declare that it abjured meddling with its neighbours, foreign conquest, and so forth; but from the first this thing was to be predicted: that old Europe and new France could not subsist *together*. A Glorious Revolution, oversetting State-Prisons and Feudalism; publishing, with outburst of Federative Cannon, in face of all the Earth, that Appearance is not Reality, how shall it subsist amid Governments which, if Appearance is *not* Reality, are—one knows not what? In death-feud, and internecine wrestle and battle, it shall subsist with them; not otherwise.

Rights of Man, printed on Cotton Handkerchiefs, in various dialects of human speech, pass over to the Frankfort Fair. What say we, Frankfort Fair? They have crossed Euphrates, and the fabulous Hydaspes; wafted themselves beyond the Ural, Altai, Himmalayah; struck off from wood stereotypes, in angular Picture-writing, they are jabbered and jingled of in China and Japan. Where will it stop? Kien-Lung smells mischief; not the remotest Dalai-Lama shall now knead his dough-pills in peace.—Hateful to us, as is the Night! Bestir yourselves, ye Defenders of Order! They do bestir themselves: all Kings and Kinglets, with their spiritual temporal array, are astir; their brows clouded with menace. Diplomatic emissaries fly swift; Conventions, privy Conclaves assemble; and wise wigs wag, taking what counsel they can.

Also, as we said, the Pamphleteer draws pen, on this side and that: zealous fists beat the Pulpit-drum. Not without issue! Did not iron Birmingham, shouting 'Church and King', itself knew not why, burst out, last July, into rage, drunkenness and fire; and your Priestleys, and the like, dining there on that Bastille day, get the maddest singeing: scandalous to consider! In which same days, as we can remark, High Potentates, Austrian and Prussian, with Emigrants, were faring towards Pilnitz in Saxony; there, on the 27th of August, they, keeping to themselves what further 'secret Treaty' there might or might not be, did publish their hopes and their threatenings, their Declaration that it was 'the common cause of Kings.'

Where a will to quarrel is, there is a way. Our readers remember that Pentecost-Night, Fourth of August 1789, when Feudalism fell in a few hours? The National Assembly, in abolishing Feudalism, promised that 'compensation' should be given; and did endeavour to give it. Nevertheless the Austrian Kaiser answers that his German Princes, for their part, cannot be unfeudalized; that they have Possessions in French Alsace, and Feudal Rights secured to them, for which no conceivable compensation will suffice. So this of the Possessioned Princes, *'Princes Possessionés,'* is bandied from Court to Court; covers acres of diplomatic paper at this day: a weariness to the world. Kaunitz argues from Vienna; Delessart responds from Paris, though perhaps not sharply enough. The Kaiser and his Possessioned Princes will too evidently come and *take* compensation—so much as they can get. Nay might one not *partition* France, as we have done Poland, and are doing; and so pacify it with a vengeance?

From South to North! For actually it is 'the common cause of Kings.' Swedish Gustav, sworn Knight of the Queen of France, will lead Coalized Armies—had not Ankarström treasonously shot him; for, indeed, there were griefs nearer home. Austria and Prussia speak at Pilnitz; all men intensely listening. Imperial Rescripts have gone out from Turin; there will be secret Convention at Vienna. Catherine of Russia beckons approvingly; will help, were she ready. Spanish Bourbon stirs amid his pillows; from him too, even from him, shall there come help. Lean Pitt, 'the Minister of Preparatives', looks out from his watch-tower in Saint James's, in a suspicious manner. Councillors plotting, Calonnes dim-hovering—alas, Sergeants rub-a-dubbing openly through all manner of German market-towns, collecting ragged valour! Look where you will, immeasurable Obscurantism is girdling this fair France; which, again, will not be girdled by it. Europe is in travail; pang after pang; what a shriek was that of Pilnitz! The birth will be: WAR.

Nay, the worst feature of the business is this last, still to be named; the Emigrants at Coblentz. So many thousands ranking there, in bitter hate and menace: King's Brothers, all Princes of the Blood except wicked D'Orléans; your duelling De Castries, your eloquent Cazalès; bull-headed Malseignes, a wargod Broglie; Distaff Seigneurs, insulted Officers, all that have ridden across the Rhine-stream; D'Artois welcoming Abbé Maury with a kiss, and clasping him publicly to his own royal heart! Emigration, flowing over the Frontiers, now in drops, now in streams, in various humours of fear, of petulance, rage and hope, ever since those first Bastille days when D'Artois went, 'to shame the citizens of Paris,'—had swollen to the size of a Phenomenon for the world. Coblentz is become a small extra-national Versailles; a Versailles *in partibus:* briguing, intriguing, favoritism, strumpetocracy itself, they say, goes on there; all the old activities, on a small scale, quickened by hungry Revenge.

Enthusiasm, of loyalty, of hatred and hope, has risen to a high pitch; as, in any Coblentz tavern you may hear, in speech and in singing. Maury assists in the interior Council; much is decided on: for one thing, they keep lists of the dates of your emigrating; a month sooner, or a month later, determines your greater or your less right to the coming Division of the Spoil. Cazalès himself, because he had occasionally spoken with a Constitutional tone, was looked on coldly at first: so pure are our principles. And arms are a-hammering at Liége; 'three thousand horses' ambling hitherward from the Fairs of Germany: Cavalry enrolling; likewise Foot-soldiers, 'in blue coat, red waistcoat and nankeen trousers.' They have their secret domestic correspondences, as their open foreign: with disaffected Crypto-Aristocrats, with contumacious Priests, with Austrian Committee in the Tuileries. Deserters are spirited over by assiduous crimps; Royal-Allemand is gone almost wholly. Their route of March, towards France and the Division of the Spoil, is marked out, were the Kaiser once ready. 'It is said, they mean to poison the sources; but,' adds Patriotism making report of it, 'they will not poison the source of Liberty'; whereat *on applaudit,* we cannot but applaud. Also they have manufactories of False Assignats; and men that circulate in the interior, distributing and disbursing the same; one of these we denounce now to Legislative Patriotism: 'a man Lebrun by name; about thirty years of age, with blonde hair and in quantity; has,' only for the time being surely, 'a black-eye, *œil poché;* goes in a *wiski* with a black horse.'—always keeping his Gig!

Unhappy Emigrants, it was their lot, and the lot of France! They are ignorant of much that they should know: of themselves, of what is around them. A Political Party that knows not *when it is beaten,* may become one of the fatallest of things, to itself, and to all. Nothing will convince these men that they cannot scatter the French Revolution at the first blast of their war-trumpet; that the French Revolution is other than a blustering Effervescence, of brawlers and spouters, which, at the flash of chivalrous broadswords, at the rustle of gallows-ropes, will burrow itself, in dens the deeper the welcomer. But, alas, what man does know and measure himself, and the things that are round him;—else where were the need of physical fighting at all? Never, till they are cleft asunder, can these heads believe that a Sansculottic arm has any vigour in it: cleft asunder, it will be too late to believe.

One may say, without spleen against his poor erring brothers of any side, that above all other mischiefs, this of the Emigrant Nobles acted fatally on France. Could they have known, could they have understood! In the beginning of 1789, a splendour and a terror still yet a little while: but its hours are numbered: Europe is coming with Four hundred and nineteen thousand and the Chivalry of France; the gallows, one may hope, will get its own.

SECTION VI

September in Paris

[In the summer of 1792 France faced invasion by a Prussian army headed by the Duke of Brunswick, who avowed his intention of restoring the ancient authority of the King, of "putting an end to the anarchy in the interior of France," and of giving the city of Paris over to "military execution." This threatening manifesto aroused fierce indignation throughout the country, and as the Legislative Assembly seemed unable to act energetically, led to an uprising in Paris and the storming of the Tuileries Palace by the mob (August 10, 1792). The Assembly broke up after decreeing the election of a National Convention to meet in September. Power was seized in Paris by the radical Commune and the provisional government headed by Danton. Thousands of suspected persons were arrested and packed into prison. Drastic measures were taken to secure the loyalty of the army and to resist the invasion to the utmost.]

351

YE HAVE ROUSED HER, then, ye Emigrants and Despots of the world; France is roused! Long have ye been lecturing and tutoring this poor Nation, like cruel uncalled-for pedagogues, shaking over her your ferulas of fire and steel: it is long that ye have pricked and fillipped and affrighted her, there as she sat helpless in her dead cerements of a Constitution, you gathering in on her from all lands, with your armaments and plots, your invadings and truculent bullyings—and lo now, ye have pricked her to the quick, and she is up, and her blood is up. The dead cerements are rent into cobwebs, and she fronts you in that terrible strength of Nature, which no man has measured, which goes down to Madness and Tophet: see now how ye will deal with her.

This month of September 1792, which has become one of the memorable months of History, presents itself under two most diverse aspects; all of black on the one side, all of bright on the other. Whatsoever is cruel in the panic frenzy of Twenty-five million men, whatsoever is great in the simultaneous death-defiance of Twenty-five million men, stand here in abrupt contrast, near by one another. As indeed is usual when a man, how much more when a Nation of men, is hurled suddenly beyond the limits. For Nature, as green as she looks, rests everywhere on dread foundations, were we further down; and Pan, to whose music the Nymphs dance, has a cry in him that can drive all men distracted.

Very frightful it is when a Nation, rending asunder its Constitutions and Regulations which were grown dead cerements for it, becomes *trans*cendental; and must now seek its wild way through the New, Chaotic—where Force is not yet distinguished into Bidden and Forbidden, but Crime and Virtue welter unseparated—in that domain of what is called the Passions; of what we call the Miracles and the Portents! It is thus that, for some three years to come, we are to contemplate France, in this final Third Volume of our History. Sansculottism reigning in all its grandeur and in all its hideousness: the Gospel (God's-Message) of Man's Rights, Man's *mights* or strengths, once more preached irrefragably abroad; along with this, and still louder for the time, the fearfullest Devil's-Message of Man's weaknesses and sins—and all on such a scale, and under such aspect: cloudy 'death-birth of a world': huge smoke-cloud, streaked with rays as of heaven on one side; girt on the other as with hell-fire! History tells us many things: but for the last thousand years and more, what thing has she told us of a sort like this? Which therefore let us too,

O Reader, dwell on willingly, for a little; and from its endless significance endeavour to extract what may, in present circumstances, be adapted for us.

It is unfortunate, though very natural, that the history of this Period has so generally been written in hysterics. Exaggeration abounds, execration, wailing; and, on the whole, darkness. But thus too, when foul old Rome had to be swept from the Earth, and those Northmen, and other horrid sons of Nature, came in, 'swallowing formulas' as the French now do, foul old Rome screamed execratively her loudest; so that the true shape of many things is lost for us. Attila's Huns had arms of such length that they could lift a stone without stooping. Into the body of the poor Tatars execrative Roman History intercalated an alphabetic letter; and so they continue Tartars, of fell Tartarean nature, to this day. Here, in like manner, search as we will in these multiform innumerable French Records, darkness too frequently covers, or sheer distraction bewilders. One finds it difficult to imagine that the Sun shone in this September month, as he does in others. Nevertheless it is an indisputable fact that the Sun did shine; and there was weather and work—nay, as to that, very bad weather for harvest-work! An unlucky Editor may do his utmost; and after all, require allowances.

At Paris, by lying Rumour which proved prophetic and veridical, the fall of Verdun was known some hours *before* it happened. It is Sunday the second of September; handiwork hinders not the speculations of the mind. Verdun gone (though some still deny it); the Prussians in full march, with gallows-ropes, with fire and faggot! Thirty-thousand Aristocrats within our own walls; and but the merest quarter-tithe of them yet put in Prison! Nay, there goes a word that even these will revolt. Sieur Jean Julien, wagoner of Vaugirard, being set in the Pillory last Friday, took all at once to crying, That he would be well revenged ere long; that the King's Friends in Prison would burst out, force the Temple, set the King on horseback, and, joined by the unimprisoned, ride roughshod over us all. This the unfortunate wagoner of Vaugirard did bawl, at the top of his lungs: when snatched off to the Townhall, he persisted in it, still bawling; yesternight, when they guillotined him, he died with the froth of it on his lips. For a man's mind, padlocked to the Pillory, may go mad; and all men's minds may go mad, and 'believe him,' as the frenetic will do, *'because it is impossible.'*

So that apparently the knot of the crisis and last agony of France is come? Make front to this, thou Improvised Commune, strong Danton, whatsoever man is strong! Readers can judge whether the Flag of Country in Danger flapped soothingly or distractively on the souls of men, that day.

But the Improvised Commune, but strong Danton is not wanting, each after his kind. Huge Placards are getting plastered to the walls; at two o'clock the storm-bell shall be sounded, the alarm-cannon fired; all Paris shall rush to the Champ-de-Mars, and have itself enrolled. Unarmed, truly, and undrilled; but desperate, in the strength of frenzy. Haste, ye men; ye very women, offer to mount guard and shoulder the brown musket: weak clucking-hens, in a state of desperation, will fly at the muzzle of the mastiff; and even conquer him—by vehemence of character! Terror itself, when once grown transcendental, becomes a kind of courage; as frost sufficiently intense, according to Poet Milton, will *burn*.—Danton, the other night, in the Legislative Committee of General Defence, when the other Ministers and Legislators had all opined, said, It would not do to quit Paris, and fly to Saumur; that they must abide by Paris; and take such attitude as would put their enemies in fear—*faire peur;* a word of his which has been often repeated, and reprinted—in italics.

At two of the clock, Beaurepaire, as we saw, has shot himself at Verdun; and, over Europe, mortals are going in for afternoon sermon. But at Paris, all steeples are clangouring not for sermon; the alarm-gun booming from minute to minute; Champ-de-Mars and Fatherland's Altar boiling with desperate terror-courage: what a *miserere* going up to Heaven from this once Capital of the Most Christian King! The Legislative sits in alternate awe and effervescence; Vergniaud proposing that Twelve shall go and dig personally on Montmartre; which is decreed by acclaim.

But better than digging personally with acclaim, see Danton enter; —the black brows clouded, the colossus-figure tramping heavy; grim energy looking from all features of the rugged man! Strong is that grim Son of France and Son of Earth; a Reality and not a Formula he too: and surely now if ever, being hurled *low* enough, it is on the Earth and on Realities that he rests. 'Legislators!' so speaks the stentor-voice, as the Newspapers yet preserve it for us, 'it is not the alarm-cannon that you hear: it is the *pas-de-charge* against our enemies. To conquer them, to hurl them back, what do we require? *Il nous faut de l'audace, et encore de l'audace, et toujours de l'audace.*

354

To dare, and again to dare, and without end to dare!'—Right so, thou brawny Titan; there is nothing left for thee but that. Old men, who heard it, will still tell you how the reverberating voice made all hearts swell, in that moment; and braced them to the sticking-place; and thrilled abroad over France, like electric virtue, as a word spoken in season.

But the Commune, enrolling in the Champ-de-Mars? But the Committee of Watchfulness, become now Committee of Public Salvation; whose conscience is Marat? The Commune enrolling enrolls many; provides Tents for them in that Mars'-Field, that they may march with dawn on the morrow: praise to this part of the Commune! To Marat and the Committee of Watchfulness not praise—not even blame, such as could be meted out in these insufficient dialects of ours; expressive silence rather! Lone Marat, the man forbid, meditating long in his Cellars of refuge, on his Stylites Pillar, could see salvation in one thing only: in the fall of 'two hundred and sixty thousand Aristocrat heads.' With so many scores of Naples Bravoes, each a dirk in his right-hand, a muff on his left, he would traverse France, and do it. But the world laughed, mocking the severe-benevolence of a People's Friend; and his idea could not become an action, but only a fixed-idea. Lo, now, however, he has come down from his Stylites Pillar, to a *Tribune particulière;* here now, without the dirks, without the *muffs* at least, were it not grown possible—now in the knot of the crisis, when salvation or destruction hangs in the hour!

The Ice-Tower of Avignon was noised of sufficiently, and lives in all memories; but the authors were not punished: nay we saw Jourdan *Coupe-tête,* borne on men's shoulders, like a copper Portent, 'traversing the cities of the South.'—What phantasms, squalid-horrid, shaking their dirk and muff, may dance through the brain of a Marat, in this dizzy pealing of tocsin-miserere and universal frenzy, seek not to guess, O Reader! Nor what the cruel Billaud 'in his short brown coat' was thinking; nor Sergent, not yet *Agate*-Sergent; nor Panis the confidant of Danton—nor, in a word, how gloomy Orcus does breed in her gloomy womb, and fashion her monsters and prodigies of Events, which thou seest her visibly bear! Terror is on these streets of Paris; terror and rage, tears and frenzy: tocsin-miserere pealing through the air; fierce desperation rushing to battle; mothers, with streaming eyes and wild hearts, sending forth their sons to die. 'Carriage-horses are seized by the bridle,' that they may draw cannon; 'the traces cut, the carriages left standing.' In such tocsin-miserere, and murky bewilderment of Frenzy, are not Murder, Até and all Furies near at hand? On slight hint—who knows on how slight?—may not Murder come; and, with *her* snaky-sparkling head, illuminate this murk!

How it was and went, what part might be premeditated, what was improvised and accidental, man will never know, till the great Day of Judgement make it known. But with a Marat for keeper of the Sovereign's Conscience—And we know what the *ultima ratio* of Sovereigns, when they are driven to it, is! In this Paris there are as wicked men, say a hundred or more, as exist in all the Earth: to be hired, and set on; to set on, of their own accord, unhired.—And yet we will remark that premeditation itself is not performance, is not surety of performance; that it is perhaps, at most, surety of *letting* whosoever will perform. From the purpose of crime to the act of crime there is an abyss; wonderful to think of. The finger lies on the pistol; but the man is not yet a murderer: nay, his whole nature staggering at such consummation, is there not a confused pause rather—one last instant of possibility for him? Not yet a murderer; it is at the mercy of light trifles whether the most fixed idea may not yet become unfixed. One slight twitch of a muscle, the death-flash bursts; and he is it, and will for Eternity be it—and Earth has become a penal Tartarus for him; his horizon girdled now not with golden hope, but with red flames of remorse; voices from the depths of Nature sounding, Woe, woe on him!

Of such stuff are we all made; on such powder-mines of bottomless guilt and criminality—'if God restrained not,' as is well said—does the purest of us walk. There are depths in man that go the length of lowest Hell, as there are heights that reach highest Heaven—for are not both Heaven and Hell made out of him, made by him, everlasting Miracle and Mystery as he is?—But looking on this Champ-de-Mars, with its tent-buildings and frantic enrolments; on this murky-simmering Paris, with its crammed Prisons (supposed about to burst), with its tocsin-miserere, its mothers' tears, and soldiers' farewell shoutings—the pious soul might have prayed, that day, that God's grace would restrain, and greatly restrain; lest on slight hest or hint, Madness, Horror and Murder rose, and this Sabbathday of September became a Day black in the Annals of men.

The tocsin is pealing its loudest, the clocks inaudibly striking *Three,* when poor Abbé Sicard, with some thirty other Nonjurant Priests, in six carriages, fare along the streets, from their preliminary House of

Detention at the Townhall, westward towards the Prison of the Abbaye. Carriages enough stand deserted on the streets; these six move on—through angry multitudes cursing as they move. Accursed Aristocrat Tartuffes, this is the pass ye have brought us to! And now ye will break the Prisons, and set Capet Veto on horseback to ride over us? Out upon you, Priests of Beelzebub and Moloch; of Tartuffery, Mammon and the Prussian Gallows—which ye name Mother-Church and God!—Such reproaches have the poor Nonjurants to endure, and worse; spoken in on them by frantic Patriots, who mount even on the carriage-steps; the very Guards hardly refraining. Pull up your carriage-blinds?—No! answers Patriotism, clapping its horny paw on the carriage-blind, and crushing it down again. Patience in oppression has limits: we are close on the Abbaye, it has lasted long: a poor Nonjurant, of quicker temper, smites the horny paw with his cane; nay, finding solacement in it, smites the unkempt head, sharply and again more sharply, twice over—seen clearly of us and of the world. It is the last that we see clearly. Alas, next moment, the carriages are locked and blocked in endless raging tumults; in yells deaf to the cry for mercy, which answer the cry for mercy with sabre-thrusts through the heart. The thirty Priests are torn out, are massacred about the Prison-Gate, one after one—only the poor Abbé Sicard, whom one Moton a watchmaker, knowing him, heroically tried to save and secrete in the Prison, escapes to tell—and it is Night and Orcus, and Murder's snaky-sparkling head *has* risen in the murk!—

From Sunday afternoon (exclusive of intervals and pauses not final) till Thursday evening, there follow consecutively a Hundred Hours. Which hundred hours are to be reckoned with the hours of the Bartholomew Butchery, of the Armagnac Massacres, Sicilian Vespers, or whatsoever is savagest in the annals of this world. Horrible the hour when man's soul, in its paroxysm, spurns asunder the barriers and rules; and shows what dens and depths are in it! For Night and Orcus, as we say, as was long prophesied, have burst forth, here in this Paris, from their subterranean imprisonment: hideous, dim-confused; which it is painful to look on; and yet which cannot, and indeed which should not, be forgotten.

The Reader, who looks earnestly through this dim Phantasmagory of the Pit, will discern few fixed certain objects; and yet still a few. He will observe, in this Abbaye Prison, the sudden massacre of the Priests being once over, a strange Court of Justice, or call it Court of Revenge and Wild-Justice, swiftly fashion itself, and take seat round a table, with the Prison-Registers spread before it—Stanislas Maillard, Bastille-hero, famed Leader of the Menads, presiding. O Stanislas, one hoped to meet thee elsewhere than here; thou shifty Riding-Usher, with an inkling of Law! This work also thou hadst to do; and then— to depart for ever from our eyes. At *La Force,* at the *Châtelet,* the *Conciergerie,* the like Court forms itself, with the like accompaniments: the thing that one man does, other men can do. There are some Seven Prisons in Paris, full of Aristocrats with conspiracies—nay not even *Bicêtre* and *Salpêtrière* shall escape, with their Forgers of Assignats: and there are seventy times seven hundred Patriot hearts in a state of frenzy. Scoundrel hearts also there are; as perfect, say, as the Earth holds—if such are needed. To whom, in this mood, law is as no-law; and killing, by what name soever called, is but work to be done.

So sit these sudden Courts of Wild-Justice, with the Prison-Registers before them; unwonted wild tumult howling all round; the Prisoners in dread expectancy within. Swift: a name is called; bolts jingle, a Prisoner is there. A few questions are put; swiftly this sudden Jury decides: Royalist Plotter or not? Clearly not; in that case, Let the Prisoner be enlarged with *Vive la Nation.* Probably yea; then still, Let the Prisoner be enlarged, but without *Vive la Nation;* or else it may run. Let the Prisoner be conducted to La Force. At La Force again their formula is, Let the Prisoner be conducted to the Abbaye.— 'To La Force then!' Volunteer bailiffs seize the doomed man; he is at the outer gate; 'enlarged', or 'conducted', not into La Force, but into a howling sea; forth, under an arch of wild sabres, axes and pikes; and sinks, hewn asunder. And another sinks, and another; and there forms itself a piled heap of corpses, and the kennels begin to run red. Fancy the yells of these men, their faces of sweat and blood; the crueller shrieks of these women, for there are women too; and a fellow-mortal hurled naked into it all! Jourgniac de Saint-Méard has seen battle, has seen an effervescent Regiment du Roi in mutiny; but the bravest heart may quail at this. The Swiss Prisoners, remnants of the Tenth of August, 'clasped each other spasmodically, and hung back; grey veterans crying: "Mercy, Messieuers; ah, mercy!" But there was no mercy. Suddenly, however, one of these men steps forward. He had on a blue frock coat; he seemed about thirty, his stature was above common, his look noble and martial. "I go first," said he, "since it must be so: adieu!" Then dashing his hat sharply behind him: "Which way?" cried he to the Brigands: "Show it me, then." They open the folding gate; he is announced to the multitude. He stands a moment motionless; then plunges forth among the pikes, and dies of a thousand wounds'.

Man after man is cut down; the sabres need sharpening, the killers refresh themselves from wine-jugs. Onward and onward goes the butchery; the loud yells wearying down into bass growls. A sombre-faced shifting multitude looks on; in dull approval, or dull disapproval; in dull recognition that it is Necessity. 'An *Anglais* in drab greatcoat' was seen, or seemed to be seen, serving liquor from his own dram-bottle;—for what purpose, 'if not set on by Pitt,' Satan and himself know best! Witty Dr. Moore grew sick on approaching, and turned into another street.—Quick enough goes this Jury-Court; and rigorous. The brave are not spared, nor the beautiful, nor the weak. Old M. de Montmorin, the Minister's Brother, was acquitted by the Tribunal of the Seventeenth; and conducted back, elbowed by howling galleries; but is not acquitted here. Princess de Lamballe has lain down on bed: 'Madame, you are to be removed to the Abbaye.' 'I do not wish to remove; I am well enough here.' There is a need-be for removing. She will arrange her dress a little, then; rude voices answer, 'You have not far to go.' She too is led to the hell-gate; a manifest Queen's-Friend. She shivers back, at the sight of bloody sabres; but there is no return: Onwards! That fair hind head is cleft with the axe; the neck is severed. The fair body is cut in fragments; with indignities, and obscene horrors of moustachio *grands-lèvres,* which human nature would fain find incredible—which shall be read in the original language only. She was beautiful, she was good, she had known no happiness. Young hearts, generation after generation, will think with themselves: O worthy of worship, thou king-descended, god-descended, and poor sister-woman! why was not I there; and some Sword Balmung or Thor's Hammer in my hand? Her head is fixed on a pike; paraded under the windows of the Temple; that a still more hated, a Marie Antoinette, may see. One Municipal, in the Temple with the Royal Prisoners at the moment, said, 'Look out.' Another eagerly whispered, 'Do not look.' The circuit of the Temple is guarded, in these hours, by a long stretched tricolor riband: terror enters, and the clangour of infinite tumult; hitherto not regicide, though that too may come.

But it is more edifying to note what thrillings of affection, what fragments of wild virtues turn up in this shaking asunder of man's existence; for of these too there is a proportion. Note old Marquis

Cazotte: he is doomed to die; but his young Daughter clasps him in her arms, with an inspiration of eloquence, with a love which is stronger than very death: the heart of the killers themselves is touched by it; the old man is spared. Yet he was guilty, if plotting for his King is guilt: in ten days more, a Court of Law condemned him, and he had to die elsewhere; bequeathing his Daughter a lock of his old grey hair. Or note old M. de Sombreuil, who also had a Daughter:—My Father is not an Aristocrat: O good gentlemen, I will swear it, and testify it, and in all ways prove it; we are not; we hate Aristocrats! 'Wilt thou drink Aristocrats' blood?' The man lifts blood (if universal Rumour can be credited); the poor maiden does drink. 'This Sombreuil is innocent then!' Yes, indeed—and now note, most of all, how the bloody pikes, at this news, do rattle to the ground; and the tiger-yells become bursts of jubilee over a brother saved; and the old man and his daughter are clasped to bloody bosoms, with hot tears; and borne home in triumph of *Vive la Nation,* the killers refusing even money! Does it seem strange, this temper of theirs? It seems very certain, well proved by Royalist testimony in other instances; and very significant.

This is the September Massacre, otherwise called 'Severe Justice of the People.' These are the Septemberers (*Septembriseurs*); a name of some note and lucency—but lucency of the Nether-fire sort; very different from that of our Bastille Heroes, who shone, disputable by no Friend of Freedom, as in Heavenly light-radiance: to such phasis of the business have we advanced since then! The numbers massacred are, in the Historical *fantasy,* 'between two and three thousand;' or indeed they are 'upwards of six thousand,' for Peltier (in vision) saw them massacring the very patients of the Bicêtre Madhouse 'with grape-shot;' nay finally they are 'twelve thousand' and odd hundreds, —not more than that. In Arithmetical ciphers, and Lists drawn up by accurate Advocate Maton, the number, including two-hundred and two priests, three 'persons unknown,' and 'one thief killed at the Bernardins,' is, as above hinted, a Thousand and Eighty-nine—not less than that.

A thousand and eighty-nine lie dead, 'two-hundred and sixty heaped carcasses on the Pont au Change' itself—among which, Robespierre pleading afterwards will 'nearly weep' to reflect that there was said to be one slain innocent. One; not two, O thou seagreen Incorruptible? If so, Themis Sansculotte must be lucky; for she was brief!—In the dim Registers of the Townhall, which are preserved to this day, men read, with a certain sickness of heart, items and entries not usual in

Town Books: 'To workers employed in preserving the salubrity of the air in the Prisons, and persons who presided over these dangerous operations', so much—in various items, nearly seven hundred pounds sterling. To carters employed to 'the Burying-grounds of Clamart, Montrouge and Vaugirard,' at so much a journey, per cart; this also is an entry. Then so many francs and odd sous 'for the necessary quantity of quick-lime!' Carts go along the streets; full of stript human corpses, thrown pellmell; limbs sticking up—seest thou that cold Hand sticking up, through the heaped embrace of brother corpses, in its yellow paleness, in its cold rigour; the palm opened towards Heaven, as if in dumb prayer, in expostulation *de profundis,* Take pity on the Sons of Men!—Mercier saw it, as he walked down 'the Rue Saint-Jacques from Montrouge, on the morrow of the Massacres:' but not a hand; it was a Foot,—which he reckons still more significant, one understands not well why. Or was it as the Foot of one *spurning* Heaven? Rushing, like a wild diver, in disgust and despair, towards the depths of Annihilation? Even there shall His hand find thee, and His right-hand hold thee—surely for right not for wrong, for good not evil! 'I saw that Foot,' says Mercier; 'I shall know it again at the great Day of Judgement, when the Eternal, throned on his thunders, shall judge both Kings and Septemberers.'

That a shriek of inarticulate horror rose over this thing, not only from French Aristocrats and Moderates, but from all Europe, and has prolonged itself to the present day, was most natural and right. The thing lay done, irrevocable; a thing to be counted beside some other things, which lie very black in our Earth's Annals, yet which will not erase therefrom. For man, as was remarked, has transcendentalisms in him; standing, as he does, poor creature, every way 'in the confluence of Infinitudes;' a mystery to himself and others: in the centre of two Eternities, of three Immensities,—in the intersection of primaeval Light with the everlasting Dark!—Thus have there been, especially by vehement tempers reduced to a state of desperation, very miserable things done. Sicilian Vespers, and 'eight thousand slaughtered in two hours,' are a known thing. Kings themselves, not in desperation, but only in difficulty, have sat hatching, for year and day (nay De Thou says for seven years), their Bartholomew Business; and then, at the right moment, also on an Autumn Sunday, this very Bell (they say it is the identical metal) of Saint-Germain l'Auxerrois was set a-pealing—with effect. Nay the same black boulder-stones of these Paris Prisons have seen Prison-massacres before now; men massacring countrymen, Burgundies massacring Armagnacs, whom they had suddenly imprisoned, till, as now, there were piled heaps of carcasses, and the streets ran red: the Mayor Pétion of the time speaking the austere language of the law, and answered by the Killers, in old French (it is some four hundred years old): *'Maugré bieu, Sire—* Sir, God's malison on your "justice," your "pity," your "right reason." Cursed be of God whoso shall have pity on these false traitorous Armagnacs, English; dogs they are; they have destroyed us, wasted this realm of France, and sold it to the English.' And so they slay, and fling aside the slain, to the extent of 'fifteen hundred and eighteen, among whom are found four bishops of false and damnable counsel, and two Presidents of Parlement.' For though it is not Satan's world this that we live in, Satan always has his place in it (underground properly); and from time to time bursts up. Well may mankind shriek, inarticulately anathematizing as they can. There are actions of such emphasis that no shrieking can be too emphatic for them. Shriek ye; acted have they.

Shriek who might in this France, in this Paris Legislative or Paris Townhall, there are Ten Men who do not shriek. A Circular goes out from the Committee of *Salut Public,* dated 3rd of September 1792; directed to all Townhalls: a State-paper too remarkable to be overlooked. 'A part of the ferocious conspirators detained in the Prisons', it says, 'have been put to death by the People; and we cannot doubt but the whole Nation, driven to the edge of ruin by such endless series of treasons, will make haste to adopt *this* means of public salvation; and all Frenchmen will cry as the men of Paris: We go to fight the enemy; but we will not leave robbers behind us, to butcher our wives and children.' To which are legibly appended these signatures: Panis; Sergent; Marat, Friend of the People; with Seven others—carried down thereby, in a strange way, to the late remembrance of Antiquarians. We remark, however, that their Circular rather recoiled on themselves. The Townhalls made no use of it; even the distracted Sansculottes made little; they only howled and bellowed, but did not bite. At Rheims 'about eight persons' were killed; and two afterwards were hanged for doing it. At Lyons, and a few other places, some attempt was made; but with hardly any effect, being quickly put down.

Less fortunate were the Prisoners of Orléans; was the good Duke de La Rochefoucault. He journeying, by quick stages, with his Mother

362

and Wife, towards the Waters of Forges, or some quieter country, was arrested at Gisors; conducted along the streets, amid effervescing multitudes, and killed dead 'by the stroke of a paving-stone hurled through the coach-window.' Killed as a once Liberal now Aristocrat; Protector of Priests, Suspender of virtuous Pétions, and most unfortunate Hot-grown-cold, detestable to Patriotism. He dies lamented of Europe; his blood spattering the cheeks of his old Mother, ninety-three years old.

As for the Orléans Prisoners, they are State Criminals: Royalists, Ministers, Delessarts, Montmorins; who have been accumulating on the High Court of Orléans, ever since that Tribunal was set up. Whom now it seems good that we should get transferred to our new Paris Court of the Seventeenth; which proceeds far quicker. Accordingly hot Fournier from Martinique, Fournier *l'Américain,* is off, missioned by Constituted Authority; with stanch National Guards, with Lazouski the Pole; sparingly provided with road-money. These, through bad quarters, through difficulties, perils, for Authorities cross each other in this time—do triumphantly bring off the Fifty or Fifty-three Orléans Prisoners, towards Paris; where a swifter Court of the Seventeenth will do justice on them. But lo, at Paris, in the interim, a still swifter and swiftest Court of the *Second,* and of *September,* has instituted itself: enter not Paris, or that will judge you!—What shall hot Fournier do? It was his duty, as volunteer Constable, had he been a perfect character, to guard those men's lives never so Aristocratic, at the expense of his own valuable life never so Sansculottic, till some Constituted Court had disposed of them. But he was an imperfect character and Constable; perhaps one of the more imperfect.

Hot Fournier, ordered to turn thither by one Authority, to turn thither by another Authority, is in a perplexing multiplicity of orders; but finally he strikes off for Versailles. His Prisoners fare in tumbrils, or open carts, himself and Guards riding and marching around: and at the last village, the worthy Mayor of Versailles comes to meet him, anxious that the arrival and locking-up were well over. It is Sunday, the ninth day of the month. Lo, on entering the Avenue of Versailles, what multitudes, stirring, swarming in the September sun, under the dull-green September foliage; the Four-rowed Avenue all humming and swarming, as if the Town had emptied itself! Our tumbrils roll heavily through the living sea; the Guards and Fournier making way with ever more difficulty; the Mayor speaking and gesturing his persuasivest; amid the inarticulate growling hum, which growls ever the deeper even by hearing itself growl, not without sharp yelpings here and there—Would to God we were out of this strait place, and wind and separation had cooled the heat, which seems about igniting here.

And yet if the wide Avenue is too strait, what will the Street *de Surintendance* be, at leaving of the same? At the corner of Surintendance Street, the compressed yelpings become a continuous yell: savage figures spring on the tumbril-shafts; first spray of an endless coming tide! The Mayor pleads, pushes, half-desperate; is pushed, carried off in men's arms: the savage tide has entrance, has mastery. Amid horrid noise, and tumult as of fierce wolves, the Prisoners sink massacred—all but some eleven, who escaped into houses, and found mercy. The Prisons, and what other Prisoners they held, were with difficulty saved. The stript clothes are burnt in bonfire; the corpses lie heaped in the ditch on the morrow morning. All France, except it be the Ten Men of the Circular and their people, moans and rages, inarticulately shrieking; all Europe rings.

But neither did Danton shriek; though, as Minister of Justice, it was more his part to do so. Brawny Danton is in the breach, as of stormed Cities and Nations; amid the sweep of Tenth-of-August cannon, the rustle of Prussian gallows-ropes, the smiting of September sabres; destruction all round him, and the rushing-down of worlds: Minister of Justice is his name; but Titan of the Forlorn Hope, and *Enfant Perdu* of the Revolution, is his quality—and the man acts according to that. 'We must put our enemies in fear!' Deep fear, is it not, as of its own accord, falling on our enemies? The Titan of the Forlorn Hope, he is not the man that would swiftest of all prevent its so falling. Forward, thou lost Titan of an *Enfant Perdu;* thou must dare, and again dare, and without end dare; there is nothing left for thee but that! *'Que mon nom soit flétri,* Let my name be blighted:' what am I? The Cause alone is great; and shall live, and not perish. So, on the whole, here too is a Swallower of Formulas; of still wider gulp than Mirabeau: this Danton, Mirabeau of the Sansculottes. In the September days, this Minister was not heard of as co-operating with strict Roland; his business might lie elsewhere—with Brunswick and the Hôtel-de-Ville. When applied to by an official person, about the Orléans Prisoners, and the risks they ran, he answered gloomily, twice over, 'Are not these men guilty?'—When pressed, he 'answered in a terrible voice,' and turned his back. A thousand slain in the Prisons; horrible if you will: but Brunswick is within a day's journey of us; and there are Five-and-twenty Millions yet, to slay or to save. Some men have tasks—frightfuller than ours! It seems strange, but is not strange, that this Minister of Moloch-Justice, when any suppliant for a friend's life got access to him, was found to have human compassion; and yielded and granted 'always;' neither did one personal enemy of Danton perish in these days'.

To shriek, we say, when certain things are acted, is proper and unavoidable. Nevertheless, articulate speech, not shrieking, is the faculty of man: when speech is not yet possible, let there be, with the shortest delay, at least—silence. Silence, accordingly, in this forty-fourth year of the business, and eighteen hundred and thirty-sixth of an 'Era called Christian as *lucus à non'*, is the thing we recommend and practise. Nay, instead of shrieking more, it were perhaps edifying to remark, on the other side, what a singular thing Customs (in Latin, *Mores*) are; and how fitly the Virtue, *Vir-tus,* Manhood or Worth, that is in a man, is called his *Morality* or *Customariness*. Fell Slaughter, one of the most authentic products of the Pit you would say, once give it Customs, becomes War, with Laws of War; and is Customary and Moral enough; and red individuals carry the tools of it girt round their haunches, not without an air of pride—which do thou nowise blame. While, see! so long as it is but dressed in hodden or russet; and Revolution, less frequent than War, has not yet got its Laws of Revolution, but the hodden or russet individuals are Uncustomary— O shrieking beloved brother blockheads of Mankind, let us close those wide mouths of ours; let us cease shrieking, and begin considering!

SECTION VII

Regicide

[*The National Convention, elected by the decree of the expiring Legislative Assembly, began sessions in Paris on September 21, 1792. On the previous day the French army, commanded by Dumouriez and Kellermann, had defeated the Prussians at Valmy, and had thus checked the invasion which threatened to destroy the*

365

revolution. In its first session the National Convention decreed the abolition of the monarchy, and within a few weeks ordered the King brought to trial. That he would be condemned was a foregone conclusion; the only real question was that of punishment. The Girondins, who had been the principal leaders in the Legislative Assembly, were opposed to the death penalty. The violent revolutionary party, forming "the Mountain" of the National Convention, was determined to force matters to extremes.]

THE THREE VOTINGS

I S LOUIS CAPET GUILTY of conspiring against Liberty? Shall our Sentence be itself final, or need ratifying by Appeal to the People? If guilty, what Punishment? This is the form agreed to, after uproar and 'several hours of tumultuous indecision:' these are the Three successive Questions, whereon the Convention shall now pronounce. Paris floods round their Hall; multitudinous, many-sounding. Europe and all Nations listen for their answer. Deputy after Deputy shall answer to his name: Guilty or Not guilty?

As to the Guilt, there is, as above hinted, no doubt in the mind of Patriot men. Overwhelming majority pronounces Guilt; the unanimous Convention votes for Guilt, only some feeble twenty-eight voting not Innocence, but refusing to vote at all. Neither does the Second Question prove doubtful, whatever the Girondins might calculate. Would not Appeal to the People be another name for civil war? Majority of two to one answers that there shall be no Appeal: this also is settled. Loud Patriotism, now at ten o'clock, may hush itself for the night; and retire to its bed not without hope. Tuesday has gone well. On the morrow comes, What Punishment? On the morrow is the tug of war.

Consider therefore if, on this Wednesday morning, there is an affluence of Patriotism; if Paris stands a-tiptoe, and all Deputies are at their post! Seven-hundred and Forty-nine honourable Deputies; only some twenty absent on mission, Duchâtel and some seven others absent by sickness. Meanwhile expectant Patriotism and Paris standing a-tiptoe, have need of patience. For this Wednesday again passes in debate and effervescence; Girondins proposing that a 'majority of

366

three-fourths' shall be required; Patriots fiercely resisting them. Danton, who has just got back from mission in the Netherlands, does obtain 'order of the day' on this Girondin proposal; nay he obtains further that we decide *sans désemparer,* in Permanent-session, till we have done.

And so, finally, at eight in the evening this Third stupendous Voting, by roll-call or *appel nominal,* does begin. What Punishment? Girondins undecided, Patriots decided, men afraid of Royalty, men afraid of Anarchy, must answer here and now. Infinite Patriotism, dusky in the lamp-light, floods all corridors, crowds all galleries; sternly waiting to hear. Shrill-sounding Ushers summon you by Name and Department; you must rise to the Tribune, and say.

Eye-witnesses have represented this scene of the Third Voting, and of the votings that grew out of it; a scene protracted, like to be endless, lasting, with few brief intervals, from Wednesday till Sunday morning,—as one of the strangest seen in the Revolution. Long night wears itself into day, morning's paleness is spread over all faces; and again the wintry shadows sink, and the dim lamps are lit: but through day and night and the vicissitudes of hours, Member after Member is mounting continually those Tribune-steps; pausing aloft there, in the clearer upper light, to speak his Fate-word; then diving down into the dusk and throng again. Like Phantoms in the hour of midnight; most spectral, pandemonial! Never did President Vergniaud, or any terrestrial President, superintend the like. A King's Life, and so much else that depends thereon, hangs trembling in the balance. Man after man mounts; the buzz hushes itself till he have spoken: Death; Banishment; Imprisonment till the Peace. Many say, Death; with what cautious well-studied phrases and Paragraphs they could devise, of explanation, of enforcement, of faint recommendation to mercy. Many too say, Banishment; something short of Death. The balance trembles, none can yet guess whitherward. Whereat anxious Patriotism bellows; irrepressible by Ushers.

The poor Girondins, many of them, under such fierce bellowing of Patriotism, say Death; justifying, *motivant,* that most miserable word of theirs by some brief casuistry and jesuitry. Vergniaud himself says, Death; justifying by jesuitry. Rich Lepelletier Saint-Fargeau had been of the Noblesse, and then of the Patriot Left Side, in the Constituent; and had argued and reported, there and elsewhere, not a little, *against* Capital Punishment: nevertheless he now says, Death; a word which may cost him dear. Manuel did surely rank with the Decided in

August last; but he has been sinking and backsliding ever since September and the scenes of September. In this Convention, above all, no word he could speak would find favour; he says now, Banishment; and in mute wrath quits the place for ever—much hustled in the corridors. Philippe Égalité votes, in his soul and conscience, Death: at the sound of which and of whom, even Patriotism shakes its head; and there runs a groan and shudder through this Hall of Doom. Robespierre's vote cannot be doubtful; his speech is long. Men see the figure of shrill Sieyès ascend; hardly pausing, passing merely, this figure says, *'La Mort sans phrase,* Death without phrases;' and fares onward and downward. Most spectral, pandemonial!

And yet if the Reader fancy it of a funereal, sorrowful or even grave character, he is far mistaken: 'the Ushers in the Mountain quarter,' says Mercier, 'had become as Box-keepers at the Opera;' opening and shutting of Galleries for privileged persons, for 'D'Orléans Égalité's mistresses,' or other high-dizened women of condition, rustling with laces and tricolor. Gallant Deputies pass and repass thitherward, treating them with ices, refreshments and small-talk; the high-dizened heads beck responsive; some have their card and pin, pricking down the Ayes and Noes, as at a game of *Rouge-et-Noir*. Further aloft reigns Mère Duchesse with her unrouged Amazons; she cannot be prevented making long *Hahas,* when the vote is not *La Mort*. In these Galleries there is refection, drinking of wine and brandy 'as in open tavern, *en pleine tabagie.'* Betting goes on in all coffeehouses of the neighbourhood. But within doors, fatigue, impatience, uttermost weariness sits now on all visages; lighted up only from time to time by turns of the game. Members have fallen asleep; Ushers come and awaken them to vote: other Members calculate whether they shall not have time to run and dine. Figures rise, like phantoms, pale in the dusky lamp-light; utter from this Tribune, only one word: Death. *'Tout est optique,'* says Mercier, 'The world is all an optical shadow.' Deep in the Thursday night, when the Voting is done, and Secretaries are summing it up, sick Duchâtel, more spectral than another, comes borne on a chair, wrapt in blankets, in 'night-gown and nightcap,' to vote for Mercy: one vote it is thought may turn the scale.

Ah no! In profoundest silence, President Vergniaud, with a voice full of sorrow, has to say: 'I declare, in the name of the Convention, that the punishment it pronounces on Louis Capet is that of Death.' Death by a small majority of Fifty-three. Nay, if we deduct from the

368

one side, and add to the other, a certain Twenty-six, who said Death but coupled some faintest ineffectual surmise of mercy with it, the majority will be but *One*.

Death is the sentence: but its execution? It is not executed yet! Scarcely is the vote declared when Louis's Three Advocates enter; with Protest in his name, with demand for Delay, for Appeal to the People. For this do Desèze and Tronchet plead, with brief eloquence: brave old Malesherbes pleads for it with eloquent want of eloquence, in broken sentences, in embarrassment and sobs; that brave time-honoured face, with its grey strength, its broad sagacity and honesty, is mastered with emotion, melts into dumb tears.—They reject the Appeal to the People; that having been already settled. But as to the Delay, what they call *Sursis,* it *shall* be considered; shall be voted for to-morrow: at present we adjourn. Whereupon Patriotism 'hisses' from the Mountain: but a 'tyrannical majority' has so decided, and adjourns.

There is still this *fourth* Vote then, growls indignant Patriotism—this vote, and who knows what other votes, and adjournments of voting; and the whole matter still hovering hypothetical! And at every new vote those Jesuit Girondins, even they who voted for Death, would so fain find a loophole! Patriotism must watch and rage. Tyrannical adjournments there have been; one, and now another at midnight on plea of fatigue—all Friday wasted in hesitation and higgling; in *re*-counting of the votes, which are found correct as they stood! Patriotism bays fiercer than ever; Patriotism, by long watching, has become red-eyed, almost rabid.

'Delay: yes or no?' men do vote it finally, all Saturday, all day and night. Men's nerves are worn out, men's hearts are desperate; now it shall end. Vergniaud, spite of the baying, ventures to say Yes, Delay; though he had voted Death. Philippe Égalité says, in his soul and conscience, No. The next Member mounting: 'Since Philippe says No, I for my part say Yes, *moi je dis Oui*'. The balance still trembles. Till finally, at three o'clock on Sunday morning, we have: *No Delay,* by a majority of Seventy; *Death within four-and-twenty hours!*

Garat, Minister of Justice, has to go to the Temple with this stern message: he ejaculates repeatedly, *'Quelle commission affreuse,* What a frightful function!' Louis begs for a Confessor; for yet three days of life, to prepare himself to die. The Confessor is granted; the three days and all respite are refused.

There is no deliverance, then? Thick stone walls answer, None. Has King Louis no friends? Men of action, of courage grown desperate, in this his extreme need? King Louis's friends are feeble and far. Not even a voice in the coffee-houses rises for him. At Méot the Restaurateur's no Captain Dampmartin now dines; or sees death-doing whiskerandoes on furlough exhibit daggers of improved structure. Méot's gallant Royalists on furlough are far across the marches; they are wandering distracted over the world: or their bones lie whitening Argonne Wood. Only some weak Priests 'leave Pamphlets on all the bourne-stones,' this night, calling for a rescue: calling for the pious women to rise; or are taken distributing Pamphlets, and sent to prison.

Nay there is one death-doer, of the ancient Méot sort, who, with effort, has done even less and worse: slain a Deputy, and set all the Patriotism of Paris on edge! It was five on Saturday evening when Lepelletier St. Fargeau, having given his vote, *No Delay,* ran over to Février's in the Palais-Royal to snatch a morsel of dinner. He had dined, and was paying. A thickset man 'with black hair and blue beard,' in a loose kind of frock, stepped up to him; it was, as Février and the bystanders bethought them, one Pâris of the old King's-Guard. 'Are you Lepelletier?' asks he.—'Yes.'—'You voted in the King's business . . . ?'—'I voted Death'.—'*Scélérat,* take that!' cries Pâris, flashing out a sabre from under his frock, and plunging it deep in Lepelletier's side. Février clutches him: but he breaks off; is gone.

The voter Lepelletier lies dead; he has expired in great pain, at one in the morning—two hours before that Vote of *No Delay* was fully summed up. Guardsman Pâris is flying over France; cannot be taken; will be found some months after, self-shot in a remote inn.—Robespierre sees reason to think that Prince d'Artois himself is privately in Town; that the Convention will be butchered in the lump. Patriotism sounds mere wail and vengeance: Santerre doubles and trebles all his patrols. Pity is lost in rage and fear; the Convention has refused the three days of life and all respite.

PLACE DE LA RÉVOLUTION

TO THIS CONCLUSION, then, hast thou come, O hapless Louis! The Son of Sixty Kings is to die on the Scaffold by form of Law. Under Sixty Kings this same form of Law, form of Society, has been fashioning itself together, these thousand years; and has become, one way and other, a most strange Machine. Surely, if needful, it is also frightful, this Machine; dead, blind; not what it should be; which, with swift stroke, or by cold slow torture, has wasted the lives and souls of innumerable men. And behold now a King himself, or say rather Kinghood in his person, is to expire here in cruel tortures— like a Phalaris shut in the belly of his own red-heated Brazen Bull! It is ever so; and thou shouldst know it, O haughty tyrannous man: injustice breeds injustice; curses and falsehoods do verily return 'always *home*,' wide as they may wander. Innocent Louis bears the sins of many generations: he too experiences that man's tribunal is not in this Earth; that if he had no Higher one, it were not well with him.

A King dying by such violence appeals impressively to the imagination; as the like must do, and ought to do. And yet at bottom it is not the King dying, but the man! Kingship is a coat: the grand loss is of the skin. The man from whom you take his Life, to him can the whole combined world do *more*? Lally went on his hurdle; his mouth filled with a gag. Miserablest mortals, doomed for picking pockets, have a whole five-act Tragedy in them, in that dumb pain, as they go to the gallows, unregarded; they consume the cup of trembling down to the lees. For Kings and for Beggars, for the justly doomed and the unjustly, it is a hard thing to die. Pity them all: thy utmost pity, with all aids and appliances and throne-and-scaffold contrasts, how far short is it of the thing pitied!

A Confessor has come; Abbé Edgeworth, of Irish extraction, whom the King knew by good report, has come promptly on this solemn mission. Leave the Earth alone, then, thou hapless King; it with its malice will go its way, thou also canst go thine. A hard scene yet remains: the parting with our loved ones. Kind hearts, environed in the same grim peril with us; to be left *here!* Let the Reader look with the eyes of Valet Cléry, through these glass-doors, where also the Municipality watches; and see the cruellest of scenes:

'At half-past eight, the door of the ante-room opened: the Queen appeared first, leading her Son by the hand; then Madame Royale and Madame Elizabeth: they all flung themselves into the arms of the King. Silence reigned for some minutes; interrupted only by sobs. The Queen made a movement to lead his Majesty towards the inner room, where M. Edgeworth was waiting unknown to them: "No," said the King, "let us go into the dining-room, it is there only that I can see you." They entered there; I shut the door of it, which was of glass. The King sat down, the Queen on his left hand, Madame Elizabeth on his right, Madame Royale almost in front; the young Prince remained standing between his Father's legs. They all leaned towards him, and often held him embraced. This scene of woe lasted an hour and three quarters; during which we could hear nothing: we could see only that always when the King spoke, the sobbings of the Princesses redoubled, continued for some minutes; and that then the King began again to speak.'—And so our meetings and our partings do now end! The sorrows we gave each other; the poor joys we faithfully shared, and all our lovings and our sufferings, and confused toilings under the earthly Sun, are over. Thou good soul, I shall never, never through all ages of Time, see thee any more!—NEVER! O Reader, knowest thou that hard word?

For nearly two hours this agony lasts; then they tear themselves asunder. 'Promise that you will see us on the morrow.' He promises— Ah yes, yes; yet once; and go now, ye loved ones; cry to God for yourselves and me!—It was a hard scene, but it is over. He will not see them on the morrow. The Queen, in passing through the anteroom, glanced at the Cerberus Municipals; and, with woman's vehemence, said through her tears, *'Vous êtes tous des scélérats.'*

King Louis slept sound, till five in the morning, when Cléry, as he had been ordered, awoke him. Cléry dressed his hair: while this went forward, Louis took a ring from his watch, and kept trying it on his finger; it was his wedding-ring, which he is now to return to the Queen as a mute farewell. At half-past six, he took the Sacrament; and continued in devotion, and conference with Abbé Edgeworth. He will not see his Family: it were too hard to bear.

At eight, the Municipals enter: the King gives them his Will, and messages and effects; which they, at first, brutally refuse to take charge of: he gives them a roll of gold pieces, a hundred and twenty-five louis; these are to be returned to Malesherbes, who had lent them. At nine, Santerre says the hour is come. The King begs yet to retire for three minutes. At the end of three minutes, Santerre again says the hour is come. 'Stamping on the ground with his right foot, Louis answers: *"Partons,* Let us go." '—How the rolling of those drums comes in, through the Temple bastions and bulwarks, on the heart of a queenly wife; soon to be a widow! He is gone, then, and has not seen us? A Queen weeps bitterly; a King's Sister and Children. Over all these Four does Death also hover: all shall perish miserably save one; she, as Duchesse d'Angoulême, will live,—not happily.

At the Temple Gate were some faint cries, perhaps from voices of Pitiful women: *'Grâce! Grâce!'* Through the rest of the streets there is silence as of the grave. No man not armed is allowed to be there: the armed, did any even pity, dare not express it, each man overawed by all his neighbours. All windows are down, none seen looking through them. All shops are shut. No wheel-carriage rolls, this morning, in these streets but one only. Eighty-thousand armed men stand ranked, like armed statues of men; cannons bristle, cannoneers with match burning, but no word or movement: it is as a city enchanted into silence and stone: one carriage with its escort, slowly rumbling, is the only sound. Louis reads, in his Book of Devotion, the Prayers of the Dying: clatter of this death-march falls sharp on the ear, in the great silence; but the thought would fain struggle heavenward, and forget the Earth.

As the clocks strike ten, behold the Place de la Révolution, once Place de Louis Quinze: the Guillotine, mounted near the old Pedestal where once stood the Statue of that Louis! Far round, all bristles with cannons and armed men: spectators crowding in the rear; D'Orléans Égalité there in cabriolet. Swift messengers, *hoquetons,* speed to the Townhall, every three minutes: near by is the Convention sitting—vengeful for Lepelletier. Heedless of all, Louis reads his Prayers of the Dying; not till five minutes yet has he finished; then the Carriage opens. What temper he is in? Ten different witnesses will give ten different accounts of it. He is in the collision of all tempers; arrived now at the black Mahlstrom and descent of Death: in sorrow, in indignation, in resignation struggling to be resigned. 'Take care of M. Edgeworth,' he straitly charges the Lieutenant who is sitting with them: then they two descend.

The drums are beating: *'Taisez-vous,* Silence!' he cries 'in a terrible voice, *d'une voix terrible.'* He mounts the scaffold, not without delay; he is in puce coat, breeches of grey, white stockings. He strips off the coat; stands disclosed in a sleeve-waistcoat of white flannel. The Executioners approach to bind him: he spurns, resists; Abbé Edgeworth has to remind him how the Saviour, in whom men trust, submitted to be bound. His hands are tied, his head bare; the fatal moment is come. He advances to the edge of the Scaffold, 'his face very red,' and says: 'Frenchmen, I die innocent: it is from the Scaffold and near appearing before God that I tell you so. I pardon my enemies; I desire that France—' A General on horseback, Santerre or another, prances out, with uplifted hand: *'Tambours!'* The drums drown the voice. 'Executioners, do your duty!' The Executioners, desperate lest themselves be murdered (for Santerre and his Armed Ranks will strike, if they do not), seize the hapless Louis: six of them desperate, him singly desperate, struggling there; and bind him to their plank. Abbé Edgeworth, stooping, bespeaks him: 'Son of Saint Louis, ascend to Heaven.' The Axe clanks down; a King's Life is shorn away. It is Monday the 21st of January 1793. He was aged Thirty-eight years four months and twenty-eight days.

Executioner Samson shows the Head: fierce shout of *Vive la République* rises, and swells; caps raised on bayonets, hats waving: students of the College of Four Nations take it up, on the far Quais; fling it over Paris. D'Orléans drives off in his cabriolet: the Townhall Councillors rub their hands, saying, 'It is done, It is done.' There is dipping of handkerchiefs, of pike-points in the blood. Headsman Samson, though he afterwards denied it, sells locks of the hair: fractions of the puce coat are long after worn in rings.—And so, in some half-hour it is done; and the multitude has all departed. Pastry-cooks, coffee-sellers, milkmen sing out their trivial quotidian cries: the world wags on, as if this were a common day. In the coffee-houses that evening, says Prudhomme, Patriot shook hands with Patriot in a more cordial manner than usual. Not till some days after, according to Mercier, did public men see what a grave thing it was.

A grave thing it indisputably is; and will have consequences. On the morrow morning, Roland, so long steeped to the lips in disgust and chagrin, sends in his demission. His accounts lie all ready, correct in black-on-white to the uttermost farthing: these he wants but to have audited, that he might retire to remote obscurity, to the country and his books. They will never be audited, those accounts; he will never get retired thither.

It was on Tuesday that Roland demitted. On Thursday comes Lepelletier St. Fargeau's Funeral, and passage to the Pantheon of Great Men. Notable as the wild pageant of a winter day. The Body is borne aloft, half-bare; the winding-sheet disclosing the death-wound: sabre and bloody clothes parade themselves; a 'lugubrious music' wailing harsh *naeniae*. Oak-crowns shower down from windows; President Vergniaud walks there, with Convention, with Jacobin Society, and all Patriots of every colour, all mourning brotherlike.

Notable also for another thing, this Burial of Lepelletier: it was the last act these men ever did with concert! All Parties and figures of Opinion, that agitate this distracted France and its Convention, now stand, as it were, face to face, and dagger to dagger; the King's Life, round which they all struck and battled, being hurled down. Dumouriez, conquering Holland, growls ominous discontent, at the head of Armies. Men say Dumouriez will have a King; that young D'Orléans Égalité shall be his King. Deputy Fauchet, in the *Journal des Amis,* curses his day, more bitterly than Job did; invokes the poniards of Regicides, of 'Arras Vipers' or Robespierres, of Pluto Dantons, of horrid Butchers Legendre and Simulacra d'Herbois, to send him swiftly to another world than *theirs.* This is *Te-Deum* Fauchet, of the Bastille Victory, of the *Cercle Social.* Sharp was the death-hail rattling round one's Flag-of-truce, on that Bastille day: but it was soft to such wreckage of High Hope as this; one's New Golden Era going down in leaden dross, and sulphurous black of the Everlasting Darkness!

At home this Killing of a King has divided all friends; and abroad it has united all enemies. Fraternity of Peoples, Revolutionary Propagandism; Atheism, Regicide; total destruction of social order in this world! All Kings, and lovers of Kings, and haters of Anarchy, rank in coalition; as in a war for life. England signifies to Citizen Chauvelin, the Ambassador or rather Ambassador's-Cloak, that he must quit the country in eight days. Ambassador's-Cloak and Ambassador, Chauvelin and Talleyrand, depart accordingly. Talleyrand, implicated in that Iron Press of the Tuileries, thinks it safest to make for America.

England has cast out the Embassy: England declares war—being shocked principally, it would seem, at the condition of the River Scheldt. Spain declares war; being shocked principally at some other thing; which doubtless the Manifesto indicates. Nay, we find it was not England that declared war first, or Spain first; but that France herself declared war first on both of them—a point of immense Parliamentary and Journalistic interest in those days, but which has become of no interest whatever in these. They all declare war. The sword is drawn, the scabbard thrown away. It is even as Danton said, in one of his all-too-gigantic figures: 'The coalized Kings threaten us; we hurl at their feet, as gage of battle, the Head of a King.'

375

The Terror

[*Immediately after the execution of the King, war was declared against Great Britain, Holland, and Spain. Through the early months of 1793 the general situation continued to deteriorate. The factional fight in the Convention between the Girondins and the Mountain grew more bitter. The financial situation became acute. A royalist revolt broke out in the Vendée. On April 6 the notorious Committee of Public Safety, headed by Danton, and later joined by Robespierre, St. Just, and Couthon, was organized, and gradually assumed virtually dictatorial powers. In June many of the Girondins were arrested, while others of the faction fled. Marat, an influential journalist and radical leader, who was particularly active in urging the purge of the Girondins, was assassinated on July 13 by Charlotte Corday. To check incipient counter-revolution in the provinces, the Committee of Public Safety sent commissioners to various centers who introduced a reign of terror. In Paris, execution of enemies and suspected enemies of the Republic went forward with increasing violence.*]

MARIE-ANTOINETTE

ON MONDAY the Fourteenth of October 1793, a Cause is pending in the Palais de Justice, in the new Revolutionary Court, such as these old stone-walls never witnessed: the Trial of Marie-Antoinette. The once brightest of Queens, now tarnished, defaced, forsaken, stands here at Fouquier-Tinville's Judgement-bar; answering for her life. The Indictment was delivered her last night. To such changes of human fortune what words are adequate? Silence alone is adequate.

There are few Printed things one meets with of such tragic, almost ghastly, significance as those bald Pages of the *Bulletin du Tribunal Révolutionnaire,* which bear title, *Trial of the Widow Capet.* Dim, dim, as if in disastrous eclipse; like the pale kingdoms of Dis! Plutonic Judges, Plutonic Tinville; encircled, nine times, with Styx and Lethe, with Fire-Phlegethon and Cocytus named of Lamentation! The very witnesses summoned are like Ghosts: exculpatory, inculpatory, they themselves are all hovering over death and doom; they are known, in our imagination, as the prey of the Guillotine. Tall *ci-devant* Count d'Estaing, anxious to show himself Patriot, cannot escape; nor Bailly, who, when asked If he knows the Accused, answers with a reverent inclination towards her, 'Ah, yes, I know Madame.' Ex-Patriots are here, sharply dealt with, as Procureur Manuel; Ex-Ministers, shorn of their splendour. We have cold Aristocratic impassivity, faithful to itself even in Tartarus; rabid stupidity, of Patriot Corporals, Patriot Washerwomen, who have much to say of Plots, Treasons, August Tenth, old Insurrection of Women. For all now has become a crime, in her who has *lost*.

Marie-Antoinette, in this her utter abandonment, and hour of extreme need, is not wanting to herself, the imperial woman. Her look, they say, as that hideous Indictment was reading, continued calm; 'she was sometimes observed moving her fingers, as when one plays on the piano.' You discern, not without interest, across that dim Revolutionary Bulletin itself, how she bears herself queenlike. Her answers are prompt, clear, often of Laconic brevity; resolution, which has grown contemptuous without ceasing to be dignified, veils itself in calm words. 'You persist, then, in denial?'—'My plan is not denial: it is the truth I have said, and I persist in that.' Scandalous Hébert has borne his testimony as to many things: as to one thing, concerning Marie-Antoinette and her little Son—wherewith Human Speech had better not further be soiled. She has answered Hébert; a Juryman begs to observe that she has not answered as to *this*. 'I have not answered,' she exclaims with noble emotion, 'because Nature refuses to answer such a charge brought against a Mother. I appeal to all the Mothers that are here.' Robespierre, when he heard of it, broke out into something almost like swearing at the brutish blockheadism of this Hébert; on whose foul head his foul lie has recoiled. At four o'clock on Wednesday morning, after two days and two nights of interrogating, jury-charging, and other darkening of counsel, the result comes out: sentence of Death. 'Have you anything to say?' The Accused shook her head, without speech. Night's candles are burning out; and with her too Time is finishing, and it will be Eternity and Day. This Hall of Tinville's is dark, ill-lighted except where she stands. Silently she withdraws from it, to die.

Two Processions, or Royal Progresses, three-and-twenty years

377

apart, have often struck us with a strange feeling of contrast. The first is of a beautiful Archduchess and Dauphiness, quitting her Mother's City, at the age of Fifteen; towards hopes such as no other Daughter of Eve then had: 'On the morrow,' says Weber an eye-witness, 'the Dauphiness left Vienna. The whole city crowded out; at first with a sorrow which was silent. She appeared: you saw her sunk back into her carriage; her face bathed in tears; hiding her eyes now with her handkerchief, now with her hands; several times putting out her head to see yet again this Palace of her Fathers, whither she was to return no more. She motioned her regret, her gratitude to the good Nation, which was crowding here to bid her farewell. Then arose not only tears; but piercing cries, on all sides. Men and women alike abandoned themselves to such expression of their sorrow. It was an audible sound of wail, in the streets and avenues of Vienna. The last Courier that followed her disappeared, and the crowd melted away.'

The young imperial Maiden of Fifteen has now become a worn dis-crowned Widow of Thirty-eight; grey before her time: this is the last Procession: 'Few minutes after the Trial ended, the drums were beat-ing to arms in all Sections; at sunrise the armed force was on foot, cannons getting placed at the extremities of the Bridges, in the Squares, Crossways, all along from the Palais de Justice to the Place de la Révolution. By ten o'clock, numerous patrols were circulating in the Streets; thirty thousand foot and horse drawn up under arms. At eleven, Marie-Antoinette was brought out. She had on an undress of *piqué blanc:* she was led to the place of execution, in the same man-ner as an ordinary criminal; bound, on a Cart; accompanied by a Constitutional Priest in Lay dress; escorted by numerous detachments of infantry and cavalry. These, and the double row of troops all along her road, she appeared to regard with indifference. On her counte-nance there was visible neither abashment nor pride. To the cries of *Vive la République* and *Down with Tyranny,* which attended her all the way, she seemed to pay no heed. She spoke little to her Confessor. The tricolor Streamers on the housetops occupied her attention, in the Streets du Roule and Saint-Honoré; she also noticed the Inscriptions on the house-fronts. On reaching the Place de la Révolution, her looks turned towards the *Jardin National,* whilom Tuileries; her face at that moment gave signs of lively emotion. She mounted the Scaf-fold with courage enough; at a quarter past Twelve, her head fell; the Executioner showed it to the people, amid universal long-continued cries of *Vive la République.*'

WHOM NEXT, O Tinville! The next are of a different colour: our poor Arrested Girondin Deputies. What of them could still be laid hold of; our Vergniaud, Brissot, Fauchet, Valazé, Gensonné; the once flower of French Patriotism, Twenty-two by the tale: *hither,* at Tinville's Bar, onward from 'safeguard of the French People,' from confinement in the Luxembourg, imprisonment in the Conciergerie, have they now, by the course of things, arrived. Fouquier-Tinville must give what account of them he can.

Undoubtedly this Trial of the Girondins is the greatest that Fouquier has yet had to do. Twenty-two, all chief Republicans, ranged in a line there; the most eloquent in France; Lawyers too; not without friends in the auditory. How will Tinville prove these men guilty of Royalism, Federalism, Conspiracy against the Republic? Vergniaud's eloquence awakes once more; 'draws tears,' they say. And Journalists report, and the Trial lengthens itself out day after day; 'threatens to become eternal,' murmur many. Jacobinism and Municipality rise to the aid of Fouquier. On the 28th of the month, Hébert and others come in deputation to inform a Patriot Convention that the Revolutionary Tribunal is quite 'shackled by Forms of Law;' that a Patriot Jury ought to have 'the power of cutting short, of *terminer les débats,* when they feel themselves convinced.' Which pregnant suggestion, of cutting short, passes itself, with all dispatch, into a Decree.

Accordingly, at ten o'clock on the night of the 30th of October, the Twenty-two, summoned back once more, receive this information, That the Jury feeling themselves convinced have cut short, have brought in their verdict; that the Accused are found guilty, and the Sentence on one and all of them is, Death with confiscation of goods.

Loud natural clamour rises among the poor Girondins; tumult; which can only be repressed by the gendarmes. Valazé stabs himself; falls down dead on the spot. The rest, amid loud clamour and confusion, are driven back to their Conciergerie; Lasource exclaiming, 'I die on the day when the People have lost their reason; ye will die when they recover it.' No help! Yielding to violence, the Doomed uplift the Hymn of the Marseillaise; return singing to their dungeon.

Riouffe, who was their Prison-mate in these last days, has lovingly recorded what death they made. To our notions, it is not an edifying death. Gay satirical *Potpourri* by Ducos; rhymed Scenes of Tragedy, wherein Barrère and Robespierre discourse with Satan; death's eve spent in 'singing' and 'sallies of gaiety,' with 'discourses on the happiness of peoples': these things, and the like of these, we have to accept for what they are worth. It is the manner in which the Girondins make *their* Last Supper. Valazé, with bloody breast, sleeps cold in death; hears not the singing. Vergniaud has his dose of poison; but it is not enough for his friends, it is enough only for himself; wherefore he flings it from him; presides at this Last Supper of the Girondins, with wild coruscations of eloquence, with song and mirth. Poor human Will struggles to assert itself; if not in this way, then in that.

But on the morrow morning all Paris is out; such a crowd as no man had seen. The Death-carts, Valazé's cold corpse stretched among the yet living Twenty-one, roll along. Bareheaded, hands bound; in their shirt-sleeves, coat flung loosely round the neck; so fare the eloquent of France; bemurmured, beshouted. To the shouts of *Vive la République,* some of them keep answering with counter-shouts of *Vive la République.* Others, as Brissot, sit sunk in silence. At the foot of the scaffold they again strike up, with appropriate variations, the Hymn of the Marseillaise. Such an act of music; conceive it well! The yet Living chant there; the chorus so rapidly wearing weak! Samson's axe is rapid; one head per minute, or little less. The chorus is wearing weak; the chorus is worn *out;*—farewell for evermore, ye Girondins. Te-Deum Fauchet has become silent; Valazé's dead head is lopped: the sickle of the Guillotine has reaped the Girondins all away. 'The eloquent, the young, the beautiful and brave!' exclaims Riouffe. O Death, what feast is toward in thy ghastly Halls?

Nor, alas, in the far Bordeaux region will Girondism fare better. In caves of Saint-Emilion, in loft and cellar, the weariest months roll on; apparel worn, purse empty; wintry November come; under Tallien and his Guillotine, all hope now gone. Danger drawing ever nigher, difficulty pressing ever straiter, they determine to separate. Not unpathetic the farewell; tall Barbaroux, cheeriest of brave men, stoops to clasp his Louvet: 'In what place soever thou findest my Mother,' cries he, 'try to be instead of a son to her: no resource of mine but I will share with thy Wife, should chance ever lead me where she is.'

Louvet went with Guadet, with Salles and Valadi; Barbaroux with Buzot and Pétion. Valadi soon went southward, on a way of his own. The two friends and Louvet had a miserable day and night; the 14th of the November month, 1793. Sunk in wet, weariness and hunger, they knock, on the morrow, for help, at a friend's country-house; the faint-hearted friend refuses to admit them. They stood therefore under trees, in the pouring rain. Flying desperate, Louvet thereupon will to Paris. He sets forth, there and then, splashing the mud on each side of him, with a fresh strength gathered from fury or frenzy. He passes villages, finding 'the sentry asleep in his box in the thick rain'; he is gone, before the man can call after him. He bilks Revolutionary Committees; rides in carriers' carts, covered carts and open; lies hidden in one, under knapsacks and cloaks of soldiers' wives on the Street of Orléans, while men search for him; has hairbreadth escapes that would fill three romances: finally he gets to Paris to his fair Helpmate; gets to Switzerland, and waits better days.

Poor Guadet and Salles were both taken, ere long; they died by the Guillotine in Bordeaux; drums beating to drown their voices. Valadi also is caught, and guillotined. Barbaroux and his two comrades weathered it longer, into the summer of 1794; but not long enough. One July morning, changing their hiding-place, as they have often to do, 'about a league from Saint-Emilion, they observe a great crowd of country-people': doubtless Jacobins come to take them? Barbaroux draws a pistol, shoots himself dead. Alas, and it was not Jacobins; it was harmless villagers going to a village wake. Two days afterwards, Buzot and Pétion were found in a Cornfield, their bodies half-eaten by dogs.

Such was the end of Girondism. They arose to regenerate France, these men; and have accomplished *this*. Alas, whatever quarrel we had with them, has not their cruel fate abolished it? Pity only survives. So many excellent souls of heroes sent down to Hades; they themselves given as a prey of dogs and all manner of birds! But, here too, the will of the Supreme Power was accomplished. As Vergniaud said: 'The Revolution, like Saturn, is devouring its own children.'

RUSHING DOWN

W E ARE NOW, THEREFORE, got to that black precipitous Abyss; whither all things have long been tending; where, having now arrived on the giddy verge, they hurl down, in confused ruin; headlong, pellmell, down, down—till Sansculottism have consummated itself; and in this wondrous French Revolution, as in a Doomsday, **a**

World have been rapidly, if not born again, yet destroyed and engulfed. Terror has long been terrible: but to the actors themselves it has now become manifest that their appointed course is one of Terror; and they say, Be it so. *'Que la Terreur soit à l'ordre du jour.'*

So many centuries, say only from Hugh Capet downwards, had been adding together, century transmitting it with increase to century, the sum of Wickedness, of Falsehood, Oppression of man by man. Kings were sinners, and Priests were, and People. Open Scoundrels rode triumphant, bediademed, becoroneted, bemitred; or the still fataller species of Secret-Scoundrels, in their fair-sounding formulas, speciosities, respectabilities, hollow within: the race of Quacks was grown many as the sands of the sea. Till at length such a sum of Quackery had accumulated itself as, in brief, the Earth and the Heavens were weary of. Slow seemed the Day of Settlement; coming on, all imperceptible, across the bluster and fanfaronade of Courtierisms, Conquering-Heroisms, Most Christian *Grand Monarque*-isms, Well-beloved Pompadourisms: yet behold it was always coming; behold it has come, suddenly, unlooked for by any man! The harvest of long centuries was ripening and whitening so rapidly of late; and now it is grown *white,* and is reaped rapidly, as it were, in one day. Reaped, in this Reign of Terror; and carried home, to Hades and the Pit!—Unhappy Sons of Adam: it is ever so; and never do they know it, nor will they know it. With cheerfully smoothed countenances, day after day, and generation after generation, they, calling cheerfully to one another, Well-speed ye, are at work, *sowing the wind.* And yet, as God lives, they *shall reap the whirlwind;* no other thing, we say, is possible—since God is a Truth and His World is a Truth.

History, however, in dealing with this Reign of Terror, has had her own difficulties. While the Phenomenon continued in its primary state, as mere 'Horrors of the French Revolution,' there was abundance to be said and shrieked. With and also without profit. Heaven knows, there were terrors and horrors enough: yet that was not all the Phenomenon; nay, more properly, that was not the Phenomenon at all, but rather was the *shadow* of it, the negative part of it. And now, in a new stage of the business, when History, ceasing to shriek, would try rather to include under her old Forms of speech or speculation this new amazing Thing; that so some accredited scientific Law of Nature might suffice for the unexpected Product of Nature, and History might get to speak of it articulately, and draw inferences and

382

profit from it; in this new stage, History, we must say, babbles and flounders perhaps in a still painfuller manner. Take, for example, the latest Form of speech we have seen propounded on the subject as adequate to it, almost in these months, by our worthy M. Roux, in his *Histoire Parlementaire.* The latest and the strangest: that the French Revolution was a dead-life effort, after eighteen hundred years of preparation, to realize—the Christian Religion! *Unity, Indivisibility, Brotherhood or Death,* did indeed stand printed on all Houses of the Living; also, on Cemeteries, or Houses of the Dead, stood printed, by order of Procureur Chaumette, *Here is Eternal Sleep:* but a Christian Religion realized by the Guillotine and Death-Eternal 'is suspect to me,' as Robespierre was wont to say, *'m'est suspecte.'*

Alas, no, M. Roux! A Gospel of Brotherhood, not according to any of the Four old Evangelists, and calling on men to repent, and amend *each his own* wicked existence, that they might be saved; but a Gospel rather, as we often hint, according to a new Fifth Evangelist Jean-Jacques, calling on men to amend *each the whole world's* wicked existence, and be saved by making the Constitution. A thing different and distant *toto coelo,* as they say: the whole breadth of the sky, and further if possible!—It is thus, however, that History, and indeed all human Speech and Reason does yet, what Father Adam began life by doing: strive to *name* the new Things it sees of Nature's producing—often helplessly enough.

But what if History were to admit, for once, that all the Names and Theorems yet known to her fall short? That this grand Product of Nature was even grand, and new, in that it came not to range itself under old recorded Laws of Nature at all, but to disclose new ones? In that case, History renouncing the pretension to *name* it at present, will *look* honestly at it, and name what she can of it! Any approximation to the right Name has value: were the right Name itself once here, the Thing is known henceforth; the Thing is then ours, and can be dealt with.

Now surely not realization, of Christianity, or of aught earthly, do we discern in this Reign of Terror, in this French Revolution of which it is the consummating. Destruction rather we discern—of all that was destructible. It is as if Twenty-five millions, risen at length into the Pythian mood, had stood up simultaneously to say, with a sound which goes through far lands and times, that this Untruth of an Existence had become insupportable. O ye Hypocrisies and Speciosities, Royal mantles, Cardinal plush-cloaks, ye Credos, Formulas,

Respectabilities, fair-painted Sepulchres full of dead men's bones—behold, ye appear to us to be altogether a Lie. Yet our Life is not a lie; yet our Hunger and Misery is not a Lie! Behold we lift up, one and all, our Twenty-five million right-hands; and take the Heavens, and the Earth and also the Pit of Tophet to witness, that either ye shall be abolished, or else we shall be abolished!

No inconsiderable Oath, truly; forming, as has been often said, the most remarkable transaction in these last thousand years. Wherefrom likewise there follow, and will follow, results. The fulfilment of this Oath; that is to say, the black desperate battle of Men against their whole Condition and Environment—a battle, alas, withal, against the Sin and Darkness that was in themselves as in others: this is the Reign of Terror. Transcendental despair was the purport of it, though not consciously so. False hopes, of Fraternity, Political Millennium, and what not, we have always seen: but the unseen heart of the whole, the transcendental despair, was not false; neither has it been of no effect. Despair, pushed far enough, completes the circle, so to speak; and becomes a kind of genuine productive hope again.

Doctrine of Fraternity, out of old Catholicism, does, it is true, very strangely in the vehicle of a Jean-Jacques Evangel, suddenly plump down out of its cloud-firmament; and from a theorem determine to make itself a practice. But just so do all creeds, intentions, customs, knowledges, thoughts and things, which the French have, suddenly plump down; Catholicism, Classicism, Sentimentalism, Cannibalism: all *isms* that make up Man in France, are rushing and roaring in that gulf; and the theorem has become a practice, and whatsoever cannot swim sinks. No Evangelist Jean-Jacques alone; there is not a Village Schoolmaster but has contributed his quota: do we not *thou* one another to the Free Peoples of Antiquity? The French Patriot, in red Phrygian night-cap of Liberty, christens his poor little red infant Cato—Censor, or else of Utica. Gracchus has become Babœuf, and edits Newspapers; Mutius Scaevola, Cordwainer of that ilk, presides in the Section Mutius-Schaevola: and in brief, there is a world wholly jumbling itself, to try what will swim.

Wherefore we will, at all events, call this Reign of Terror a very strange one. Dominant Sansculottism makes, as it were, free arena; one of the strangest temporary states Humanity was ever seen in. A nation of men, full of wants and void of habits! The old habits are gone to wreck because they were old: men, driven forward by Necessity and fierce Pythian Madness, have, on the spur of the instant, to devise for the want the *way* of satisfying it. The Wonted tumbles down; by imitation, by invention, the Unwonted hastily builds itself up. What the French National head has in it comes out: if not a great result, surely one of the strangest.

Neither shall the Reader fancy that it was all black, this Reign of Terror: far from it. How many hammermen and squaremen, bakers and brewers, washers and wringers, over this France, must ply their old daily work, let the Government be one of Terror or one of Joy! In this Paris there are Twenty-three Theatres nightly; some count as many as Sixty Places of Dancing. The Playwright manufactures pieces of a strictly Republican character. Ever fresh Novel-garbage, as of old, fodders the Circulating Libraries. The 'Cesspool of *Agio,*' now in a time of Paper Money, works with a vivacity unexampled, unimagined; exhales from itself 'sudden fortunes,' like Aladdin-Palaces: really a kind of miraculous Fata-Morganas, since you *can* live in them, for a time. Terror is as a sable ground, on which the most variegated of scenes paints itself. In startling transitions, in colours all intensated, the sublime, the ludicrous, the horrible succeed one another; or rather, in crowding tumult, accompany one another.

Here, accordingly, if anywhere, the 'hundred tongues,' which the old Poets often clamour for, were of supreme service! In defect of any such organ on our part, let the Reader stir up his own imaginative organ: let us snatch for him this or the other significant glimpse of things, in the fittest sequence we can.

DEATH

IN THE EARLY DAYS of November, there is one transient glimpse of things that is to be noted: the last transit to his long home of Philippe d'Orléans Égalité. Philippe was 'decreed accused,' along with the Girondins, much to his and their surprise; but not tried along with them. They are doomed and dead, some three days, when Philippe, after his long half-year of durance at Marseilles, arrives in Paris. It is, as we calculate, the third of November 1793.

On which same day, two notable Female Prisoners are also put in ward there: Dame Dubarry, and Josephine Beauharnais. Dame whilom Countess Dubarry, Unfortunate-female, had returned from London; they snatched her, not only as Ex-harlot of a whilom Majesty, and therefore suspect; but as having 'furnished the Emigrants with money.' Contemporaneously with whom there comes the wife Beauharnais, soon to be the widow: she that is Josephine Tascher Beauharnais; that shall be Josephine Empress Bonaparte— for a black Divineress of the Tropics prophesied long since that she should be a Queen and more. Likewise, in the same hours, poor Adam Lux, nigh turned in the head, who, according to Forster, 'has taken no food these three weeks,' marches to the Guillotine for his Pamphlet on Charlotte Corday: he 'sprang to the scaffold;' said 'he died for her with great joy.' Amid such fellow-travellers does Philippe arrive. For, be the month named Brumaire year 2 of Liberty, or November year 1793 of Slavery, the Guillotine goes always, *Guillotine va toujours*.

Enough, Philippe's indictment is soon drawn, his jury soon convinced. He finds himself made guilty of Royalism, Conspiracy and much else; nay, it is a guilt in him that he voted Louis's Death, though he answers, 'I voted in my soul and conscience.' The doom he finds is death forthwith; this present sixth dim day of November is the last day that Philippe is to see. Philippe, says Montgaillard, thereupon called for breakfast: sufficiency of 'oysters, two cutlets, best part of an excellent bottle of claret;' and consumed the same with apparent relish. A Revolutionary Judge, or some official Convention Emissary, then arrived, to signify that he might still do the State some service by revealing the truth about a plot or two. Philippe answered that, on him, in the pass things had come to, the State had, he thought, small claim; that nevertheless, in the interest of Liberty, he, having still some leisure on his hands, was willing, were a reasonable question asked him, to give a reasonable answer. And so, says Montgaillard, he leant his elbow on the mantel-piece, and conversed in an undertone, with great seeming composure; till the leisure was done, or the Emissary went his ways.

At the door of the Conciergerie, Philippe's attitude was erect and easy, almost commanding. It is five years, all but a few days, since Philippe, within these same stone walls, stood up with an air of graciosity, and asked King Louis, 'Whether it was a Royal Session, then, or a Bed of Justice?' O Heaven!—Three poor blackguards were to ride and die with him: some say, they objected to such company, and had to be flung in, neck and heels; but it seems not true. Objecting or not objecting, the gallows-vehicle gets under way. Philippe's dress is remarked for its elegance; green frock, waistcoat of white *piqué*, yellow buckskins, boots clear as Warren: his air, as before, entirely composed, impassive, not to say easy and Brummellean-polite. Through street after street; slowly, amid execrations;—past the Palais Égalité, whilom Palais Royal! The cruel Populace stopped him there, some minutes: Dame de Buffon, it is said, looked out on him, in Jezebel headtire; along the ashlar Wall there ran these words in huge tricolor print, REPUBLIC ONE AND INDIVISIBLE; LIBERTY, EQUALITY, FRATERNITY OR DEATH: *National Property*. Philippe's eyes flashed hell-fire, one instant; but the next instant it was gone, and he sat impassive, Brummellean-polite. On the scaffold, Samson was for drawing off his boots: 'Tush,' said Philippe, 'they will come better off *after;* let us have done, *dépêchons-nous!'*

So Philippe was not without virtue, then? God forbid that there should be any living man without it! He had the virtue to keep living for five-and-forty years—other virtues perhaps more than we know of. But probably no mortal ever had such things recorded of him: such facts, and also such lies. For he was a *Jacobin Prince of the Blood;* consider what a combination! Also, unlike any Nero, any Borgia, he lived in the Age of Pamphlets. Enough for us: Chaos *has* reabsorbed him; may it late or never bear his like again!—Brave young Orléans Égalité, deprived of all, only not deprived of himself, is gone to Coire in the Grisons, under the name of Corby, to teach Mathematics. The Égalité Family is at the darkest depths of the Nadir.

A far nobler Victim follows; one who will claim remembrance from several centuries: Jeanne-Marie Philipon, the Wife of Roland. Queenly, sublime in her uncomplaining sorrow, seemed she to Riouffe in her Prison. 'Something more than is usually found in the looks of women painted itself,' says Riouffe, 'in those large black eyes of hers, full of expression and sweetness. She spoke to me often, at the Grate: we were all attentive round her, in a sort of admiration and astonishment; she expressed herself with a purity, with a harmony and prosody that made her language like music, of which the ear could never have enough. Her conversation was serious, not cold; coming from the mouth of a beautiful woman, it was frank and courageous as that of a great man. . . . And yet her maid said: "Before you, she collects her strength; but in her own room, she will sit three hours sometimes leaning on the window, and weeping."' She has been in Prison, liberated once, but recaptured the same hour, ever since the first of June: in agitation and uncertainty; which has gradually settled down into the last stern certainty, that of death. In the Abbaye Prison, she occupied Charlotte Corday's apartment. Here in the Conciergerie, she speaks with Riouffe, with Ex-Minister Clavière; calls the beheaded Twenty-two *'Nos amis,* our Friends',—whom we are soon to follow. During these five months, those *Memoirs* of hers were written, which all the world still reads.

But now, on the 8th of November, 'clad in white,' says Riouffe, 'with her long black hair hanging down to her girdle,' she is gone to the Judgement-bar. She returned with a quick step; lifted her finger, to signify to us that she was doomed: her eyes seemed to have been wet. Fouquier-Tinville's questions had been 'brutal;' offended female honour flung them back on him, with scorn, not without tears. And now, short preparation soon done, she too shall go her last road. There went with her a certain Lamarche, 'Director of Assignat-printing;' whose dejection she endeavoured to cheer. Arrived at the foot of the scaffold, she asked for pen and paper, 'to write the strange thoughts that were rising in her:' a remarkable request; which was refused. Looking at the Statue of Liberty which stands there, she says bitterly: 'O Liberty, what things are done in thy name!' For Lamarche's sake, she will die first; show him how easy it is to die: 'Contrary to the order,' said Samson.—'Pshaw, you cannot refuse the last request of a Lady;' and Samson yielded.

Noble white Vision, with its high queenly face, its soft proud eyes, long black hair flowing down to the girdle; and as brave a heart as ever beat in woman's bosom! Like a white Grecian Statue, serenely complete, she shines in that black wreck of things—long memorable. Honour to great Nature who, in Paris City, in the Era of Noble-Sentiment and Pompadourism, can make a Jeanne Philipon, and nourish her to clear perennial Womanhood, though but on Logics, *Encyclopédies,* and the Gospel according to Jean-Jacques! Biography will long remember that trait of asking for a pen 'to write the strange thoughts that were rising in her.' It is as a little light-beam, shedding softness, and a kind of sacredness, over all that preceded: so in her too there was an Unnameable; she too was a Daughter of the Infinite; there were mysteries which Philosophism had not dreamt of!—She left long written counsels to her little Girl; she said her Husband would not survive her.

Still crueller was the fate of poor Bailly, First National President, First Mayor of Paris: doomed now for Royalism, Fayettism; for that Red-Flag Business of the Champ-de-Mars—one may say in general, for leaving his Astronomy to meddle with Revolution. It is the 10th of November 1793, a cold bitter drizzling rain, as poor Bailly is led through the streets; howling Populace covering him with curses, with mud; waving over his face a burning or smoking mockery of a Red Flag. Silent, unpitied, sits the innocent old man. Slow faring through the sleety drizzle, they have got to the Champ-de-Mars: Not there! vociferates the cursing Populace; such Blood ought not to stain an Altar of the Fatherland: not there; but on that dung-heap by the Riverside! So vociferates the cursing Populace; Officiality gives ear to them. The Guillotine is taken down, though with hands numbed by the sleety drizzle; is carried to the Riverside; is there set up again, with slow numbness; pulse after pulse still counting itself out in the old man's weary heart. For hours long; amid curses and bitter frost-rain! 'Bailly, thou tremblest,' said one. '*Mon ami,* it is for cold,' said Bailly, '*c'est de froid.*' Crueller end had no mortal.

Some days afterwards, Roland, hearing the news of what happened on the 8th, embraces his kind Friends at Rouen, leaves their kind house which had given him refuge; goes forth, with farewell too sad for tears. On the morrow morning, 16th of the month, 'some four leagues from Rouen, Paris-ward, near Bourg-Baudoin, in M. Normand's Avenue,' there is seen sitting leant against a tree the figure of a rigorous wrinkled man; stiff now in the rigour of death; a cane-sword run through his heart; and at his feet this writing: 'Whoever thou art that findest me lying, respect my remains: they are those of a man who consecrated all his life to being useful; and who has died as he lived, virtuous and honest. . . . Not fear, but indignation, made me quit my retreat, on learning that my Wife had been murdered. I wished not to remain longer on an Earth polluted with crimes.'

Barnave's appearance at the Revolutionary Tribunal was of the bravest; but it could not stead him. They have sent for him from Grenoble; to pay the common smart. Vain is eloquence, forensic or other, against the dumb Clotho-shears of Tinville. He is still but two-and-thirty, this Barnave, and has known such changes. Short while ago, we saw him at the top of Fortune's wheel, his word a law to all Patriots: and now surely he is at the *bottom* of the wheel; in stormful altercation with a Tinville Tribunal, which is dooming him to die! And Pétion, once also of the Extreme Left, and named *Pétion Virtue,* where is he? Civilly dead; in the Caves of Saint-Emilion; to be devoured of dogs. And Robespierre, who rode along with him on the shoulders of the people, is in Committee of *Salut;* civilly alive: not to live always. So giddy-swift whirls and spins this immeasurable *tormentum* of a Revolution; wild-booming; not to be followed by the eye. Barnave, on the Scaffold, stamped with his foot; and looking upwards was heard to ejaculate, 'This then is my reward?'

Deputy Ex-Procureur Manuel is already gone; and Deputy Osselin, famed also in August and September, is about to go: and Rabaut, discovered treacherously between his two walls, and the Brother of Rabaut. National Deputies not a few! And Generals: the memory of General Custine cannot be defended by his Son; his Son is already guillotined. Custine the Ex-Noble was replaced by Houchard the Plebeian: he too could not prosper in the North; for him too there was no mercy; he has perished in the Place de la Révolution, after attempting suicide in Prison. And Generals Biron, Beauharnais, Brunet, whatsoever General prospers not; tough old Lückner, with his eyes grown rheumy; Alsatian Westermann, valiant and diligent in La Vendée: *none of them can,* as the Psalmist sings, *his soul from death deliver.*

How busy are the Revolutionary Committees; Sections with their Forty Halfpence a-day! Arrestment on arrestment falls quick, continual; followed by death. Ex-Minister Clavière has killed himself in Prison. Ex-Minister Lebrun, seized in a hayloft, under the disguise of a working man, is instantly conducted to death. Nay, withal, is it not what Barrère calls 'coining money on the Place de la Révolution? For always the 'property of the guilty, if property he have,' is confiscated. To avoid accidents, we even make a Law that suicide shall not defraud us; that a criminal who kills himself does not the less incur forfeiture of goods. Let the guilty tremble, therefore, and the suspect, and the rich, and in a word all manner of Culottic men! Luxembourg Palace, once Monsieur's, has become a huge loathsome Prison; Chantilly Palace too, once Condé's:—And their Landlords are at Blankenberg, on the wrong side of the Rhine. In Paris are now some Twelve Prisons; in France some Forty-four Thousand: thitherward, thick as brown leaves in Autumn, rustle and travel the suspect; shaken down by Revolutionary Committees, they are swept thitherward, as into their storehouse—to be consumed by Samson and Tinville. 'The Guillotine goes not ill, *La Guillotine ne va pas mal*'.

DESTRUCTION

THE SUSPECT MAY WELL TREMBLE; but how much more the open rebels; the Girondin Cities of the South! Revolutionary Army is gone forth, under Ronsin the Playwright; six thousand strong; 'in red nightcap, in tricolor waistcoat, in black-shag trousers, black-shag spencer, with enormous moustachios, enormous sabre,—in *carmagnole complète,'* and has portable guillotines. Representative Carriers has got to Nantes, by the edge of blazing La Vendée, which Rossignol has literally set on fire: Carrier will try what captives you make; what accomplices they have, Royalist or Girondin: his guillotine goes always, *va toujours;* and his wool-capped 'Company of Marat.' Little children are guillotined, and aged men. Swift as the machine is, it will not serve; the Headsman and all his valets sink worn down with work; declare that the human muscles can no more. Whereupon you must try fusillading; to which perhaps still frightfuller methods may succeed.

In Brest, to like purpose, rules Jean-Bon Saint-André; with an Army of Red Nightcaps. In Bordeaux rules Tallien, with his Isabeau and henchmen; Guadets, Cussys, Salleses, many fall; the bloody Pike and Nightcap bearing supreme sway; the Guillotine coining money. Bristly fox-haired Tallien, once Able Editor, still young in years, is now become most gloomy, potent; a Pluto on Earth, and has the keys of Tartarus. One remarks, however, that a certain Senhorina Cabarus, or call her rather *Senhora* and wedded not yet widowed *Dame de Fontenai,* brown beautiful woman, daughter of Cabarus the Spanish Merchant, has softened the red bristly countenance; pleading for herself and friends; and prevailing. The keys of Tartarus, or any kind of power, are something to a woman; gloomy Pluto himself is not insensible to love. Like a new Proserpine, she, by this red gloomy Dis, is gathered; and, they say, softens his stone heart a little.

Maignet, at Orange in the South; Lebon, at Arras in the North, become world's wonders. Jacobin Popular Tribunal, with its National Representative, perhaps where Girondin Popular Tribunal had lately been, rises here and rises there; wheresoever needed. Fouchés, Maignets, Barrasses, Frérons scour the Southern Departments; like reapers with their guillotine-sickle. Many are the labourers, great is the harvest. By the hundred and the thousand, men's lives are cropped; cast like brands into the burning.

Marseilles is taken, and put under martial law: lo, at Marseilles, what one besmutted red-bearded corn-ear is this which they cut— one gross Man, we mean, with copper-studded face; plenteous beard, or beard-stubble, of a tile-colour? By Nemesis and the Fatal Sisters, it is Jourdan Coupe-tête! Him they have clutched, in these martial-law districts; him too, with their 'national razor,' their *rasoir national,* they sternly shave away. Low now is Jourdan the Headsman's own head low as Deshuttes's and Varigny's, which he sent on pikes, in the Insurrection of Women! No more shall he, as a copper Portent, be seen gyrating through the Cities of the South; no more sit judging, with pipes and brandy, in the Ice-tower of Avignon. The all-hiding Earth has received him, the bloated Tilebeard: may we never look upon his like again!—Jourdan one names; the other Hundreds are not named. Alas, they, like confused faggots, lie massed together for us; counted by the cart-load: and yet not an individual faggot-twig of them but had a Life and History; and was cut, not without pangs as when a Kaiser dies!

Least of all cities can Lyons escape. Lyons, which we saw in dread sunblaze, that Autumn night when the Powder-tower sprang aloft, was clearly verging towards a sad end. Inevitable: what could des-perate valour and Précy do; Dubois-Crancé, deaf as Destiny, stern as Doom, capturing their 'redoubts of cotton-bags;' hemming them in, ever closer, with his Artillery-lava? Never would that *ci-devant* D'Autichamp arrive; never any help from Blankenberg. The Lyons Jacobins were hidden in cellars; the Girondin Municipality waxed pale, in famine, treason and red fire. Précy drew his sword, and some Fifteen Hundred with him; sprang to saddle, to cut their way to Switzerland. They cut fiercely; and were fiercely cut, and cut down; not hundreds, hardly units of them ever saw Switzerland. Lyons, on the 9th of October, surrenders at discretion; it is become a devoted Town. Abbé Lamourette, now Bishop Lamourette, whilom Legis-lator, he of the old *Baiser-l'Amourette* or Delilah-Kiss, is seized here; is sent to Paris to be guillotined: 'he made the sign of the cross,' they say, when Tinville intimated his death-sentence to him; and died as an eloquent Constitutional Bishop. But woe now to all Bishops, Priests, Aristocrats and Federalists that are in Lyons! The *manes* of Chalier are to be appeased; the Republic, maddened to the Sibylline pitch, has bared her right arm. Behold! Representative Fouché, it is Fouché of Nantes, a name to become well known; he with a Patriot company goes duly, in wondrous Procession, to raise the corpse of

Chalier. An Ass housed in Priest's cloak, with a mitre on his head, and trailing the Mass-Books, some say the very Bible, at its tail, paces through Lyons streets: escorted by multitudinous Patriotism, by clangour as of the Pit; towards the grave of Martyr Chalier. The body is dug up, and burnt: the ashes are collected in an Urn; to be worshipped of Paris Patriotism. The Holy Books were part of the funeral pile; their ashes are scattered to the wind. Amid cries of 'Vengeance! Vengeance!'—which, writes Fouché, shall be satisfied.

Lyons in fact is a Town to be abolished; not Lyons henceforth, but *'Commune Affranchie,* Township Freed:' the very name of it shall perish. It is to be razed, this once great City, if Jacobinism prophesy right; and a Pillar to be erected on the ruins, with this Inscription, *Lyons rebelled against the Republic; Lyons is no more.* Fouché, Couthon, Collot, Convention Representatives succeed one another: there is work for the hangman; work for the hammerman, *not* in building. The very Houses of Aristocrats, we say, are doomed. Paralytic Couthon, borne in a chair, taps on the wall, with emblematic mallet, saying, *'La Loi te frappe,* The Law strikes thee;' masons, with wedge and crowbar, begin demolition. Crash of downfall, dim ruin and dust-clouds fly in the winter wind. Had Lyons been of soft stuff, it had all vanished in those weeks, and the Jacobin prophecy had been fulfilled. But Towns are not built of soap-froth; Lyons Town is built of stone. Lyons, though it rebelled against the Republic, *is* to this day.

Neither have the Lyons Girondins all one neck, that you could dispatch it at one swoop. Revolutionary Tribunal here, and Military Commission, guillotining, fusillading, do what they can: the kennels of the Place des Terreaux run red; mangled corpses roll down the Rhone. Collot d'Herbois, they say, was once hissed on the Lyons stage: but with what sibilation, of world-catcall or hoarse Tartarean Trumpet, will ye hiss him now, in this his new character of Convention Representative—not to be repeated! Two-hundred and nine men are marched forth over the River, to be shot in mass, by musket and cannon, in the Promenade of the Brotteaux. It is the second of such scenes; the first was of some Seventy. The corpses of the first were flung into the Rhone, but the Rhone stranded some; so these now, of the second lot, are to be buried on land. Their one long grave is dug; they stand ranked, by the loose mould-ridge; the younger of them singing the Marseillaise. Jacobin National Guards give fire; but have again to give fire, and again; and to take the bayonet and the

393

spade, for though the doomed all fall, they do not all die—and it becomes a butchery too horrible for speech. So that the very Nationals, as they fire, turn away their faces. Collot, snatching the musket from one such National, and levelling it with unmoved countenance, says, 'It is thus a Republican ought to fire.'

This is the second Fusillade, and happily the last: it is found too hideous; even inconvenient. There were Two-hundred and nine marched out; one escaped at the end of the Bridge: yet behold, when you count the corpses, they are Two-hundred and *ten*. Rede us this riddle, O Collot? After long guessing, it is called to mind that two individuals, here in the Brotteaux ground, did attempt to leave the rank, protesting with agony that they were not condemned men, that they were Police Commissaries: which two we repulsed, and disbelieved, and shot with the rest! Such is the vengeance of an enraged Republic. Surely this, according to Barrère's phrase, is Justice 'under rough forms, *sous des formes acerbes'*. But the Republic, as Fouché says, must 'march to Liberty over corpses.' Or again, as Barrère has it: 'None but the dead do not come back, *Il n'y a que les morts qui ne reviennent pas.'* Terror hovers far and wide: 'the Guillotine goes not ill.'

But before quitting those Southern regions, over which History can cast only glances from aloft, she will alight for a moment, and look fixedly at one point: the Siege of Toulon. Much battering and bombarding, heating of balls in furnaces or farm-houses, serving of artillery well and ill, attacking of Ollioules Passes, Forts Malbosquet, there has been: as yet to small purpose. We have had General Cartaux here, a whilom Painter elevated in the troubles of Marseilles; General Doppet, a whilom Medical man elevated in the troubles of Piemont, who, under Crancé, took Lyons, but cannot take Toulon. Finally we have General Dugommier, a pupil of Washington. Convention *Représentants* also we have had; Barrases, Salicettis, Robespierre the Younger:—also an Artillery *Chef de brigade,* of extreme diligence, who often takes his nap of sleep among the guns; a short, taciturn, olive-complexioned young man, not unknown to us, by name Bonaparte; one of the best Artillery-officers yet met with. And still Toulon is not taken. It is the fourth month now; December, in slave-style; *Frostarious* or *Frimaire,* in new-style: and still their cursed Red-Blue Flag flies there. They are provisioned from the Sea; they have seized all heights, felling wood, and fortifying themselves; like the coney, they have built their nest in the rocks.

Meanwhile, *Frostarious* is not yet become *Snowous* or *Nivose,* when a Council of War is called; Instructions have just arrived from Government and *Salut Public.* Carnot, in *Salut Public,* has sent us a plan of siege: on which plan General Dugommier has this criticism to make, Commissioner Salicetti has that; and criticisms and plans are very various; when that young Artillery-Officer ventures to speak; the same whom we saw snatching sleep among the guns, who has emerged several times in this History—the name of him Napoleon Bonaparte. It is his humble opinion, for he has been gliding about with spy-glasses, with thoughts, That a certain Fort l'Eguillette can be clutched, as with lion-spring, on the sudden; wherefrom, were it once ours, the very heart of Toulon might be battered; the English Lines were, so to speak, turned inside out, and Hood and our Natural Enemies must next day either put to sea, or be burnt to ashes. Commissioners arch their eyebrows, with negatory sniff: who is this young gentleman with more wit than we all? Brave veteran Dugommier, however, thinks the idea worth a word; questions the young gentleman; becomes convinced; and there is for issue, Try it.

On the taciturn bronze-countenance therefore, things being now all ready, there sits a grimmer gravity than ever, compressing a hotter central-fire than ever. Yonder, thou seest, is Fort l'Eguillette; a desperate lion-spring, yet a possible one; this day to be tried!—Tried it is; and found *good.* By stratagem and valour, stealing through ravines, plunging fiery through the fire-tempest, Fort l'Eguillette is clutched at, is carried; the smoke having cleared, we see the Tricolor fly on it: the bronze-complexioned young man was right. Next morning, Hood, finding the interior of his lines exposed, his defences turned inside out, makes for his shipping. Taking such Royalists as wished it on board with him, he weighs anchor; on this 19th of December 1793, Toulon is once more the Republic's!

Cannonading has ceased at Toulon; and now the guillotining and fusillading may begin. Civil horrors, truly: but at least that infamy of an English domination is purged away. Let there be Civic Feast universally over France: so reports Barrère, or Painter David; and the Convention assist in a body. Nay, it is said, these infamous English (with an attention rather to their own interests than to ours) set fire to our store-houses, arsenals, warships in Toulon Harbour, before weighing; some score of brave war-ships, the only ones we now had! However, it did not prosper, though the flame spread far and high; some two ships were burned, not more; the very galley-slaves ran with buckets to quench. These same proud Ships, Ship *l'Orient* and the rest, have to carry this same young Man to Egypt first: not yet can they be changed to ashes, or to Sea-Nymphs; not yet to sky-rockets, O ship *l'Orient;* nor become the prey of England,—before their time!

And so, over France universally, there is Civic Feast and high-tide: and Toulon sees fusillading, grape-shotting in mass, as Lyons saw; and 'death is poured out in great floods, *vomie à grands flots;'* and Twelve-thousand Masons are requisitioned from the neighbouring country, to raze Toulon from the face of the Earth. For it is to be razed, so reports Barrère; all but the National Shipping Establishments; and to be called henceforth not Toulon, but *Port of the Mountain.* There in black death-cloud we must leave it—hoping only that Toulon too is built of stone; that perhaps even Twelve-thousand Masons cannot pull it down, till the fit pass.

One begins to be sick of 'death vomited in great floods.' Nevertheless, hearest thou not, O Reader (for the sound reaches through centuries), in the dead December and January nights, over Nantes Town, confused noises, as of musketry and tumult, as of rage and lamentation; mingling with the everlasting moan of the Loire waters there? Nantes Town is sunk in sleep; but *Représentant* Carrier is not sleeping, the wool-capped Company of Marat is not sleeping. Why unmoors that flatbottomed craft, that *gabarre;* about eleven at night; with Ninety Priests under hatches? They are going to Belle Isle? In the middle of the Loire stream, on signal given, the gabarre is scuttled; she sinks with all her cargo. 'Sentence of Deportation,' writes Carrier, 'was executed *vertically.'* The Ninety Priests, with their gabarre-coffin, lie deep! It is the first of the *Noyades,* what we may call *Drownages,* of Carrier; which have become famous for ever.

Guillotining there was at Nantes, till the Headsman sank worn out: then fusillading 'in the Plain of Saint-Mauve;' little children fusilladed, and women with children at the breast; children and women, by the hundred and twenty; and by the five hundred, so hot is La Vendée: till the very Jacobins grew sick, and all but the Company of Marat cried, Hold! Wherefore now we have got Noyading; and on the 24th night of *Frostarious* year 2, which is 14th of December 1793, we have a second Noyade; consisting of 'a Hundred and Thirty-eight persons.'

Or why waste a gabarre, sinking it with them? Fling them out; fling them out, with their hands tied: pour a continual hail of lead over all the space, till the last struggler of them be sunk! Unsound sleepers of Nantes, and the Sea-Villages thereabouts, hear the musketry amid the night-winds; wonder what the meaning of it is. And women were in that gabarre; whom the Red Nightcaps were stripping naked; who begged, in their agony, that their smocks might not be stripped from them. And young children were thrown in, their mothers vainly pleading: 'Wolflings,' answered the Company of Marat, 'who would grow to be wolves.'

By degrees, daylight itself witnesses Noyades: women and men are tied together, feet and feet, hands and hands; and flung in: this they call *Mariage Républicain,* Republican Marriage. Cruel is the panther of the woods, the she-bear bereaved of her whelps: but there is in man a hatred crueller than that. Dumb, out of suffering now, as pale swoln corpses, the victims tumble confusedly seaward along the Loire stream; the tide rolling them back: clouds of ravens darken the River; wolves prowl on the shoal-places: Carrier writes, *'Quel torrent révolutionnaire,* What a torrent of Revolution!' For the man is rabid; and the Time is rabid. These are the Noyades of Carrier; twenty-five by the tale, for what is done in darkness comes to be investigated in sunlight: not to be forgotten for centuries.—We will turn to another aspect of the Consummation of Sansculotism; leaving this as the blackest.

But indeed men are all rabid; as the Time is. Representative Lebon, at Arras, dashes his sword into the blood flowing from the Guillotine; exclaims, 'How I like it!' Mothers, they say, by his order, have to stand by while the Guillotine devours their children: a band of music is stationed near; and, at the fall of every head, strikes up its *Ça ira.* In the Burgh of Bedouin, in the Orange region, the Liberty-tree has been cut down overnight. Representative Maignet, at Orange, hears of it; burns Bedouin Burgh to the last dog-hutch; guillotines the inhabitants, or drives them into the caves and hills. Republic One and Indivisible! She is the newest Birth of Nature's waste inorganic Deep, which men named Orcus, Chaos, primaeval Night; and knows one law, that of self-preservation. *Tigresse Nationale:* meddle not with a whisker of her! Swift-rending is her stroke; look what a paw she spreads—pity has not entered into her heart.

Prudhomme, the dull-blustering Printer and Able Editor, as yet a Jacobin Editor, will become a renegade one, and publish large volumes, on these matters, *Crimes of the Revolution;* adding innumerable lies withal, as if the truth were not sufficient. We, for our part, find it more edifying to know, one good time, that this Republic and National Tigress *is* a New-Birth; a Fact of Nature among Formulas, in

an Age of Formulas; and to look, oftenest in silence, how the so genuine Nature-Fact will demean itself among these. For the Formulas
are partly genuine, partly delusive, supposititious: we call them, in the
language of metaphor, regulated modelled *shapes;* some of which
have bodies and life still in them; most of which, according to a German Writer, have only emptiness, 'glass-eyes glaring on you with a
ghastly affectation of life, and in their interior unclean accumulation
of beetles and spiders!' But the Fact, let all men observe, is a genuine
and sincere one; the sincerest of Facts; terrible in its sincerity, as very
Death. Whatsoever is equally sincere may front it, and beard it; but
whatsoever is *not?*—

SECTION IX

The Terror at Height

THE GODS ARE ATHIRST

WHAT THEN IS THIS Thing, called *La Révolution,* which, like an
Angel of Death, hangs over France, noyading, fusillading, fighting, gun-boring, tanning human skins? *La Révolution* is but so many
Alphabetic Letters; a thing nowhere to be laid hands on, to be
clapped under lock and key: where is it? what is it? It is the Madness
that dwells in the hearts of men. In this man it is, and in that man; as
a rage or as a terror, it is in all men. Invisible, impalpable; and yet no
black Azrael, with wings spread over half a continent, with sword
sweeping from sea to sea, could be a truer Reality.

To explain, what is called explaining, the march of this Revolutionary Government, be no task of ours. Man cannot explain it. A
paralytic Couthon, asking in the Jacobins, 'What hast thou done to be
hanged if Counter-Revolution should arrive?' a sombre Saint-Just, not
yet six-and-twenty, declaring that 'for Revolutionists there is no rest
but in the tomb;' a seagreen Robespierre converted into vinegar and
gall; much more an Amar and Vadier, a Collot and Billaud: to inquire what thoughts, predetermination or prevision, might be in the
head of these men! Record of their thought remains not; Death and

Darkness have swept it out utterly. Nay, if we even had their thought, all that they could have articulately spoken to us, how insignificant a fraction were that of the Thing which realized itself, which decreed itself, on signal given by them! As has been said more than once, this Revolutionary Government is not a self-conscious but a blind fatal one. Each man, enveloped in his ambient-atmosphere of revolutionary fanatic Madness, rushes on, impelled and impelling; and has become a blind brute Force; no rest for him but in the grave! Darkness and the mystery of horrid cruelty cover it for us, in History; as they did in Nature. The chaotic Thunder-cloud, with its pitchy black, and its tumult of dazzling jagged fire, in a world all electric: thou wilt not undertake to show how that comported itself—what the secrets of its dark womb were; from what sources, with what specialties, the lightning it held did, in confused brightness of terror, strike forth, destructive and self-destructive, till it ended? Like a Blackness naturally of Erebus, which by will of Providence had for once mounted itself into dominion and the Azure: is not this properly the nature of Sansculottism consummating itself? Of which Erebus Blackness be it enough to discern that this and the other dazzling fire-bolt, dazzling fire-torrent, does by small Volition and great Necessity, verily issue—in such and such succession; destructive so and so, self-destructive so and so: till it end.

Royalism is extinct; 'sunk,' as they say, 'in the mud of the Loire;' Republicanism dominates without and within: what, therefore, on the 15th day of March 1794, is this? Arrestment, sudden really as a bolt out of the Blue, has hit strange victims: Hébert *Père Duchesne,* Bibliopolist Momoro, Clerk Vincent, General Ronsin; high Cordelier Patriots, redcapped Magistrates of Paris, Worshippers of Reason, Commanders of Revolutionary Army! Eight short days ago, their Cordelier Club was loud, and louder than ever, with Patriot denunciations. Hébert *Père Duchesne* had 'held his tongue and his heart these two months, at sight of Moderates, Crypto-Aristocrats, Camilles, *Scélérats* in the Convention itself: but could not do it any longer; would, if other remedy were not, invoke the sacred right of Insurrection.' So spake Hébert in Cordelier Session; with vivats, till the roofs rang again. Eight short days ago; and now already! They rub their eyes: it is no dream; they find themselves in the Luxembourg. Goose Gobel too; and they that burn Churches! Chaumette himself, potent Procureur, *Agent National* as they now call it, who could 'recognize the Suspect by the very face of them,' he lingers but three days; on the third day he too is hurled in. Most chopfallen, blue, enters the National Agent this Limbo whither he has sent so many. Prisoners crowd round, jibing and jeering; 'Sublime National Agent,' says one, 'in virtue of thy immortal Proclamation, lo there! I am suspect, thou art suspect, he is suspect, we are suspect, ye are suspect, they are suspect!'

The meaning of these things? Meaning! It is a Plot; Plot of the most extensive ramifications; which, however, Barrère holds the threads of. Such Church-burning and scandalous masquerades of Atheism, fit to make the Revolution odious: where indeed could they originate but in the gold of Pitt? Pitt indubitably, as Preternatural Insight will teach one, did hire this Faction of *Enragés,* to play their fantastic tricks; to roar in their Cordeliers Club about Moderatism; to print their *Père Duchesne;* worship skyblue Reason in red nightcap; rob all Altars— and bring the spoil to *us!*

Still more indubitable, visible to the mere bodily sight, is this: that the Cordeliers Club sits pale, with anger and terror; and has 'veiled the Rights of Man,'—without effect. Likewise that the Jacobins are in considerable confusion; busy 'purging themselves, *s'épurant,*' as in times of Plot and public Calamity they have repeatedly had to do. Not even Camille Desmoulins but has given offence: nay there have risen murmurs against Danton himself; though he bellowed them down, and Robespierre finished the matter by 'embracing him in the Tribune.'

Whom shall the Republic and a jealous Mother-Society trust? In these times of temptation, of Preternatural Insight! For there are Factions of the Stranger, *'de l'étranger,'* Factions of Moderates, of Enraged; all manner of Factions: we walk in a world of Plots; strings universally spread, of deadly gins and falltraps, baited by the gold of Pitt! Clootz, Speaker of Mankind so-called, with his *Evidences of Mahometan Religion,* and babble of Universal Republic, him an incorruptible Robespierre has purged away. Baron Clootz, and Paine rebellious Needleman lie, these two months, in the Luxembourg; limbs of the Faction *de l'étranger.* Representative Phélippeaux is purged out: he came back from La Vendée with an ill report in his mouth against rogue Rossignol, and our method of warfare there. Recant it, O Phélippeaux, we entreat thee! Phélippeaux will not recant; and is purged out. Representative Fabre d'Eglantine, famed Nomenclator of Romme's Calendar, is purged out; nay, is cast into the Luxembourg: accused of Legislative Swindling 'in regard to moneys of the India Company.' There with his Chabots, Bazires, guilty of the like, let

400

Fabre wait his destiny. And Westermann, friend of Danton, he who led the Marseillaise on the Tenth of August, and fought well in La Vendée, but spoke not well of rogue Rossignol, is purged out. Lucky, if he too go not to the Luxembourg. And your Prolys, Guzmans, of the Faction of the Stranger, they have gone; Pereyra, though he fled, is gone, 'taken in the disguise of a Tavern Cook.' I am suspect, thou art suspect, he is suspect!—

The great heart of Danton is weary of it. Danton is gone to native Arcis, for a little breathing-time of peace: Away, black Arachne-webs, thou world of Fury, Terror and Suspicion; welcome, thou ever-lasting Mother, with thy spring greenness, thy kind household loves and memories; true art thou, were all else untrue! The great Titan walks silent, by the banks of the murmuring Aube, in young native haunts that knew him when a boy; wonders what the end of these things may be.

But strangest of all, Camille Desmoulins is purged out. Couthon gave as a test in regard to Jacobin purgation the question, 'What hast thou done to be hanged if Counter-Revolution should arrive?' Yet Camille, who could so well answer this question, is purged out! The truth is, Camille, early in December last, began publishing a new Journal, or Series of Pamphlets, entitled the *Vieux Cordelier,* Old Cordelier. Camille, not afraid at one time to 'embrace Liberty on a heap of dead bodies,' begins to ask now, Whether among so many ar-resting and punishing Committees, there ought not to be a 'Commit-tee of Mercy?' Saint-Just, he observes, is an extremely solemn young Republican, who 'carries his head as if it were a *Saint-Sacrement,'* adorable Hostie, or divine Real Presence! Sharply enough, this *old* Cordelier—Danton and he were of the earliest primary Cordeliers—shoots his glittering war-shafts into your *new* Cordeliers, your Héberts, Momoros, with their brawling brutalities and despicabilities; say, as the Sun-god (for poor Camille is a Poet) shot into that Python Ser-pent, sprung of mud.

Whereat, as was natural, the Hébertist Python did hiss and writhe amazingly; and threaten 'sacred right of Insurrection;' and, as we saw, get cast into Prison. Nay, with all the old wit, dexterity and light graceful poignancy, Camille, translating 'out of *Tacitus,* from the Reign of Tiberius,' pricks into the *Law of the Suspect* itself; making it odious! Twice, in the Decade, his wild Leaves issue; full of wit, nay of humour, of harmonious ingenuity and insight—one of the strangest phenomena of that dark time; and smite, in their wild-sparkling way, at various monstrosities, Saint-Sacrament heads, and Juggernaut idols, in a rather reckless manner. To the great joy of Josephine Beauharnais, and the other Five-thousand and odd Suspects, who fill the Twelve Houses of Arrest; on whom a ray of hope dawns! Robespierre, at first approbatory, knew not at last what to think; then thought, with his Jacobins, that Camille must be expelled. A man of true Revolutionary spirit, this Camille; but with the unwisest sallies; whom Aristocrats and Moderates have the art to corrupt! Jacobinism is in uttermost crisis and struggle; enmeshed wholly in plots, corruptibilities, neck-gins and baited falltraps of Pitt *Ennemi du Genre Humain.* Camille's First Number begins with '*O Pitt!*'—his last is dated 15 Pluviose Year 2, 3rd February 1794; and ends with these words of Montezuma's, '*Les dieux ont soif,* The gods are athirst.'

Be this as it may, the Hébertists lie in Prison only some nine days. On the 24th of March, therefore, the Revolution Tumbrils carry through that Life-tumult a new cargo: Hébert, Vincent, Momoro, Ronsin, Nineteen of them in all; with whom, curious enough, sits Clootz Speaker of Mankind. They have been massed swiftly into a lump, this miscellany of Nondescripts; and travel now their last road. No help. They too must 'look through the little window;' they too must 'sneeze into the sack,' *éternuer dans le sac;* as they have done to others, so is it done to them. *Sainte-Guillotine,* meseems, is worse than the old Saints of Superstition; a man-devouring Saint? Clootz, still with an air of polished sarcasm, endeavours to jest, to offer cheering 'arguments of Materialism;' he requested to be executed last, 'in order to establish certain principles'—which hitherto, I think, Philosophy has got no good of. General Ronsin too, he still looks forth with some air of defiance, eye of command: the rest are sunk in a stony paleness of despair. Momoro, poor Bibliopolist, no Agrarian Law yet realized—they might as well have hanged thee at Evreux, twenty months ago, when Girondin Buzot hindered them. Hébert *Père Duchesne* shall never in this world rise in sacred right of insurrection; he sits there low enough, head sunk on breast; Red Nightcaps shouting round him, in frightful parody of his Newspaper Articles, 'Grand choler of the Père Duchesne!' Thus perish they; the sack receives all their heads. Through some section of History, Nineteen spectre-chimeras shall flit, squeaking and gibbering; till Oblivion swallow them.

In the course of a week, the Revolutionary Army itself is disbanded; the General having become spectral. This Faction of Rabids, therefore, is also purged from the Republican soil; here also the baited falltraps of that Pitt have been wrenched up harmless; and anew there is joy over a Plot discovered. The Revolution, then, is verily devouring its own children? All Anarchy, by the nature of it, is not only destructive but *self*-destructive.

DANTON, NO WEAKNESS

DANTON, MEANWHILE, has been pressingly sent for from Arcis: he must return instantly, cried Camille, cried Phélippeaux and Friends, who scented danger in the wind. Danger enough! A Danton, a Robespierre, chief-products of a victorious Revolution, are now arrived in immediate front of one another; must ascertain how they will live together, rule together. One conceives easily the deep mutual incompatibility that divided these two: with what terror of feminine hatred the poor seagreen Formula looked at the monstrous colossal Reality, and grew greener to behold him—the Reality, again, struggling to think no ill of a chief-product of the Revolution; yet feeling at bottom that such chief-product was little other than a chief windbag, blown large by Popular air; not a man, with the heart of a man, but a poor spasmodic incorruptible pedant, with a logic-formula instead of heart; of Jesuit or Methodist-Parson nature; full of sincere-cant, incorruptibility, or virulence, poltroonery; barren as the eastwind! Two such chief-products are too much for one Revolution.

Friends, trembling at the results of a quarrel on their part, brought them to meet. 'It is right,' said Danton, swallowing much indignation, 'to repress the Royalists: but we should not strike except where it is useful to the Republic; we should not confound the innocent and the guilty.'—'And who told you,' replied Robespierre with a poisonous look, 'that one innocent person had perished?'—'*Quoi,*' said Danton, turning round to Friend Pâris self-named Fabricius, Juryman in the Revolutionary Tribunal: '*Quoi,* not one innocent? What sayest thou of it, Fabricius!'—Friends, Westermann, this Pâris and others urged him to show himself, to ascend the Tribune and act. The man Danton was not prone to show himself; to act, or uproar for his own safety. A man of careless, large, hoping nature; a large nature that could rest: he would sit whole hours, they say, hearing Camille talk, and liked

403

nothing so well. Friends urged him to fly; his Wife urged him: 'Whither fly?' answered he: 'If freed France cast me out, there are only dungeons for me elsewhere. One carries not his country with him at the sole of his shoe!' The man Danton sat still. Not even the arrestment of Friend Hérault, a member of *Salut,* yet arrested by *Salut,* can rouse Danton.—On the night of the 30th of March Jury-man Pâris came rushing in; haste looking through his eyes: A clerk of the *Salut Committee* had told him Danton's warrant was made out, he is to be arrested this very night! Entreaties there are and trepidation, of poor Wife, of Pâris and Friends: Danton sat silent for a while; then answered, *'Ils n'oseraient,* They dared not;' and would take no measures. Murmuring 'They dared not,' he goes to sleep as usual.

And yet, on the morrow morning, strange rumour spreads over Paris City: Danton, Camille, Phélippeaux, Lacroix have been arrested overnight! It is verily so: the corridors of the Luxembourg were all crowded, Prisoners crowding forth to see this giant of the Revolution enter among them. 'Messieurs,' said Danton politely, 'I hoped soon to have got you all out of this: but here I am myself; and one sees not where it will end.'—Rumour may spread over Paris: the Convention clusters itself into groups; wide-eyed, whispering, 'Danton arrested!' Who then is safe? Legendre, mounting the Tribune, utters, at his own peril, a feeble word for him; moving that he be heard at that Bar before indictment; but Robespierre frowns him down: 'Did you hear Chabot, or Bazire? Would you have two weights and measures?' Legendre cowers low: Danton, like the others, must take his doom.

Danton's Prison-thoughts were curious to have; but are not given in any quantity: indeed few such remarkable men have been left so obscure to us as this Titan of the Revolution. He was heard to ejaculate: 'This time twelvemonth, I was moving the creation of that same Revolutionary Tribunal. I crave pardon for it of God and man. They are all Brothers Cain; Brissot would have had me guillotined as Robespierre now will. I leave the whole business in a frightful welter (*gâchis épouvantable*): not one of them understands anything of government. Robespierre will follow me; I drag down Robespierre. O, it were better to be a poor fisherman than to meddle with governing of men.'—Camille's young beautiful Wife, who had made him rich not in money alone, hovers round the Luxembourg, like a disembodied spirit, day and night. Camille's stolen letters to her still exist; stained with the mark of his tears. 'I carry my head like a Saint-

Sacrament?' so Saint-Just was heard to mutter: 'perhaps he will carry his like a Saint-Denis.'

Unhappy Danton, thou still unhappier light Camille, once light *Procureur de la Lanterne,* ye also have arrived, then, at the Bourne of Creation, where, like Ulysses Polytlas at the limit and utmost Gades of his voyage, gazing into that dim Waste beyond Creation, a man does see *the Shade of his Mother,* pale, ineffectual—and days when his Mother nursed and wrapped him are all too sternly contrasted with this day! Danton, Camille, Hérault, Westermann, and the others, very strangely massed up with Bazires, Swindler Chabots, Fabre d'Eglantines, Banker Freys, a most motley Batch, *'Fournée'* as such things will be called, stand ranked at the Bar of Tinville. It is the 2nd of April 1794. Danton has had but three days to lie in Prison; for the time presses.

What is your name? place of abode? and the like, Fouquier asks; according to formality. 'My name is Danton', answers he; 'a name tolerably known in the Revolution: my abode will soon be Annihilation (*dans le Néant*); but I shall live in the Pantheon of History.' A man will endeavour to say something forcible, be it by nature or not! Hérault mentions epigrammatically that he 'sat in this Hall, and was detested of Parlementeers.' Camille makes answer, 'My age is that of the *bon Sansculotte Jésus;* an age fatal to Revolutionists.' O Camille, Camille! And yet in that Divine Transaction, let us say, there did lie, among other things, the fatallest Reproof ever uttered here below to Worldly Right-honourableness; 'the highest fact,' so devout Novalis calls it, 'in the Rights of Man.' Camille's real age, it would seem, is thirty-four. Danton is one year older.

Some five months ago, the Trial of the Twenty-two Girondins was the greatest that Fouquier had then done. But here is a still greater to do; a thing which tasks the whole faculty of Fouquier; which makes the very heart of him waver. For it is the voice of Danton that reverberates now from these domes; in passionate words, piercing with their wild sincerity, winged with wrath. Your best Witnesses he shivers into ruin at one stroke. He demands that the Committee-men themselves come as Witnesses, as Accusers; he 'will cover them with ignominy.' He raises his huge stature, he shakes his huge black head, fire flashes from the eyes of him—piercing to all Republican hearts: so that the very Galleries, though we filled them by ticket, murmur sympathy; and are like to burst down, and raise the People, and deliver him! He complains loudly that he is classed with Chabots, with swindling Stockjobbers; that his Indictment is a list of platitudes and horrors. 'Danton hidden on the 10th of August?' reverberates he, with the roar of a lion in the toils: 'where are the men that had to press Danton to show himself, that day? Where are these high-gifted souls of whom he borrowed energy? Let them appear, these Accusers of mine: I have all the clearness of my self-possession when I demand them. I will unmask the three shallow scoundrels,' *les trois plats coquins,* Saint-Just, Couthon, Lebas, 'who fawn on Robespierre, and lead him towards his destruction. Let them produce themselves here; I will plunge them into Nothingness, out of which they ought never to have risen.' The agitated President agitates his bell; enjoins calmness, in a vehement manner: 'What is it to thee how I defend myself?' cries the other: 'the right of *dooming* me is thine always. The voice of a man speaking for his honour and his life may well drown the jingling of thy bell!' Thus Danton, higher and higher; till the lion-voice of him 'dies away in his throat': speech will not utter what is in that man. The Galleries murmur ominously; the first day's Session is over.

O Tinville, President Herman, what will ye do? They have two days more of it, by strictest Revolutionary Law. The Galleries already murmur. If this Danton were to burst your meshwork!—Very curious indeed to consider. It turns on a hair: and what a Hoitytoity were *there,* Justice and Culprit changing places; and the whole History of France running changed! For in France there is this Danton only that could still try to govern France. He only, the wild amorphous Titan; —and perhaps that other olive-complexioned individual, the Artillery-Officer at Toulon, whom we left pushing his fortune in the South?

On the evening of the second day, matters looking not better but worse and worse, Fouquier and Herman, distraction in their aspect, rush over to *Salut Public.* What is to be done? *Salut Public* rapidly concocts a new Decree; whereby if men 'insult Justice', they may be 'thrown out of the Debates.' For indeed, withal, is there not 'a Plot in the Luxembourg Prison?' *Ci-devant* General Dillon, and others of the Suspect, plotting with Camille's Wife to distribute *assignats;* to force the Prisons, overset the Republic? Citizen Laflotte, himself Suspect but desiring enfranchisement, has reported said Plot for us: —a report that may bear fruit! Enough, on the morrow morning, an obedient Convention passes this Decree. *Salut* rushes off with it to the aid of Tinville, reduced now almost to extremities. And so, *Hors de*

Débats, Out of the Debates, ye insolents! Policemen do your duty! In such manner, with a dead-lift effort, *Salut,* Tinville, Herman, Leroi *Dix-Août,* and all stanch jurymen setting heart and shoulder to it, the Jury becomes 'sufficiently instructed;' Sentence is passed, is sent by an Official, and torn and trampled on: *Death this day.* It is the 5th of April 1794. Camille's poor Wife may cease hovering about this Prison. Nay, let her kiss her poor children; and prepare to enter it, and to follow!—

Danton carried a high look in the Death-cart. Not so Camille: it is but one week, and all is so topsyturvied; angel Wife left weeping; love, riches, Revolutionary fame, left all at the Prison-gate; carnivorous Rabble now howling round. Palpable, and yet incredible; like a madman's dream! Camille struggles and writhes; his shoulders shuffle the loose coat off them, which hangs knotted, the hands tied: 'Calm, my friend,' said Danton; 'heed not that vile canaille (*laissez là cette vile canaille*)'. At the foot of the Scaffold, Danton was heard to ejaculate: 'O my Wife, my well-beloved, I shall never see thee more then!'—but, interrupting himself: 'Danton, no weakness!' He said to Hérault-Séchelles stepping forward to embrace him: 'Our heads will meet *there,*' in the Headsman's sack. His last words were to Samson the Headsman himself: 'Thou wilt show my head to the people; it is worth showing.'

So passes, like a gigantic mass, of valour, ostentation, fury, affection and wild revolutionary force and manhood, this Danton, to his unknown home. He was of Arcis-sur-Aube; born of 'good farmer-people' there. He had many sins; but one worst sin he had not, that of Cant. No hollow Formalist, deceptive and self-deceptive, *ghastly* to the natural sense, was this; but a very Man: with all his dross he was a Man; fiery-real, from the great fire-bosom of Nature herself. He saved France from Brunswick; he walked straight his own wild road, whither it led him. He may live for some generations in the memory of men.

THE TUMBRILS

Next week, it is still but the 10th of April, there comes a new Nineteen; Chaumette, Gobel, Hébert's Widow, the Widow of Camille: these also roll their fated journey; black Death devours them. Mean Hébert's Widow was weeping, Camille's Widow tried to

speak comfort to her. O ye kind Heavens, azure, beautiful, eternal behind your tempests and Time-clouds, is there not pity in store for all!
Gobel, it seems, was repentant; he begged absolution of a Priest; died
as a Gobel best could. For Anaxagoras Chaumette, the sleek head
now stript of its *bonnet rouge,* what hope is there? Unless Death *were*
'an eternal sleep?' Wretched Anaxagoras, God shall judge thee, not I.

Hébert, therefore, is gone, and the Hébertists; they that robbed
Churches, and adored blue Reason in red nightcap. Great Danton,
and the Dantonists; they also are gone. Down to the catacombs; they
are become silent men! Let no Paris Municipality, no Sect or Party of
this hue or that, resist the will of Robespierre and *Salut.* Mayor
Pache, not prompt enough in denouncing these Pitt Plots, may con-
gratulate about them now. Never so heartily; it skills not! His course
likewise is to the Luxembourg. We appoint one Fleuriot-Lescot In-
terim-Mayor in his stead: an 'architect from Belgium,' they say, this
Fleuriot; he is a man one can depend on. Our new Agent-National is
Payan, lately Juryman; whose cynosure also is Robespierre.

Thus then, we perceive, this confusedly electric Erebus-cloud of
Revolutionary Government has altered its shape somewhat. Two
masses, or wings, belonging to it; an over-electric mass of Cordelier
Rabids, and an under-electric of Dantonist Moderates and Clemency-
men—these two masses, shooting bolts at one another, so to speak,
have annihilated one another. For the Erebus-cloud, as we often
remark, is of suicidal nature; and, in jagged irregularity, darts its
lightning withal into itself. But now these two discrepant masses
being mutually annihilated, it is as if the Erebus-cloud had got to
internal composure; and did only pour its hell-fire lightning on the
World that lay under it. In plain words, Terror of the Guillotine was
never terrible till now. Systole, diastole, swift and ever swifter goes
the Axe of Samson. Indictments cease by degrees to have so much
as plausibility: Fouquier chooses from the Twelve Houses of Arrest
what he calls Batches, *'Fournées,'* a score or more at a time; his Jurymen are charged to make *feu de file,* file-firing till the ground be *clear.*
Citizen Laflotte's report of Plot in the Luxembourg is verily bearing
fruit! If no speakable charge exist against a man, or Batch of men,
Fouquier has always this: a Plot in the Prison. Swift and ever swifter
goes Samson; up, finally, to three score and more at a Batch. It is
the highday of Death: none but the Dead return not.

O dusky D'Espréménil, what a day is this, the 22nd of April, thy
last day! The Palais Hall here is the same stone Hall, where thou,

five years ago, stoodest perorating, amid endless pathos of rebellious Parlement, in the grey of the morning; bound to march with D'Agoust to the Isles of Hières. The stones are the same stones: but the rest, Men, Rebellion, Pathos, Peroration, see! it has all fled, like a gibbering troop of ghosts, like the phantasms of a dying brain. With D'Espréménil, in the same line of Tumbrils, goes the mournfullest medley. Chapelier goes, *ci-devant* popular President of the Constituent; whom the Menads and Maillard met in his carriage, on the Versailles Road. Thouret likewise, *ci-devant* President, father of Constitutional Law-acts; he whom we heard saying, long since, with a loud voice, 'The Constituent Assembly has fulfilled its mission!' And the noble old Malesherbes, who defended Louis and could not speak, like a grey old rock dissolving into sudden water: he journeys here now, with his kindred, daughters, sons and grandsons, his Lamoignons, Château-briands; silent, towards Death.—One young Châteaubriand alone is wandering amid the Natchez, by the roar of Niagara Falls, the moan of endless forests: Welcome thou great Nature, savage, but not false, not unkind, unmotherly; no Formula thou, or rabid jangle of Hypothesis, Parliamentary Eloquence, Constitution-building and the Guillotine; speak thou to me, O Mother, and sing my sick heart thy mystic everlasting lullaby-song, and let all the rest be far!—

Another row of Tumbrils we must notice: that which holds Elizabeth, the Sister of Louis. Her Trial was like the rest; for Plots, for Plots. She was among the kindliest, most innocent of women. There sat with her, amid four-and-twenty others, a once timorous Marchioness de Crussol; courageous now; expressing towards her the liveliest loyalty. At the foot of the Scaffold, Elizabeth with tears in her eyes thanked this Marchioness; said she was grieved she could not reward her. 'Ah, Madame, would your Royal Highness deign to embrace me, my wishes were complete!'—'Right willingly, Marquise de Crussol, and with my whole heart.' Thus they: at the foot of the Scaffold. The Royal Family is now reduced to two: a girl and a little boy. The boy, once named Dauphin, was taken from his Mother while she yet lived; and given to one Simon, by trade a Cordwainer, on service then about the Temple-Prison, to bring him up in principles of Sansculottism. Simon taught him to drink, to swear, to sing the *carmagnole*. Simon is now gone to the Municipality: and the poor boy, hidden in a tower of the Temple, from which in his fright and bewilderment and early decrepitude he wishes not to stir out, lies perishing, 'his shirt not changed for six months;' amid squalor and darkness, lamentably—so as none but poor Factory Children and the like are wont to perish, and *not* be lamented!

The Spring sends its green leaves and bright weather, bright May, brighter than ever: Death pauses not. Lavoisier, famed Chemist, shall die and not live: Chemist Lavoisier was Farmer-General Lavoisier too, and now 'all the Farmers-General are arrested;' all, and shall give an account of their moneys and incomings; and die for 'putting water in the tobacco' they sold. Lavoisier begged a fortnight more of life, to finish some experiments: but 'the Republic does not need such;' the axe must do its work. Cynic Chamfort, reading these inscriptions of *Brotherhood or Death*, says 'it is a Brotherhood of Cain': arrested, then liberated; then about to be arrested again, this Chamfort cuts and slashes himself with frantic uncertain hand; gains, not without difficulty, the refuge of death. Condorcet has lurked deep, these many months; Argus-eyes watching and searching for him. His concealment is become dangerous to others and himself; he has to fly again, to skulk, round Paris, in thickets and stone-quarries. And so at the Village of Clamars, one bleared May morning, there enters a Figure, ragged, rough-bearded, hunger-stricken; asks breakfast in the tavern there. Suspect, by the look of him! 'Servant out of place, sayest thou?' Committee-President of Forty-Sous finds a Latin Horace on him: 'Art thou not one of those *Ci-devants* that were wont to keep servants? *Suspect!'* He is haled forthwith, breakfast unfinished, towards Bourg-la-Reine, on foot: he faints with exhaustion; is set on a peasant's horse; is flung into his damp prison-cell: on the morrow, recollecting him, you enter; Condorcet lies dead on the floor. They die fast, and disappear: the Notabilities of France disappear, one after one, like lights in a Theatre, which you are snuffing out.

Under which circumstances, is it not singular, and almost touching, to see Paris City drawn out, in the meek May nights, in civic ceremony, which they call *'Souper Fraternel,'* Brotherly Supper? Spontaneous; or partially spontaneous, in the twelfth, thirteenth, fourteenth nights of this May month, it is seen. Along the Rue Saint-Honoré, and main Streets and Spaces, each Citoyen brings forth what of supper the stingy *Maximum* has yielded him, to the open air; joins it to his neighbour's supper; and with common table, cheerful light burning frequent, and what due modicum of cut-glass and other garnish and relish is convenient, they eat frugally together, under the kind stars. See it, O Night! With cheerfully pledged wine-cup, hob-

410

nobbing to the Reign of Liberty, Equality, Brotherhood, with their wives in best ribands, with their little ones romping round, the Citoyens, in frugal Love-feast, sit there. Night in her wide empire sees nothing similar. O my brothers, why is the reign of Brotherhood not come! It is come, it shall have come, say the Citoyens frugally hobnobbing.—Ah me! these everlasting stars, do they not look down 'like glistening eyes, bright with immortal pity, over the lot of man!'

One lamentable thing, however, is, that individuals will attempt assassination—of Representatives of the People. Representative Collot, Member even of *Salut,* returning home, 'about one in the morning,' probably touched with liquor, as he is apt to be, meets on the stairs the cry *'Scélérat!'* and also the snap of a pistol: which latter flashes in the pan; disclosing to him, momentarily, a pair of truculent saucer-eyes, swart grim-clenched countenance; recognizable as that of our little fellow-lodger, Citoyen Amiral, formerly 'a clerk in the Lotteries!' Collot shouts *Murder,* with lungs fit to awaken all the *Rue Favart;* Amiral snaps a second time; a second time flashes in the pan; then darts up into his apartment; and, after there firing, still with inadequate effect, one musket at himself and another at his captor, is clutched and locked in Prison. An indignant little man this Amiral, of Southern temper and complexion, of 'considerable muscular force.' He denies not that he meant to 'purge France of a Tyrant;' nay avows that he had an eye to the Incorruptible himself, but took Collot as more convenient!

Rumour enough hereupon; heaven-high congratulation of Collot, fraternal embracing, at the Jacobins and elsewhere. And yet, it would seem, the assassin mood proves catching. Two days more, it is still but the 23rd of May, and towards nine in the evening, Cécile Rénault, Paper-dealer's daughter, a young woman of soft blooming look, presents herself at the Cabinet-maker's in the Rue Saint-Honoré; desires to see Robespierre. Robespierre cannot be seen; she grumbles irreverently. They lay hold of her. She has left a basket in a shop hard by: in the basket are female change of raiment and two knives! Poor Cécile, examined by Committee, declares she 'wanted to see what a tyrant was like:' the change of raiment was 'for my own use in the place I am surely going to.'—'What place?'—'Prison; and then the Guillotine,' answered she.—Such things come of Charlotte Corday; in a people prone to imitation, and monomania! Swart choleric men try Charlotte's feat, and their pistols miss fire; soft blooming young women try it, and, only half-resolute, leave their knives in a shop.

411

O Pitt, and ye Faction of the Stranger, shall the Republic never have rest; but be torn continually by baited springes, by wires of explosive spring-guns? Swart Amiral, fair young Cécile, and all that knew them, and many that did not know them, lie locked, waiting the scrutiny of Tinville.

MUMBO-JUMBO

BUT ON THE DAY they call *Décadi,* New-Sabbath, 20 *Prairial,* 8th June by old style, what thing is this going forward in the Jardin National, whilom Tuileries Garden?

All the world is there, in holyday clothes: foul linen went out with the Hébertists; nay Robespierre, for one, would never once countenance that; but went always elegant and frizzled, not without vanity even—and had his room hung round with seagreen Portraits and Busts. In holyday clothes, we say, are the innumerable Citoyens and Citoyennes: the weather is of the brightest; cheerful expectation lights all countenances. Juryman Vilate gives breakfast to many a Deputy, in his official Apartment, in the Pavillon *ci-devant* of Flora; rejoices in the bright-looking multitudes, in the brightness of leafy June, in the auspicious *Décadi,* or New-Sabbath. This day, if it please Heaven, we are to have, on improved Anti-Chaumette principles: a New Religion.

Catholicism being burned out, and Reason-worship guillotined, was there not need of one? Incorruptible Robespierre, not unlike the Ancients, as Legislator of a free people, will now also be Priest and Prophet. He has donned his sky-blue coat, made for the occasion; white silk waistcoat broidered with silver, black silk breeches, white stockings, shoe-buckles of gold. He is President of the Convention; he has made the Convention *decree,* so they name it, *décréter* the 'Existence of the Supreme Being,' and likewise *'ce principe consolateur* of the Immortality of the Soul.' These consolatory principles, the basis of rational Republican Religion, are getting decreed; and here, on this blessed *Décadi,* by help of Heaven and Painter David, is to be our first act of worship.

See, accordingly, how after Decree passed, and what has been called 'the scraggiest Prophetic Discourse ever uttered by man,' Mahomet Robespierre, in sky-blue coat and black breeches, frizzled

412

and powdered to perfection, bearing in his hand a bouquet of flowers and wheat-ears, issues proudly from the Convention Hall; Convention following him, yet, as is remarked, with an interval. Amphitheatre has been raised, or at least *Monticule* or Elevation; hideous Statues of Atheism, Anarchy and such like, thanks to Heaven and Painter David, strike abhorrence into the heart. Unluckily, however, our Monticule is too small. On the top of it not half of us can stand; wherefore there arises indecent shoving, nay treasonous irreverent growling. Peace, thou Bourdon de l'Oise; peace, or it may be worse for thee!

The seagreen Pontiff takes a torch, Painter David handing it; mouths some other froth-rant of vocables, which happily one cannot hear; strides resolutely forward, in sight of expectant France; sets his torch to Atheism and Company, which are but made of pasteboard steeped in turpentine. They burn up rapidly; and, from within, there rises 'by machinery,' an incombustible Statue of Wisdom, which, by ill hap, gets besmoked a little; but does stand there visible in as serene attitude as it can.

And then? Why, then, there is other Processioning, scraggy Discoursing, and—this *is* our Feast of the *Être Suprême;* our new Religion, better or worse, is come!—Look at it one moment, O Reader, not two. The shabbiest page of Human Annals: or is there, that thou wottest of, one shabbier? Mumbo-Jumbo of the African woods to me seems venerable beside this new Deity of Robespierre; for this is a *conscious* Mumbo-Jumbo, and *knows* that he is machinery. O seagreen Prophet, unhappiest of windbags blown nigh to bursting, what distracted Chimera among realities art thou growing to! This then, this common pitch-link for artificial fireworks of turpentine and pasteboard; *this* is the miraculous Aaron's Rod thou wilt stretch over a hag-ridden hell-ridden France, and bid her plagues cease? Vanish, thou and it!—'*Avec ton Être Suprême,*' said Billaud, '*tu commences m'embêter:* With thy Être Suprême thou beginnest to be a bore to me.'

Catherine Théot, on the other hand, 'an ancient serving-maid seventy-nine years of age,' inured to Prophecy and the Bastille from of old, sits in an upper room in the Rue de Contrescarpe, poring over the Book of Revelations, with an eye to Robespierre; finds that this astonishing thrice-potent Maximilien really is the Man spoken of by Prophets, who is to make the Earth young again. With her sit devout old Machionesses, *ci-devant* honourable women; among whom Old-

413

Constituent Dom Gerle, with his addle-head, cannot be wanting. They sit there, in the Rue de Contrescarpe; in mysterious adoration: Mumbo is Mumbo, and Robespierre is his Prophet. A conspicuous man this Robespierre. He has his volunteer Bodyguard of *Tappe-durs,* let us say *Strike-sharps,* fierce Patriots with feruled sticks; and Jacobins kissing the hem of his garment. He enjoys the admiration of many, the worship of some; and is well worth the wonder of one and all.

The grand question and hope, however is: Will not this Feast of the Tuileries Mumbo-Jumbo be a sign perhaps that the Guillotine is to abate? Far enough from that! Precisely on the second day after it, Couthon, one of the 'three shallow scoundrels,' gets himself lifted into the Tribune; produces a bundle of papers. Couthon proposes that, as Plots still abound, the *Law of the Suspect* shall have extension, and Arrestment new vigour and facility. Further that, as in such case business is like to be heavy, our Revolutionary Tribunal too shall have extension; be divided, say, into Four Tribunals, each with its President, each with its Fouquier or Substitute of Fouquier, all labouring at once, and any remnant of shackle or dilatory formality be struck off: in this way it may perhaps still overtake the work. Such is Couthon's *Decree of the Twenty-second Prairial,* famed in those times. At hearing of which Decree, the very Mountain gasped, awestruck; and one Ruamps ventured to say that if it passed without adjournment and discussion, he, as one Representative, 'would blow his brains out.' Vain saying! The Incorruptible knit his brows; spoke a prophetic fateful word or two: the *Law of Prairial* is Law; Ruamps glad to leave his rash brains where they are. Death then, and always Death! Even so, Fouquier is enlarging his borders; making room for Batches of a Hundred and fifty at once—getting a Guillotine set up of improved velocity, and to work under cover, in the apartment close by. So that *Salut* itself has to intervene, and forbid him: 'Wilt thou *demoralize* the Guillotine,' asks Collot, reproachfully, *'démoraliser le supplice!'*

There is indeed danger of that; were not the Republican faith great, it were already done. See, for example, on the 17th of June, what a *Batch,* Fifty-four at once! Swart Amiral is here, he of the pistol that missed fire; young Cécile Rénault, with her father, family, entire kith and kin; the Widow of D'Espréménil; old M. de Sombreuil of the Invalides, with his Son—poor old Sombreuil, seventy-three years old, his Daughter saved him in September, and it was but for

414

this. Faction of the Stranger, fifty-four of them! In red shirts and smocks, as Assassins and Faction of the Stranger, they flit along there; red baleful Phantasmagory, towards the land of Phantoms.

Meanwhile will not the people of the Place de la Révolution, the inhabitants along the Rue Saint-Honoré as these continual Tumbrils pass, begin to look gloomy? Republicans too have bowels. The Guillotine is shifted, then again shifted; finally set up at the remote extremity of the Southeast: Suburbs Saint-Antoine and Saint-Marceau, it is to be hoped, if they have bowels, have very tough ones.

SECTION X

Epilogue

[*After the purging of Danton and his followers, Robespierre dominated the government. In July, 1794, a group in the Convention, fearing for their own lives, formed a conspiracy against him. On July 27 (9 Thermidor, according to the revolutionary calendar) he and his most important followers were declared outlaws.*]

THE END OF ROBESPIERRE

OUR FIFTH-ACT, of this natural Greek Drama, with its natural unities, can only be painted in gross; somewhat as that antique Painter, driven desperate, did the *foam.* For through this blessed July night, there is clangour, confusion very great, of marching troops; of Sections going this way, Sections going that; of Missionary Representatives reading Proclamations by torchlight; Missionary Legendre, who has raised force somewhere, emptying out the Jacobins, and flinging their key on the Convention table: 'I have locked their door; it shall be Virtue that reopens it.' Paris, we say, is set against itself, rushing confused, as Ocean-currents do: a huge Mahlstrom, sounding there, under cloud of night. Convention sits permanent on this hand; Municipality most permanent on that. The poor prisoners hear tocsin and rumour; strive to bethink them of the signals apparently of hope.

415

Meek continual Twilight streaming up, which will be Dawn and a To-morrow, silvers the Northern hem of Night; it wends and wends there, that meek brightness, like a silent prophecy, along the great ring-dial of the Heaven. So still, eternal! and on Earth all is confused shadow and conflict; dissidence, tumultuous gloom and glare; and 'Destiny as yet sits wavering, and shakes her doubtful urn.'

About three in the morning, the dissident Armed Forces have *met*. Henriot's Armed Force stood ranked in the Place de Grève; and now Barras's, which he has recruited, arrives there; and they front each other, cannon bristling against cannon. Citoyens! cries the voice of Discretion loudly enough, Before coming to bloodshed, to endless civil-war, hear the Convention Decree read: 'Robespierre and all rebels Out of Law!'—Out of Law? There is terror in the sound. Unarmed Citoyens disperse rapidly home. Municipal Cannoneers, in sudden whirl, anxiously unanimous, range themselves on the Convention side, with shouting. At which shout, Henriot descends from his upper room, far gone in drink as some say; finds his Place de Grève empty; the cannons' mouth turned *towards* him; and on the whole—that it is now the catastrophe!

Stumbling in again, the wretched drunk-sobered Henriot announces: 'All is lost!' *'Misérable,* it is thou that hast lost it!' cry they; and fling him, or else he flings himself, out of window: far enough down; into masonwork and horror of cesspool; not into death but worse. Augustin Robespierre follows him; with the like fate. Saint-Just, they say, called on Lebas to kill him; who would not. Couthon crept under a table; attempting to kill himself; not doing it.—On entering that Sanhedrim of Insurrection, we find all as good as extinct; undone, ready for seizure. Robespierre was sitting on a chair, with pistol-shot blown through not his head but his under-jaw; the suicidal hand had failed. With prompt zeal, not without trouble, we gather these wrecked Conspirators; fish up even Henriot and Augustin, bleeding and foul; pack them all, rudely enough, into carts; and shall, before sunrise, have them safe under lock and key. Amid shoutings and embracings.

Robespierre lay in an anteroom of the Convention Hall, while his Prison-escort was getting ready; the mangled jaw bound up rudely with bloody linen: a spectacle to men. He lies stretched on a table, a deal-box his pillow; the sheath of the pistol is still clenched convulsively in his hand. Men bully him, insult him: his eyes still indicate intelligence; he speaks no word. 'He had on the sky-blue coat he had got made for the Feast of the *Être Suprême.*'—O Reader, can thy hard heart hold out against that? His trousers were nankeen; the stockings had fallen down over the ankles. He spake no word more in this world.

And so, at six in the morning, a victorious Convention adjourns. Report flies over Paris as on golden wings; penetrates the Prisons; irradiates the faces of those that were ready to perish: turnkeys and *moutons,* fallen from their high estate, look mute and blue. It is the 28th day of July, called 10th of Thermidor, year 1794.

Fouquier had but to identify; his Prisoners being already Out of Law. At four in the afternoon, never before were the streets of Paris seen so crowded. From the Palais de Justice to the Place de la Révo-lution, for *thither* again go the Tumbrils this time, it is one dense stir-ring mass; all windows crammed; the very roofs and ridge-tiles bud-ding forth human Curiosity, in strange gladness. The Death-tumbrils, with their motley Batch of Outlaws, some Twenty-three or so, from Maximilien to Mayor Fleuriot and Simon the Cordwainer, roll on. All eyes are on Robespierre's Tumbril, where he, his jaw bound in dirty linen, with his half-dead Brother, and half-dead Henriot, lie shattered; their 'seventeen hours' of agony about to end. The Gendarmes point their swords at him, to show the people which is he. A woman springs on the Tumbril; clutching the side of it with one hand; waving the other Sibyl-like; and exclaims: 'The death of these gladdens my very heart, *m'enivre de joie;'* Robespierre opened his eyes; '*Scélérat,* go down to Hell, with the curses of all wives and mothers!'—At the foot of the scaffold, they stretched him on the ground till his turn came. Lifted aloft, his eyes again opened; caught the bloody axe. Samson wrenched the coat off him; wrenched the dirty linen from his jaw: the jaw fell powerless, there burst from him a cry;—hideous to hear and see. Samson, thou canst not be too quick!

Samson's work done, there bursts forth shout on shout of applause. Shout, which prolongs itself not only over Paris, but over France, but over Europe, and down to this generation. Deservedly, and also unde-servedly. O unhappiest Advocate of Arras, wert thou worse than other Advocates? Stricter man, according to his Formula, to his Credo and his Cant, of probities, benevolences, pleasures-of-virtue, and such like, lived not in that age. A man fitted, in some luckier settled age, to have become one of those incorruptible barren Pattern-Figures,

417

and have had marble-tablets and funeral-sermons. His poor landlord, the Cabinet-maker in the Rue Saint-Honoré, loved him; his Brother died for him. May God be merciful to him, and to us!

This is the end of the Reign of Terror; new glorious *Revolution* named *of Thermidor;* of Thermidor 9th, year 2; which being interpreted into old slave-style means 27th of July 1794. Terror is ended; and death in the Place de la Révolution, were the *'Tail* of Robespierre' once executed; which service Fouquier in large Batches is swiftly managing.

DECADENT

How LITTLE did any one suppose that here was the end not of Robespierre only, but of the Revolution System itself! Least of all did the mutinying Committee-men suppose it; who had mutinied with no view whatever except to continue the National Regeneration with their own heads on their shoulders. And yet so it verily was. The insignificant stone they had struck out, so insignificant anywhere else, proved to be the Keystone; the whole arch-work and edifice of Sansculottism began to loosen, to crack, to yawn; and tumbled piecemeal, with considerable rapidity, plunge after plunge; till the Abyss had swallowed it all, and in this upper world Sansculottism was no more.

For despicable as Robespierre himself might be, the death of Robespierre was a signal at which great multitudes of men, struck dumb with terror heretofore, rose out of their hiding-places; and, as it were, saw one another, how multitudinous they were; and began speaking and complaining. They are countable by the thousand and the million; who have suffered cruel wrong. Ever louder rises the plaint of such a multitude; into a universal sound, into a universal continuous peal, of what they call Public Opinion. Camille had demanded a 'Committee of Mercy,' and could not get it; but now the whole Nation resolves itself into a Committee of Mercy: the Nation has tried Sansculottism, and is weary of it. Force of Public Opinion! What King or Convention can withstand it? You in vain struggle: the thing that is rejected as 'calumnious' to-day must pass as veracious with triumph another day: gods and men have declared that Sansculottism cannot be. Sansculottism, on that Ninth night of Thermidor, suicidally 'fractured its under-jaw;' and lies writhing, never to rise more.

418

So much is getting abolished; fleeting swiftly into the Inane. For the Press speaks, and the human tongue; Journals, heavy and light, in Philippic and Burlesque: a renegade Fréron, a renegade Prud-homme, loud they as ever, only the contrary way. And *Ci-devants* show themselves, almost parade themselves; resuscitated as from death-sleep; publish what death-pains they have had. The very Frogs of the Marsh croak with emphasis. Your protesting Seventy-three shall, with a struggle, be emitted out of Prison, back to their seats; your Louvets, Isnards, Lanjuinais, and wrecks of Girondism, recalled from their haylofts, and caves in Switzerland, will resume their place in the Convention: natural foes of Terror!

Thermidorian Talliens, and mere foes of Terror, rule in this Con-vention, and out of it. The compressed Mountain shrinks silent more and more. Moderatism rises louder and louder: not as a tempest, with threatenings; say rather, as the rushing of a mighty organ-blast, and melodious deafening Force of Public Opinion, from the Twenty-five million windpipes of a Nation all in Committee of Mercy: which how shall any detached body of individuals withstand?

GRILLED HERRINGS

So DIES SANSCULOTTISM, the body of Sansculottism; or is changed. Its ragged Pythian Carmagnole-dance has transformed itself into a Pyrrhic, into a dance of Cabarus Balls. Sansculottism is dead; ex-tinguished by new *isms* of that kind, which were its own natural progeny; and is buried, we may say, with such deafening jubilation and disharmony of funeral-knell on their part, that only after some half-century or so does one begin to learn clearly why it was ever alive.

And yet a meaning lay in it: Sansculottism verily was alive, a New-Birth of TIME; nay it still lives, and is not dead but changed. The *soul* of it still lives; still works far and wide, through one bodily shape into another less amorphous, as is the way of cunning Time with his New-Births:—till, in some perfected shape, it embrace the whole cir-cuit of the world! For the wise man may now everywhere discern that he must found on his manhood, not on the garnitures of his manhood. He who, in these Epochs of our Europe, founds on garni-tures, formulas, culottisms of what sort soever, is founding on old cloth and sheepskin, and cannot endure. But as for the body of Sansculottism, that is dead and buried—and one hopes, need not reappear, in primary amorphous shape, for another thousand years.

It was the frightfullest thing ever born of Time? One of the frightfullest. This Convention, now grown Antijacobin, did, with an eye to justify and fortify itself, publish Lists of what the Reign of Terror had perpetrated: Lists of Persons Guillotined. The Lists, cries splenetic Abbé Montgaillard, were not complete. They contain the names of, How many persons thinks the Reader?—Two-thousand all but a few. There were above four-thousand, cries Montgaillard: so many were guillotined, fusilladed, noyaded, done to dire death; of whom Nine-hundred were women. It is a horrible sum of human lives, M. l'Abbé: some ten times as many shot rightly on a field of battle, and one might have had his Glorious-Victory with *Te-Deum*. It is not far from the two-hundredth part of what perished in the entire Seven-Years War. By which Seven-Years War, did not the great Fritz wrench Silesia from the great Theresa; and a Pompadour, stung by epigrams, satisfy herself that she could not be an Agnes Sorel? The head of man is a strange vacant sounding-shell, M. l'Abbé; and studies Cocker to small purpose.

But what if History somewhere on this Planet were to hear of a Nation, the third soul of whom had not, for thirty weeks each year, as many third-rate potatoes as would sustain him? History, in that case, feels bound to consider that starvation is starvation: that starvation from age to age presupposes much; History ventures to assert that the French Sansculotte of Ninety-three, who, roused from long death-sleep, could rush at once to the frontiers, and die fighting for an immortal Hope and Faith of Deliverance for him and his, was but the *second*-miserablest of men! The Irish Sans-potato, had he not senses then, nay not a soul! In his frozen darkness, it was bitter for him to die famishing; bitter to see his children famish. It was bitter for him to be a beggar, a liar and a knave. Nay, if that dreary Greenland-wind of benighted Want, perennial from sire to son, had frozen him into a kind of torpor and numb callosity, so that he saw not, felt not—was this, for a creature with a soul in it, some assuagement; or the cruellest wretchedness of all?

Such things were; such things are; and they go on in silence peaceably—and Sansculottism follow them. History, looking back over this France through long times, back to Turgot's time for instance, when dumb Drudgery staggered up to its King's Palace, and in wide-expanse of sallow faces, squalor and winged raggedness, presented

420

hieroglyphically its Petition of Grievances; and for answer got hanged on a 'new gallows forty feet high,'—confesses mournfully that there is no period to be met with, in which the general Twenty-five Millions of France suffered *less* than in this period which they name Reign of Terror! But it was not the Dumb Millions that suffered here; it was the Speaking Thousands, and Hundreds and Units; who shrieked and published, and made the world ring with their wail, as they could and should: that is the grand peculiarity. The frightfullest Births of Time are never the loud-speaking ones, for these soon die; they are the silent ones, which can live from century to century! Anarchy, hateful as Death, is abhorrent to the whole nature of man; and so must itself soon die.

Wherefore let all men know what of depth and of height is still revealed in man; and, with fear and wonder, with just sympathy and just antipathy, with clear eye and open heart, contemplate it and appropriate it; and draw innumerable inferences from it. This inference, for example, among the first: That 'if the gods of this lower world will sit on their glittering thrones, indolent as Epicurus' gods, with the living Chaos of Ignorance and Hunger weltering uncared-for at their feet, and smooth Parasites preaching, Peace, peace, when there is no peace,' then the dark Chaos, it would seem, will rise,— has risen, and O Heavens! has it not tanned their skins into breeches for itself? That there be no second Sansculottism in our Earth for a thousand years, let us understand well what the first was; and let Rich and Poor of us go and do *otherwise*.

FINIS

HOMER'S EPOS, it is remarked, is like a Bas-Relief sculpture: it does not conclude, but merely ceases. Such, indeed, is the Epos of Universal History itself. Directorates, Consulates, Emperorships, Restorations, Citizen-Kingships succeed this Business in due series, in due genesis one out of the other. Nevertheless the First-parent of all these may be said to have gone to air in the way we see. A Babœuf Insurrection, next year, will die in the birth; stifled by the Soldiery. A Senate, if tinged with Royalism, can be purged by the Soldiery; and an Eighteenth of Fructidor transacted by the mere show of bayonets. Nay Soldiers' bayonets can be used *à posteriori* on a Senate, and make it leap out of window—still bloodless; and produce an Eighteenth of

Brumaire. Such changes must happen: but they are managed by intriguings, caballings, and then by orderly word of command; almost like mere changes of Ministry. Not in general by sacred right of Insurrection, but by milder methods growing ever milder, shall the events of French History be henceforth brought to pass.

It is admitted that this Directorate, which owned, at its starting, these three things, an 'old table, a sheet of paper, and an inkbottle,' and no visible money arrangement whatever, did wonders: that France, since the Reign of Terror hushed itself, has been a new France, awakened like a giant out of torpor; and has gone on, in the Internal Life of it, with continual progress. As for the External form and forms of Life, what can we say, except that out of the Eater there comes Strength; out of the Unwise there comes *not* Wisdom! Shams are burnt up; nay, what as yet is the peculiarity of France, the very Cant of them is burnt up. The new Realities are not yet come: ah no, only Phantasms, Paper models, tentative Prefigurements of such! In France there are now Four Million Landed Properties; that black portent of an Agrarian Law is, as it were, *realized*. What is still stranger, we understand all Frenchmen have 'the right of duel;' the Hackney-coachman with the Peer, if insult be given: such is the law of Public Opinion. Equality at least in death! The Form of Government is by Citizen King, frequently shot at, not yet shot.

On the whole, therefore, has it not been fulfilled what was prophesied, *ex-post facto* indeed, by the Arch-quack Cagliostro, or another? He, as he looked in rapt vision and amazement into these things, thus spake: 'Ha! What is *this?* Angels, Uriel, Anachiel, and ye other Five; Pentagon of Rejuvenescence; Power that destroyedst Original Sin; Earth, Heaven, and thou Outer Limbo, which men name Hell! Does the EMPIRE OF IMPOSTURE waver! Burst there, in starry sheen updarting, Light-rays from out of *its* dark foundation; as it rocks and heaves, not in travail-throes but in death-throes? Yea, Light-rays, piercing, clear, that salute the Heavens,—lo, they *kindle* it; their starry clearness becomes as red Hellfire!

'IMPOSTURE is in flames, Imposture is burnt up: one red sea of Fire, wild-bellowing, enwraps the World; with its fire-tongue licks at the very Stars. Thrones are hurled into it, and Dubois Mitres, and Prebendal Stalls that drop fatness, and—ha! what see I?—all the *Gigs* of Creation: all, all! Woe is me! Never since Pharaoh's Chariots, in the Red Sea of water, was there wreck of Wheel-vehicles like this

422

in the Sea of Fire. Desolate, as ashes, as gases, shall they wander in the wind.

'Higher, higher yet flames the Fire-Sea; crackling with new dislocated timber; hissing with leather and prunella. The metal Images are molten; the marble Images become mortar-lime; the stone Mountains sulkily explode. RESPECTABILITY, with all her collected Gigs inflamed for funeral pyre, wailing, leaves the Earth: not to return save under new Avatar. Imposture how it burns, through generations: how it is burnt up; for a time. The World is black ashes;—which, ah, when will they grow green? The Images all run into amorphous Corinthian brass; all Dwellings of men destroyed; the very mountains peeled and riven, the valleys black and dead: it is an empty World! Woe to them that shall be born then!—A King, a Queen (ah me!) were hurled in; did rustle once; flew aloft, crackling, like paper-scroll. Iscariot Égalité was hurled in; thou grim de Launay, with thy grim Bastille; whole kindreds and peoples; five millions of mutually destroying Men. For it is the End of the dominion of IMPOSTURE (which is Darkness and opaque Firedamp); and the burning up, with unquenchable fire, of all the Gigs that are in the Earth.' This Prophecy, we say, has it not been fulfilled, is it not fulfilling?

And so here, O Reader, has the time come for us two to part. Toilsome was our journeying together; not without offence; but it is done. To me thou wert as a beloved shade, the disembodied or not yet embodied spirit of a Brother. To thee I was but as a Voice. Yet was our relation a kind of sacred one; doubt not that! For whatsoever once sacred things become hollow jargons, yet while the Voice of Man speaks with Man, hast thou not there the living fountain out of which all sacredness sprang, and will yet spring? Man, by the nature of him, is definable as 'an incarnated Word.' Ill stands it with me if I have spoken falsely: thine also it was to hear truly. Farewell.

Andrew Hamilton's

SPEECH

DEFENDING

FREEDOM OF

THE PRESS

August 4, 1735

HOME COURSE APPRECIATION

THREE LOUD HUZZAS BURST from the spectators in the hot crowded courtroom when the jury delivered the verdict, "Not guilty." One shout was surely for Counsel for the Defense; the others were certainly for freedom of the press and fair trial by jury. The three cheers were, really, one great hurrah—for Liberty.

The charge was "seditious libel."

The case should have been a simple one. The trial should have taken a few hours at the most, and the whole thing should have passed into history, to become of interest only to scholars searching for some knowledge of our past.

Instead, the case was complicated and dragged on for months. The trial occupied a whole hot summer—and the details, the participants, the event itself became a bright, shiny star on the chart of man's search for political freedom.

The defendant was John Peter Zenger, thirty-eight years old. He had come to America from Germany when he was thirteen; a year later he was apprenticed to William Bradford, the famous printer, whom he served for nine years. At twenty-nine he set up his own printing business in New York City; at thirty-six—in November 1733,

Andrew Hamilton addressing the Court.

to be exact—he began to publish his own newspaper, the *New York Weekly Journal*. This was not merely a business venture, and the risks involved were far from purely financial.

One such "risk" was to be found in the person of William Cosby, who had been appointed governor of New York Colony in 1732. His tyrannical, high-handed, self-interested sort of government soon aroused the animosity of all classes of people and resulted in a bitter alignment of popular party against government party. The antagonism developed into open conflict when Cosby started "rigging" the courts: the popular party began to use a new, highly effective weapon—an opposition newspaper.

In choosing John Peter Zenger as editor and publisher of the *New*

York Weekly Journal, the leaders of the popular party selected a man whose English was poor and whose printing was indifferent, but whose courage was undaunted. It was also a dramatic choice, because until November 5, 1773—the day the first issue of the newspaper appeared —there had been only one newspaper in New York Colony: the *New York Gazette,* founded in 1725 by Zenger's master, William Bradford. But Bradford was on the side of the colonial government and his newspaper was its "mouthpiece."

For a year each issue of the *Weekly Journal* contained scathing attacks on the governor and his government. Finally, in November 1734, unable to abide it any longer, Cosby ordered certain issues of the paper burned. The court refused the order and the sheriff's own slave had to carry out the command. A few days later Zenger was arrested on a charge of libel. Unable to raise the extraordinarily high bail, Zenger remained in prison for ten months; but the paper appeared every Monday—his wife receiving her husband's instructions "through the hole in the door of the prison."

In April 1735 Zenger was finally brought to trial. When his lawyers questioned the appointment of certain judges they were promptly disbarred—leaving Zenger practically defenseless, since the few remaining lawyers were either on the side of the government or too intimidated to take the case. Secretly, Zenger's lawyers wrote to Andrew Hamilton in Philadelphia.

Hamilton was almost eighty. In his youth he had kept a classical school in Virginia; he had gone to London to study law, returned to America and settled in Philadelphia where he had become prominent in public affairs: Attorney General of Pennsylvania, Recorder of Philadelphia, Vice Admiralty Judge, Speaker of the Assembly—these only begin to describe the range of his activities. He belonged to no political party and adhered to no religious creed. He was old, he suffered painfully from the gout; but his spirit was still independent, his mind still vigorous—and he was known as the best lawyer in North America.

His appearance in the courtroom on Nassau and Wall Streets on August 4, 1735, was a dramatic surprise in this history-making trial.

There were two important issues of freedom at stake and Hamilton's eloquent oratory won a victory for both. He denied that the complaints of a number of men who suffer under a bad administration could be considered "libeling that administration," and his victory on this point affirmed the principle that a free press the only orderly means by which the people could voice their objections to a deficient government. He persuaded the jury to decide not only whether the said articles were published—which was the limit of their appointed task, the character of these articles being determined later by the judge himself—but also to decide whether the articles were actually libelous. In asserting that judgment of the law was as much the task of the jury as of the judge, he was insisting on actual trial by jury. Fifty-six years later this principle was made law in the House of Commons.

When Hamilton left for Philadelphia the day after the trial, the ships in the harbor sounded their guns in salute. The cheers in the courtroom and the booming guns were a triumphant echo of Hamilton's words, that "without liberty life is a misery."

MAY IT PLEASE your honors, I agree with Mr. Attorney [Richard Bradley] that government is a sacred thing, but I differ very widely from him when he would insinuate that the just complaints of a number of men, who suffer under a bad administration, is libeling that administration. Had I believed that to be law, I should not have given the court the trouble of hearing anything that I could say in this cause. I own when I read the information, I had not the art to find out (without the help of Mr. Attorney's innuendoes) that the Governor was the person meant in every period of that newspaper; and I was inclined to believe that they were written by some who, from an extraordinary zeal for liberty, had misconstrued the conduct of some persons in authority into crimes; and that Mr. Attorney, out of his too great zeal for power, had exhibited this information to correct the indiscretion of my client, and at the same time to show his superiors the great concern he had, lest they should be treated with any undue freedom. But from what Mr. Attorney had just now said, to wit, that this prosecution was directed by the Governor and council, and from the extraordinary appearance of people of all conditions which I observe in court upon this occasion, I have reason to think that those in the administration have by this prosecution something more in view, and that the people believe they have a good deal more at stake than I apprehended; and therefore, as it is become my duty to be both plain and particular in this cause, I beg leave to bespeak the patience of the court.

427

I was in hopes as that terrible court where those dreadful judgments were given and that law established, which Mr. Attorney has produced for authorities to support this cause, was long ago laid aside as the most dangerous court to the liberties of the people of England that ever was known in that kingdom, that Mr. Attorney, knowing this, would not have attempted to set up a Star Chamber here, nor to make their judgments a precedent to us; for it is well known that what would have been judged treason in those days for a man to speak, I think, has since not only been practiced as lawful, but the contrary doctrine has been held to be law.

There is heresy in law as well as in religion, and both have changed very much; and we well know that it is not two centuries ago that a man would have been burned as a heretic for owning such opinions in matters of religion as are publicly written and printed at this day. They were fallible men, it seems, and we take the liberty, not only to differ from them in religious opinion, but to condemn them and their opinions too; and I must presume that in taking these freedoms in thinking and speaking about matters of faith or religion, we are in the right; for, though it is said there are very great liberties of this kind taken in New York, yet I have heard of no information preferred by Mr. Attorney for any offenses of this sort. From which I think it is pretty clear that in New York a man may make very free with his God, but he must take special care what he says of his Governor. It is agreed upon by all men that this is a reign of liberty, and while men keep within the bounds of truth, I hope they may with safety both speak and write their sentiments of the conduct of men of power; I mean of that part of their conduct only which affects the liberty or property of the people under their administration; were this to be denied, then the next step may make them slaves. For what notions can be entertained of slavery beyond that of suffering the greatest injuries and oppressions without the liberty of complaining; or if they do, to be destroyed, body and estate, for so doing?

It is said, and insisted upon by Mr. Attorney, that government is a sacred thing; that it is to be supported and reverenced; it is government that protects our persons and estates; that prevents treasons, murders, robberies, riots, and all the train of evils that overturn kingdoms and states and ruin particular persons; and if those in the administration, especially the supreme magistrates, must have all their conduct censured by private men, government cannot subsist. This is called a licentiousness not to be tolerated. It is said that it brings the rulers of the people into contempt so that their authority is not regarded, and so that in the end the laws cannot be put in execution. These, I say, and such as these, are the general topics insisted upon by men in power and their advocates. But I wish it might be considered at the same time how often it has happened that the abuse of power has been the primary cause of these evils, and that it was the injustice and oppression of these great men which has commonly brought them into contempt with the people. The craft and art of such men are great, and who that is the least acquainted with history or with law can be ignorant of the specious pretenses which have often been made use of by men in power to introduce arbitrary rule and destroy the liberties of a free people. . . .

This is the second information for libeling of a governor that I have known in America. And the first, though it may look like a romance, yet, as it is true, I will beg leave to mention it. Governor Nicholson, who happened to be offended with one of his clergy, met him one day upon the road; and, as it was usual with him (under the protection of his commission), used the poor parson with the worst of language, threatened to cut off his ears, slit his nose, and, at last, to shoot him through the head. The parson, being a reverend man, continued all this time uncovered in the heat of the sun until he found an opportunity to fly for it; and coming to a neighbor's house felt himself very ill of a fever, and immediately wrote for a doctor; and that his physician might be the better judge of his distemper, he acquainted him with the usage he had received, concluding that the Governor was certainly mad, for that no man in his senses would have behaved in that manner. The doctor, unhappily, showed the parson's letter; the Governor came to hear of it, and so an information was preferred against the poor man for saying he believed the Governor was mad; and it was laid in the information to be false, scandalous, and wicked, and written with intent to move sedition among the people and bring his Excellency into contempt. But, by an order from the late Queen Anne, there was a stop put to the prosecution, with sundry others set on foot by the same Governor against gentlemen of the greatest worth and honor in that government.

And may not I be allowed, after all this, to say that, by a little countenance, almost anything which a man writes may, with the help of that useful term of art called an innuendo, be construed to be a libel, according to Mr. Attorney's definition of it; that whether the words are spoken of a person of a public character or of a private

429

man, whether dead or living, good or bad, true or false, all make a libel; for, according to Mr. Attorney, after a man hears a writing read, or reads and repeats it, or laughs at it, they are all punishable. It is true, Mr. Attorney is so good as to allow, after the party knows it to be a libel; but he is not so kind as to take the man's word for it.

If a libel is understood in the large and unlimited sense urged by Mr. Attorney, there is scarce a writing I know that may not be called a libel, or scarce any person safe from being called to account as a libeler, for Moses, meek as he was, libeled Cain; and who is it that has not libeled the devil? For, according to Mr. Attorney, it is no justification to say one has a bad name. Eachard has libeled our good King William; Burnet has libeled, among many others, King Charles and King James; and Rapin has libeled them all. How must a man speak or write, or what must he hear, read, or sing? Or when must he laugh, so as to be secure from being taken up as a libeler? I sincerely believe that were some persons to go through the streets of New York nowadays and read a part of the Bible, if it were not known to be such, Mr. Attorney, with the help of his innuendoes, would easily turn it into a libel. As for instance: Isaiah 11:16: "The leaders of the people cause them to err, and they that are led by them are destroyed." But should Mr. Attorney go about to make this a libel, he would read it thus: "The leaders of the people" (*innuendo,* the Governor and council of New York) "cause them" (*innuendo,* the people of this province) "to err, and they" (the Governor and council, meaning) "are destroyed" (*innuendo,* are deceived into the loss of their liberty), "which is the worst kind of destruction." Or if some person should publicly repeat, in a manner not pleasing to his betters, the tenth and the eleventh verses of the fifty-sixth chapter of the same book, there Mr. Attorney would have a large field to display his skill in the artful application of his innuendoes. The words are: "His watchmen are blind, they are ignorant," etc. "Yea, they are greedy dogs, they can never have enough." But to make them a libel, there is, according to Mr. Attorney's doctrine, no more wanting but the aid of his skill in the right adapting his innuendoes. As, for instance, "His watchmen" (*innuendo,* the Governor's council and assembly) "are blind, they are ignorant" (*innuendo,* will not see the dangerous designs of his Excellency). "Yea, they" (the Governor and council, meaning) "are greedy dogs, which can never have enough" (*innuendo,* enough of riches and power). Such an instance as this seems only fit to be laughed at, but I may appeal to Mr. Attorney himself whether these are not at least equally proper to be applied to his Excellency and his ministers as some of the inferences and innuendoes in his information against my client. Then, if Mr. Attorney be at liberty to come into court and file an information in the King's name without leave, who is secure whom he is pleased to prosecute as a libeler? And as the crown law is contended for in bad times, there is no remedy for the greatest oppression of this sort, even though the party prosecuted be acquitted with honor. And give me leave to say, as great men as any in Britain have boldly asserted that the mode of prosecuting by information (when a grand jury will not find *billa vera*) is a national grievance and greatly inconsistent with that freedom which the subjects of England enjoy in most other cases. But if we are so unhappy as not to be able to ward off this stroke of power directly, let us take care not to be cheated out of our liberties by forms and appearances; let us always be sure that the charge in the information is made out clearly, even beyond a doubt; for, though matters in the information may be called form upon trial, yet they may be, and often have been found to be, matters of substance upon giving judgment.

Gentlemen, the danger is great in proportion to the mischief that may happen through our too-great credulity. A proper confidence in a court is commendable, but as the verdict (whatever it is) will be yours, you ought to refer no part of your duty to the discretion of other persons. If you should be of opinion that there is no falsehood in Mr. Zenger's papers, you will, nay (pardon me for the expression), you ought to say so; because you do not know whether others (I mean the court) may be of that opinion. It is your right to do so, and there is much depending upon your resolution, as well as upon your integrity.

The loss of liberty to a generous mind is worse than death; and yet we know there have been those in all ages who, for the sake of preferment or some imaginary honor, have freely lent a helping hand to oppress, nay, to destroy, their country. This brings to my mind that saying of the immortal Brutus, when he looked upon the creatures of Caesar, who were very great men, but by no means good men: "You Romans," said Brutus, "if yet I may call you so, consider what you are doing; remember that you are assisting Caesar to forge those very chains which one day he will make yourselves wear." This is what every man that values freedom ought to consider; he should act by judgment and not by affection or self-interest; for where those prevail, no ties of either country or kindred are regarded; as, upon the other hand, the man who loves his country prefers its liberty to all other considerations, well knowing that without liberty life is a misery. . . .

Power may justly be compared to a great river; while kept within its bounds, it is both beautiful and useful, but when it overflows its banks, it is then too impetuous to be stemmed; it bears down all before it, and brings destruction and desolation wherever it comes. If, then, this be the nature of power, let us at least do our duty, and, like wise men who value freedom, use our utmost care to support liberty, the only bulwark against lawless power, which, in all ages, has sacrificed to its wild lust and boundless ambition the blood of the best men that ever lived.

I hope to be pardoned, sir, for my zeal upon this occasion. It is an old and wise caution that "when our neighbor's house is on fire, we ought to take care of our own." For though, blessed be God, I live in a government where liberty is well understood and freely enjoyed, yet experience has shown us all (I am sure it has to me) that a bad precedent in one government is soon set up for an authority in another; and therefore I cannot but think it mine and every honest man's duty that, while we pay all due obedience to men in authority, we ought, at the same time, to be upon our guard against power wherever we apprehend that it may affect ourselves or our fellow subjects.

I am truly very unequal to such an undertaking, on many accounts. And you see I labor under the weight of many years and am borne down with great infirmities of body; yet old and weak as I am, I should think it my duty, if required, to go to the utmost part of the land, where my service could be of any use in assisting to quench the flame of prosecutions upon informations, set on foot by the government to deprive a people of the right of remonstrating, and complaining too, of the arbitrary attempts of men in power. Men who injure and oppress the people under their administration provoke them to cry out and complain, and then make that very complaint the foundation for new oppressions and prosecutions. I wish I could say there were no instances of this kind. But, to conclude, the question before the court, and you, gentlemen of the jury, is not of small nor private concern; it is not the cause of a poor printer, nor of New York alone, which you are now trying. No! It may, in its consequence, affect every free man that lives under a British government on the main continent of America. It is the best cause; it is the cause of liberty; and I make no doubt but your upright conduct, this day, will not only entitle you to the love and esteem of your fellow citizen, but every man who prefers freedom to a life of slavery will bless and honor you as men who have baffled the attempt of tyranny, and, by an impartial and uncorrupt verdict, have laid a noble foundation for securing to ourselves, our posterity, and our neighbors that to which nature and the laws of our country have given us a right—the liberty of both exposing and opposing arbitrary power (in these parts of the world at least) by speaking and writing truth.

Pliny the Younger

A LETTER

DESCRIBING THE

ERUPTION OF

MOUNT VESUVIUS

HOME COURSE APPRECIATION

N OTHING WAS TO BE HEARD but the shrieks of women, the
screams of children, and the cries of men. . . ."
Across nearly 2,000 years these cries may still be heard
by the imaginative visitor to Pompeii—just as they are described in the
words of Gaius Plinius Caecilius Secundus, who survived one of the
worst disasters in history. Pliny the Younger, as we call him today, was
only eighteen in A.D. 79 when volcanic Mount Vesuvius erupted and
buried Pompeii and Herculaneum, two of the most beautiful cities in
the Roman Empire.

Mount Vesuvius, about six miles southeast of Naples on the eastern
shore of the Bay of Naples, was a richly cultivated mountain covered
with very fertile vineyards and surrounded by cities and towns.
Ancient historians describe the volcano as burning, but their reports
of its luxurious vegetation give us cause to believe that the volcano
never erupted. Pompeii, a flourishing port and popular resort, was on
the southeastern side of the mountain; Herculaneum, also a city of fine
villas, was at its western base.

In A.D. 63, Pompeii and the surrounding neighborhood were shattered by an earthquake, and for the next sixteen years successive

"Nothing was to be heard but the shrieks of women,
   the screams of children, and the cries of men. . . . "

disturbances caused much damage to the area. On August 24, in the year 79, this series of earthquakes culminated in a violent explosion. Pompeii was buried under fiery cinders, smoking stones, and burning ashes; at Herculaneum these falling substances mixed with water and hardened into porous rock which covered the city to an average depth of eighteen to twenty feet.

Years later, Pliny the Younger wrote his graphic accounts of the catastrophe in two letters to his good friend Tacitus, the Roman historian. Tacitus, who was collecting data for his famous *Annals,* had written to Pliny asking for details of his uncle's death. This uncle, known to us as Pliny the Elder, was the celebrated author of the *Natural History,* an encyclopedia of natural science. Pliny the Younger was his adopted son.

Pliny the Younger, a cultivated Roman lawyer and writer, complied with his friend's request. His perfect prose subtly reconstructs the horror of the disaster, from his mother's observation of the dark cloud that "shot up to a great height in the form of a very tall trunk" to his uncle's scientific interest which quickly led him to heroic action and finally death by suffocation from the poisonous fumes.

This reply brought forth a second request from Tacitus: that Pliny describe the dangers he himself had experienced during the eruption.

If the first letter is an ideal report by a detached observer, the second is a model account by an eye witness. It has all the dramatic elements that accompany disasters: the casual coincidences that mean the difference between life and death, the agitated friend who arrives with solicitude and departs with self-concern, the mother who urges her son to flee and leave her behind, and the son who endangers himself by leading his aged mother to safety. There are panic-stricken crowds caught in the midst of real terrors: rocking earth, bursting flames, rolling smoke, and showers of dust and ashes.

Religious leaders felt that these cities were chosen for destruction because they had been centers of luxury and vice. The ancient philosophers had predicted that the world would be destroyed by fire and all things would fall back into original chaos. Pliny himself believed that the end had come, and indeed in one sense, it had, for untold numbers of people perished that night. Herculaneum remained buried until 1709 and Pompeii until 1748.

Slowly over the years, the cities have been excavated. A magnificent library, precious marble statues, luxurious villas, paintings still perfect in color have been reclaimed from the layers of ashes and lava that preserved them. Even the dice that were being thrown and the bread that was being baked on that fatal day have been brought to light. And so, a disaster that wreaked death and destruction in bygone centuries has become the source of much of our knowledge of Roman life and art.

THE LETTER which, in compliance with your request, I wrote to you, concerning the death of my uncle,* has raised, it seems, your curiosity to know what terrors and dangers attended me while I continued at Misenum †; for there, I think, the account in my former [letter] broke off. "Though my shock'd soul recoils, my tongue shall tell."

My uncle having left us, I continued the employment which prevented my going with him, till it was time to bathe; after which I went to supper, and then fell into a short and unquiet sleep. There had been, during many days before, some shocks of an earthquake, which the less alarmed us as they are frequent in Campania. They were so particularly violent that night that they not only shook everything about us, but seemed, indeed, to threaten total destruction. My mother flew to my chamber, where she found me rising in order to awaken her. We went out into a small court belonging to the house, which separated the sea from the buildings.

As I was at that time but eighteen years of age, I know not whether I should call my behavior, in this perilous conjuncture, courage or rashness. I took up Livy, and amused myself with turning over that author, and even making extracts from him, as if I had been perfectly at my ease. While we were in this situation, a friend of my uncle's, who was just come from Spain to pay him a visit, joined us,

* Pliny the Elder.
† Miseno, northwest of the Bay of Naples.

437

and observing me sitting by my mother with a book in my hand, reproved her patience, and my security. Nevertheless, I still went on with my author. It was now morning, but the light was exceedingly faint and languid. The buildings all around us tottered. Though we stood upon open ground, the place was narrow and confined and there was no remaining without imminent danger. We, therefore, resolved to leave the town.

The people followed us in the utmost consternation, and—as to a mind distracted with terror, every suggestion seems more prudent than its own—pressed in great crowds about us in our way out. Being advanced at a convenient distance from the houses, we stood still, in the midst of a most hazardous and tremendous scene. The chariots, which we had ordered to be drawn out, were so agitated backward and forward, though upon the most level ground, that we could not keep them steady, even by supporting them with large stones. The sea seemed to roll back upon itself, and to be driven from its banks by the convulsive motion of the earth. It is certain, at least, the shore was considerably enlarged, and several sea-animals were left upon it. On the other side a black and dreadful cloud bursting with an igneous serpentine vapor darted out a long train of fire, resembling flashes of lightning, but much larger. Upon this, our Spanish friend, whom I mentioned above, addressed himself to my mother and me, with great warmth and earnestness: "If," said he, "your brother and your uncle, are safe, your uncle certainly wishes you may be so too; but if he perished, it was his desire, no doubt, that you might both survive him. Why, therefore, do you delay your escape a moment?" We could never think of our own safety, we replied, while we were uncertain of his; upon which our friend left us, and withdrew from the danger with the utmost precipitation.

Soon afterwards, the cloud seemed to descend, and cover the whole ocean; as, indeed, it entirely hid the island of Caprea *, and the promontory of Misenum. My mother conjured me to make my escape, at any rate, which, as I was young, I might easily effect. As for herself, she said her age and corpulence rendered all attempts of that sort impossible; however, she would willingly meet death, if she could have the satisfaction of seeing that she was not the occasion of mine. But I absolutely refused to leave her and taking her by the hand, I led her on. She complied with great reluctance, and not without many reproaches to herself for being the occasion of retarding my flight.

* Capri.

438

LETTER DESCRIBING ERUPTION OF MOUNT VESUVIUS

The ashes now began to fall upon us, though in no great quantity. I turned my head and observed behind us a thick smoke, which came rolling after us like a torrent. I proposed, while we had yet any light, to turn out of the high road, lest she should be pressed to death in the dark, by the crowd that followed us.

We had scarcely stepped out of the path, when darkness overspread us, not like that of a cloudy night or when there is no moon, but of a room when it is shut up and all the lights extinct. Nothing, then, was to be heard but the shrieks of women, the screams of children, and the cries of men. Some were calling for their children, others for their parents, others for their husbands. They could only distinguish each other by their voices. One lamented his own fate, another that of his family; some wished to die, from the very fear of dying; some lifted their hands to the gods; but the greater part imagined that the last and eternal night was come, which was to destroy both the gods and the world together. Among these there were some who augmented the real terrors by imaginary ones, and made the frightened multitude falsely believe that Misenum was actually in flames. At length, a glimmering light appeared, which we imagined to be rather the forerunner of an approaching burst of flames (as in fact it was) than the return of day; however, the fire fell at a distance from us. Then again we were immersed in thick darkness, and a heavy shower of ashes rained upon us, which we were obliged every now and then to shake off, otherwise we should have been overwhelmed and buried in the heap.

I might boast that during all this scene of horror, not a sigh, or expression of fear escaped from me, had not my support been founded on that miserable, though strong consolation, that all mankind were involved in the same calamity. And I imagined I was perishing with the world itself. At last, this terrible darkness was dissipated by degrees, like a cloud or smoke. The real day returned and even the sun appeared, though very faintly, and as when an eclipse is coming on. Every object that presented itself to our eyes, which were extremely weakened, seemed changed, being covered with white ashes, as with a deep snow. We returned to Misenum, where we refreshed ourselves as well as we could, and passed an anxious night between hope and fear though, indeed, with a much larger share of the latter, for the earth still continued to shake. Several enthusiastic persons ran wildly among the people, throwing out terrifying predictions, and making a kind of frantic sport of their own and their friends' wretched situation. However, my mother and I, notwithstanding the danger we had passed, and that which still threatened us, had no intention of leaving Misenum till we should receive some account of my uncle.

And now, you will read this narrative without any view of inserting it in your history, of which it is by no means worthy; and, indeed, you must impute it to your own request, if it should appear not to deserve even the trouble of a letter. Farewell.

THE

DIVINE

COMEDY

by *Dante Alighieri*

Translated Into Verse By H. F. Cary

A CONDENSATION

NOTE: *The translator's "Argument" or summary of each canto of* The Inferno *is given complete, even where the canto has been condensed or omitted. The editor's explanatory notes appear italicized and in brackets throughout the text.*

HOME COURSE APPRECIATION

FROM TORMENTED BEGINNINGS to everlasting joy, from the realization of error to a moment of supreme vision—this is the range of the *Divine Comedy*.

Few poets have ever had the courage to guide a reader through the mysterious afterlife: in the medieval imagination, down the circles of Hell, up the side of Mount Purgatory, through the spheres of Paradise. Few poets have ever dared to pronounce an all-inclusive moral judgment upon the world, to consign thousands of souls to their eternal destinies. And of that handful of poets who have explored their worlds so exhaustively, none is a surer, firmer guide than Dante.

Yet, for all its cosmic sweep and limitless references, the poet's creation, like most great works of art, is a work of basic simplicity and almost perfect form. It is the story of a journey, a questing, and is not unlike the ancient epics of Virgil and Homer in this respect; but on how many levels of meaning we can interpret it!

Dante, despite whatever other pretensions he had, did not call his poem an epic; he called it simply *The Comedy*. To the modern ear, it may seem strange that a poem about sin and salvation should bear such a title, but the reason for this choice has become obscured. In medieval times, a comedy was a work written in the language of common speech, in this case Italian, as opposed to a work written in the more literary "tragic" Latin. Dante's choice also follows the classic definition that applied the term "comedy" to any work that ended happily. Certainly there is no happier ending to any work than the ultimate vision of God in Dante's closing canto. Only in later times was the work called *Divine,* because it spoke of the ways of God and spoke of them so beautifully.

THE STORY OF THE POEM

The journey begins in a straightforward way. On the evening before Good Friday in the year 1300, when the poet is thirty-five years old, he awakens in a gloomy wood. He sees a mountain which he decides to climb, but his course is blocked by three beasts. Discouraged, almost in despair, he is about to give up when the figure of Virgil, the great Latin poet, appears. The reader may ask himself why Virgil should appear as guide—aside from the fact that he had already written of Aeneas' visit to the Underworld in the *Aeneid;* he may also wonder what the significance of the gloomy wood and the three beasts is; but if he lets Virgil and the other characters speak and if he lets Dante describe the places visited, he will be carried along by the thread of the story and he will grasp Dante's moral judgments without any trouble.

The way to approach Dante, then, is simply to let him speak for himself. If we are told that Virgil signifies "Human Reason," the over-all structure of the poem may have deeper meaning. Even without this explanation, the character of the ancient poet, the loving teacher who can never ascend to Heaven, will impress itself on the reader's mind.

The *Divine Comedy* appeals to us because the dramatic power of the poem is so intense; sinners and saints speak with equal clarity and force. The reader always knows where he stands; he is never confused about the virtue of the characters he meets, because he sees them in the midst of their final rewards, carrying on in death what they have only begun in life.

THE PLACES OF THE POEM

THIS IS, AFTER ALL, A POEM about the "other world"; yet the genius of it lies in the fact that it constantly relates to our world. In Hell, the labors of the damned are simply the extensions of the sins they committed on earth; there is a whole society based on the *lack* of society; and the horror of their damnation lies in the realization that these people who lived in error on earth must live so even in Hell, with no mingling among the good, far from God, with no word of Christ or Mary on their lips. Hell is a place where time is measured by the distant phases of the moon; it is a place where any thought of our world brings only anguish.

Things change as the poets move from the frozen pit of Hell (where no life can exist) and begin climbing the cool verdant Mount Purgatory. Here there is very much a feeling of society; even the labors, so disconnected and self-destroying in Hell, are co-ordinated. In Purgatory there is a strong sense of time because every day (there is sun to measure the day) the penitents move closer to Heaven. Here there is very much an awareness of our world, because the souls in Purgatory are not far removed from life, and the prayers of the living help them on their journeys upward toward perfection. Purgatory is a place where feelings are mixed: the souls are tormented by their past sins, but are uplifted by their hopes of eventual salvation. At the top of the mount is the Earthly Paradise—a picture of what life could have been on earth; this dream world is tragic in terms of the present, yet reassuring in terms of the future.

In Paradise, of course, we find ultimate perfection; here is a perfect society, moving in the harmony of the dance or forming the flawless pattern of the rose. In Paradise, there is interest in the living world; here Beatrice, Dante's final guide and inspiration for his redemption, gives him his final teaching, ending the journey that she watched over. Beatrice guides him toward God, revealed in an ineffable vision of light.

WHAT DOES THE POEM MEAN?

ANY READER WHO FOLLOWS THE THREAD of the *Divine Comedy* will find some meaning in a literal interpretation; yet if he wishes, he may uncover a fuller meaning. No one has ever been able to say exactly what the poem means, because it is rich in meanings. Yet certain conclusions can be drawn.

We may believe that the poem affirms—or better, dramatizes—Christian beliefs in the redemption of the soul, in the freedom of man's will to choose between damnation and salvation, and the conviction that his choice will endure for eternity. If we think of Dante as a living soul with the power to choose and the people he meets as those who have already chosen their fates, then the poem becames a drama, a living enactment of the wonderful promise of revelation. When the poem ends, Dante would have us find that the journey we have taken in fiction is one we are taking in actual life; and the choice given to Dante (either to continue wandering in the wood or to begin the hard ascent) must also be ours. As we follow Dante, the moving center of the poem, we likewise feel ourselves members of two worlds.

"Within these ardors are the spirits,
each swathed in consuming fire."

What does it mean when the poem is called a great Christian allegory, when Beatrice is called Revelation and Virgil Human Reason? Although we can think of them primarily as characters, it can deepen our insight if we see that certain characters stand for certain things. Simple allegory is a way of using things as characters; thus in medieval legends, Everyman must ward off the attacks of Sir Sin and Baron Pride to win the hand of Lady Virtue.

Even the most casual reader, however, can see that Dante does not write on such a bald allegorical level. Indeed, if his characters reflect certain philosophical ideas, these ideas are always embodied in the people talking. Allegorical figures are often one-sided; Baron Pride can only act proud, he can never act humble. Yet Paolo and Francesca in the Hell circle of Lust are more than Carnal Sinners; in fact, so heartbreaking is their fate that Dante himself swoons when he hears the tale of it. Any allegorical readings then, must not overlook the dramatic structure of the poem; for Dante's characters are never one-sided; even the saved in Purgatory, such as Sapia of Siena, still show traces of those errors that led to their final destinies.

Yet if we look at the symbols in the allegory in another way, they can prove illuminating. If we think of Virgil as a symbol of Human Reason, it helps us understand two things. First, we assume that since he is guiding Dante (a soul striving toward light), then Reason must be a primary means toward salvation. The Church has always considered man a rational being, not a being governed by chance or the subconscious mind or mere surroundings. Reason is essential for moral choice; because we can tell the difference between good and evil, reason points the way. Then too, we understand why Virgil cannot enter Paradise; he was a pagan and never was baptized. Virgil lived a just life, as had the other Greeks and Romans now in Limbo, but he could never know the joy of salvation. Therefore he must let others guide Dante through Purgatory to Paradise. Man by his own wisdom can go only so far; then Divine Grace and Revelation must show the way.

Dante states his subject in a letter to his good friend, Can Grande: "Man by his good or evil merits in exercising his free choice becomes liable to rewarding or punishing justice."

DANTE'S CHARACTERS

ONCE WE HAVE ACCEPTED DANTE'S CHARACTERS as symbols, we are freed from certain burdens: we do not need to know their exact histories, we do not need to worry about the justness of their rewards, and especially, we cannot condemn Dante for vanity in assigning friends to Heaven and enemies to Hell. In other words, despite the fact that his characters are often real people, we can treat them largely as fictional characters. Sometimes, of course, a bit of historical background is needed. Although Count Ugolino's plight was known to many Italians in Dante's fourteenth century audience, the modern reader cannot tell from his dramatic speech why he was placed in prison and why, if he suffered so unjustly at the hands of the Pisans, he has ended his fate in Hell. These points can be explained by a footnote.

The dramatic qualities of Dante's characters have already been mentioned, but a word may be added about their variety: morally, of course, they range from saint to sinner; geographically, from Dante's native city of Florence to the remoter parts of the known world; historically, from the age of myth to the year of the vision, 1300, and in a few cases, after that date.

COMEDY AND TRAGEDY

Some of Dante's characters, such as Ciacco the Glutton, are comic; some of the episodes, such as the Battle of the Demons, approach burlesque. Other stories are tragic, such as the fruitless generosity of Farinata degli Uberti or the doom of Guido da Montefeltro. Dante's judgments of his characters from the individual viewpoint and his judgments from the viewpoint of a profound moralist may seem ironic: the "dear and kind" Brunetto Latini, his teacher, is encountered in the depths of Hell; Emperor Constantine, whose Donation was considered by Dante the cause of much of the world's corruption, is in Paradise.

No matter how sympathetic Dante makes his characters, morality is always master. To him, all virtues and vices proceed from some kind of love. A love for mankind, as well as a love for Beatrice and God, may be considered his reason for writing about his journey. But to understand his judgments, we need, in addition to our understanding of Christian morality, some knowledge of the times in which he lived.

THE WORLD OF DANTE

AT THE BEGINNING OF THE THIRTEENTH CENTURY, the nation we now know as Italy did not exist. The Italy of that time was a group of city-republics and monarchies held together by a common religious allegiance to Rome and by the tradition of the Holy Roman

"Before my sight appeared with open wings,
The beauteous image, in fruition sweet,
Gladdening the thronged spirits."

Empire. Whatever unification did exist was tenuous, for the republics—Florence or Venice or Milan—constantly feuded and made alliances for private interests. Besides this constant unrest, the Italian nobility within the states was always at war with itself, split into numerous factions and too powerful to be controlled by laws.

The greatest conflict of Dante's time was the struggle between two parties, the Guelphs and the Ghibellines. The Ghibellines opposed the Pope and supported the German Emperor, who they hoped would re-establish the Roman Empire. The Guelphs, a more liberal party, supported constitutional government by the various states under the leadership of the Pope. The dividing issues were not clear-cut, for the Guelphs and the Ghibellines allied and fought as often as the various nobles and the republics. And so, battles between Empire and Papacy, Guelph and Ghibelline, raged for years; the contest was finally decided for Dante's native city when the Florentine Guelphs won the Battle of Benevento in 1266, a year after the poet's birth near the end of May, 1265.

DANTE'S YOUTH

Dante was born to a Guelph family which, though of good blood, was not among the nobility. His mother died before he was six; his father when he was twelve. His parents seem to have associated with the upper classes, for by the time Dante was twelve, his father had arranged the boy's future marriage to Gemma, a daughter of the aristocratic Donati clan.

His education was excellent, including probably a year of study at the University of Bologna, where he associated with two fellow poets, Guido Guinicelli and Guido Cavalcanti. Dante meets the latter's father, Cavalcante Cavalcanti, and informs him of Guido's death in a very moving scene in the *Inferno*. We have already discussed his meeting with Brunetto Latini, another friend and teacher.

Dante wrote poetry at an early age, conducted the business of his family while still in his teens, and took part in military campaigns. During the last decade of the thirteenth century he studied Provençal and Latin and read extensively in philosophy, theology, science, and literature.

DANTE THE POLITICIAN

UNDER THE CONSTITUTION ESTABLISHED by the Guelphs, it was necessary to be a member of one of the guilds to qualify for higher government posts. Dante joined the Guild of Physicians and

Apothecaries, whose members included the booksellers. He became ambassador for a special mission, and was eventually elected to the Priorate, the highest governing body of Florence. His future seemed bright, but the "lamb," as he describes himself in the *Comedy,* was not safe among the "wolves," the Florentines.

Dante entered his priorate during one of the worst political schisms in Florence. The Guelphs split into two parties, the Blacks and the Whites; Dante's sympathies were divided: he was a White, but his wife's family was foremost among the Blacks. And so, Dante found himself exiling his own relatives and even his friend Guido Cavalcanti, who died of malaria in banishment. Toward the end of 1301, Dante and others went to Pope Boniface VII to try to negotiate a peace. While he was discoursing with Boniface, whose policies he condemns in the *Comedy,* the Blacks gained control of the city.

Charged with corruption and conspiracy against Florence, Dante was summoned to stand trial, but he refused to pay the fine because any payment would have been an admission of guilt. As a result, his property was confiscated and he was threatened with death by fire if he was ever found again on Florentine ground.

Thus in 1302 began one of the most famous exiles in history. For the remaining twenty years of his life, Dante wandered; we hear of him in Bologna, Verona, Padua, and finally in Ravenna. During these last years of exile, from 1307 to 1321, Dante wrote his *Comedy,* putting into it many of the characters and events of Florentine politics and Italian history.

Once during the exile, in 1309, when Emperor Henry VII marched on King Robert of Sicily, Dante felt great hope for the return of the modern Roman Empire, united with the Church, but Henry died and the dream of peace and unity faded. Dante died in Ravenna on September 14, 1321; Ravenna and his native Florence have battled for his bones, but his adopted city still claims her treasure in the guarded Tomb of Dante.

BEATRICE

TIME MAY HAVE TURNED DANTE'S LOVE for Florence to hatred and then pity, but nothing could change the quality and strength of his love for Beatrice. Beatrice is a recurring note through Dante's life and *Comedy.*

He met her first when he was nine and she was eight. From the moment he first looked at her, his love for her governed his soul. She seemed to him a manifestation on earth of heavenly glory, a divine spirit in an earthly body. They did not speak again for ten years, but her salutation then raised him to bliss. He never mentions her marriage, but when her husband died, he grieved with her; when she died a year later, at the age of twenty-four, it was as if all light had gone out of the world.

In his autobiographical work called *The New Life,* written when he was still in his twenties, Dante tries to explain his love for her. Using both poetry and prose, he describes that moment of revelation which filled his being with love for the whole world. Toward the end of the book, he begins to transform Beatrice into a symbol of heavenly love, and he ends with a wonderful vision: "wherein I saw things which determined me that I would say nothing further of this most blessed one, until such time as I could discourse more worthily concerning her. . . . It is my hope that I shall yet write concerning her what hath not before been written of any woman."

THE FRAMEWORK OF THE "DIVINE COMEDY"

Dante constructed his epic on the mystical number three. In the original Italian, the verses are arranged in units of three lines, with an intricate triple rhyme scheme. In the broad structure, the work is composed of three books—*Inferno, Purgatory,* and *Paradise.* There are thirty-three cantos in *Paradise* and *Purgatory;* the *Inferno* has thirty-three plus an introductory canto, making a total of one hundred for the entire poem.

Each part of the Trinity is expressed in one of the books: the Power of the Father in the *Inferno;* the Wisdom of the Son in the *Purgatory;* and the Love of the Holy Spirit in the *Paradise.* In the opening cantos of the *Inferno,* the recurrence of the number three can be seen in the appearance of the three beasts that block the poet's path, the three ladies who attend him in Heaven, and the three guides who will show him the way.

THE RICHNESS OF THE POEM

FOR ALL ITS REFERENCES to religion, philosophy, politics, and history, the *Divine Comedy* is still essentially a work of vivid imagination. Attentive reading yields many striking images. A fiend drops to the ground and Dante gives us an image from the sea:

> *As sails, full spread and bellying with the wind,*
> *Drop suddenly collapsed, if the mast split. . . .*

Dante, growing faint, at one point receives new vigor:

> As florets, by frosty air of night
> Bent down and closed, when day has blanched
>   their leaves,
> Rise all unfolded on their spiry stems. . . .

Dante's images add more than just color to the poem. They are means by which our world of the living is compared with the world of afterlife. In Hell, the images are painful; a sinner running over a flaming plain is likened to an athlete darting over the green to win a prize; the contrast of flaming fire and dew-glistening grass, the contrast of winning a prize and losing one's soul, are poignantly brought home. By these figures of speech, not by description alone, we learn what Hell is like.

Dante has sometimes been criticized for a lack of taste and a delight in gory detail; yet we must not confuse Dante, the dramatic character journeying in Hell, with Dante, the poet who is writing the work and has already seen his vision. The similes make us aware of this larger, more mature personality who can look back with some humor at how he swooned, faltered, and fainted at the start of his travels.

In Purgatory and Paradise, the figures of speech are more subdued and more complex: the rose or the reflection of light in water or on glass are used to give us notions of things incomprehensible by description alone. Finally, in the ultimate vision, even the clarity which is so characteristic of Dante fails him. He cannot tell us what he saw at the end because no words can describe the power of God revealed. The vision itself vanishes from him, but the hope and inspiration remain; and so, he returns to Earth to share this hope with us. If we ourselves have not seen the vision, we at least have Dante to assure us that it exists; and Dante will show the way.

PART ONE—The Inferno

CANTO I

The writer, having lost his way in a gloomy forest, and being hindered by certain wild beasts from ascending a mountain, is met by Virgil, who promises to show him the punishments of Hell, and afterwards of Purgatory; and that he shall then be conducted by Beatrice into Paradise. He follows the Roman poet.

IN THE midway of this our mortal life,
   I found me in a gloomy wood, astray *
Gone from the path direct: and e'en to tell,
It were no easy task, how savage wild
That forest, how robust and rough its growth,
Which to remember only, my dismay
Renews, in bitterness not far from death.
Yet, to discourse of what there good befell,
All else will I relate discovered there.
  How first I entered it I scarce can say,
Such sleepy dullness in that instant weighed
My senses down, when the true path I left;

* The imagined time is Good Friday, 1300, when Dante was 35, midway to the Psalmist's "threescore years and ten." He has gone "astray" in the wood of sin.

But when a mountain's foot I reached, where closed
The valley that had pierced my heart with dread,
I looked aloft, and saw his shoulders broad
Already vested with that planet's beam,
Who leads all wanderers safe through every way.*
    Then was a little respite to the fear,
That in my heart's recesses deep had lain
All of that night, so pitifully past:
And as a man, with difficult short breath,
Forspent with toiling, 'scaped from sea to shore,
Turns to the perilous wide waste, and stands
At gaze; e'en so my spirit, that yet failed,
Struggling with terror, turned to view the straits
That none hath past and lived. My weary frame
After short pause recomforted, again
I journeyed on over that lonely steep,
The hinder foot still firmer. Scarce the ascent
Began, when, lo! a panther, nimble, light,
And covered with a speckled skin, appeared; †
Nor, when it saw me, vanished; rather strove
To check my onward going; that oft-times,
With purpose to retrace my steps, I turned.
    The hour was morning's prime, and on his way
Aloft the sun ascended with those stars
That with him rose when Love Divine first moved
Those its fair works: so that with joyous hope
All things conspired to fill me, the gay skin
Of that swift animal, the matin dawn,
And the sweet season. Soon that joy was chased,
And by new dread succeeded, when in view
A lion came, 'gainst me as it appeared,
With his head held aloft and hunger-mad,
That e'en the air was fear-struck. A she-wolf
Was at his heels, who in her leanness seem'd
Full of all wants, and many a land hath made
Disconsolate ere now. She with such fear

---

* The mountain is the mountain of the Lord, the "holy hill" of the Psalms.
The "planet's beam" is that of the sun, symbolic of Divine Light.
† A traditional interpretation makes the panther (or leopard), the lion, and the
she-wolf, stand for Lust, Pride and Avarice.

O'erwhelmed me, at the sight of her appalled,
That of the height all hope I lost. As one,
Who, with his gain elated, sees the time
When all unwares is gone, he inwardly
Mourns with heart-griping anguish; such was I,
Haunted by that fell beast, never at peace,
Who coming o'er against me, by degrees
Impelled me where the sun in silence rests.

While to the lower space with backward step
I fell, my ken discerned the form of one
Whose voice seemed faint through long disuse of speech.
When him in that great desert I espied,
"Have mercy on me," I cried out aloud,
"Spirit! or living man! whate'er thou be."
He answered: "Now not man, man once I was,
And born of Lombard parents, Mantuans both
By country, when the power of Julius yet
Was scarcely firm. At Rome my life was passed,
Beneath the mild Augustus, in the time
Of fabled deities and false. A bard
I was, and made Anchises' upright son
The subject of my song, who came from Troy,
When the flames preyed on Ilium's haughty towers.
But thou, say wherefore to such perils past
Returnest thou? wherefore not this pleasant mount
Ascendest, cause and source of all delight?"
"And art thou then that Virgil, that well-spring,
From which such copious floods of eloquence
Have issued?" I with front abashed replied.
"Glory and light of all the tuneful train!
May it avail me, that I long with zeal
Have sought thy volume, and with love immense
Have conned it o'er. My master thou, and guide!
Thou he from whom alone I have derived
That style, which for its beauty into fame
Exalts me. See the beast, from whom I fled.
O save me from her, thou illustrious sage!
For every vein and pulse throughout my frame
She hath made tremble." He, soon as he saw
That I was weeping, answered, "Thou must needs

445

Another way pursue, if thou wouldst 'scape
From out that savage wilderness. This beast,
At whom thou criest, her way will suffer none
To pass, and no less hindrance makes than death:
So bad and so accursed in her kind,
That never sated is her ravenous will,
Still after food more craving than before.
To many an animal in wedlock vile
She fastens, and shall yet to many more,
Until that Greyhound * come, who shall destroy
Her with sharp pain. He will not life support
By earth nor its base metals, but by love,
Wisdom, and virtue; and his land shall be
The land 'twixt either Feltro. In his might
Shall safety to Italia's plains arise,
For whose fair realm, Camilla, virgin pure,
Nisus, Euryalus, and Turnus fell.
He, with incessant chase, through every town
Shall worry, until he to Hell at length
Restore her, thence by envy first let loose.
I, for thy profit pondering, now devise
That thou mayst follow me; and I, thy guide,
Will lead thee hence through an eternal space,
Where thou shalt hear despairing shrieks, and see
Spirits of old tormented, who invoke
A second death; and those next view, who dwell
Content in fire, for that they hope to come,
Whene'er the time may be, among the blest,
Into whose regions if thou then desire
To ascend, a spirit worthier than I
Must lead thee, in whose charge, when I depart,
Thou shalt be left: for that Almighty King,
Who reigns above, a rebel to His law
Adjudges me; and therefore hath decreed
That, to His city, none through me should come.
He in all parts hath sway; there rules, there holds
His citadel and throne. O happy those,
Whom there He chooses!" I to him in few:

* A mythical savior.

446

"Bard! by that God, whom thou didst not adore,
I do beseech thee (that this ill and worse
I may escape) to lead me where thou said'st,
That I Saint Peter's gate may view, and those
Who, as thou tell'st, are in such dismal plight."
   Onward he moved, I close his steps pursued.

CANTO II

After the invocation, which poets are used to prefix to their works, he
shows, that, on a consideration of his own strength, he doubted whether it
sufficed for the journey proposed to him, but that, being comforted by
Virgil, he at last took courage, and followed him as his guide and master.

NOW WAS THE DAY departing, and the air,
   Imbrowned with shadows, from their toils released
All animals on earth; and I alone
Prepared myself the conflict to sustain,
Both of sad pity, and that perilous road,
Which my unerring memory shall retrace.
   O Muses! O high genius! now vouchsafe
Your aid. O mind! that all I saw hast kept
Safe in a written record, here thy worth
And eminent endowments come to proof.
   I thus began: "Bard! thou who art my guide,
Consider well, if virtue be in me
Sufficient, ere to this high enterprise
Thou trust me. Thou hast told that Father Aeneas,
Yet clothed in corruptible flesh, among
The immortal tribes had entrance, and was there
Sensibly present. Yet if Heaven's great Lord,
Almighty foe to ill, such favor showed
In contemplation of the high effect,
Both what and who from him should issue forth,
It seems in reason's judgment well deserved;
Sith he of Rome and of Rome's empire wide,
In Heaven's empyreal height was chosen sire:

Both which, if truth be spoken, were ordained
And stablished for the holy place, where sits
Who to great Peter's sacred chair succeeds.
He from this journey, in thy song renowned,
Learned things, that to his victory gave rise
And to the papal robe. In after-times
The Chosen Vessel * also traveled there,
To bring us back assurance in that faith
Which is the entrance to salvation's way.
But I, why should I there presume? or who
Permits it? not Æneas I, nor Paul.
Myself I deem not worthy, and none else
Will deem me. I, if on this voyage then
I venture, fear it will in folly end.
Thou, who art wise, better my meaning knowest,
Than I can speak." As one, who unresolves
What he hath late resolved, and with new thoughts
Changes his purpose, from his first intent
Removed; e'en such was I on that dun coast,
Wasting in thought my enterprise, at first
So eagerly embraced. "If right thy words
I scan," replied that shade magnanimous,
"Thy soul is by vile fear assailed, which oft
So overcasts a man, that he recoils
From noblest resolution, like a beast
At some false semblance in the twilight gloom.
That from this terror thou mayst free thyself,
I will instruct thee why I came, and what
I heard in that same instant, when for thee
Grief touched me first. I was among the tribe
Who rest suspended, when a dame, so blest
And lovely I besought her to command,
Called me; her eyes were brighter than the star
Of day; and she, with gentle voice and soft,
Angelically tuned, her speech addressed:
'O courteous shade of Mantua! thou whose fame
'Yet lives, and shall live long as nature lasts!
'A friend of mine, and not the friend of fortune,

* According to a once well-known medieval legend, the "Chosen Vessel," St. Paul, visited Hell.

448

'On the wide desert in his road has met
'Hindrance so great, that he through fear has turned.
'Now much I dread lest he past help have strayed,
'And I be risen too late for his relief,
'From what in heaven of him I heard. Speed now,
'And by thy eloquent persuasive tongue,
'And by all means for his deliverance meet,
'Assist him. So to me will comfort spring.
'I, who now bid thee on this errand forth,
'Am Beatrice; from a place I come
'Revisited with joy. Love brought me thence,
'Who prompts my speech. When in my Master's sight
'I stand, thy praise to him I oft will tell.'

"She then was silent, and I thus began:
'O Lady! by whose influence alone
'Mankind excels whatever is contained
'Within that heaven which hath the smallest orb,
'So thy command delights me, that to obey,
'If it were done already, would seem late.
'No need hast thou farther to speak thy will:
'Yet tell the reason, why thou art not loath
'To leave that ample space, where to return
'Thou burnest, for this center here beneath.'

"She then: 'Since thou so deeply wouldst inquire,
'I will instruct thee briefly why no dread
'Hinders my entrance here. Those things alone
'Are to be feared whence evil may proceed;
'None else, for none are terrible beside.
'I am so framed by God, thanks to his grace!
'That any sufferance of your misery
'Touches me not, nor flame of that fierce fire
'Assails me. In high Heaven a blessed Dame *
'Resides, who mourns with such effectual grief
'That hindrance, which I send thee to remove,
'That God's stern judgment to her will inclines.
'To Lucia calling, her she thus bespake: †
"Now doth thy faithful servant need thy aid,
"And I commend him to thee." At her word

* The Blessed Virgin Mary.
† St. Lucia stands for Illuminating Grace.

'Sped Lucia, of all cruelty the foe,
'And coming to the place, where I abode
'Seated with Rachel, her of ancient days,
'She thus addressed me: "Thou true praise of God!
"Beatrice! why is not thy succor lent
"To him, who so much loved thee, as to leave
"For thy sake all the multitude admires?
"Dost thou not hear how pitiful his wail,
"Nor mark the death, which in the torrent flood,
"Swoln mightier than a sea, him struggling holds?"
'Ne'er among men did any with such speed
'Haste to their profit, flee from their annoy,
'As, when these words were spoken, I came here,
'Down from my blessed seat, trusting the force
'Of thy pure eloquence, which thee, and all
'Who well have marked it, into honor brings.'
    "When she had ended, her bright beaming eyes
Tearful she turned aside; whereat I felt
Redoubled zeal to serve thee. As she willed,
Thus am I come: I saved thee from the beast,
Who thy near way across the goodly mount
Prevented. What is this comes o'er thee then?
Why, why dost thou hang back? why in thy breast
Harbor vile fear? why hast not courage there,
And noble daring; since three maids, so blest,
Thy safety plan, e'en in the court of Heaven;
And so much certain good my words forebode?"
    As florets, by the frosty air of night
Bent down and closed, when day has blanched their leaves,
Rise all unfolded on their spiry stems;
So was my fainting vigor new restored,
And to my heart such kindly courage ran,
That I as one undaunted soon replied:
"O full of pity she, who undertook
My succor! and thou kind, who didst perform
So soon her true behest! With such desire
Thou hast disposed me to renew my voyage,
That my first purpose fully is resumed.
Lead on: one only will is in us both.
Thou art my guide, my master thou, and lord."

450

So spake I; and when he had onward moved,
I entered on the deep and woody way.

CANTO III

Dante, following Virgil, comes to the gate of Hell; where, after having
read the dreadful words that are written thereon, they both enter. Here,
as he understands from Virgil, those were punished who had passed their
time (for living it could not be called) in a state of apathy and indifference
both to good and evil. Then pursuing their way, they arrive at the river
Acheron; and there find the old ferryman Charon, who takes the spirits
over to the opposite shore; where as soon as Dante arrives, he is seized
with terror, and falls into a trance.

THROUGH ME you pass into the city of woe:
Through me you pass into eternal pain:
Through me among the people lost for aye.
Justice the founder of my fabric moved:
To rear me was the task of Power divine,
Supremest Wisdom, and primeval Love.
Before me things create were none, save things
Eternal, and eternal I endure.
All hope abandon, ye who enter here."
Such characters, in color dim, I marked
Over a portal's lofty arch inscribed.
Whereat I thus: "Master, these words import
Hard meaning." He as one prepared replied:
"Here thou must all distrust behind thee leave;
Here be vile fear extinguished. We are come
Where I have told thee we shall see the souls
To misery doomed, who intellectual good
Have lost." And when his hand he had stretched forth
To mine, with pleasant looks, whence I was cheered,
Into that secret place he led me on.
Here sighs, with lamentations and loud moans,
Resounded through the air pierced by no star,
That e'en I wept at entering. Various tongues,
Horrible languages, outcries of woe,
Accents of anger, voices deep and hoarse,

451

With hands together smote that swelled the sounds,
Made up a tumult, that for ever whirls
Round through that air with solid darkness stained,
Like to the sand that in the whirlwind flies.

I then, with error yet encompassed, cried:
"O master! what is this I hear? what race
Are these, who seem so overcome with woe?"

He thus to me: "This miserable fate
Suffer the wretched souls of those, who lived
Without or praise or blame, with that ill band
Of angels mixed, who nor rebellious proved,
Nor yet were true to God, but for themselves
Were only. From his bounds Heaven drove them forth,
Not to impair his luster; nor the depth
Of Hell receives them, lest the accursed tribe
Should glory thence with exultation vain."

I then: "Master! what doth aggrieve them thus,
That they lament so loud?" He straight replied:
"That will I tell thee briefly. These of death
No hope may entertain: and their blind life
So meanly passes, that all other lots
They envy. Fame of them the world hath none,
Nor suffers; Mercy and Justice scorn them both.
Speak not of them, but look, and pass them by."

And I, who straightway looked, beheld a flag,
Which whirling ran around so rapidly,
That it no pause obtained: and following came
Such a long train of spirits, I should ne'er
Have thought that death so many had despoiled.

When some of these I recognized, I saw
And knew the shade of him, who to base fear
Yielding, abjured his high estate. Forthwith
I understood, for certain, this the tribe
Of those ill spirits both to God displeasing
And to His foes. These wretches, who ne'er lived,
Went on in nakedness, and sorely stung
By wasps and hornets, which bedewed their cheeks
With blood, that, mixed with tears, dropped to their feet,
And by disgustful worms was gathered there.

Then looking further onwards, I beheld

452

A throng upon the shore of a great stream:
Whereat I thus: "Sir! grant me now to know
Whom here we view, and whence impelled they seem
So eager to pass o'er, as I discern
Through the blear light?" He thus to me in few:
"This shalt thou know, soon as our steps arrive
Beside the woeful tide of Acheron."

    Then with eyes downward cast, and filled with shame,
Fearing my words offensive to his ear,
Till we had reached the river, I from speech
Abstained. And lo! toward us in a bark
Comes on an old man, hoary white with age,
Crying, "Woe to you, wicked spirits! hope not
Ever to see the sky again. I come
To take you to the other shore across,
Into eternal darkness, there to dwell
In fierce heat and in ice. And thou, who there
Standest, live spirit! get thee hence, and leave
These who are dead." But soon as he beheld
I left them not, "By other way," said he,
"By other haven shalt thou come to shore,
Not by this passage; thee a nimbler boat
Must carry." Then to him thus spake my guide:
"Charon! thyself torment not: so 'tis willed,
Where will and power are one: ask thou no more."

    Straightway in silence fell the shaggy cheeks
Of him, the boatman o'er the livid lake,
Around whose eyes glared wheeling flames. Meanwhile
Those spirits, faint and naked, color changed,
And gnashed their teeth, soon as the cruel words
They heard. God and their parents they blasphemed,
The human kind, the place, the time, and seed,
That did engender them and give them birth.

    Then all together sorely wailing drew
To the curst strand, that every man must pass
Who fears not God. Charon, demoniac form,
With eyes of burning coal, collects them all,
Beckoning, and each, that lingers, with his oar
Strikes. As fall off the light autumnal leaves,
One still another following, till the bough

Strews all its honors on the earth beneath;
E'en in like manner Adam's evil brood
Cast themselves, one by one, down from the shore,
Each at a beck, as falcon at his call.

Thus go they over through the shadowed wave;
And ever they on the opposing bank
Be landed, on this side another throng
Still gathers. "Son," thus spake the courteous guide,
"Those who die subject to the wrath of God
All here together come from every clime,
And to o'erpass the river are not loath:
For so Heaven's justice goads them on, that fear
Is turned into desire. Hence ne'er hath passed
Good spirit. If of thee Charon complain,
Now mayst thou know the import of his words."

This said, the gloomy region trembling shook
So terribly, that yet with clammy dews
Fear chills my brow. The sad earth gave a blast,
That, lightening, shot forth a vermilion flame,
Which all my senses conquered quite, and I
Down dropped, as one with sudden slumber seized.

CANTO IV

The Poet, being roused by a clap of thunder, and following his guide onwards, descends into Limbo, which is the first circle of Hell, where he
finds the souls of those, who, although they have lived virtuously and
have not to suffer for great sins, nevertheless, through lack of baptism,
merit not the bliss of Paradise. Hence he is led on by Virgil to descend
into the second circle.

B ROKE THE DEEP slumber in my brain a crash
Of heavy thunder, that I shook myself,
As one by main force roused. Risen upright,
My rested eyes I moved around, and searched,
With fixed ken, to know what place it was
Wherein I stood. For certain, on the brink
I found me of the lamentable vale,
The dread abyss, that joins a thundrous sound

Of plaints innumerable. Dark and deep,
And thick with clouds o'erspread, mine eye in vain
Explored its bottom, nor could aught discern.

"Now let us to the blind world there beneath
Descend"; the bard began, all pale of look:
"I go the first, and thou shalt follow next."

Then I, his altered hue perceiving, thus:
"How may I speed, if thou yieldest to dread,
Who still art wont to comfort me in doubt?"

He then: "The anguish of that race below
With pity stains my cheek, which thou for fear
Mistakest. Let us on. Our length of way
Urges to haste." Onward, this said, he moved;
And entering led me with him, on the bounds
Of the first circle that surrounds the abyss.

Here, as mine ear could note, no plaint was heard
Except of sighs, that made the eternal air
Tremble, not caused by tortures, but from grief
Felt by those multitudes, many and vast,
Of men, women, and infants. Then to me
The gentle guide: "Inquirest thou not what spirits
Are these which thou beholdest? Ere thou pass
Farther, I would thou know, that these of sin
Were blameless; and if aught they merited,
It profits not, since baptism was not theirs,
The portal to thy faith. If they before
The Gospel lived, they served not God aright;
And among such am I. For these defects,
And for no other evil, we are lost;
Only so far afflicted, that we live
Desiring without hope." Sore grief assailed
My heart at hearing this, for well I knew
Suspended in that Limbo many a soul
Of mighty worth. "O tell me, sire revered!
Tell me, my master!" I began, through wish
Of full assurance in that holy faith
Which vanquishes all error; "say, did e'er
Any, or through his own or other's merit,
Come forth from thence, who afterward was blest?"

Piercing the secret purport of my speech,

He answered: "I was new to that estate,
When I beheld a puissant one * arrive
Amongst us, with victorious trophy crowned.
He forth the shade of our first parent drew,
Abel his child, and Noah righteous man,
Of Moses lawgiver for faith approved,
Of patriarch Abraham, and David king,
Israel with his sire and with his sons,
Nor without Rachel whom so hard he won,
And others many more, whom He to bliss
Exalted. Before these, be thou assured,
No spirit of human kind was ever saved."

We, while he spake, ceased not our onward road,
Still passing through the wood; for so I name
Those spirits thick beset. We were not far
On this side from the summit, when I saw
A flame, that o'er the darkened hemisphere
Prevailing shined. Yet we a little space
Were distant, not so far but I in part
Discovered that a tribe in honor high
That place possessed. "O thou, who every art
And science valuest! who are these, that boast
Such honor, separate from all the rest?"

He answered: "The renown of their great names
That echoes through your world above, acquires
Favor in Heaven, which holds them thus advanced."
Meantime a voice I heard: "Honor the bard
Sublime! his shade returns, that left us late!"
No sooner ceased the sound, than I beheld
Four mighty spirits toward us bend their steps,
Of semblance neither sorrowful nor glad.

When thus my master kind began: "Mark him,
Who in his right hand bears that falchion keen,
The other three preceding, as their lord.
This is that Homer, of all bards supreme:
Horace the next, in satire's vein excelling;

---

* The "puissant one" was Christ in His descent into Limbo (which means "border" or "edge"). The reader will observe that the names of Christ and Mary do not occur in "The Inferno."

The third is Ovid; Lucan is the last.
Because they all that appellation own,
With which the voice singly accosted me,
Honoring they greet me thus, and well they judge."
    So I beheld united the bright school
Of him the monarch of sublimest song,
That o'er the others like an eagle soars.
    When they together short discourse had held,
They turned to me, with salutation kind
Beckoning me; at which my master smiled:
Nor was this all; but greater honor still
They gave me, for they made me of their tribe;
And I was sixth amid that learnéd band.
    Far as the luminous beacon on we passed,
Speaking of matters, then befitting well
To speak, now fitter left untold. At foot
Of a magnificent castle we arrived,
Seven times with lofty walls begirt, and round
Defended by a pleasant stream. O'er this
As o'er dry land we passed. Next, through seven gates,
I with those sages entered, and we came
Into a meadow fresh with verdure bright.
There dwelt a race, who slow their eyes around
Majestically moved, and in their port
Bore eminent authority: they spake
Seldom, but all their words were tuneful sweet.
    We to one side retired, into a place
Open and bright and lofty, whence each one
Stood manifest to view. Incontinent,
There on the green enamel of the plain
Were shown me the great spirits, by whose sight
I am exalted in my own esteem.
    Of all to speak at full were vain attempt;
For my wide theme so urges, that oft-times
My words fall short of what bechanced. In two
The six associates part. Another way
My sage guide leads me, from that air serene,
Into a climate ever vexed with storms:
And to a part I come, where no light shines.

Coming into the second circle of Hell, Dante at the entrance beholds
Minos the Infernal Judge, by whom he is admonished to beware how he
enters those regions. Here he witnesses the punishment of carnal sinners,
who are tossed about ceaselessly in the dark air by the most furious winds.
Among these, he meets with Francesca of Rimini, through pity at whose
sad tale he falls fainting to the ground.

FROM THE FIRST circle I descended thus
   Down to the second, which, a lesser space
Embracing, so much more of grief contains,
Provoking bitter moans. There Minos stands,
Grinning with ghastly feature: he, of all
Who enter, strict examining the crimes,
Gives sentence, and dismisses them beneath,
According as he foldeth him around:
For when before him comes the ill-fated soul,
It all confesses; and that judge severe
Of sins, considering what place in Hell
Suits the transgression, with his tail so oft
Himself encircles, as degrees beneath
He dooms it to descend. Before him stand
Always a numerous throng; and in his turn
Each one to judgment passing, speaks, and hears
His fate, thence downward to his dwelling hurled.
   "O thou! who to this residence of woe
Approachest!" when he saw me coming, cried
Minos, relinquishing his dread employ,
"Look how thou enter here; beware in whom
Thou place thy trust; let not the entrance broad
Deceive thee to thy harm." To him my guide:
"Wherefore exclaimest? Hinder not his way
By destiny appointed; so 'tis willed,
Where will and power are one. Ask thou no more."
   Now are the rueful wailings to be heard.
Now am I come where many a plaining voice
Smites on my ear. Into a place I came
Where light was silent all. Bellowing there groaned
A noise, as of a sea in tempest torn

By warring winds. The stormy blast of Hell
With restless fury drives the spirits on,
Whirled round and dashed amain with sore annoy.
When they arrive before the ruinous sweep,
There shrieks are heard, there lamentations, moans,
And blasphemies 'gainst the good Power in Heaven.
    I understood, that to this torment sad
The carnal sinners are condemned, in whom
Reason by lust is swayed. As in large troops
And multitudinous, when winter reigns,
The starlings on their wings are borne abroad;
So bears the tyrannous gust those evil souls.
On this side and on that, above, below,
It drives them: hope of rest to solace them
Is none, nor e'en of milder pang. As cranes,
Chanting their dolorous notes, traverse the sky,
Stretched out in long array; so I beheld
Spirits, who came loud wailing, hurried on
By their dire doom. Then I: "Instructor! who
Are these, by the black air so scourged?"—"The first
Of those, of whom thou questionest," he replied,
"O'er many tongues was empress. She in vice
Of luxury was so shameless, that she made
Liking be lawful by promulged decree,
To clear the blame she had herself incurred.
This is Semiramis, of whom 'tis writ,
That she succeeded Ninus her espoused;
And held the land, which now the Sultan rules.
The next * in amorous fury slew herself,
And to Sicheus' ashes broke her faith:
Then follows Cleopatra, lustful queen."
    There marked I Helen, for whose sake so long
The time was fraught with evil; there the great
Achilles, who with love fought to the end.
Paris I saw, and Tristan; and beside,
A thousand more he showed me, and by name
Pointed them out, whom love bereaved of life.
    When I had heard my sage instructor name
Those dames and knights of antique days, o'erpowered

* Dido, the widowed queen of Carthage, who killed herself for love of Aeneas.

By pity, well-nigh in amaze my mind
Was lost; and I began: "Bard! willingly
I would address those two together coming,
Which seem so light before the wind." He thus:
"Note thou, when nearer they to us approach.
Then by that love which carries them along,
Entreat; and they will come." Soon as the wind
Swayed them towards us, I thus framed my speech:
"O wearied spirits! come, and hold discourse
With us, if by none else restrained." As doves
By fond desire invited, on wide wings
And firm, to their sweet nest returning home,
Cleave the air, wafted by their will along;
Thus issued, from that troop where Dido ranks,
They, through the ill air speeding: with such force
My cry prevailed, by strong affection urged.

  "O gracious creature and benign! who go'st
Visiting, through this element obscure,
Us, who the world with bloody stain imbrued;
If, for a friend, the King of all, we owned,
Our prayer to him should for thy peace arise,
Since thou hast pity on our evil plight.
Of whatsoe'er to hear or to discourse
It pleases thee, that will we hear, of that
Freely with thee discourse, while e'er the wind,
As now, is mute. The land, that gave me birth,
Is situate on the coast, where Po descends
To rest in ocean with his sequent streams.

  "Love, that in gentle heart is quickly learnt,
Entangled him by that fair form, from me
Ta'en in such cruel sort, as grieves me still:
Love, that denial takes from none beloved,
Caught me with pleasing him so passing well,
That, as thou seest, he yet deserts me not.
Love brought us to one death: Caïna waits
The soul, who spilt our life." * Such were their words;
At hearing which, downward I bent my looks,

* Francesca, daughter of the Lord of Ravenna, and wife of Gianciotto Malatesta of Rimini. The lover, Paolo, was the handsome brother of the husband, who was deformed.

460

And held them there so long, that the bard cried:
"What art thou pondering?" I in answer thus:
"Alas! by what sweet thoughts, what fond desire
Must they at length to that ill pass have reached!"
    Then turning, I to them my speech addressed,
And thus began: "Francesca! your sad fate
Even to tears my grief and pity moves.
But tell me; in the time of your sweet sighs,
By what, and how Love granted, that ye knew
Your yet uncertain wishes?" She replied:
"No greater grief than to remember days
Of joy, when misery is at hand. Thy wise guide
Knows that well. Yet so eagerly
If thou art bent to know the primal root,
From whence our dear love sprang, I will do
As one, who weeps and tells his tale. One day,
For our delight we read of Lancelot,
How him love thralled. Alone we were, and no
Suspicion near us. Oft-times by that reading
Our eyes were drawn together, and the hue
Fled from our altered cheek. But at one point
Alone we fell. When of that smile we read,
The wished smile, so rapturously kissed
By one so deep in love, then he, who ne'er
From me shall separate, at once my lips
All trembling kissed. The book and writer both
Were love's purveyors. In its leaves that day
We read no more." While thus one spirit spake,
The other wailed so sorely, that heart-struck
I, through compassion fainting, seemed not far
From death, and like a corpse fell to the ground.

CANTO VI

On his recovery, the Poet finds himself in the third circle, where the gluttonous are punished. Their torment is to lie in the mire, under a continual and heavy storm of hail, snow, and discolored water; Cerberus meanwhile barking over them with his threefold throat, and rending them piecemeal. One of these, who on earth was named Ciacco, foretells the divisions with which Florence is about to be distracted. Dante proposes a question to his guide, who solves it; and they proceed towards the fourth circle.

M Y SENSE reviving, that erewhile had drooped
    With pity for the kindred shades, whence grief
O'ercame me wholly, straight around I see
New torments, new tormented souls, which way
Soe'er I move, or turn, or bend my sight.
In the third circle I arrive, of showers
Ceaseless, accursed, heavy and cold, unchanged
For ever, both in kind and in degree.
Large hail, discolored water, sleety flaw
Through the dun midnight air streamed down amain:
Stank all the land whereon that tempest fell.

    Cerberus, cruel monster, fierce and strange,
Through his wide threefold throat, barks as a dog
Over the multitude immersed beneath.
His eyes glare crimson, black his unctuous beard,
His belly large, and clawed the hands, with which
He tears the spirits, flays them, and their limbs
Piecemeal disparts. Howling there spread, as curs,
Under the rainy deluge, with one side
The other screening, oft they roll them round,
A wretched, godless crew. When that great worm
Descried us, savage Cerberus, he oped
His jaws, and the fangs showed us; not a limb
Of him but trembled. Then my guide, his palms
Expanding on the ground, thence filled with earth
Raised them, and cast it in his ravenous maw.
E'en as a dog, that yelling bays for food
His keeper, when the morsel comes, lets fall
His fury, bent alone with eager haste
To swallow it; so dropped the loathsome cheeks
Of demon Cerberus, who thundering stuns
The spirits, that they for deafness wish in vain.

    We, o'er the shades thrown prostrate by the brunt
Of the heavy tempest passing, set our feet
Upon their emptiness, that substance seemed.
    They all along the earth extended lay,

Save one, that sudden raised himself to sit,
Soon as that way he saw us pass. "O thou!"
He cried, "who through the infernal shades art led,
Own, if again thou know'st me. Thou wast framed
Or ere my frame was broken." I replied:
"The anguish thou endurest perchance so takes
Thy form from my remembrance, that it seems
As if I saw thee never. But inform
Me who thou art, that in a place so sad
Art set, and in such torment, that although
Other be greater, none disgusteth more."
He thus in answer to my words rejoined:
"Thy city, heaped with envy to the brim,
Aye, that the measure overflows its bounds,
Held me in brighter days. Ye citizens
Were wont to name me Ciacco.* For the sin
Of gluttony, damned vice, beneath this rain,
E'en as thou seest, I with fatigue am worn:
Nor I sole spirit in this woe: all these
Have by like crime incurred like punishment."

  No more he said, and I my speech resumed:
"Ciacco! thy dire affliction grieves me much,
Even to tears. But tell me, if thou know'st,
What shall at length befall the citizens
Of the divided city; whether any
Just one live there: tell the cause,
Whence jarring Discord hath assailed it thus."

[*After some political discussion Dante inquires after the fate of certain Florentines and is told:*]

"These are yet blacker spirits. Various crimes
Have sunk them deeper in the dark abyss.
If thou so far descendest, thou mayst see them.
But to the pleasant world, when thou return'st,
Of me make mention, I entreat thee, there.
No more I tell thee, answer thee no more."
    This said, his fixed eyes he turned askance,
A little eyed me, then bent down his head,
And 'midst his blind companions back he fell.

* In English: Hog

When thus my guide: "No more his bed he leaves,
Ere the last angel-trumpet blow. The Power
Adverse to these shall then in glory come,
Each one forthwith to his sad tomb repair,
Resume his fleshly vesture and his form,
And hear the eternal doom re-echoing rend
The vault." So passed we through that mixture foul
Of spirits and rain, with tardy steps; meanwhile
Touching, though slightly, on the life to come.
For thus I questioned: "Shall these tortures, Sir!
When the great sentence passes, be increased,
Or mitigated, or as now severe?"

He then: "Consult thy knowledge; that decides,
That, as each thing to more perfection grows,
It feels more sensibly both good and pain.
Though ne'er to true perfection may arrive
This race accurst, yet nearer then, than now,
They shall approach it." Compassing that path,
Circuitous we journeyed; and discourse,
Much more than I relate, between us passed:
Till at the point, whence the steps led below,
Arrived, there Plutus, the great foe, we found.*

CANTO VII

In the present Canto, Dante describes his descent into the fourth circle, at
the beginning of which he sees Plutus stationed. Here one like doom awaits
the prodigal and the avaricious; which is, to meet in direful conflict, rolling great weights against each other with mutual upbraidings. From hence
Virgil takes occasion to show how vain the goods that are committed into
the charge of Fortune; and this moves our author to inquire what being
that Fortune is, of whom he speaks: which question being resolved, they
go down into the fifth circle, where they find the wrathful and gloomy tormented in the Stygian lake. Having made a compass round great part of
this lake, they come at last to the base of a lofty tower.

A H ME! O Satan! Satan!" loud exclaimed
Plutus, in accent hoarse of wild alarm;

* The god of riches.

And the kind sage, whom no event surprised,
To comfort me thus spake: "Let not thy fear
Harm thee, for power in him, be sure, is none
To hinder down this rock thy safe descent."
Then to that swollen lip turning, "Peace!" he cried,
"Curst wolf! thy fury inward on thyself
Prey, and consume thee! Through the dark profound,
Not without cause, he passes. So 'tis willed
On high, there where the great Archangel poured
Heaven's vengeance on the first adulterer proud."

As sails, full spread and bellying with the wind,
Drop suddenly collapsed, if the mast split;
So to the ground down dropped the cruel fiend.

Thus we, descending to the fourth steep ledge,
Gained on the dismal shore, that all the woe
Hems in of all the universe. Ah me!
Almighty Justice! in what store thou heapest
New pains, new troubles, as I here beheld.
Wherefore doth fault of ours bring us to this?

E'en as a billow, on Charybdis rising,
Against encountered billow dashing breaks;
Such is the dance this wretched race must lead,
Whom more than elsewhere numerous here I found.
From one side and the other, with loud voice,
Both rolled on weights, by main force of their breasts,
Then smote together, and each one forthwith
Rolled them back voluble, turning again;
Exclaiming these, "Why holdest thou so fast?"
Those answering, "Why castest thou away?"
So, still repeating their despiteful song,
They to the opposite point, on either hand,
Traversed the horrid circle; then arrived,
Both turned them round, and through the middle space
Conflicting met again. At sight whereof
I, stung with grief, thus spake: "O say, my guide!
What race is this? Were these, whose heads are shorn,
On our left hand, all separate to the Church?"

He straight replied: "In their first life, these all
In mind were so distorted, that they made,
According to due measure, of their wealth

No use. This clearly from their words collect,
Which they howl forth, at each extremity
Arriving of the circle, where their crime
Contrary in kind disparts them. To the Church
Were separate those, that with no hairy cowls
Are crowned, both Popes and Cardinals, o'er whom
Avarice dominion absolute maintains."

I then: " 'Mid such as these some needs must be,
Whom I shall recognize, that with the blot
Of these foul sins were stained." He answering thus:
"Vain thought conceivest thou. That ignoble life,
Which made them vile before, now makes them dark
And to all knowledge indiscernible.
For ever they shall meet in this rude shock:
These from the tomb with clenched grasp shall rise,
Those with close-shaven locks. That ill they gave,
And ill they kept, hath of the beauteous world
Deprived, and set them at this strife, which needs
No labored phrase of mine to set it off.
Now mayst thou see, my son! how brief, how vain,
The goods committed into Fortune's hands,
For which the human race keep such a coil!
Not all the gold that is beneath the moon,
Or ever hath been, of these toil-worn souls
Might purchase rest for one." I thus rejoined:
"My guide! of thee this also would I learn;
This Fortune, that thou speak'st of, what it is,
Whose talons grasp the blessings of the world."

He thus: "O beings blind! what ignorance
Besets you! Now my judgment hear and mark.
He, whose transcendent wisdom passes all,
The heavens creating, gave them ruling powers
To guide them; so that each part shines to each,
Their light in equal distribution poured.
By similar appointment he ordained,
Over the world's bright images to rule,
Superintendence of a guiding hand
And general minister, which, at due time,
May change the empty vantages of life
From race to race, from one to other's blood,

Beyond prevention of man's wisest care:
Wherefore one nation rises into sway,
Another languishes, e'en as her will
Decrees, from us concealed, as in the grass
The serpent train. Against her nought avails
Your utmost wisdom. She with foresight plans,
Judges, and carries on her reign, as theirs
The other powers divine. Her changes know
No intermission: by necessity
She is made swift, so frequent come who claim
Succession in her favors. This is she,
So execrated e'en by those whose debt
To her is rather praise: they wrongfully
With blame requite her, and with evil word;
But she is blessed, and for that recks not:
Amidst the other primal beings glad,
Rolls on her sphere, and in her bliss exults.
Now on our way we pass, to heavier woe
Descending: for each star is falling now,
That mounted at our entrance, and forbids
Too long our tarrying." We the circle crossed
To the next steep, arriving at a well,
That boiling pours itself down to a foss
Sluiced from its source. Far murkier was the wave
Than blackest grain: and we in company
Of the inky waters, journeying by their side,
Entered, though by a different track, beneath.
Into a lake, the Stygian named, expands
The dismal stream, when it hath reached the foot
Of the gray withered cliffs. Intent I stood
To gaze, and in the marish sunk descried
A miry tribe, all naked, and with looks
Betokening rage. They not with hands alone
Struck out, but with the head, the breast, the feet,
Cutting each other piecemeal with their fangs.
    The good instructor spake: "Now seest thou, son!
The souls of those whom anger overcame.
This, too, for certain know, that underneath
The water dwells a multitude, whose sighs
Into these bubbles make the surface heave,

As thine eye tells thee wheresoe'er it turn.
Fixed in the slime, they say: 'Sad once were we,
'In the sweet air made gladsome by the sun,
'Carrying a foul and lazy mist within:
'Now in these murky settlings are we sad.'
Such dolorous strain they gurgle in their throats,
But word distinct can utter none." Our route
Thus compassed we, a segment widely stretched
Between the dry embankment and the core
Of the loathed pool, turning meanwhile our eyes
Downward on those who gulped its muddy lees;
Nor stopped, till to a tower's low base we came.

CANTO VIII

A signal having been made from the tower, Phlegyas, the ferryman of the
lake, speedily crosses it, and conveys Virgil and Dante to the other side.
On their passage, they meet with Filippo Argenti, whose fury and torment
are described. They then arrive at the city of Dis, the entrance whereto is
denied, and the portals closed against them by many Demons.

M Y THEME pursuing, I relate, that ere
  We reached the lofty turret's base, our eyes
Its height ascended, where we marked uphung
Two beacons and another saw from far
Return the signal, so remote that scarce
The eye could catch its beam. I, turning round
To the deep source of knowledge, thus inquired:
"Say what this means; and what, that other light
In answer set: what agency doth this?"
    "There on the filthy waters," he replied,
"E'en now what next awaits us mayst thou see,
If the marsh-gendered fog conceal it not."
    Never was arrow from the cord dismissed,
That ran its way so nimbly through the air,
As a small bark, that through the waves I spied
Toward us coming, under the sole sway
Of one that ferried it, who cried aloud:

"Art thou arrived, fell spirit?"—"Phlegyas, Phlegyas,*
This time thou criest in vain," my lord replied;
"No longer shalt thou have us, but while o'er
The slimy pool we pass." As one who hears
Of some great wrong he hath sustained, whereat
Inly he pines; so Phlegyas inly pined
In his fierce ire. My guide, descending, stepped
Into the skiff, and bade me enter next,
Close at his side; nor, till my entrance, seemed
The vessel freighted. Soon as both embarked,
Cutting the waves, goes on the ancient prow,
More deeply than with others it is wont.

While we our course o'er the dead channel held,
One drenched in mire before me came, and said:
"Who art thou, that thus comest ere thine hour?"
I answered: "Though I come, I tarry not:
But who art thou, that art become so foul?"
"One, as thou seest, who mourn," he straight replied.
To which I thus: "In mourning and in woe,
Curst spirit! tarry thou. I know thee well,
E'en thus in filth disguised." Then stretched he forth
Hands to the bark; whereof my teacher sage
Aware, thrusting him back: "Away! down there
To the other dogs!" then, with his arms my neck
Encircling, kissed my cheek, and spake: "O soul,
Justly disdainful! blest was she in whom
Thou wast conceived. He in the world was one
For arrogance noted: to his memory
No virtue lends its luster; even so
Here is his shadow furious. There above,
How many now hold themselves mighty kings,
Who here like swine shall wallow in the mire,
Leaving behind them horrible dispraise."
I then: "Master! him fain would I behold
Whelmed in these dregs, before we quit the lake."
He thus: "Or ever to thy view the shore
Be offered, satisfied shall be that wish,

* Dante mingles mythical personages freely with historical. Phlegyas, when
Apollo wronged his daughter, set fire to the god's temple at Delphi. Virgil has
him uttering warnings in Tartarus.

Which well deserves completion." Scarce his words
Were ended, when I saw the miry tribes
Set on him with such violence, that still
For that I render thanks to God, and praise.
"To Filippo Argenti!" cried they all:
And on himself the moody Florentine
Turned his avenging fangs. Him here we left,
Nor speak I of him more. But on mine ear
Sudden a sound of lamentation smote,
Whereat mine eye unbarred I sent abroad.

    And thus the good instructor: "Now, my son,
Draws near the city, that of Dis is named,
With its grave denizens, a might throng."

    I thus: "The minarets already, Sir!
There, certes, in the valley I descry,
Gleaming vermilion, as if they from fire
Had issued." He replied: "Eternal fire,
That inward burns, shows them with ruddy flame
Illumed; as in this nether Hell thou seest."

    We came within the fosses deep, that moat
This region comfortless. The walls appeared
As they were framed of iron. We had made
Wide circuit, ere a place we reached, where loud
The mariner cried vehement: "Go forth:
The entrance is here." Upon the gates I spied
More than a thousand, who of old from Heaven
Were showered. With ireful gestures, "Who is this,"
They cried, "that, without death first felt, goes through
The regions of the dead?" My sapient guide
Made sign that he for secret parley wished;
Whereat their angry scorn abating, thus
They spake: "Come thou alone; and let him go,
Who hath so hardily entered this realm.
Alone return he by his witless way;
If well he know it, let him prove. For thee,
Here shalt thou tarry, who through clime so dark
Hast been his escort." Now bethink thee, reader!
What cheer was mine at sound of those curst words.
I did believe I never should return.

    "O my loved guide! who more than seven times

470

Security hast rendered me, and drawn
From peril deep, whereto I stood exposed,
Desert me not," I cried, "in this extreme.
And, if our onward going be denied,
Together trace we back our steps with speed."

My liege, who thither had conducted me,
Replied: "Fear not: for of our passage none
Hath power to disappoint us, by such high
Authority permitted. But do thou
Await me here; meanwhile, thy wearied spirit
Comfort, and feed with kindly hope, assured
I will not leave thee in this lower world."

This said, departs the sire benevolent
And quits me. Hesitating I remain
At war, 'twixt will and will not, in my thoughts.

I could not hear what terms he offered them,
But they conferred not long, for all at once
Pellmell rushed back within. Closed were the gates,
By those our adversaries, on the breast
Of my liege lord: excluded, he returned
To me with tardy steps. Upon the ground
His eyes were bent, and from his brow erased
All confidence, while thus in sighs he spake:
"Who hath denied me these abodes of woe?"
Then thus to me: "That I am angered, think
No ground of terror: in this trial I
Shall vanquish, use what arts they may within."

CANTO IX

After some hindrances, and having seen the hellish furies and other monsters, the Poet, by the help of an Angel, enters the city of Dis, wherein
he discovers that the heretics are punished in tombs burning with intense
fire: and he, together with Virgil, passes onwards between the sepulchers
and the walls of the city.

I, SOON as entered, throw mine eye around,
And see, on every part, wide-stretching space,

Replete with bitter pain and torment ill.

As where Rhone stagnates on the plains of Arles,
Or as at Pola, near Quarnaro's gulf,
That closes Italy and laves her bounds,
The place is all thick spread with sepulchers;
So was it here, save what in horror here
Excelled: for 'midst the graves were scattered flames,
Wherewith intensely all throughout they burned,
That iron for which no craft hotter needs.

Their lids all hung suspended; and beneath
From them forth issued lamentable moans,
Such as the sad and tortured well might raise.

I thus: "Master! say who are these, interred
Within these vaults, of whom distinct we hear
The dolorous sighs." He answer thus returned:
"The arch-heretics are here, accompanied
By every sect their followers; and much more,
Than thou believest, the tombs are freighted: like
With like is buried; and the monuments
Are different in degrees of heat." This said,
He to the right hand turning, on we passed
Betwixt the afflicted and the ramparts high.

CANTO X

Dante, having obtained permission from his guide, holds discourse with
Farinata degli Uberti and Cavalcante Cavalcanti, who lie in their fiery
tombs, that are yet open, and not to be closed up till after the last judgment. Farinata predicts the Poet's exile from Florence; and shows him
that the condemned have knowledge of future things, but are ignorant of
what is at present passing, unless it be revealed by some newcomer from
earth.

Now by a secret pathway we proceed,
    Between the walls that hem the region round,
And the tormented souls: my master first,
I close behind his steps. "Virtue supreme!"
I thus began: "who through these ample orbs

In circuit lead me, even as thou will;
Speak thou, and satisfy my wish. May those,
Who lie within these sepulchers, be seen?
Already all the lids are raised, and none
O'er them keeps watch." He thus in answer spake:
"They shall be closed all, what-time they here
From Josaphat returned shall come, and bring
Their bodies, which above they now have left.
The cemetery on this part obtain,
With Epicurus, all his followers,
Who with the body make the spirit die.
Here therefore satisfaction shall be soon,
Both to the question asked, and to the wish
Which thou conceal'st in silence." I replied:
"I keep not, guide beloved! from thee my heart
Secreted, but to shun vain length of words;
A lesson erewhile taught me by thyself."

"O Tuscan! thou, who through the city of fire
Alive art passing, so discreet of speech:
Here, please thee, stay awhile. Thy utterance
Declares the place of thy nativity
To be that noble land, with which perchance
I too severely dealt." Sudden that sound
Forth issued from a vault, whereat, in fear,
I somewhat closer to my leader's side
Approaching, he thus spake: "What dost thou? Turn:
Lo! Farinata * there, who hath himself
Uplifted: from his girdle upwards, all
Exposed, behold him." On his face was mine
Already fixed: his breast and forehead there
Erecting, seemed as in high scorn he held
E'en Hell. Between the sepulchers, to him
My guide thrust me, with fearless hands and prompt;
This warning added: "See thy words be clear."

He, soon as I there stood at the tomb's foot,
Eyed me a space; then in disdainful mood
Addressed me: "Say what ancestors were thine."

---

* Farinata degli Uberti, leader of the Ghibellines in Florence, is put among
the heretics for having maintained, with Epicurus, that the soul dies with the
body.

I, willing to obey him, straight revealed
The whole, nor kept back aught: whence he, his brow
Somewhat uplifting, cried: "Fiercely were they
Adverse to me, my party, and the blood
From whence I sprang: twice, therefore, I abroad
Scattered them." * "Though driven out, yet they each time
From all parts," answered I, "returned; an art
Which yours have shown they are not skilled to learn."

Then, peering forth from the unclosed jaw,
Rose from his side a shade,† high as the chin,
Leaning, methought, upon its knees upraised.
It looked around, as eager to explore
If there were other with me; but perceiving
That fond imagination quenched, with tears
Thus spake: "If thou through this blind prison goest,
Led by thy lofty genius and profound,
Where is my son? ‡ and wherefore not with thee?"

I straight replied: "Not of myself I come;
By him, who there expects me, through this clime
Conducted, whom perchance Guido thy son
Had in contempt." Already had his words
And mode of punishment read me his name,
Whence I so fully answered. He at once
Exclaimed, up starting, "How! said'st thou, he *had?*
No longer lives he? Strikes not on his eye
The blessed daylight?" Then, of some delay
I made ere my reply, aware, down fell
Supine, nor after forth appeared he more.

Meanwhile the other, great of soul, near whom
I yet was stationed, changed not countenance stern,
Nor moved the neck, nor bent his ribbed side.
"And if," continuing the first discourse,
"They in this art," he cried, "small skill have shown;
That doth torment me more e'en than this bed.
But not yet fifty times shall be relumed

* An allusion to the expulsion of the Guelfs from Florence in 1249 and 1260.
Dante belonged originally to the Guelf faction, which sided with the Pope
rather than the Emperor.
† Cavalcante Cavalcanti, though a Guelf, was a neo-Epicurean, like Farinata.
‡ Guido Cavalcanti, a poet. was a friend of Dante.

Her aspect, who reigns here queen of this realm,*
Ere thou shalt know the full weight of that art."
    "So may thy lineage find at last repose,"
I thus adjured him, "as thou solve this knot,
Which now involves my mind. If right I hear,
Ye seem to view beforehand that which time
Leads with him, of the present uninformed."
    "We view, as one who hath an evil sight,"
He answered, "plainly, objects far remote;
So much of his large splendor yet imparts
The Almighty Ruler: but when they approach,
Or actually exist, our intellect
Then wholly fails; nor of your human state,
Except what others bring us, know we aught.
Hence therefore mayst thou understand, that all
Our knowledge in that instant shall expire,
When on futurity the portals close."
    Then conscious of my fault, and by remorse
Smitten, I added thus: "Now shalt thou say
To him there fallen, that his offspring still
Is to the living joined; and bid him know,
That if from answer, silent, I abstained,
'Twas that my thought was occupied, intent
Upon that error, which thy help hath solved."
    But now my master summoning me back
I heard, and with more eager haste besought
The spirit to inform me, who with him
Partook his lot. He answer thus returned:
"More than a thousand with me here are laid.
Within is Frederick, second of that name,†
And the Lord Cardinal; and of the rest
I speak not." He, this said, from sight withdrew.
But I my steps toward the ancient bard
Reverting, ruminated on the words
Betokening me such ill. Onward he moved,

* The moon is the measure of time in the infernal regions. Farinata means
that fifty months shall not pass before Dante himself experiences how hard it
is to return to Florence after exile.
† The Emperor Frederick II was notorious for his dissolute ways. The "Lord
Cardinal" Ottaviano degli Ubaldini was supposed to have said, "If there be
any soul, I have lost mine for the Ghibellines."

475

And thus, in going, questioned: "Whence the amaze
That holds thy senses wrapt?" I satisfied
The inquiry, and the sage enjoined me straight:
"Let thy safe memory store what thou hast heard
To thee importing harm; and note thou this,"
With his raised finger bidding me take heed,
"When thou shalt stand before her gracious beam,
Whose bright eye all surveys, she of thy life
The future tenor will to thee unfold."

Forthwith he to the left hand turned his feet:
We left the wall, and towards the middle space
Went by a path that to a valley strikes,
Which e'en thus high exhaled its noisome steam.

CANTO XI

Dante arrives at the verge of a rocky precipice which encloses the seventh circle, where he sees the sepulcher of Anastasius the Heretic. He pauses briefly behind the lid, to make himself capable by degrees of enduring the fetid smell that steams upward from the abyss. He is instructed by Virgil concerning the manner in which the three following circles are disposed, and what description of sinners is punished in each. He then inquires the reason why the carnal, the gluttonous, the avaricious and prodigal, the wrathful and gloomy, suffer not their punishments within the city of Dis. He next asks how the crime of usury is an offense against God; and at length the two Poets go towards the place from which a passage leads down to the seventh circle.

UPON THE utmost verge of a high bank,
    By craggy rocks walled round, we came,
Where woes beneath, more cruel yet, were suffered.

"My son! within these rocks," my guide began,
"Are three close circles in gradation placed,
As these which now thou leavest. Each one is full
Of spirits accurst; but that the sight alone
Hereafter may suffice thee, listen how
And for what cause in durance they abide.

"Of all malicious act abhorred in Heaven,
The end is injury; and all such end
Either by force or fraud works other's woe.
But fraud, because of man peculiar evil,

476

To God is more displeasing; and beneath,
The fraudulent are therefore doomed to endure
Severer pang. The violent occupy
All the first circle; and because, to force,
Three persons are obnoxious, in three rounds,
Each within other separate, is it framed.
To God, his neighbor, and himself, by man
Force may be offered; to himself I say,
And his possessions, as thou soon shalt hear
At full. Death, violent death, and painful wounds
Upon his neighbor he inflicts; and wastes,
By devastation, pillage, and the flames,
His substance. Slayers, and each one that smites
In malice, plunderers, and all robbers, hence
The torment undergo of the first round,
In different herds. Man can do violence
To himself and his own blessings: and for this,
He, in the second round must aye deplore
With unavailing penitence his crime,
Whoe'er deprives himself of life and light,
In reckless lavishment his talent wastes,
And sorrows there where he should dwell in joy.
To God may force be offered, in the heart
Denying and blaspheming His high power,
And Nature with her kindly law condemning.
And thence the inmost round marks with its seal
Sodom, and Cahors,* and all such as speak
Contemptuously of the Godhead in their hearts.
   "Fraud, that in every conscience leaves a sting,
May be by man employed on one, whose trust
He wins, or on another who withholds
Strict confidence. Seems as the latter way
Broke but the bond of love which Nature makes.
Whence in the second circle have their nest,
Dissimulation, witchcraft, flatteries,
Theft, falsehood, simony, all who seduce
To lust, or set their honesty at pawn,
With such vile scum as these. The other way

* Sodom is synonymous with sexual perversion; Cahors, in southern France,
with usury.

Forgets both Nature's general love, and that
Which thereto added afterward gives birth
To special faith. Whence in the lesser circle,*
Point of the universe, dread seat of Dis,
The traitor is eternally consumed."

  I thus: "Instructor, clearly thy discourse
Proceeds, distinguishing the hideous chasm
And its inhabitants with skill exact.
But tell me this: they of the dull, fat pool,
Whom the rain beats, or whom the tempest drives,
Or who with tongues so fierce conflicting meet,
Wherefore within the city fire-illumed
Are not these punished, if God's wrath be on them?
And if it be not, wherefore in such guise
Are they condemned?" He answer thus returned:
"Wherefore in dotage wanders thus thy mind,
Not so accustomed? or what other thoughts
Possess it? Dwell not in thy memory
The words, wherein thy ethic page describes
Three dispositions adverse to Heaven's will,
Incontinence, malice, and mad brutishness,
And how incontinence the least offends
God, and least guilt incurs? If well thou note
This judgment, and remember who they are,
Without these walls to vain repentance doomed,
Thou shalt discern why they apart are placed
From these fell spirits, and less doleful pours
Justice Divine on them its vengeance down."

CANTO XII

Descending by a very rugged way into the seventh circle, where the violent
are punished, Dante and his leader find it guarded by the Minotaur; whose
fury being pacified by Virgil, they step downwards from crag to crag; till,
drawing near the bottom, they descry a river of blood, wherein are tormented such as have committed violence against their neighbor. At these,

* It is "the lesser circle" because it is farther down, Dante's Hell being a cone
down to the center of the earth, a hole made by Satan when he fell from
Heaven.

when they strive to emerge from the blood, a troop of Centaurs, running along the side of the river, aim their arrows; and three of their band opposing our travelers at the foot of the steep, until Virgil prevails upon one of them to carry them both across the stream; and on their passage, Dante is informed by him of the course of the river, and of those that are punished therein.

THE PLACE, where to descend the precipice
   We came, was rough as Alp; and on its verge
Such object lay, as every eye would shun.
   As is that ruin, which Adice's stream
On this side Trento struck, shouldering the wave,
Or loosed by earthquake or for lack of prop;
For from the mountain's summit, whence it moved
To the low level, so the headlong rock
Is shivered, that some passage it might give
To him who from above would pass; e'en such
Into the chasm was that descent: and there
At point of the disparted ridge lay stretched
The infamy of Crete, detested brood *
Of the feigned heifer: and at sight of us
It gnawed itself, as one with rage distract.
To him my guide exclaimed: "Perchance thou deemest
The king of Athens here, who, in the world
Above, thy death contrived. Monster! avaunt!
He comes not tutored by thy sister's art,
But to behold your torments is he come."
   Like to a bull, that with impetuous spring
Darts, at the moment when the fatal blow
Hath struck him, but unable to proceed
Plunges on either side; so saw I plunge
The Minotaur; whereat the sage exclaimed:
"Run to the passage! while he storms, 'tis well
That thou descend." Thus down our road we took
Through those dilapidated crags, that oft
Moved underneath my feet, to weight like theirs
Unused. I pondering went, and thus he spake:
"Perhaps thy thoughts are of this ruined steep,
Guarded by the brute violence, which I

* The Minotaur, half-bull, half-man, symbol of violence and bestiality in this seventh circle.

Have vanquished now. Know then, that when I first
Hither descended to the nether Hell,
This rock was not yet fallen. But past doubt
(If well I mark), not long ere He arrived,
Who carried off from Dis the mighty spoil
Of the highest circle, then through all its bounds
Such trembling seized the deep concave and foul,
I thought the universe was thrilled with love,
Whereby, there are who deem, the world hath oft
Been into chaos turned: and in that point,
Here, and elsewhere, that old rock toppled down.
But fix thine eyes beneath: the river of blood
Approaches, in which all those are steeped,
Who have by violence injured." O blind lust!
O foolish wrath! who so dost goad us on
In the brief life, and in the eternal then
Thus miserably o'erwhelm us. I beheld
An ample foss, that in a bow was bent,
As circling all the plain; for so my guide
Had told. Between it and the rampart's base,
On trail ran Centaurs, with keen arrows armed,
As to the chase they on the earth were wont.

    At seeing us descend they each one stood;
And issuing from the troop, three sped with bows
And missile weapons chosen first; of whom
One cried from far: "Say, to what pain ye come
Condemned, who down this steep have journeyed. Speak
From whence ye stand, or else the bow I draw."

    To whom my guide: "Our answer shall be made
To Chiron, there, when nearer him we come.
Ill was thy mind, thus ever quick and rash."
Then me he touched, and spake: "Nessus is this,
Who for the fair Deïanira died,
And wrought himself revenge for his own fate.
He in the midst, that on his breast looks down,
Is the great Chiron who Achilles nursed;
That other, Pholus, prone to wrath." Around
The foss these go by thousands, aiming shafts
At whatsoever spirit dares emerge
From out the blood, more than his guilt allows.

We to those beasts, that rapid strode along,
Drew near; when Chiron took an arrow forth,
And with the notch pushed back his shaggy beard
To the cheek-bone, then, his great mouth to view
Exposing, to his fellows thus exclaimed:
"Are ye aware, that he who comes behind
Moves what he touches? The feet of the dead
Are not so wont." My trusty guide, who now
Stood near his breast, where the two natures join,
Thus made reply: "He is indeed alive,
And solitary so must needs by me
Be shown the gloomy vale, thereto induced
By strict necessity, not by delight.
She left her joyful music in the sky,
Who this new office to my care consigned.
He is no robber, no dark spirit I.
But by that virtue, which empowers my step
To tread so wild a path, grant us, I pray,
One of thy band, whom we may trust secure,
Who to the ford may lead us, and convey
Across, him mounted on his back; for he
Is not a spirit that may walk the air."

Then on his right breast turning, Chiron thus
To Nessus spake: "Return, and be their guide.
And if ye chance to cross another troop,
Command them keep aloof." Onward we moved,
The faithful escort by our side, along
The border of the crimson-seething flood,
Whence, from those steeped within, loud shrieks arose.

Some there I marked, as high as to their brow
Immersed, of whom the mighty Centaur thus:
"These are the souls of tyrants, who were given
To blood and rapine. Here they wail aloud
Their merciless wrongs. Here Alexander dwells,
And Dionysius fell, who many a year
Of woe wrought for fair Sicily. That brow,
Whereon the hair so jetty clustering hangs,
Is Azzolino; that with flaxen locks
Obizzo of Este, in the world destroyed
By his foul step-son." To the bard revered

481

I turned me round, and thus he spake: "Let him
Be to thee now first leader, me but next
To him in rank." Then farther on a space
The Centaur paused, near some, who to the throat
Were upright from the wave; and, showing us
A spirit by itself apart retired,
Exclaimed: "He in God's bosom smote the heart,*
Which yet is honored on the bank of Thames."

    A race I next espied who held the head,
And even all the bust, above the stream.
'Midst these I many a face remembered well.
Thus shallow more and more the blood became,
So that at last it but imbrued the feet;
And there our passage lay athwart the foss.

    "As ever on this side the boiling wave
Thou seest diminishing," the Centaur said,
"So on the other, be thou well assured,
It lower still and lower sinks its bed,
Till in that part it re-uniting join,
Where 'tis the lot of tyranny to mourn.
There Heaven's stern justice lays chastising hand
On Attila, who was the scourge of earth,
On Sextus and on Pyrrhus, and extracts
Tears ever by the seething flood unlocked
From the Rinieri, of Corneto this,
Pazzo the other named, who filled the ways †
With violence and war." This said, he turned,
And quitting us, alone repassed the ford.

CANTO XIII

Still in the seventh circle, Dante enters its second compartment, which contains both those who have done violence on their own persons and those who have violently consumed their goods; the first changed into rough and knotted trees whereon the harpies build their nests, the latter chased and torn by black female mastiffs. Among the former, Piero delle

* Guy de Montfort murdered Prince Henry of England in 1271, "in God's bosom,"—i.e. in the church at Viterbo.
† The two Italians were highwaymen.

Vigne is one who tells him the cause of his having committed suicide, and moreover in what manner the souls are transformed into those trunks. Of the latter crew, he recognizes Lano, a Sienese, and Giacomo, a Paduan: and lastly, a Florentine, who had hung himself from his own roof, speaks to him of the calamities of his countrymen.

ERE NESSUS yet had reached the other bank,
   We entered on a forest, where no track
Of steps had worn a way. Not verdant there
The foliage, but of dusky hue; not light
The boughs and tapering, but with knares deformed
And matted thick: fruits there were none, but thorns
Instead, with venom filled. Less sharp than these,
Less intricate the brakes, wherein abide
Those animals, that hate the cultured fields,
Betwixt Corneto and Cecina's stream.
   Here the brute Harpies make their nest, the same
Who from the Strophades the Trojan band
Drove with dire boding of their future woe.
Broad are their pennons, of the human form
Their neck and countenance, armed with talons keen
The feet, and the huge belly fledged with wings.
These sit and wail on the drear mystic wood.
   The kind instructor in these words began:
"Ere farther thou proceed, know thou art now
In the second round, and shalt be, till thou come
Upon the horrid sand: look therefore well
Around thee, and such things thou shalt behold,
As would my speech discredit." On all sides
I heard sad plainings breathe, and none could see
From whom they might have issued. In amaze
Fast bound I stood. He, as it seemed, believed
That I had thought so many voices came
From some amid those thickets close concealed,
And thus his speech resumed: "If thou lop off
A single twig from one of those ill plants,
The thought thou hast conceived shall vanish quite."
   Thereat a little stretching forth my hand,
From a great wilding gathered I a branch,
And straight the trunk exclaimed: "Why pluck thou me?"

Then, as the dark blood trickled down its side,
These words it added: "Wherefore tear me thus?
Is there no touch of mercy in thy breast?
We once were men, that now are rooted here.
Thy hand might well have spared us, had we been
The souls of serpents." As a brand yet green,
That burning at one end from the other sends
A groaning sound, and hisses with the wind
That forces out its way, so burst at once
Forth from the broken splinter words and blood.
   I, letting fall the bough, remained as one
Assailed by terror; and the sage replied:
"If he, O injured spirit! could have believed
What he hath seen but in my verse described,
He never against thee had stretched his hand.
But I, because the thing surpassed belief,
Prompted him to this deed, which even now
Myself I rue. But tell him, who thou wast;
That, for this wrong to do thee some amends,
In the upper world (for thither to return
Is granted him) thy fame he may revive."
   "That pleasant word of thine," the trunk replied,
"Hath so inveigled me, that I from speech
Cannot refrain, wherein if I indulge
A little longer, in the snare detained,
Count it not grievous. I it was, who held
Both keys to Frederick's heart, and turned the wards,
Opening and shutting, with a skill so sweet,
That besides me, into his inmost breast
Scarce any other could admittance find.
The faith I bore to my high charge was such,
It cost me the life-blood that warmed my veins.
That Envy, who ne'er turned her gloating eyes
From Cæsar's household, common vice and pest
Of courts, 'gainst me inflamed the minds of all;
And to Augustus they so spread the flame,
That my glad honors changed to bitter woes.
My soul, disdainful and disgusted, sought
Refuge in death from scorn, and I became,

484

Just as I was, unjust toward myself.
By the new roots, which fix this stem, I swear,
That never faith I broke to my liege lord,
Who merited such honor; and of you,
If any to the world indeed return,
Clear he from wrong my memory, that lies
Yet prostrate under envy's cruel blow."

First somewhat pausing, till the mournful words
Were ended, then to me the bard began:
"Lose not the time; but speak, and of him ask,
If more thou wish to learn." Whence I replied:
"Question thou him again of whatsoe'er
Will, as thou think'st, content me; for no power
Have I to ask, such pity is at my heart."

He thus resumed: "So may he do for thee
Freely what thou entreatest, as thou yet
Be pleased, imprisoned spirit! to declare,
How in these gnarled joints the soul is tied;
And whether any ever from such frame
Be loosened, if thou canst, that also tell."

Thereat the trunk breathed hard, and the wind soon
Changed into sounds articulate like these:
"Briefly ye shall be answered. When departs
The fierce soul from the body, by itself
Thence torn asunder, to the seventh gulf
By Minos doomed, into the wood it falls,
No place assigned, but wheresoever chance
Hurls it; there sprouting, as a grain of spelt,
It rises to a sapling, growing thence
A savage plant. The Harpies, on its leaves
Then feeding, cause both pain, and for the pain
A vent to grief. We, as the rest, shall come
For our own spoils, yet not so that with them
We may again be clad; for what a man
Takes from himself it is not just he have.
Here we perforce shall drag them; and throughout
The dismal glade our bodies shall be hung,
Each on the wild thorn of his wretched shade."

Attentive yet to listen to the trunk

485

We stood, expecting further speech, when us
A noise surprised; as when a man perceives
The wild boar and the hunt approach his place
Of stationed watch, who of the beasts and boughs
Loud rustling round him hears. And lo! there came
Two naked, torn with briers, in headlong flight,
That they before them broke each fan o' the wood.
"Haste now," the foremost cried, "now haste thee, death!"
The other, as seemed, impatient of delay,
Exclaiming, "Lano! not so bent for speed
Thy sinews, in the lists of Toppo's field."
And then, for that perchance no longer breath
Sufficed him, of himself and of a bush
One group he made. Behind them was the wood
Full of black female mastiffs, gaunt and fleet
As greyhounds that have newly slipped the leash.
On him, who squatted down, they stuck their fangs,
And having rent him piecemeal bore away
The tortured limbs. My guide then seized my hand,
And led me to the thicket, which in vain
Mourned through its bleeding wounds: "O Giacomo
Of Sant' Andrea! what avails it thee,"
It cried, "that of me thou hast made thy screen?
For thy ill life, what blame on me recoils?"
    When o'er it he had paused, my master spake:
"Say who wast thou, that at so many points
Breathest out with blood thy lamentable speech?"
    He answered: "O ye spirits! arrived in time
To spy the shameful havoc that from me
My leaves hath severed thus, gather them up,
And at the foot of their sad parent-tree
Carefully lay them. In that city I dwelt,
Who for the Baptist her first patron changed,
Whence he for this shall cease not with his art
To work her woe: and if there still remained not
On Arno's passage some faint glimpse of him,
Those citizens, who reared once more her walls
Upon the ashes left by Attila,
Had labored without profit of their toil.
I slung the fatal noose from my own roof."

They arrive at the beginning of the third of those compartments into which this seventh circle is divided. It is a plain of dry and hot sand, where three kinds of violence are punished; namely, against God, against Nature, and against Art; and those who have thus sinned are tormented by flakes of fire, which are eternally showering down upon them. Among the violent against God is found Capaneus, whose blasphemies they hear. Next, turning to the left along the forest of self-slayers, and having journeyed a little onwards, they meet with a streamlet of blood that issues from the forest and traverses the sandy plain. Here Virgil speaks to our Poet of a huge ancient statue that stands within Mount Ida in Crete, from a fissure in which statue there is a dripping of tears, from which the said streamlet, together with the three other infernal rivers, is formed.

SOON AS THE charity of native land
   Wrought in my bosom, I the scattered leaves
Collected, and to him restored, who now
Was hoarse with utterance. To the limit thence
We came, which from the third the second round
Divides, and where of justice is displayed
Contrivance horrible. Things then first seen
More clear to manifest, I tell how next
A plain we reached, that from its sterile bed
Each plant repelled. The mournful wood waves round
Its garland on all sides, as round the wood
Spreads the sad foss. There, on the very edge,
Our steps we stayed. It was an area wide
Of arid sand and thick, resembling most
The soil that once by Cato's foot was trod.

   Vengeance of Heaven! Oh! how shouldst thou be feared
By all, who read what here mine eyes beheld.

   Of naked spirits many a flock I saw,
All weeping piteously, to different laws
Subjected; for on the earth some lay supine,
Some crouching close were seated, others paced
Incessantly around; the latter tribe
More numerous, those fewer who beneath
The torment lay, but louder in their grief.

   O'er all the sand fell slowly wafting down
Dilated flakes of fire, as flakes of snow

487

On Alpine summit, when the wind is hushed.
Unceasing was the play of wretched hands,
Now this, now that way glancing, to shake off
The heat, still falling fresh. I thus began:
"Instructor! thou who all things overcomest,
Except the hardy demons that rushed forth
To stop our entrance at the gate, say who
Is yon huge spirit, that, as seems, heeds not
The burning, but lies there in proud scorn,
As by the sultry tempest immatured?"

    Straight he himself, who was aware I asked
My guide of him, exclaimed: "Such as I was
When living, dead such now I am. If Jove
Weary his workman out, from whom in ire
He snatched the lightnings, that at my last day
Transfixed me; if the rest he weary out,
At their black smithy laboring by turns,
In Mongibello, while he cries aloud,

    'Help, help, good Mulciber!' * as once he cried
In the Phlegræan warfare; and the bolts
Launch he, full aimed at me, with all his might;
He never should enjoy a sweet revenge."

    Then thus my guide, in accent higher raised
Than I before had heard him: "Capaneus! †
Thou art more punished, in that this thy pride
Lives yet unquenched: no torment, save thy rage,
Were to thy fury pain proportioned full."

    Next turning round to me, with milder voice
He spake: "This of the seven kings was one,
Who girt the Theban walls with siege, and held,
As still he seems to hold, God in disdain,
And sets His high omnipotence at nought.
But, as I told him, his despiteful mood
Is ornament well suits the breast that wears it.
Follow me now; and look thou set not yet
Thy foot in the hot sand, but to the wood

---

* Mulciber is Vulcan, who forged in Mongibello (Mount Aetna) the thunder-bolts of Jove. Phlegra was the scene of the war between the gods and the giants.
† Capaneus, when he was besieging Thebes, defied Jupiter to protect it, and was struck by lightning as he scaled the wall. He is the type of the blasphemer.

488

Keep ever close." Silently we passed
To where there gushes from the forest's bound
A little brook, whose crimsoned wave yet lifts
My hair with horror. As the rill, that runs
From Bulicame, to be portioned out
Among the sinful women; so ran this
Down through the sand; its bottom and each bank
Stone-built, and either margin at its side,
Whereon I straight perceived our passage lay.
    "Of all that I have shown thee, since that gate
We entered first, whose threshold is to none
Denied, nought else so worthy of regard,
As is this river, has thine eye discerned,
O'er which the flaming volley all is quenched."
    So spake my guide; and I him thence besought,
That having given me appetite to know,
The food he too would give, that hunger craved.
    "In midst of ocean," forthwith he began,
"A desolate country lies, which Crete is named;
Under whose monarch, in old times, the world
Lived pure and chaste. A mountain rises there,
Called Ida, joyous once with leaves and streams,
Deserted now like a forbidden thing.
It was the spot which Rhea, Saturn's spouse,
Chose for the secret crib of Jupiter;
And better to conceal him, drowned in shouts
His infant cries. Within the mount, upright
An ancient form there stands, and huge, that turns
His shoulders towards Damiata; and at Rome,
As in his mirror, looks. Of finest gold
His head is shaped, pure silver are the breast
And arms, thence to the middle is of brass,
And downward all beneath well-tempered steel,
Save the right foot of potter's clay, on which
Than on the other more erect he stands.
Each part, except the gold, is rent throughout;
And from the fissure tears distil, which joined
Penetrate to that cave.* They in their course,

* The metals comprising the "ancient form" stand for the Golden, Silver,
Bronze, and Iron Ages. The tears of Time—or of all human generations since
the Golden Age—form the infernal rivers that flow into Cocytus.

Thus far precipitated down the rock,
From Acheron, and Styx, and Phlegethon;
Then by this straitened channel passing hence
Beneath, e'en to the lowest depth of all,
Form there Cocytus, of whose lake (thyself
Shalt see it) I here give thee no account."

Then I to him: "If from our world this sluice
Be thus derived; wherefore to us but now
Appears it at this edge?" He straight replied:
"The place, thou know'st, is round; and though great part
Thou have already passed, still to the left
Descending to the nethermost, not yet
Hast thou the circuit made of the whole orb.
Wherefore, if aught of new to us appear,
It needs not bring up wonder in thy looks."

Then I again inquired: "Where flow the streams
Of Phlegethon and Lethe? for of one
Thou tell'st not; and the other, of that shower,
Thou say'st, is formed." He answer thus returned:
"Doubtless thy questions all well pleased I hear.
Yet the red seething wave might have resolved
One thou proposest. Lethe thou shalt see,
But not within this hollow, in the place
Whither, to lave themselves, the spirits go,
Whose blame hath been by penitence removed."
He added: "Time is now we quit the wood.
Look thou my steps pursue: the margins give
Safe passage, unimpeded by the flames;
For over them all vapor is extinct."

CANTO XV

Taking their way upon one of the mounds by which the streamlet, spoken
of in the last Canto, was embanked, and having gone so far that they
could no longer have discerned the forest if they had turned round to look
for it, they meet a troop of spirits that come along the sand by the side
of the pier. These are they who have done violence to Nature; and
amongst them Dante distinguishes Brunetto Latini, who had been formerly

490

his master; with whom, turning a little backward, he holds a discourse which occupies the remainder of this Canto.

ONE OF THE solid margins bears us now
    Enveloped in the mist, that, from the stream
Arising, hovers o'er, and saves from fire
Both piers and water. As the Flemings rear
Their mound, 'twixt Ghent and Bruges, to chase back
The ocean, fearing his tumultuous tide
That drives toward them; or the Paduans theirs
Along the Brenta, to defend their towns
And castles, ere the genial warmth be felt
On Chiarentana's top; such were the mounds,
So framed, though not in height or bulk to these
Made equal, by the master, whosoe'er
He was, that raised them here. We from the wood
Were now so far removed, that turning round
I might not have discerned it, when we met
A troop of spirits, who came beside the pier.
    They each one eyed us, as at eventide
One eyes another under a new moon;
And toward us sharpened their sight, as keen
As an old tailor at his needle's eye.
    Thus narrowly explored by all the tribe,
One knew my face. He by the skirt
Caught me, and cried, "What wonder have we here?"
    And I, when he to me outstretched his arm,
Intently fixed my ken on his parched looks,
That, although smirched with fire, they hindered not
But I remembered him; and towards his face
My hand inclining, answered: "Ser Brunetto!
And are ye here?" He thus to me: "My son!
Oh let it not displease thee, if Brunetto
Latini but a little space with thee
Turn back, and leave his fellows to proceed."
    I thus to him replied: "Much as I can,
I thereto pray thee; and if thou be willing
That I here seat me with thee, I consent;
His leave, with whom I journey, first obtained."
    "O son!" said he, "whoever of this throng

491

One instant stops, lies then a hundred years,
No fan to ventilate him, when the fire
Smites sorest. Pass thou therefore on. I close
Will at thy garments walk, and then rejoin
My troop, who go mourning their endless doom."

    I dared not from the path descend to tread
On equal ground with him, but held my head
Bent down, as one who walks in reverent guise.

    "What chance or destiny," thus he began,
"Ere the last day, conducts thee here below?
And who is this that shows to thee the way?"

    "There up aloft," I answered, "in the life
Serene, I wandered in a valley lost,
Before mine age had to its fullness reached.
But yester-morn I left it: then once more
Into that vale returning, him I met;
And by this path homeward he leads me back."

    "If thou," he answered, "follow but thy star,
Thou canst not miss at last a glorious haven;
Unless in fairer days my judgment erred.
And if my fate so early had not chanced,
Seeing the Heavens thus bounteous to thee, I
Had gladly given thee comfort in thy work.
But that ungrateful and malignant race,
Who in old times came down from Fiesole,*
Ay and still smack of their rough mountain-flint,
Will for thy good deeds show thee enmity.
Nor wonder; for amongst ill-savored crabs
It suits not the sweet fig-tree lay her fruit.
Old fame reports them in the world for blind,
Covetous, envious, proud. Look to it well:
Take heed thou cleanse thee of their ways. For thee,
Thy fortune hath such honor in reserve,
That thou by either party shalt be craved
With hunger keen: but be the fresh herb far
From the goat's tooth. The herd of Fiesole

---

* Brunetto had written in his Treasure: "Afterwards the Romans besieged Fiesole, till at last they conquered it and brought it into subjection. Then they built upon the plain, which is at the foot of the high rocks on which that city stood, another city, that is now called Florence."

492

May of themselves make litter, not touch the plant,
If any such yet spring on their rank bed,
In which the holy seed revives, transmitted
From those true Romans, who still there remained,
When it was made the nest of so much ill."

    "Were all my wish fulfilled," I straight replied,
"Thou from the confines of man's nature yet
Hadst not been driven forth; for in my mind
Is fixed, and now strikes full upon my heart,
The dear, benign, paternal image, such
As thine was, when so lately thou didst teach me
The way for man to win eternity:
And how I prized the lesson, it behooves,
That, long as life endures, my tongue should speak.
What of my fate thou tell'st, that write I down;
For her I keep it, the celestial dame,
Who will know all, if I to her arrive.
This only would I have thee clearly note:
That, so my conscience have no plea against me,
Do Fortune as she list, I stand prepared.
Not new or strange such earnest to mine ear.
Speed Fortune then her wheel, as likes her best;
The clown his mattock; all things have their course."

    Thereat my sapient guide upon his right
Turned himself back, then looked at me, and spake:
"He listens to good purpose who takes note."

    I not the less still on my way proceed,
Discoursing with Brunetto, and inquire
Who are most known and chief among his tribe.

    "To know of some is well"; he thus replied,
"But of the rest silence may best beseem.
Time would not serve us for report so long.
In brief I tell thee, that all these were clerks,
Men of great learning and no less renown,
By one same sin polluted in the world.
With them is Priscian; and Accorso's son,*

---

* Priscian was a Latin grammarian, Francesco d'Accorso a jurist. The "servants' Servant" is the Pope who transferred Andrea de' Mozzi from the bishopric of Florence to the see of Vicenza (on the Bacchiglione).

493

Francesco herds among that wretched throng:
And, if the wish of so impure a blotch
Possessed thee, him thou also mightst have seen,
Who by the servants' Servant was transferred
From Arno's seat to Bacchiglione, where
His ill-strained nerves he left. I more would add,
But must from further speech and onward way
Alike desist; for yonder I behold
A mist new-risen on the sandy plain.
A company, with whom I may not sort,
Approaches. I commend my *Treasure* to thee,
Wherein I yet survive; my sole request."

This said, he turned, and seemed as one of those
Who o'er Verona's champain try their speed
For the green mantle; and of them he seemed,
Not he who loses but who gains the prize.

CANTO XVI

Journeying along the pier, which crosses the sand, they are now so near the end of it as to hear the noise of the stream falling into the eighth circle, when they meet the spirits of three military men. Judging Dante, from his dress, to be a countryman of theirs, they entreat him to stop. He complies, and speaks with them. The two Poets then reach the place where the water descends, this being the termination of the third compartment in the seventh circle. Here Virgil having thrown down into the hollow a cord, wherewith Dante was girdled, they behold at that signal a monstrous and horrible figure come swimming up to them.

NOW CAME I where the water's din was heard,
As down it fell into the other round,
Resounding like the hum of swarming bees:
When forth together issued from a troop,
That passed beneath the fierce tormenting storm,
Three spirits, running swift. They towards us came,
And each one cried aloud, "Oh! do thou stay,
Whom, by the fashion of thy garb, we deem
To be some inmate of our evil land."

Ah me! what wounds I marked upon their limbs,
Recent and old, inflicted by the flames.

E'en the remembrance of them grieves me yet.
   Attentive to their cry, my teacher paused,
And turned to me his visage, and then spake:
"Wait now: our courtesy these merit well:
And were 't not for the nature of the place,
Whence glide the fiery darts, I should have said,
That haste had better suited thee than them."
   They, when we stopped, resumed their ancient wail,
And, soon as they had reached us, all the three
Whirled round together in one restless wheel.
As naked champions, smeared with slippery oil,
Are wont, intent, to watch their place of hold
And vantage, ere in closer strife they meet;
Thus each one, as he wheeled, his countenance
At me directed, so that opposite
The neck moved ever to the twinkling feet.
   "If woe of this unsound and dreary waste,"
Thus one began, "added to our sad cheer
Thus peeled with flame, do call forth scorn on us
And our entreaties, let our great renown
Incline thee to inform us who thou art,
That dost imprint, with living feet unharmed,
The soil of Hell. He, in whose track thou seest
My steps pursuing, naked though he be
And reft of all, was of more high estate
Than thou believest; grandchild of the chaste
Gualdrada, him they Guidoguerra called,
Who in his lifetime many a noble act
Achieved, both by his wisdom and his sword.
The other, next to me that beats the sand,
Is Aldobrandi, name deserving well,
In the upper world, of honor; and myself,
Who in this torment do partake with them,
Am Rusticucci, whom, past doubt, my wife,
Of savage temper, more than aught beside
Hath to this evil brought." If from the fire
I had been sheltered, down amidst them straight
I then had cast me; nor my guide, I deem,
Would have restrained my going: but that fear
Of the dire burning vanquished the desire,

Which made me eager of their wished embrace.

I then began: "Not scorn, but grief much more,
Such as long time alone can cure, your doom
Fixed deep within me, soon as this my lord
Spake words, whose tenor taught me to expect
That such a race, as ye are, was at hand.
I am a countryman of yours, who still
Affectionate have uttered, and have heard
Your deeds and names renowned. Leaving the gall,
For the sweet fruit I go, that a sure guide
Hath promised to me. But behooves that far
As to the center first I downward tend."

"So may long space thy spirit guide thy limbs,"
He answer straight returned; "and so thy fame
Shine bright when thou art gone, as thou shalt tell,
If courtesy and valor, as they wont,
Dwell in our city, or have vanished clean."

"An upstart multitude and sudden gains,
Pride and excess, O Florence! have in thee
Engendered, so that now in tears thou mourn'st!"

Thus cried I, with my face upraised, and they
All three, who for an answer took my words,
Looked at each other, as men look when truth
Comes to their ear. "If at so little cost,"
They all at once rejoined, "thou satisfy
Others who question thee, O happy thou!
Gifted with words so apt to speak thy thought.
Wherefore, if thou escape this darksome clime,
Returning to behold the radiant stars,
When thou with pleasure shalt retrace the past,
See that of us thou speak among mankind."

This said, they broke the circle, and so swift
Fled, that as pinions seemed their nimble feet.

Not in so short a time might one have said
"Amen," as they had vanished. Straight my guide
Pursued his track. I followed: and small space
Had we passed onward, when the water's sound
Was now so near at hand, that we had scarce
Heard one another's speech for the loud din.

E'en as the river, that first holds its course

Unmingled, from the Mount of Vesulo,
On the left side of Apennine, toward
The east, which Acquacheta higher up
They call, ere it descend into the vale,
At Forlì, by that name no longer known,
Rebellows o'er Saint Benedict, rolled on
From the Alpine summit down a precipice,
Where space enough to lodge a thousand spreads;
Thus downward from a craggy steep we found
That this dark wave resounded, roaring loud,
So that the ear its clamor soon had stunned.

I had a cord that braced my girdle round,
Wherewith I once had thought fast bound to take
The painted leopard. This when I had all
Unloosened from me (so my master bade)
I gathered up, and stretched it forth to him.
Then to the right he turned, and from the brink
Standing few paces distant, cast it down
Into the deep abyss. "And somewhat strange,"
Thus to myself I spake, "signal so strange
Betokens, which my guide with earnest eye
Thus follows." Ah! what caution must men use
With those who look not at the deed alone,
But spy into the thoughts with subtle skill.

"Quickly shall come," he said, "what I expect;
Thine eye discover quickly that, whereof
Thy thought is dreaming." Ever to that truth,
Which but the semblance of a falsehood wears,
A man, if possible, should bar his lip;
Since, although blameless, he incurs reproach.
But silence here were vain; and by these notes,
Which now I sing, reader, I swear to thee,
So may they favor find to latest times!
That through the gross and murky air I spied
A shape come swimming up, that might have quelled
The stoutest heart with wonder; in such guise
As one returns, who hath been down to loose
An anchor grappled fast against some rock,
Or to aught else that in the salt wave lies,
Who, upward springing, close draws in his feet.

The monster Geryon is described; to whom while Virgil is speaking in order that he may carry them both down to the next circle, Dante, by permission, goes a little farther along the edge of the void, to descry the third species of sinners contained in this compartment, namely, those who have done violence to Art; and then returning to his master, they both descend, seated on the back of Geryon.

Lo! THE FELL monster with the deadly sting,
  Who passes mountains, breaks through fenced walls
And firm embattled spears, and with his filth
Taints all the world." Thus me my guide addressed,
And beckoned him, that he should come to shore,
Near to the stony causeway's utmost edge.
    Forthwith that image vile of Fraud appeared,
His head and upper part exposed on land,
But laid not on the shore his bestial train.
His face the semblance of a just man's wore,
So kind and gracious was its outward cheer;
The rest was serpent all: two shaggy claws
Reached to the arm-pits; and the back and breast,
And either side, were painted o'er with nodes
And orbits. Colors variegated more
Nor Turks nor Tartars e'er on cloth of state
With interchangeable embroidery wove,
Nor spread Arachne o'er her curious loom.
As oft-times a light skiff, moored to the shore,
Stands part in water, part upon the land;
Or, as where dwells the greedy German boor,
The beaver settles, watching for his prey;
So on the rim, that fenced the sand with rock,
Sat perched the fiend of evil. In the void
Glancing, his tail upturned its venomous fork,
With sting like scorpion's armed. Then thus my guide:
"Now need our way must turn few steps apart,
Far as to that ill beast, who couches there."
    Thereat, toward the right our downward course
We shaped, and, better to escape the flame
And burning marle, ten paces on the verge

Proceeded. Soon as we to him arrive,
A little farther on mine eye beholds
A tribe of spirits, seated on the sand
Near to the void. Forthwith my master spake:
"That to the full thy knowledge may extend
Of all this round contains, go now, and mark
The mien these wear: but hold not long discourse.
Till thou returnest, I with him meantime
Will parley, that to us he may vouchsafe
The aid of his strong shoulders." Thus alone,
Yet forward on the extremity I paced
Of that seventh circle, where the mournful tribe
Were seated. At the eyes forth gushed their pangs.
Against the vapors and the torrid soil
Alternately their shifting hands they plied.
Thus use the dogs in summer still to ply
Their jaws and feet by turns, when bitten sore
By gnats, or flies, or gadflies swarming round.

   Noting the visages of some, who lay
Beneath the pelting of that dolorous fire,
One of them all I knew not; but perceived
That, pendent from his neck, each bore a pouch
With colors and with emblems various marked,
On which it seemed as if their eye did feed.

   My guide already seated on the haunch
Of the fierce animal I found; and thus
He me encouraged. "Be thou stout: be bold.
Down such a steep flight must we now descend.
Mount thou before: for, that no power the tail
May have to harm thee, I will be in the midst."

   As one who hath an ague fit so near,
His nails already are turned blue, and he
Quivers all o'er, if he but eye the shade;
Such was my cheer at hearing of his words.
But shame soon interposed her threat, who makes
The servant bold in presence of his lord.

   I settled me upon those shoulders huge,
And would have said, but that the words to aid
My purpose came not, "Look thou clasp me firm."
   But he whose succor then not first I proved,

Soon as I mounted, in his arms aloft,
Embracing, held me up; and thus he spake:
"Geryon! now move thee: be thy wheeling gyres
Of ample circuit, easy thy descent.
Think on the unusual burden thou sustainest."

As a small vessel, backening out from land,
Her station quits; so thence the monster loosed,
And, when he felt himself at large, turned round
There, where the breast had been, his forked tail.
Thus, like an eel, outstretched at length he steered,
Gathering the air up with retractile claws.

Not greater was the dread, when Phaëton
The reins let drop at random, whence high heaven,
Whereof signs yet appear, was wrapped in flames;
Nor when ill-fated Icarus perceived,
By liquefaction of the scalded wax,
The trusted pennons loosened from his loins,
His sire exclaiming loud, "Ill way thou keep'st";
Than was my dread, when round me on each part
The air I viewed, and other object none,
Save the fell beast. He, slowly sailing, wheels
His downward motion, unobserved of me,
But that the wind, arising to my face,
Breathes on me from below. Now on our right
I heard the cataract beneath us leap
With hideous crash; whence bending down to explore,
New terror I conceived at the steep plunge;
For flames I saw, and wailings smote mine ear:
So that, all trembling, close I crouched my limbs,
And then distinguished, unperceived before,
By the dread torments that on every side
Drew nearer, how our downward course we wound.

As falcon, that hath long been on the wing,
But lure nor bird hath seen, while in despair
The falconer cries, "Ah me! thou stoop'st to earth,"
Wearied descends, whence nimbly he arose
In many an airy wheel, and lighting sits
At distance from his lord in angry mood;
So Geryon lighting places us on foot
Low down at base of the deep-furrowed rock.

And, of his burden there discharged, forthwith
Sprang forward, like an arrow from the string.

CANTO XVIII

The Poet describes the situation and form of the eighth circle, divided into
ten gulfs, which contain as many different descriptions of fraudulent sinners; but in the present Canto he treats only of two sorts: the first is of
those who, either for their own pleasure, or for that of another, have
seduced any woman from her duty; and these are scourged of demons in
the first gulf: the other sort is of flatterers, who in the second gulf are
condemned to remain immersed in filth.

THERE IS A place within the depths of Hell
    Called Malebolge, all of rock dark-stained
With hue ferruginous, e'en as the steep
That round it circling winds. Right in the midst
Of that abominable region yawns
A spacious gulf profound, whereof the frame
Due time shall tell. The circle, that remains,
Throughout its round, between the gulf and base
Of the high craggy banks, successive forms
Ten bastions, in its hollow bottom raised.

    As where, to guard the walls, full many a foss
Begirds some stately castle, sure defense
Affording to the space within; so here
Were modeled these: and as like fortresses,
E'en from their threshold to the brink without,
Are flanked with bridges; from the rock's low base
Thus flinty paths advanced, that 'cross the moles
And dikes struck onward far as to the gulf,
That in one bound collected cuts them off.
Such was the place, wherein we found ourselves
From Geryon's back dislodged. The bard to left
Held on his way, and I behind him moved.

    On our right hand new misery I saw,
New pains, new executioners of wrath,
That swarming peopled the first chasm. Below
Were naked sinners. Hitherward they came,

Meeting our faces, from the middle point;
With us beyond, but with a larger stride.
E'en thus the Romans, when the year returns
Of Jubilee, with better speed to rid
The thronging multitudes, their means devise
For such as pass the bridge; that on one side
All front toward the Castle, and approach
Saint Peter's fane, on the other towards the Mount.

Each diverse way, along the grisly rock,
Horned demons I beheld, with lashes huge,
That on their back unmercifully smote.
Ah! how they made them bound at the first stripe!
None for the second waited, nor the third.

Meantime, as on I passed, one met my sight,
Whom soon as viewed, "Of him," cried I, "not yet
Mine eye hath had his fill." I therefore stayed
My feet to scan him, and the teacher kind
Paused with me, and consented I should walk
Backward a space; and the tormented spirit,
Who thought to hide him, bent his visage down,
But it availed him nought; for I exclaimed:
"Thou who dost cast thine eye upon the ground,
Unless thy features do belie thee much,
Venedico art thou. But what brings thee
Into this bitter seasoning?" He replied:
"Unwillingly I answer to thy words.
But thy clear speech, that to my mind recalls
The world I once inhabited, constrains me.
Know then 't was I who led fair Ghisola
To do the Marquis' will, however fame
The shameful tale have bruited. Nor alone,
Bologna hither sendeth me to mourn;
Rather with us the place is so o'erthronged,
That not so many tongues this day are taught,
Betwixt the Reno and Savena's stream,
To answer *Sipa* * in their country's phrase.
And if of that securer proof thou need,
Remember but our craving thirst for gold."

* Bologna is situated between the two above-named rivers. *Sipa* is *sì* (yes) in
the Bolognese dialect.

Him speaking thus, a demon with his thong
Struck and exclaimed, "Away, corrupter! here
Women are none for sale." Forthwith I joined
My escort, and few paces thence we came
To where a rock forth issued from the bank.
That easily ascended, to the right
Upon its splinter turning, we depart
From those eternal barriers. When arrived
Where, underneath, the gaping arch lets pass
The scourged souls: "Pause here," the teacher said,
"And let these others miserable now
Strike on thy ken; faces not yet beheld,
For that together they with us have walked."

From the old bridge we eyed the pack, who came
From the other side toward us, like the rest,
Excoriate from the lash. My gentle guide,
By me unquestioned, thus his speech resumed:
"Behold that lofty shade, who this way tends,
And seems too woe-begone to drop a tear.
How yet the regal aspect he retains!
Jason is he, whose skill and prowess won
The ram from Colchis. To the Lemnian isle
His passage thither led him, when those bold
And pitiless women had slain all their males.
There he with tokens and fair witching words
Hypsipyle beguiled, a virgin young,
Who first had all the rest herself beguiled.
Impregnated, he left her there forlorn:
Such is the guilt condemns him to this pain;
Here, too, Medea's injuries are avenged.
All bear him company, who like deceit
To his have practiced. And thus much to know
Of the first vale suffice thee, and of those
Whom its keen torments urge." Now had we come
Where, crossing the next pier, the straitened path
Bestrides its shoulders to another arch.

Hence, in the second chasm we heard the ghosts,
Who gibber in low melancholy sounds,
With wide-stretched nostrils snort, and on themselves
Smite with their palms. Upon the banks a scurf,

503

From the foul steam condensed, encrusting hung,
That held sharp combat with the sight and smell.

So hollow is the depth, that from no part,
Save on the summit of the rocky span,
Could I distinguish aught. Thus far we came;
And thence I saw, within the foss below,
A crowd immersed in ordure, that appeared
Draff of the human body. There beneath
Searching with eye inquisitive, I marked
One with his head so grimed, 'twere hard to deem
If he were clerk or layman. Loud he cried:
"Why greedily thus bendest more on me,
Than on these other filthy ones, thy ken?"

"Because, if true my memory," I replied,
"I heretofore have seen thee with dry locks;
And thou Alessio art, of Lucca sprung.
Therefore than all the rest I scan thee more."

Then beating on his brain, these words he spake:
"Me thus low down my flatteries have sunk,
Wherewith I ne'er enough could glut my tongue."

My leader thus: "A little farther stretch
Thy face, that thou the visage well mayst note
Of that besotted, sluttish courtesan,
Who there doth rend her with defiled nails,
Now crouching down, now risen on her feet.
Thaïs is this, the harlot, whose false lip
Answered her doting paramour that asked,
'Thankest me much?'—'Say rather, wondrously.'
And, seeing this, here satiate be our view."

CANTO XIX

They come to the third gulf, wherein are punished those who have been guilty of simony. These are fixed with the head downwards in certain apertures, so that no more of them than the legs appears without, and on the soles of their feet are seen burning flames. Dante is taken down by his guide into the bottom of the gulf; and there finds Pope Nicholas the Fifth, whose evil deeds, together with those of other pontiffs, are bitterly reprehended. Virgil then carries him up again to the arch, which affords them a passage over the following gulf.

504

WOE TO THEE, Simon Magus! woe to you,
His wretched followers! who the things of God,
Which should be wedded unto goodness, them,
Rapacious as ye are, do prostitute
For gold and silver in adultery.
Now must the trumpet sound for you, since yours
Is the third chasm. Upon the following vault
We now had mounted, where the rock impends
Directly o'er the center of the foss.

Wisdom Supreme! how wonderful the art,
Which Thou dost manifest in Heaven, in earth,
And in the evil world, how just a meed
Allotting by Thy virtue unto all.

I saw the livid stone, throughout the sides
And in its bottom full of apertures,
All equal in their width, and circular each.
Nor ample less nor larger they appeared
Than, in Saint John's fair dome of me beloved,
Those framed to hold the pure baptismal streams,
One of the which I brake, some few years past,
To save a whelming infant: and be this
A seal to undeceive whoever doubts
The motive of my deed. From out the mouth
Of every one emerged a sinner's feet,
And of the legs high upward as the calf.
The rest beneath was hid. On either foot
The soles were burning; whence the flexile joints
Glanced with such violent motion, as had snapped
Asunder cords or twisted withes. As flame,
Feeding on unctuous matter, glides along
The surface, scarcely touching where it moves;
So here, from heel to point, glided the flames.

"Master! say who is he, than all the rest
Glancing in fiercer agony, on whom
A ruddier flame doth prey?" I thus inquired.

"If thou be willing," he replied, "that I
Carry thee down, where least the slope bank falls,
He of himself shall tell thee, and his wrongs."

I then: "As pleases thee, to me is best.
Thou art my lord; and know'st that ne'er I quit

Thy will: what silence hides, that knowest thou."
Thereat on the fourth pier we came, we turned,
And on our left descended to the depth,
A narrow strait, and perforated close.
Nor from his side my leader set me down,
Till to his orifice he brought, whose limb
Quivering expressed his pang. "Whoe'er thou art,
Sad spirit! thus reversed, and as a stake
Driven in the soil," I in these words began;
"If thou be able, utter forth thy voice."

    He shouted: "Ha! already standest there?
Already standest there, O Boniface! *
By many a year the writing played me false.
So early dost thou surfeit with the wealth,
For which thou feared not in guile to take
The lovely lady, and then mangle her?"

    I felt as those who, piercing not the drift
Of answer made them, stand as if exposed
In mockery, nor know what to reply;
When Virgil thus admonished: "Tell him quick,
'I am not he, not he whom thou believest.' "

    And I, as was enjoined me, straight replied.

    That heard, the spirit all did wrench his feet,
And, sighing, next in woeful accent spake:
"What then of me requirest? If to know
So much imports thee, who I am, that thou
Hast therefore down the bank descended, learn
That in the mighty mantle I was robed,
And of a she-bear was indeed the son,
So eager to advance my whelps, that there
My having in my purse above I stowed,
And here myself. Under my head are dragged
The rest, my predecessors in the guilt
Of simony. Stretched at their length, they lie
Along an opening in the rock. 'Midst them
I also low shall fall, soon as he comes,

---

* The speaker, Pope Nicholas III, mistakes Dante for Boniface VIII, who was pope at the time of the vision, dying in 1303. Boniface was an illustrious pope, but was accused (wrongly) of having wrested the Church, "the lovely lady," by guile from Celestine V.

For whom I took thee, when so hastily
I questioned. But already longer time
Hath passed, since my soles kindled, and I thus
Upturned have stood, than is his doom to stand
Planted with fiery feet. For after him,
One yet of deeds more ugly shall arrive,
From forth the west, a shepherd without law,*
Fated to cover both his form and mine.

    I know not if I here too far presumed,
But in this strain I answered: "Tell me now,
What treasures from Saint Peter at the first
Our Lord demanded, when he put the keys
Into his charge? Surely He asked no more
But 'Follow me!' Nor Peter, nor the rest,
Or gold or silver of Matthias took,
When lots were cast upon the forfeit place
Of the condemned soul. Abide thou then;
Thy punishment of right is merited:
And look thou well to that ill-gotten coin,
Which against Charles thy hardihood inspired.†
If reverence of the keys restrained me not,
Which thou in happier time didst hold, I yet
Severer speech might use. Your avarice
O'ercasts the world with mourning, under foot
Treading the good, and raising bad men up.
Of gold and silver ye have made your god,
Differing wherein from the idolater,
But that he worships one, a hundred ye?
Ah, Constantine! to how much ill gave birth,
Not thy conversion, but that plenteous dower
Which the first wealthy Father gained from thee."

    Meanwhile, as thus I sung, he, whether wrath
Or conscience smote him, violent upsprang
Spinning on either sole. I do believe
My teacher well was pleased, with so composed
A lip he listened ever to the sound
Of the true words I uttered. In both arms

* Dante damns another post-1300 pontiff, Clement V, who was responsible for the transfer of the papacy to Avignon.
† Nicholas III in vain endeavored to marry his niece to a nephew of Charles of Anjou, King of Naples and Sicily.

He caught, and, to his bosom lifting me,
Upward retraced the way of his descent.

Nor weary of his weight, he pressed me close,
Till to the summit of the rock we came,
Our passage from the fourth to the fifth pier.
His cherished burden there gently he placed
Upon the rugged rock and steep, a path
Not easy for the clambering goat to mount.

Thence to my view another vale appeared.

CANTO XX

The Poet relates the punishment of such as presumed, while living, to
predict future events. It is to have their faces reversed and set the contrary
way on their limbs, so that, being deprived of the power to see before
them, they are constrained ever to walk backwards. Among these Virgil
points out to him Amphiaraüs, Tiresias, Aruns, and Manto (from the
mention of whom he takes occasion to speak of the origin of Mantua),
together with several others, who had practiced the arts of divination and
astrology.

AND NOW the verse proceeds to torments new,
    Fit argument of this the twentieth strain
Of the first song, whose awful theme records
The spirits whelmed in woe. Earnest I looked
Into the depth that opened to my view,
Moistened with tears of anguish, and beheld
A tribe that came along the hollow vale,
In silence weeping: such their step as walk
Choirs, chanting solemn litanies, on earth.

As on them more direct mine eye descends,
Each wondrously seemed to be reversed
At the neck-bone, so that the countenance
Was from the reins averted; and because
None might before him look, they were compelled
To advance with backward gait. Thus one perhaps
Hath been by force of palsy clean transposed,
But I ne'er saw it nor believe it so.

Now, reader! think within thyself, so God
Fruit of thy reading give thee! how I long

Could keep my visage dry, when I beheld
Near me our form distorted in such guise,
That on the hinder parts fallen from the face
The tears down-streaming rolled. Against a rock
I leant and wept, so that my guide exclaimed:
"What, and art thou, too, witless as the rest?
Here pity most doth show herself alive,
When she is dead. What guilt exceedeth his,
Who with Heaven's judgment in his passion strives?
Raise up thy head, raise up, and see the man
Before whose eyes earth gaped in Thebes, when all
Cried out 'Amphiaraüs, whither rushest? *
Why leavest thou the war?' He not the less
Fell ruining far as to Minos down,
Whose grapple none eludes. Lo! how he makes
The breast his shoulders; and who once too far
Before him wished to see, now backward looks,
And treads reverse his path. Tiresias note,
Who semblance changed, when woman he became
Of male, through every limb transformed; and then
Once more behooved with his rod to strike
The two entwining serpents, ere the plumes,†
That marked the better sex, might shoot again."

 "See next the wretches, who the needle left,
The shuttle and the spindle, and became
Diviners: baneful witcheries they wrought
With images and herbs. But onward now:
For now doth Cain with fork of thorns ‡ confine
On either hemisphere, touching the wave
Beneath the towers of Seville. Yesternight
The moon was round. Thou mayst remember well:
For she good service did thee in the gloom
Of the deep wood." This said, both onward moved.

* The prophet Amphiaraüs was swallowed up by an earthquake at the siege
of the seven against Thebes.
† By "plumes" is meant the beard of this famous soothsayer of Thebes, who
was turned into a woman when he separated two serpents with his staff, and
seven years later, on meeting and striking the same serpents, was changed
back to a man.
‡ Cain with his thorns is similar to "the Man in the Moon." The moon is
setting in the sea west of Seville. It is approximately dawn on Saturday morning.

CANTO XXI

Still in the eighth circle, which bears the name of Malebolge, they look down from the bridge that passes over its fifth gulf, upon the barterers or public peculators. These are plunged in a lake of boiling pitch, and guarded by Demons, to whom Virgil, leaving Dante apart, presents himself; and license being obtained to pass onward, both pursue their way.

CANTO XXII

Virgil and Dante proceed, accompanied by the Demons, and see other sinners of the same description in the same gulf. The device of Ciampolo, one of these, to escape from the Demons, who had laid hold on him.

IT HATH BEEN heretofore my chance to see
 Horsemen with martial order shifting camp,
To onset sallying, or in muster ranged,
Or in retreat sometimes outstretched for flight:
Light-armed squadrons and fleet foragers
Scouring thy plains, Arezzo! have I seen,
And clashing tournaments, and tilting jousts,
Now with the sound of trumpets, now of bells,
Tabors, or signals made from castled heights,
And with inventions multiform, our own,
Or introduced from foreign land; but ne'er
To such a strange recorder I beheld
In evolution moving, horse nor foot,
Nor ship, that tacked by sign from land or star.
 With the ten demons on our way we went;
Ah, fearful company! but in the church
With saints, with gluttons at the tavern's mess.
 Still earnest on the pitch I gazed, to mark
All things whate'er the chasm contained, and those
Who burned within. As dolphins that, in sign
To mariners, heave high their arched backs,
That thence forewarned they may advise to save
Their threatened vessel; so, at intervals,
To ease the pain, his back some sinner showed,

510

Then hid more nimbly than the lightning-glance.
    E'en as the frogs, that of a watery moat
Stand at the brink, with the jaws only out,
Their feet and of the trunk all else concealed,
Thus on each part the sinners stood; but soon
As Barbariccia was at hand, so they
Drew back under the wave. I saw, and yet
My heart doth stagger, one, that waited thus,
As it befalls that oft one frog remains,
While the next springs away: and Graffiacan,
Who of the fiends was nearest, grappling seized
His clotted locks, and dragged him sprawling up,
That he appeared to me an otter. Each
Already by their names I knew, so well
When they were chosen I observed, and marked
How one the other called. "O Rubicant!
See that his hide thou with thy talons flay,"
Shouted together all the cursed crew.
    Then I: "Inform thee, Master! if thou may,
What wretched soul is this, on whom their hands
His foes have laid." My leader to his side
Approached, and whence he came inquired; to whom
Was answered thus: "Born in Navarre's domain,
My mother placed me in a lord's retinue;
For she had borne me to a villain vile,
A spendthrift of his substance and himself.
The good king Thibault after that I served:
To peculating here my thoughts were turned,
Whereof I give account in this dire heat."
    Straight Ciriatto, from whose mouth a tusk
Issued on either side, as from a boar,
Ripped him with one of these. 'Twixt evil claws
The mouse had fallen: but Barbariccia cried,
Seizing him with both arms: "Stand thou apart,
While I do fix him on my prong transpierced."
Then added, turning to my guide his face,
"Inquire of him, if more thou wish to learn,
Ere he again be rent." My leader thus:
"Then tell us of the partners in thy guilt;
Knowest thou any sprung of Latian land

511

Under the tar?"—"I parted," he replied,
"But now from one, who sojourned not far thence:
So were I under shelter now with him,
Nor hook nor talon then should scare me more."

"Too long we suffer," Libicocco cried;
Then, darting forth a prong, seized on his arm,
And mangled bore away the sinewy part.
Him Draghignazzo by his thighs beneath
Would next have caught; whence angrily their chief,
Turning on all sides round, with threatening brow
Restrained them. When their strife a little ceased,
Of him, who yet was gazing on his wound,
My teacher thus without delay inquired:
"Who was the spirit, from whom by evil hap
Parting, as thou hast told, thou camest to shore?"—

"It was the friar Gomita," he rejoined,
"He of Gallura, vessel of all guile,
Who had his master's enemies in hand,
And used them so that they commend him well.
Money he took, and them at large dismissed;
So he reports; and in each other charge
Committed to his keeping played the part
Of barterer to the height. With him doth herd
The chief of Logodoro, Michel Zanche; *
Sardinia is a theme whereof their tongue
Is never weary. Out! alas! behold
That other, how he grins. More would I say,
But tremble lest he mean to maul me sore."

Their captain then to Farfarello turning,
Who rolled his moony eyes in act to strike,
Rebuked him thus: "Off, cursed bird! avaunt!"

"If ye desire to see or hear," he thus
Quaking with dread resumed, "or Tuscan spirits
Or Lombard, I will cause them to appear.
Meantime let these ill talons bate their fury,
So that no vengeance they may fear from them;
And I, remaining in this self-same place,
Will, for myself but one, make seven appear,

* Friar Gomita went to the gallows for accepting bribes. Michel Zanche, a
fellow Sardinian, was murdered by his son-in-law.

When my shrill whistle shall be heard: for so
Our custom is to call each other up."
   Cagnazzo at that word deriding grinned,
Then wagged the head and spake: "Hear his device,
Mischievous as he is, to plunge him down."
   Whereto he thus, who failed not in rich store
Of nice-wove toils: "Mischief, forsooth, extreme!
Meant only to procure myself more woe."
   No longer Alichino then refrained,
But thus, the rest gainsaying, him bespake:
"If thou do cast thee down, I not on foot
Will chase thee, but above the pitch will beat
My plumes. Quit we the vantage ground, and let
The bank be as a shield; that we may see,
If singly thou prevail against us all."
   Now, reader, of new sport expect to hear.
   They each one turned his eyes to the other shore,
He first, who was the hardest to persuade.
The spirit of Navarre chose well his time,
Planted his feet on land, and at one leap
Escaping, disappointed their resolve.
   Them quick resentment stung, but him the most,
Who was the cause of failure: in pursuit
He therefore sped, exclaiming, "Thou art caught."
   But little it availed; terror outstripped
His following flight; the other plunged beneath,
And he with upward pinion raised his breast:
E'en thus the water-fowl, when she perceives
The falcon near, dives instant down, while he
Enraged and spent retires. That mockery
In Calcabrina fury stirred, who flew
After him, with desire of strife inflamed;
And, for the barterer had 'scaped, so turned
His talons on his comrade. O'er the dyke
In grapple close they joined; but the other proved
A goshawk able to rend well his foe;
And in the boiling lake both fell. The heat
Was umpire soon between them; but in vain
To lift themselves they strove, so fast were glued
Their pennons. Barbariccia, as the rest,

513

That chance lamenting, four in flight dispatched
From the other coast, with all their weapons armed.
They, to their post on each side speedily
Descending, stretched their hooks toward the fiends,
Who floundered, inly burning from their scars:
And we departing left them to that broil.

CANTO XXIII

The enraged Demons pursue Dante, but he is preserved from them by
Virgil. On reaching the sixth gulf, he beholds the punishment of the
hypocrites; which is, to pace continually round the gulf under the pressure
of cloaks and hoods, that are gilt on the outside, but leaden within. He is
addressed by two of these, Catalano and Loderingo, knights of Saint Mary,
otherwise called Joyous Friars, of Bologna. Caïaphas is seen fixed to a
cross on the ground, and lies so stretched along the way, that all tread
on him in passing.

IN SILENCE and in solitude we went,
    One first, the other following his steps,
As minor friars journeying on their road.
    The present fray had turned my thoughts to muse
Upon old Æsop's fable, where he told
What fate unto the mouse and frog befell; *
For language hath not sounds more like in sense,
Than are these chances, if the origin
And end of each be heedfully compared.
And as one thought bursts from another forth,
So afterward from that another sprang,
Which added doubly to my former fear.
For thus I reasoned: "These through us have been
So foiled, with loss and mockery so complete,
As needs must sting them sore. If anger then
Be to their evil will conjoined, more fell
They shall pursue us, than the savage hound
Snatches the wild hare panting 'twixt his jaws."
    Already I perceived my hair stand all

* While a mouse and frog were struggling to see which was superior, a kite
came down and gobbled them both.

514

On end with terror, and looked eager back.
"Teacher," I thus began, "if speedily
Thyself and me thou hide not, much I dread
Those evil talons. Even now behind
They urge us: quick imagination works
So forcibly, that I already feel them."

He answered: "Were I formed of leaded glass,
I should not sooner draw unto myself
Thy outward image, than I now imprint
That from within. This moment came thy thoughts
Presented before mine, with similar act
And countenance similar, so that from both
I one design have framed. If the right coast
Incline so much, that we may thence descend
Into the other chasm, we shall escape
Secure from this imagined pursuit."

He had not spoke his purpose to the end,
When I from far beheld them with spread wings
Approach to take us. Suddenly my guide
Caught me, even as a mother that from sleep
Is by the noise aroused, and near her sees
The climbing fires, who snatches up her babe
And flies ne'er pausing, careful more of him
Than of herself, that but a single vest
Clings round her limbs. Down from the jutting beach
Supine he cast him to that pendent rock,
Which closes on one part the other chasm.

Never ran water with such hurrying pace
Adown the tube to turn a land-mill's wheel,
When nearest it approaches to the spokes,
As then along that edge my master ran,
Carrying me in his bosom, as a child,
Not a companion. Scarcely had his feet
Reached to the lowest of the bed beneath,
When over us the steep they reached: but fear
In him was none; for that high Providence,
Which placed them ministers of the fifth foss,
Power of departing thence took from them all.

There in the depth we saw a painted tribe,
Who paced with tardy steps around, and wept,

515

Faint in appearance and o'ercome with toil.
Cloaks had they on, with hoods, that fell low down
Before their eyes, in fashion like to those
Worn by the monks in Cologne. Their outside
Was overlaid with gold, dazzling to view,
But leaden all within, and of such weight!
Oh, everlasting wearisome attire!

We yet once more with them together turned
To leftward, on their dismal moan intent.
But, by the weight oppressed, so slowly came
The fainting people, that our company
Was changed at every movement of the step.

Whence I my guide addressed: "See that thou find
Some spirit, whose name may by his deeds be known;
And to that end look round thee as thou goest."

Then one, who understood the Tuscan voice,
Cried after us aloud: "Hold in your feet,
Ye who so swiftly speed through the dusk air.
Perchance from me thou shalt obtain thy wish."

Whereat my leader, turning, me bespake:
"Pause, and then onward at their pace proceed."

I stayed, and saw two spirits in whose look
Impatient eagerness of mind was marked
To overtake me; but the load they bore
And narrow path retarded their approach.

Soon as arrived, they with an eye askance
Perused me, but spake not: then turning, each
To other thus conferring said: "This one
Seems, by the action of his throat, alive;
And, be they dead, what privilege allows
They walk unmantled by the cumbrous stole?"

Then thus to me: "Tuscan, who visitest
The college of the mourning hypocrites,
Disdain not to instruct us who thou art."

"By Arno's pleasant stream," I thus replied,
"In the great city I was bred and grew,
And wear the body I have ever worn.
But who are ye, from whom such mighty grief,
As now I witness, courseth down your cheeks?
What torment breaks forth in this bitter woe?"

"Our *mantles* gleaming bright with orange hue,"
One of them answer'd, "are so leaden gross,
That with their weight they make the balances
To crack beneath them. Joyous Friars we were,
Bologna's natives; Catalano I,
He Loderingo named; and by thy land
Together taken, as men used to take
A single and indifferent arbiter,
To reconcile their strifes. How there we sped,
Gardingo's vicinage can best declare." *
    "O friars!" I began, "your miseries—"
But there broke off, for one had caught mine eye,
Fixed to a cross with three stakes on the ground:
He, when he saw me, writhed himself, throughout
Distorted, ruffling with deep sighs his beard.
And Catalano, who thereof was 'ware,
Thus spake: "That pierced spirit, whom intent
Thou view'st, was he who gave the Pharisees
Counsel, that it were fitting for one man
To suffer for the people. He doth lie
Transverse; nor any passes, but him first
Behooves make feeling trial how each weighs.
In straits like this along the foss are placed
The father of his consort, and the rest
Partakers in that council, seed of ill
And sorrow to the Jews." I noted then,
How Virgil gazed with wonder upon him,
Thus abjectly extended on the cross
In banishment eternal. To the friar
He next his words addressed: "We pray ye tell,
If so be lawful, whether on our right
Lies any opening in the rock, whereby
We both may issue hence, without constraint
On the Dark Angels, that compelled they come
To lead us from this depth." He thus replied:
"Nearer than thou dost hope, there is a rock
From the great circle moving, which o'ersteps

* These two founders of the "Joyous Friars," after being invited as magistrates to Florence, were accused of corruption; they destroyed the Gardingo section of the city.

Each vale of horror, save that here his cope
Is shattered. By the ruin ye may mount:
For on the side it slants, and most the height
Rises below." With head bent down awhile
My leader stood; then spake: "He warned us ill,
Who yonder hangs the sinners on his hook."

    To whom the friar: "At Bologna once
I many vices of the Devil heard;
Among the rest was said, 'He is a liar,
And the father of lies!' " When he had spoke,
My leader with large strides proceeded on,
Somewhat disturbed with anger in his look.

    I therefore left the spirits heavy laden,
And, following, his beloved footsteps marked.

CANTO XXIV

Under the escort of his faithful master, Dante, not without difficulty,
makes his way out of the sixth gulf; and, in the seventh, sees the robbers
tormented by venomous and pestilent serpents. The soul of Vanni Fucci,
who had pillaged the sacristy of Saint James in Pistoia, predicts some
calamities that impended over that city, and over the Florentines.

IN THE YEAR's early nonage, when the sun
   Tempers his tresses in Aquarius' urn,
And now towards equal day the nights recede;
Whenas the frost upon the earth puts on
Her dazzling sister's image, but not long
Her milder sway endures; then riseth up
The village hind, whom fails his wintry store,
And looking out beholds the plain around
All whitened; whence impatiently he smites
His thighs, and to his hut returning in,
There paces to and fro, wailing his lot,
As a discomfited and helpless man;
Then comes he forth again, and feels new hope
Spring in his bosom, finding e'en thus soon
The world hath changed its countenance, grasps his crook,
And forth to pasture drives his little flock:
So me my guide disheartened, when I saw

518

His troubled forehead; and so speedily
That ill was cured; for at the fallen bridge
Arriving, towards me with a look as sweet,
He turned him back, as that I first beheld
At the steep mountain's foot. Regarding well
The ruin, and some counsel first maintained
With his own thought, he opened wide his arm
And took me up. As one, who, while he works,
Computes his labor's issue, that he seems
Still to foresee the effect; so lifting me
Up to the summit of one peak, he fixed
His eye upon another. "Grapple that,"
Said he, "but first make proof, if it be such
As will sustain thee." For one *cloaked* with lead
This were no journey. Scarcely he, though light,
And I, though onward pushed from crag to crag,
Could mount. And if the precinct of this coast
Were not less ample than the last, for him
I know not, but my strength had surely failed.
But Malebolge all toward the mouth
Inclining of the nethermost abyss,
The site of every valley hence requires
That one side upward slope, the other fall.

At length the point from whence the utmost stone
Juts down, we reached; soon as to that arrived,
So was the breath exhausted from my lungs,
I could no farther, but did seat me there.

"Now needs thy best of man"; so spake my guide:
"For not on downy plumes, nor under shade
Of canopy reposing, fame is won;
Without which whosoe'er consumes his days
Leaveth such vestige of himself on earth,
As smoke in air or foam upon the wave.
Thou therefore rise: vanquish thy weariness
By the mind's effort, in each struggle formed
To vanquish, if she suffer not the weight
Of her corporeal frame to crush her down.
A longer ladder yet remains to scale:
From these to have escaped sufficeth not;
If well thou note me, profit by my words."

I straightway rose, and showed myself less spent
Than I in truth did feel me. "On," I cried,
"For I am stout and fearless." Up the rock
Our way we held, more rugged than before,
Narrower, and steeper far to climb. From talk
I ceased not, as we journeyed, so to seem
Least faint; whereat a voice from the other foss
Did issue forth, for utterance suited ill.
Though on the arch that crosses there I stood,
What were the words I knew not, but who spake
Seemed moved in anger. Down I stooped to look;
But my quick eye might reach not to the depth
For shrouding darkness; wherefore thus I spake:
"To the next circle, teacher, bend thy steps,
And from the wall dismount we; for as hence
I hear and understand not, so I see
Beneath, and nought discern."—"I answer not,"
Said he, "but by the deed. To fair request
Silent performance maketh best return."

We from the bridge's head descended, where
To the eighth mound it joins; and then, the chasm
Opening to view, I saw a crowd within
Of serpents terrible, so strange of shape
And hideous, that remembrance in my veins
Yet shrinks the vital current. Of her sands
Let Lybia vaunt no more: if Jaculus,
Pareas and Chelyder be her brood,
Cenchris and Amphisbæna, plagues so dire
Or in such numbers swarming ne'er she showed,
Not with all Ethiopia, and whate'er
Above the Erythræan sea is spawned.

Amid this dread exuberance of woe
Ran naked spirits winged with horrid fear,
Nor hope had they of crevice where to hide,
Or heliotrope to charm them out of view.
With serpents were their hands behind them bound,
Which through their reins infixed the tail and head,
Twisted in folds before. And lo! on one
Near to our side, darted an adder up,
And, where the neck is on the shoulders tied,

Transpierced him. Far more quickly than e'er pen
Wrote O or I, he kindled, burned, and changed
To ashes all, poured out upon the earth.
When there dissolved he lay, the dust again
Uprolled spontaneous, and the self-same form
Instant resumed. So mighty sages tell,
The Arabian Phœnix, when five hundred years
Have well-nigh circled, dies, and springs forthwith
Renascent: blade nor herb throughout his life
He tastes, but tears of frankincense alone
And odorous amomum: swaths of nard
And myrrh his funeral shroud. As one that falls,
He knows not how, by force demoniac dragged
To earth, or through obstruction fettering up
In chains invisible the powers of man,
Who, risen from his trance, gazeth around,
Bewildered with the monstrous agony
He hath endured, and wildly staring sighs;
So stood aghast the sinner when he rose.

    Oh! how severe God's judgment, that deals out
Such blows in stormy vengeance. Who he was,
My teacher next inquired; and thus in few
He answered: "Vanni Fucci am I called,
Not long since rained down from Tuscany
To this dire gullet. Me the bestial life
And not the human pleased, mule that I was,
Who in Pistoia found my worthy den."

    I then to Virgil: "Bid him stir not hence;
And ask what crime did thrust him hither: once
A man I knew him, choleric and bloody."

    The sinner heard and feigned not, but towards me
His mind directing and his face, wherein
Was dismal shame depictured, thus he spake:
"It grieves me more to have been caught by thee
In this sad plight, which thou beholdest, than
When I was taken from the other life.
I have no power permitted to deny
What thou inquirest. I am doomed thus low
To dwell, for that the sacristy by me
Was rifled of its goodly ornaments,

521

And with the guilt another falsely charged.
But that thou mayst not joy to see me thus,
So as thou e'er shalt 'scape this darksome realm,
Open thine ears and hear what I forebode.
Reft of the Neri first Pistoia pines;
Then Florence changeth citizens and laws;
From Valdimagra, drawn by wrathful Mars,
A vapor rises, wrapped in turbid mists,
And sharp and eager driveth on the storm
With arrowy hurtling o'er Piceno's field,
Whence suddenly the cloud shall burst, and strike
Each helpless Bianco prostrate to the ground.
This have I told, that grief may rend thy heart."

CANTO XXV

The sacrilegious Fucci vents his fury in blasphemy, is seized by serpents, and flying is pursued by Cacus in the form of a Centaur, who is described with a swarm of serpents on his haunch, and a dragon on his shoulders breathing forth fire. Our Poet then meets with the spirits of three of his countrymen, two of whom undergo a marvelous transformation in his presence.

WHEN HE HAD spoke, the sinner raised his hands
Pointed in mockery, and cried: "Take them, God!
I level them at thee." From that day forth
The serpents were my friends; for round his neck
One of them rolling twisted, as it said,
"Be silent, tongue!" Another, to his arms
Upgliding, tied them, riveting itself
So close, it took from them the power to move.

Pistoia! ah, Pistoia! why dost doubt
To turn thee into ashes, cumbering earth
No longer, since in evil act so far
Thou hast outdone thy seed? I did not mark,
Through all the gloomy circles of the abyss,
Spirit, that swelled so proudly 'gainst his God;
Not him, who headlong fell from Thebes. He fled,
Nor uttered more; and after him there came

A Centaur full of fury, shouting, "Where,
Where is the caitiff?" On Maremma's marsh
Swarm not the serpent tribe, as on his haunch
They swarmed, to where the human face begins.
Behind his head, upon the shoulders, lay
With open wings a dragon, breathing fire
On whomsoe'er he met. To me my guide:
"Cacus is this, who underneath the rock
Of Aventine spread oft a lake of blood.
He, from his brethren parted, here must tread
A different journey, for his fraudful theft
Of the great herd that near him stalled; whence found
His felon deeds their end, beneath the mace
Of stout Hercules, that perchance laid on
A hundred blows, and not the tenth was felt."
　　While yet he spake, the Centaur sped away:
And under us three spirits came, of whom
Nor I nor he was ware, till they exclaimed,
"Say who are ye!" We then broke off discourse,
Intent on these alone. I knew them not:
But, as it chanceth oft, befell that one
Had need to name another. "Where," said he,
"Doth Cianfa lurk?" I, for a sign my guide
Should stand attentive, placed against my lips
The finger lifted. If, O reader! now
Thou be not apt to credit what I tell,
No marvel; for myself do scarce allow
The witness of mine eyes. But as I looked
Toward them, lo! a serpent with six feet
Springs forth on one, and fastens full upon him:
His midmost grasped the belly, a forefoot
Seized on each arm (while deep in either cheek
He fleshed his fangs); the hinder on the thighs
Were spread, 'twixt which the tail inserted curled
Upon the reins behind. Ivy ne'er clasped
A doddered oak, as round the other's limbs
The hideous monster intertwined his own.
Then, as they both had been of burning wax,
Each melted into other, mingling hues,
That which was either now was seen no more.

Thus up the shrinking paper, ere it burns,
A brown tint glides, not turning yet to black,
And the clean white expires. The other two
Looked on, exclaiming, "Ah! how dost thou change,
Agnello! See! Thou art nor double now,
Nor only one." The two heads now became
One, and two figures blended in one form
Appeared, where both were lost. Of the four lengths
Two arms were made: the belly and the chest,
The thighs and legs, into such members changed
As never eye hath seen. Of former shape
All trace was vanished. Two, yet neither, seemed
That image miscreate, and so passed on
With tardy steps. As underneath the scourge
Of the fierce dog-star that lays bare the fields,
Shifting from brake to brake the lizard seems
A flash of lightning, if he thwart the road;
So toward the entrails of the other two
Approaching seemed an adder all on fire,
As the dark pepper-grain livid and swart.
In that part, whence our life is nourished first,
One he transpierced; then down before him fell
Stretched out. The pierced spirit looked on him,
But spake not; yea, stood motionless and yawned,
As if by sleep or feverous fit assailed.
He eyed the serpent, and the serpent him;
One from the wound, the other from the mouth
Breathed a thick smoke, whose vapory columns joined.
  Lucan in mute attention now may hear,
Nor thy disastrous fate, Sabellus, tell,
Nor thine, Nasidius. Ovid now be mute.
What if in warbling fiction he record
Cadmus and Arethusa, to a snake
Him changed, and her into a fountain clear,
I envy not; for never face to face
Two natures thus transmuted did he sing,
Wherein both shapes were ready to assume
The other's substance. They in mutual guise
So answered that the serpent split his train
Divided to a fork, and the pierced spirit

Drew close his steps together, legs and thighs
Compacted, that no sign of juncture soon
Was visible: the tail, disparted, took
The figure which the spirit lost; its skin
Softening, his indurated to a rind.
The shoulders next I marked, that entering joined
The monster's arm-pits, whose two shorter feet
So lengthened, as the others dwindling shrunk.
The feet behind then twisting up became
That part that man conceals, which in the wretch
Was cleft in twain. While both the shadowy smoke
With a new color veils, and generates
The excrescent pile on one, peeling it off
From the other body, lo! upon his feet
One upright rose, and prone the other fell.
Nor yet their glaring and malignant lamps
Were shifted, though each feature changed beneath.
Of him who stood erect, the mounting face
Retreated towards the temples, and what there
Superfluous matter came, shot out in ears
From the smooth cheeks; the rest, not backward dragged,
Of its excess did shape the nose; and swelled
Into due size protuberant the lips.
He, on the earth who lay, meanwhile extends
His sharpened visage, and draws down the ears
Into the head, as doth the slug his horns.
His tongue, continuous before and apt
For utterance, severs; and the other's fork
Closing unites; that done, the smoke was laid.
The soul, transformed into the brute, glides off,
Hissing along the vale, and after him
The other talking sputters; but soon turned
His new-grown shoulders on him, and in few
Thus to another spake: "Along this path
Crawling, as I have done, speed Buoso now!"
So saw I fluctuate in successive change
The unsteady ballast of the seventh hold:
And here if aught my pen have swerved, events
So strange may be its warrant. O'er mine eyes
Confusion hung, and on my thoughts amaze.

Remounting by the steps, down which they had descended to the seventh gulf, they go forward to the arch that stretches over the eighth, and from thence behold numberless flames wherein are punished the evil counsellors, each flame containing a sinner—save one, in which were Diomede and Ulysses, the latter of whom relates the manner of his death.

FLORENCE, exult! for thou so mightily
   Hast thriven, that o'er land and sea thy wings
Thou beatest, and thy name spreads over Hell.
Among the plunderers, such the three I found,
Thy citizens; whence shame to me thy son,
And no proud honor to thyself redounds.

   But if our minds, when dreaming near the dawn,
Are of the truth presageful, thou ere long
Shalt feel what Prato (not to say the rest)
Would fain might come upon thee; and that chance
Were in good time, if it befell thee now.
Would so it were, since it must needs befall!
For as time wears me, I shall grieve the more.

   We from the depth departed; and my guide
Remounting scaled the flinty steps, which late
We downward traced, and drew me up the steep.
Pursuing thus our solitary way
Among the crags and splinters of the rock,
Sped not our feet without the help of hands.

   Then sorrow seized me, which e'en now revives,
As my thought turns again to what I saw,
And, more than I am wont, I reign and curb
The powers of nature in me, lest they run
Where Virtue guides not; that, if aught of good
My gentle star or something better gave me,
I envy not myself the precious boon.

   As in that season, when the sun least veils
His face that lightens all, what time the fly
Gives way to the shrill gnat, the peasant then,
Upon some cliff reclined, beneath him sees
Fire-flies innumerous spangling o'er the vale,
Vineyard or tilth, where his day-labor lies;

With flames so numberless throughout its space
Shone the eighth chasm, apparent, when the depth
Was to my view exposed. As he, whose wrongs
The bears avenged, at its departure saw
Elijah's chariot, when the steeds erect
Raised their steep flight for heaven; his eyes, meanwhile,
Straining pursued them, till the flame alone,
Upsoaring like a misty speck, he kenned:
E'en thus along the gulf moves every flame,
A sinner so enfolded close in each,
That none exhibits token of the theft.

Upon the bridge I forward bent to look,
And grasped a flinty mass, or else had fallen,
Though pushed not from the height. The guide, who marked
How I did gaze attentive, thus began:
"Within these ardors are the spirits, each
Swathed in confining fire."—"Master! thy word,"
I answered, "hath assured me; yet I deemed
Already of the truth, already wished
To ask thee who is in yon fire, that comes
So parted at the summit, as it seemed
Ascending from that funeral pile where lay
The Theban brothers." He replied: "Within,
Ulysses there and Diomede endure
Their penal tortures, thus to vengeance now
Together hasting, as erewhile to wrath.
These in the flame with ceaseless groans deplore
The ambush of the horse, that opened wide
A portal for that goodly seed to pass,
Which sowed imperial Rome; nor less the guile
Lament they, whence, of her Achilles 'reft,
Deïdamia yet in death complains.*
And there is rued the stratagem that Troy
Of her Palladium spoiled."—"If they have power
Of utterance from within these sparks," said I,
"O Master! think my prayer a thousand-fold

* Dante sides with the Trojans, whom Virgil represented as the ancestors of
the Romans. Ulysses and Diomede, typically guileful Greeks, are punished for
the Trojan horse, for coaxing Achilles to Troy, and for stealing the sacred
image of Pallas upon which the safety of that city depended.

In repetition urged, that thou vouchsafe
To pause till here the horned flame arrive.
See, how toward it with desire I bend."
    He thus: "Thy prayer is worthy of much praise,
And I accept it therefore; but do thou
Thy tongue refrain: to question them be mine;
For I divine thy wish; and they perchance,
For they were Greeks, might shun discourse with thee."
    When there the flame had come, where time and place
Seemed fitting to my guide, he thus began:
"O ye, who dwell two spirits in one fire!
If, living, I of you did merit aught,
Whate'er the measure were of that desert,
When in the world my lofty strain I poured,
Move ye not on, till one of you unfold
In what clime death o'ertook him self-destroyed."
    Of the old flame forthwith the greater horn
Began to roll, murmuring, as a fire
That labors with the wind; then to and fro
Wagging the top, as a tongue uttering sounds,
Threw out its voice, and spake: "When I escaped
From Circe, who beyond a circling year
Had held me near Caieta by her charms,
Ere thus Æneas yet had named the shore;
Nor fondness for my son, nor reverence
Of my old father, nor return of love,
That should have crowned Penelope with joy,
Could overcome in me the zeal I had
To explore the world, and search the ways of life,
Man's evil and his virtue. Forth I sailed
Into the deep illimitable main,
With but one bark, and the small faithful band
That yet cleaved to me. As Iberia far,
Far as Morocco, either shore I saw,
And the Sardinian and each isle beside
Which round that ocean bathes. Tardy with age
Were I and my companions, when we came
To the strait pass, where Hercules ordained
The boundaries not to be o'erstepped by man.
The walls of Seville to my right I left,

On the other hand already Ceuta past.
'O brothers!' I began, 'who to the west
'Through perils without number now have reached;
'To this the short remaining watch, that yet
'Our senses have to wake, refuse not proof
'Of the unpeopled world, following the track
'Of sun. Call to mind from whence ye sprang:
'Ye were not formed to live the lives of brutes,
'But virtue to pursue and knowledge high.'
With these few words I sharpened for the voyage
The mind of my associates, that I then
Could scarcely have withheld them. To the dawn
Our poop we turned, and for the witless flight
Made our oars wings, still gaining on the left.
Each star of the other pole night now beheld,
And ours so low, that from the ocean floor
It rose not. Five times re-illumed, as oft
Vanished the light from underneath the moon,
Since the deep way we entered, when from far
Appeared a mountain dim, loftiest methought
Of all I e'er beheld. Joy seized us straight;
But soon to mourning changed. From the new land
A whirlwind sprung, and at her foremost side
Did strike the vessel. Thrice it whirled her round
With all the waves; the fourth time lifted up
The poop, and sank the prow: so fate decreed:
And over us the booming billow closed."

CANTO XXVII

The Poet, treating of the same punishment as in the last Canto, relates that he turned towards a flame in which was the Count Guido da Montefeltro, whose inquiries respecting the state of Romagna he answers; and Guido is thereby induced to declare who he is, and why condemned to that torment.

CANTO XXVIII

Virgil and Dante arrive in the ninth gulf, where the sowers of scandal and schismatics are seen with their limbs miserably maimed or divided in

different ways. Among these the Poet finds Mohammed, Piero de Medi-
cina, Curio, Mosca, and Bertrand de Born.

>   . . . A barrel, that hath lost
> Its middle or side stave, gapes not so wide
> As one I marked torn from the chin throughout
> Down to the hinder passage: 'twixt the legs
> Dangling his entrails hung, the midriff lay
> Open to view, and wretched ventricle,
> That turns the englutted aliment to dross.
>   Whilst eagerly I fix on him my gaze,
> He eyed me, with his hands laid his breast bare,
> And cried, "Now mark how I do rip me: lo!
> How is Mohammed mangled: before me
> Walks Ali weeping, from the chin his face
> Cleft to the forelock; and the others all,
> Whom here thou seest, while they lived, did sow
> Scandal and schism, and therefore thus are rent.
> A fiend is here behind, who with his sword
> Hacks us thus cruelly, slivering again
> Each of this ream, when we have compast round
> The dismal way; for first our gashes close
> Ere we repass before him.

CANTO XXIX

Dante, at the desire of Virgil, proceeds onward to the bridge that crosses
the tenth gulf, from whence he hears the cries of the alchemists and
forgers, who are tormented therein; but not being able to discern anything on account of the darkness, they descend the rock, that bounds this
the last of the compartments in which the eighth circle is divided, and
then behold the spirits who are afflicted by divers plagues and diseases.
Two of them, namely, Griffolino of Arezzo and Capocchio of Siena, are
introduced speaking.

> So were mine eyes inebriate with the view
>   Of the vast multitude, whom various wounds
> Disfigured, that they longed to stay and weep.
>   But Virgil roused me: "What yet gazest on?
> Wherefore doth fasten yet thy sight below

Among the maimed and miserable shades?
Thou hast not shown in any chasm beside
This weakness. Know, if thou wouldst number them,
That two-and-twenty miles the valley winds
Its circuit, and already is the moon
Beneath our feet: the time permitted now
Is short; and more, not seen, remains to see."

    . . . Soon as we came
O'er the last cloister in the dismal rounds
Of Malebolge, and the brotherhood
Were to our view exposed, then many a dart
Of sore lament assailed me, headed all
With points of thrilling pity, that I closed
Both ears against the volley with mine hands.

 As were the torment, if each poor-house
Of Valdichiana, in the sultry time
'Twixt July and September, with the isle
Sardinia and Maremma's pestilent fen,
Had heaped their maladies all in one foss
Together; such was here the torment: dire
The stench, as issuing steams from festered limbs.

 We on the utmost shore of the long rock
Descended still to leftward. Then my sight
Was livelier to explore the depth, wherein
The minister of the most mighty Lord,
All-searching Justice, dooms to punishment
The forgers noted on her dread record.

 More rueful was it not methinks to see
The nation in Ægina * droop, what time
Each living thing, e'en to the little worm,
All fell, so full of malice was the air
(And afterward, as bards of yore have told,
The ancient people were restored anew
From seed of emmets), than was here to see
The spirits, that languished through the murky vale,
Up-piled on many a stack. Confused they lay,
One o'er the belly, o'er the shoulders one
Rolled of another; sideling crawled a third

---

* Ovid describes the plague of Aegina and its re-population by Jupiter's turning ants into men.

Along the dismal pathway. Step by step
We journeyed on, in silence looking round,
And listening those diseased, who strove in vain
To lift their forms. Then two I marked, that sat
Propped 'gainst each other, as two brazen pans
Set to retain the heat. From head to foot,
A tetter barked them round. Nor saw I e'er
Groom currying so fast, for whom his lord
Impatient waited, or himself perchance
Tired with long watching, as of these each one
Plied quickly his keen nails, through furiousness
Of ne'er abated pruriency. The crust
Came drawn from underneath in flakes, like scales
Scraped from the bream, or fish of broader mail.
    "O thou! who with thy fingers rendest off
Thy coat of proof," thus spake my guide to one,
"And sometimes makest tearing pincers of them,
Tell me if any born of Latian land
Be among these within: so may thy nails
Serve thee for everlasting to this toil."
    "Both are of Latium," weeping he replied,
"Whom tortured thus thou seest: but who art thou
That hast inquired of us?" To whom my guide:
"One that descend with this man, who yet lives,
From rock to rock, and show him hell's abyss."
    Then started they asunder, and each turned
Trembling toward us, with the rest, whose ear
Those words resounding struck. To me my liege
Addressed him: "Speak to them whate'er thou list."
    And I therewith began: "So may no time
Filch your remembrance from the thoughts of men
In the upper world, but after many suns
Survive it, as ye tell me, who ye are,
And of what race ye come. Your punishment,
Unseemly and disgustful in its kind,
Deter you not from opening thus much to me."
    "Arezzo was my dwelling," answered one,
"And me Albero of Siena brought,
To die by fire: but that, for which I died,
Leads me not here. True is, in sport I told him,

That I had learned to wing my flight in air;
And he, admiring much, as he was void
Of wisdom, willed me to declare to him
The secret of mine art: and only hence,
Because I made him not a Dædalus,
Prevailed on one supposed his sire to burn me.
But Minos to this chasm, last of the ten,
For that I practiced alchemy on earth,
Has doomed me. Him no subterfuge eludes."

Then to the bard I spake: "Was ever race
Light as Siena's? Sure not France herself
Can show a tribe so frivolous and vain."

The other leprous spirit heard my words,
And thus returned: "Be Stricca from this charge
Exempted, he who knew so temperately
To lay out fortune's gifts; and Niccolò,
Who first the spice's costly luxury
Discovered in that garden, where such seed
Roots deepest in the soil; and be that troop
Exempted, with whom Caccia of Asciano
Lavished his vineyards and wide-spreading woods,
And his rare wisdom Abbagliato showed
A spectacle for all.* That thou mayst know
Who seconds thee against the Sienese
Thus gladly, bend this way thy sharpened sight,
That well my face may answer to thy ken;
So shalt thou see I am Capocchio's ghost,
Who forged transmuted metals by the power
Of alchemy; and if I scan thee right,
Thou needs must well remember how I aped
Creative nature by my subtle art."

CANTO XXX

In the same gulf, other kinds of impostors, as those who have counter-
feited the persons of others, or debased the current coin, or deceived by

* The whole speech is of course ironical and refers to a club of Sienese spend-
thrifts. The speaker, Capocchio, was burned alive in that city in 1293 for
practicing alchemy.

speech under false pretenses, are described as suffering various diseases. Sinon of Troy and Adamo of Brescia mutually reproach each other with their several impostures.

CANTO XXXI

The poets, following the sound of a loud horn, are led by it to the ninth circle, in which there are four rounds, one enclosed within the other, and containing as many sorts of Traitors; but the present Canto shows only that the circle is encompassed with Giants, one of whom, Antæus, takes them both in his arms and places them at the bottom of the circle.

TURNING OUR BACK upon the vale of woe,
    We crossed the encircled mound in silence. There
Was less than day and less than night, that far
Mine eye advanced not: but I heard a horn
Sounded so loud, the peal it rang had made
The thunder feeble. Following its course
The adverse way, my strained eyes were bent
On that one spot. So terrible a blast
Orlando blew not, when that dismal rout
O'erthrew the host of Charlemagne, and quenched
His saintly warfare. Thitherward not long
My head was raised, when many a lofty tower
Methought I spied. "Master," said I, "what land
Is this?" He answered straight: "Too long a space
Of intervening darkness has thine eye
To traverse: thou hast therefore widely erred
In thy imagining. Thither arrived
Thou well shalt see, how distance can delude
The sense. A little therefore urge thee on."
    Then tenderly he caught me by the hand;
"Yet know," said he, "ere farther we advance,
That it less strange may seem, these are not towers,
But giants. In the pit they stand immersed,
Each from his navel downward, round the bank."
    As when a fog disperseth gradually,
Our vision traces what the mist involves
Condensed in air; so piercing through the gross

534

And gloomy atmosphere, as more and more
We neared toward the brink, mine error fled
And fear came o'er me. As with circling round
Of turrets, Montereggion crowns his walls;
E'en thus the shore, encompassing the abyss,
Was turreted with giants, half their length
Uprearing, horrible, whom Jove from Heaven
Yet threatens, when his muttering thunder rolls.

Of one already I descried the face,
Shoulders, and breast, and of the belly huge
Great part, and both arms down along his ribs.

All-teeming Nature, when her plastic hand
Left framing of these monsters, did display
Past doubt her wisdom, taking from mad War
Such slaves to do his bidding; and if she
Repent her not of the elephant and whale,
Who ponders well confesses her therein
Wiser and more discreet; for when brute force
And evil will are backed with subtlety,
Resistance none avails. His visage seemed
In length and bulk, as doth the pine that tops
Saint Peter's Roman fane; and the other bones
Of like proportion, so that from above
The bank, which girdled him below, such height
Arose his stature, that three Frieslanders
Had striven in vain to reach but to his hair.
Full thirty ample palms was he exposed
Downward from whence a man his garment loops.
"Raphel baï ameth, sabì almì":
So shouted his fierce lips, which sweeter hymns
Became not; and my guide addressed him thus:
"O senseless spirit! let thy horn for thee
Interpret: therewith vent thy rage, if rage
Or other passion wring thee. Search thy neck,
There shalt thou find the belt that binds it on.
Spirit confused! lo, on thy mighty breast
Where hangs the baldrick!" Then to me he spake:
"He doth accuse himself. Nimrod is this,
Through whose ill counsel in the world no more
One tongue prevails. But pass we on, nor waste

Our words; for so each language is to him,
As his to others, understood by none."
    Then to the leftward turning sped we forth,
And at a sling's throw found another shade
Far fiercer and more huge. I cannot say
What master hand had girt him; but he held
Behind the right arm fettered, and before,
The other, with a chain, that fastened him
From the neck down; and five times round his form
Apparent met the wreathed links. "This proud one
Would of his strength against almighty Jove
Make trial," said my guide: "whence he is thus
Requited: Ephialtes they call him.
Great was his prowess, when the giants brought
Fear on the gods: those arms, which then he plied,
Now moves he never." Forthwith I returned:
"Fain would I, if 't were possible, mine eyes,
Of Briareus immeasurable, gained
Experience next." He answered: "Thou shalt see
Not far from hence Antæus, who both speaks
And is unfettered, who shall place us there
Where guilt is at its depth. Far onward stands
Whom thou wouldst fain behold, in chains, and made
Like to this spirit, save that in his looks
More fell he seems." By violent earthquake rocked
Ne'er shook a tower, so reeling to its base,
As Ephialtes. More than ever then
I dreaded death; nor than the terror more
Had needed, if I had not seen the cords
That held him fast. We, straightway journeying on,
Came to Antæus, who, five ells complete
Without the head, forth issued from the cave.
    "O thou, who in the fortunate vale, that made
Great Scipio heir of glory, when his sword
Drove back the troop of Hannibal in flight,
Who thence of old didst carry for thy spoil
An hundred lions; and if thou hadst fought
In the high conflict on thy brethren's side,
Seems as men yet believed, that through thine arm
The sons of earth had conquered; now vouchsafe

To place us down beneath, where numbing cold
Locks up Cocytus. Force not that we crave
Or Tityus' help or Typhon's. Here is one
Can give what in this realm ye covet. Stoop
Therefore, nor scornfully distort thy lip.
He in the upper world can yet bestow
Renown on thee; for he doth live, and looks
For life yet longer, if before the time
Grace call him not unto herself." Thus spake
The teacher. He in haste forth stretched his hands,
And caught my guide. Hercules long ago felt
That grapple, straitened sore. Soon as my guide
Had felt it, he bespake me thus: "This way,
That I may clasp thee"; then so caught me up,
That we were both one burden. As appears
Bologna's leaning tower from beneath
Where it doth lean, if chance a passing cloud
So sail across, that opposite it hangs;
Such then Antæus seemed, as at mine ease
I marked him stooping. I were fain at times
To have passed another way. Yet in the abyss,
That Lucifer with Judas low ingulfs,
Lightly he placed us; nor, there leaning, stayed;
But rose, as in a bark the stately mast.

CANTO XXXII

This Canto treats of the first, and, in part, of the second of those rounds,
into which the ninth and last, or frozen circle, is divided. In the former,
called Caïna, Dante finds Camiccione de' Pazzi, who gives him an account of other sinners who are there punished; and in the next, named
Antenora, he hears in like manner from Bocca degli Abati who his fellow-
sufferers are.

COULD I command rough rhymes and hoarse, to suit
That hole of sorrow o'er which every rock
His firm abutment rears, then might the vein
Of fancy rise full springing: but not mine
Such measures, and with faltering awe I touch

537

The mighty theme; for to describe the depth
Of all the universe, is no emprize
To jest with, and demands a tongue not used
To infant babbling. But let them assist
My song, the tuneful Muses, by whose aid
Amphion walled in Thebes; so with the truth
My speech shall best accord. Oh ill-starred folk,
Beyond all others wretched! who abide
In such a mansion, as scarce thought finds words
To speak of, better had ye here on earth
Been flocks, or mountain goats. As down we stood
In the dark pit beneath the giants' feet,
But lower far than they, and I did gaze
Still on the lofty battlement, a voice
Bespake me thus: "Look how thou walkest. Take
Good heed, thy soles do tread not on the heads
Of thy poor brethren." Thereupon I turned,
And saw before and underneath my feet
A lake, whose frozen surface liker seemed
To glass than water. Not so thick a veil
In winter e'er hath Austrian Danube spread
O'er his still course, nor Tanais far remote
Under the chilling sky. Rolled o'er that mass
Had Tabernich or Pietrapana fallen,
Not e'en its rim had creaked. As peeps the frog
Croaking above the wave, what time in dreams
The village gleaner oft pursues her toil,
So, to where modest shame appears, thus low
Blue pinched and shrined in ice the spirits stood,
Moving their teeth in shrill note like the stork.
His face each downward held; their mouth the cold,
Their eyes expressed the dolor of their heart.

A space I looked around, then at my feet
Saw two so strictly joined, that of their head
The very hairs were mingled. "Tell me ye,
Whose bosoms thus together press," said I,
"Who are ye?" At that sound their necks they bent;
And when their looks were lifted up to me,
Straightway their eyes, before all moist within,
Distilled upon their lips, and the frost bound

The tears betwixt those orbs, and held them there.
Plank unto plank hath never cramp closed up
So stoutly. Whence, like two enraged goats,
They clashed together: them such fury seized.

  And one, from whom the cold both ears had reft,
Exclaimed, still looking downward: "Why on us
Dost speculate so long? If thou wouldst know
Who are these two, the valley, whence his wave
Bisenzio slopes, did for its master own
Their sire Alberto, and next him themselves.
They from one body issued: and throughout
Caïna thou mayst search, nor find a shade
More worthy in congealment to be fixed; *
Not him, whose breast and shadow Arthur's hand
At that one blow dissevered; not Focaccia;
No, not this spirit, whose o'erjutting head
Obstructs my onward view: he bore the name
Of Mascheroni: † Tuscan if thou be,
Well knowest who he was. And to cut short
All further question, in my form behold
What once was Camiccione. I await
Carlino here my kinsman, whose deep guilt
Shall wash out mine." ‡ A thousand visages
Then marked I, which the keen and eager cold
Had shaped into a doggish grin; whence creeps
A shivering horror o'er me, at the thought
Of those frozen shallows. While we journeyed on
Toward the middle, at whose point unites
All heavy substance, and I trembling went
Through that eternal chillness, I know not
If will it were, or destiny, or chance,
But, passing 'midst the heads, my foot did strike
With violent blow against the face of one.

* The two sons of Alberto treacherously slew eath other. Caïna, the first of the four rounds of the ninth and last circle, takes its name from the first fratricide.
† The references are to Mordred, King Arthur's traitor nephew, and two kin-slaying Tuscans.
‡ Camiccione, who murdered his kinsman Ubertino, is yet not so wicked as Carlino, who betrayed his country and therefore, when he dies, will go to the second round of the ninth circle, Antenora (named after the betrayer of Troy), where "a thousand visages" send "a shivering horror" over Dante.

"Wherefore dost bruise me?" weeping he exclaimed;
"Unless thy errand be some fresh revenge
For Montaperto, wherefore troublest me?"
    I thus: "Instructor, now await me here,
That I through him may rid me of my doubt:
Thenceforth what haste thou wilt." The teacher paused;
And to that shade I spake, who bitterly
Still cursed me in his wrath. "What art thou, speak,
That railest thus on others?" He replied:
"Now who art thou, that smiting others' cheeks,
Through Antenora roamest, with such force
As were past sufferance, wert thou living still?"
    "And I am living, to thy joy perchance,"
Was my reply, "if fame be dear to thee,
That with the rest I may thy name enroll."
    "The contrary of what I covet most,"
Said he, "thou tender'st: hence! nor vex me more.
Ill knowest thou to flatter in this vale."
    Then seizing on his hinder scalp I cried:
"Name thee, or not a hair shall tarry here."
    "Rend all away," he answered, "yet for that
I will not tell, nor show thee, who I am,
Though at my head thou pluck a thousand times."
    Now I had grasped his tresses, and stripped off
More than one tuft, he barking, with his eyes
Drawn in and downward, when another cried,
"What ails thee, Bocca? * Sound not loud enough
Thy chattering teeth, but thou must bark outright?
What devil wrings thee?"—"Now," said I, "be dumb,
Accursed traitor! To thy shame, of thee
True tidings will I bear."—"Off!" he replied;
"Tell what thou list: but, as thou scape from hence,
To speak of him whose tongue hath been so glib,
Forget not: here he wails the Frenchman's gold.
'Him of Duera,' thou canst say, 'I marked,
'Where the starved sinners pine.' If thou be asked
What other shade was with them, at thy side
Is Beccaria, whose red gorge distained

* The treason of Bocca degli Abati at the battle of Montaperti (1260), caused the defeat of the Guelfs.

The biting axe of Florence. Farther on,
If I misdeem not, Soldanieri bides,
With Ganellon, and Tribaldello, him
Who oped Faenza when the people slept."
    We now had left him, passing on our way,
When I beheld two spirits by the ice
Pent in one hollow, that the head of one
Was cowl unto the other; and as bread
Is ravened up through hunger, the uppermost
Did so apply his fangs to the other's brain,
Where the spine joins it. Not more furiously
On Menalippus' temples Tydeus gnawed,
Than on that skull and on its garbage he.
    "O thou! who show'st so beastly sign of hate
'Gainst him thou prey'st on, let me hear," said I,
"The cause, on such condition, that if right
Warrant thy grievance, knowing who ye are,
And what the color of his sinning was,
I may repay thee in the world above,
If that wherewith I speak be moist so long."

CANTO XXXIII

The Poet is told by Count Ugolino de' Gherardeschi of the cruel manner
in which he and his children were famished in the tower at Pisa, by command of the Archbishop Ruggieri. He next discourses of the third round,
called Ptolomea, wherein those are punished who have betrayed others
under the semblance of kindness; and among these he finds the Friar
Alberigo de' Manfredi, who tells him of one whose soul was already tormented in that place, though his body appeared still to be alive upon the
earth, being yielded up to a fiend.

H IS JAWS uplifting from their fell repast,
    That sinner wiped them on the hairs o' the head,
Which he behind had mangled, then began:
"Thy will obeying, I call up afresh
Sorrow past cure; which, but to think of, wrings
My heart, or ere I tell on 't. But if words,
That I may utter, shall prove seed to bear

Fruit of eternal infamy to him,
The traitor whom I gnaw at, thou at once
Shalt see me speak and weep. Who thou mayst be
I know not, nor how here below art come:
But Florentine thou seemest of a truth,
When I do hear thee. Know, I was on earth
Count Ugolino, and the Archbishop he
Ruggieri. Why I neighbor him so close,
Now list. That through effect of his ill thoughts
In him my trust reposing, I was ta'en
And after murdered, need is not I tell.
What therefore thou canst not have heard, that is,
How cruel was the murder, shalt thou hear,
And know if he have wronged me. A small grate
Within that mew, which for my sake the name
Of famine bears, where others yet must pine,
Already through its opening several moons
Had shown me, when I slept the evil sleep
That from the future tore the curtain off.
This one, methought, as master of the sport,
Rode forth to chase the gaunt wolf, and his whelps,
Unto the mountain which forbids the sight
Of Lucca to the Pisan. With lean hounds
Inquisitive and keen, before him ranged
Lanfranchi with Sismondi and Gualandi.
After short course the father and the sons
Seemed tired and lagging, and methought I saw
The sharp tusks gore their sides. When I awoke,
Before the dawn, amid their sleep I heard
My sons (for they were with me) weep and ask
For bread. Right cruel art thou, if no pang
Thou feel at thinking what my heart foretold;
And if not now, why use thy tears to flow?
Now had they wakened; and the hour drew near
When they were wont to bring us food; the mind
Of each misgave him through his dream, and I
Heard, at its outlet underneath, locked up
The horrible tower: whence, uttering not a word,
I looked upon the visage of my sons.
I wept not: so all stone I felt within.

542

They wept: and one, my little Anselm, cried,
'Thou lookest so! Father, what ails thee?' Yet
I shed no tear, nor answered all that day
Nor the next night, until another sun
Came out upon the world. When a faint beam
Had to our doleful prison made its way,
And in four countenances I descried
The image of my own, on either hand
Through agony I bit; and they, who thought
I did it through desire of feeding, rose
O' the sudden, and cried, 'Father, we should grieve
'Far less, if thou wouldst eat of us: thou gavest
'These weeds of miserable flesh we wear;
'And do thou strip them off from us again.'
Then, not to make them sadder, I kept down
My spirit in stillness. That day and the next
We all were silent. Ah, obdurate earth!
Why open'dst not upon us? When we came
To the fourth day, then Gaddo at my feet
Outstretched did fling him, crying, 'Hast no help
'For me, my father!' There he died; and e'en
Plainly as thou seest me, saw I the three
Fall one by one 'twixt the fifth day and sixth:
Whence I betook me, now grown blind, to grope
Over them all, and for three days aloud
Called on them who were dead. Then, fasting got
The mastery of grief." * Thus having spoke,
Once more upon the wretched skull his teeth
He fastened like a mastiff's 'gainst the bone,
Firm and unyielding. Oh, thou Pisa! shame
Of all the people, who their dwelling make
In that fair region, where the Italian voice
Is heard; since that thy neighbors are so slack
To punish, from their deep foundations rise
Capraia and Gorgona, and dam up
The mouth of Arno; that each soul in thee

---

* This probably does not mean that Count Ugolino was compelled by hunger
to start feeding on the bodies of his sons; rather, starvation did what grief had
failed to do, killed him.

543

May perish in the waters. What if fame
Reported that thy castles were betrayed
By Ugolino, yet no right hadst thou
To stretch his children on the rack. For them,
Brigata, Uguccione, and the pair
Of gentle ones, of whom my song hath told,
Their tender years, thou modern Thebes, did make
Uncapable of guilt. Onward we passed,
Where others, scarffed in rugged folds of ice,
Not on their feet were turned, but each reversed.

    There, very weeping suffers not to weep;
For, at their eyes, grief, seeking passage, finds
Impediment, and rolling inward turns
For increase of sharp anguish: the first tears
Hang clustered, and like crystal vizors show,
Under the socket brimming all the cup.

    Now though the cold had from my face dislodged
Each feeling, as 't were callous, yet me seemed
Some breath of wind I felt. "Whence cometh this,"
Said I, "my Master? Is not here below
All vapor quenched?" "Thou shalt be speedily,"
He answered, "where thine eyes shall tell thee whence,
The cause descrying of this airy shower."

    Then cried out one, in the chill crust who mourned:
"O souls! so cruel, that the farthest post
Hath been assigned you,* from this face remove
The hardened veil; that I may vent the grief
Impregnate at my heart, some little space,
Ere it congeal again." I thus replied:
"Say who thou wast, if thou wouldst have mine aid;
And if I extricate thee not, far down
As to the lowest ice may I descend."

    "The friar Alberigo," answered he,
"Am I, who from the evil garden plucked
Its fruitage, and am here repaid, the date

---

* The speaker thinks that Dante and Virgil are dead souls doomed to Judecca, the bottom round of the last circle. He himself is in Ptolomea, the round above, where betrayers of hospitality go. Alberigo invited his brother and brother's son to a banquet, where, at the signal "Bring the fruit," hired murderers rushed in and stabbed them.

More luscious for my fig."—"Hah!" I exclaimed,
"Art thou too dead?"—"How in the world aloft
It fareth with my body," answered he,
"I am right ignorant. Such privilege
Hath Ptolomea, that oft-times the soul
Drops hither, ere by Atropos divorced.
And that thou mayst wipe out more willingly
The glazed tear-drops that o'erlay mine eyes,
Know that the soul, that moment she betrays,
As I did, yields her body to a fiend
Who after moves and governs it at will,
Till all its time be rounded: headlong she
Falls to this cistern. And perchance above
Doth yet appear the body of a ghost,
Who here behind me winters. Him thou knowest,
If thou but newly art arrived below.
The years are many that have passed away,
Since to this fastness Branca Doria came."
    "Now," answered I, "methinks thou mockest me;
For Branca Doria never yet hath died,
But doth all natural functions of a man,
Eats, drinks, and sleeps, and putteth raiment on." *
    He thus: "Not yet unto that upper foss
By th' evil talons guarded, where the pitch
Tenacious boils, had Michel Zanche reached,
When this one left a demon in his stead
In his own body, and of one his kin,
Who with him treachery wrought. But now put forth
Thy hand, and ope mine eyes." I oped them not.
Ill manners were best courtesy to him.
    Ah Genoese! men perverse in every way,
With every foulness stained, why from the earth
Are ye not canceled? Such a one of yours
I with Romagna's darkest spirit found,
As, for his doings, even now in soul
Is in Cocytus plunged, and yet doth seem
In body still alive upon the earth.

---

* Branca Doria, aided by a kinsman, slew his father-in-law at a banquet.
Alberigo and Branca being still alive in 1300, Dante declares a fiend is ani-
mating each of their bodies on earth.

In the fourth and last round of the ninth circle, those who have betrayed their benefactors, are wholly covered with ice. And in the midst is Lucifer, at whose back Dante and Virgil ascend, till by a secret path they reach the surface of the other hemisphere of the earth, and once more obtain sight of the stars.

THE BANNERS of Hell's Monarch do come forth
　　Toward us; therefore look," so spake my guide,
"If thou discern him." As when breathes a cloud
Heavy and dense, or when the shades of night
Fall on our hemisphere, seems viewed from far
A windmill, which the blast stirs briskly round;
Such was the fabric then methought I saw.
　　To shield me from the wind, forthwith I drew
Behind my guide: no covert else was there.
　　Now came I (and with fear I bid my strain
Record the marvel) where the souls were all
Whelmed underneath, transparent, as through glass
Pellucid the frail stem. Some prone were laid;
Others stood upright, this upon the soles,
That on his head, a third with face to feet
Arched like a bow. When to the point we came,
Whereat my guide was pleased that I should see
The creature eminent in beauty once,
He from before me stepped and made me pause.
　　"Lo!" he exclaimed, "lo Dis; and lo the place,
Where thou hast need to arm thy heart with strength."
　　How frozen and how faint I then became,
Ask me not, reader! for I write it not;
Since words would fail to tell thee of my state.
I was not dead nor living. Think thyself,
If quick conception work in thee at all,
How I did feel. That Emperor, who sways
The realm of sorrow, at mid-breast from the ice
Stood forth; and I in stature am more like
A giant, than the giants are his arms.
Mark now how great that whole must be, which suits
With such a part. If he were beautiful

As he is hideous now, and yet did dare
To scowl upon his Maker, well from him
May all our misery flow. Oh what a sight!
How passing strange it seemed, when I did spy
Upon his head three faces: one in front
Of hue vermilion, the other two with this
Midway each shoulder joined and at the crest;
The right 'twixt wan and yellow seemed; the left
To look on, such as come from whence old Nile
Stoops to the lowlands. Under each shot forth
Two mighty wings, enormous as became
A bird so vast. Sails never such I saw
Outstretched on the wide sea. No plumes had they,
But were in texture like a bat; and these
He flapped in the air, that from him issued still
Three winds, wherewith Cocytus to its depth
Was frozen. At six eyes he wept: the tears
Adown three chins distilled with bloody foam.
At every mouth his teeth a sinner champed,
Bruised as with ponderous engine; so that three
Were in this guise tormented. But far more
Than from that gnawing, was the foremost panged
By the fierce rending, whence oft-times the back
Was stripped of all its skin. "That upper spirit,
Who hath worst punishment," so spake my guide,
"Is Judas, he that hath his head within
And plies the feet without. Of th' other two,
Whose heads are under, from the murky jaw
Who hangs, is Brutus: lo! how he doth writhe
And speaks not. The other, Cassius, that appears
So large of limb. But night now re-ascends;
And it is time for parting. All is seen."
    I clipped him round the neck; for so he bade:
And noting time and place, he, when the wings
Enough were oped, caught fast the shaggy sides,
And down from pile to pile descending stepped
Between the thick fell and the jagged ice.
    Soon as he reached the point whereat the thigh
Upon the swelling of the haunches turns,
My leader there, with pain and struggling hard,

Turned round his head where his feet stood before,
And grappled at the fell as one who mounts;
That into Hell methought we turned again.
   "Expect that by such stairs as these," thus spake
The teacher, panting like a man forespent,
"We must depart from evil so extreme":
Then at a rocky opening issued forth,
And placed me on the brink to sit, next joined
With wary step my side. I raised mine eyes,
Believing that I Lucifer should see
Where he was lately left, but saw him now
With legs held upward. Let the grosser sort,
Who see not what the point was I had passed,
Bethink them if sore toil oppressed me then.
   "Arise," my master cried, "upon thy feet.
The way is long, and very rough the road;
And now within one hour and half of noon
The sun returns." It was no palace-hall
Lofty and luminous wherein we stood,
But natural dungeon where ill-footing was
And scant supply of light. "Ere from the abyss
I separate," thus when risen I began:
"My guide! vouchsafe few words to set me free
From error's thralldom. Where is now the ice?
How standeth he in posture thus reversed?
And how from eve to morn in space so brief
Hath the sun made his transit?" He in few
Thus answering spake: "Thou deemest thou art still
On the other side the center, where I grasped
The abhorred worm that boreth through the world.
Thou wast on the other side, so long as I
Descended; when I turned, thou didst o'erpass
That point, to which from every part is dragged
All heavy substance. Thou art now arrived
Under the hemisphere opposed to that,
Which the great continent doth overspread,
And underneath whose canopy expired
The Man, that was born sinless and so lived.
Thy feet are planted on the smallest sphere,

Whose other aspect is Judecca. Morn
Here rises, when there evening sets: and he,
Whose shaggy pile we scaled, yet standeth fixed,
As at the first. On this part he fell down
From Heaven; and th' earth, here prominent before,
Through fear of him did veil her with the sea,
And to our hemisphere retired.* Perchance,
To shun him, was the vacant space left here,
By what of firm land on this side appears,
That sprang aloof." There is a place beneath,
From Beelzebub as distant, as extends
The vaulted tomb; discovered not by sight,
But by the sound of brooklet, that descends
This way along the hollow of a rock,
Which, as it winds with no precipitous course,
The wave hath eaten. By that hidden way
My guide and I did enter, to return
To the fair world: and heedless of repose
We climbed, he first, I following his steps,
Till on our view the lovely lights of Heaven
Dawned through a circular opening in the cave:
Thence issuing we again beheld the stars.†

PART TWO: Purgatory

[*Dante and Virgil slowly begin the ascent of the Mount of Purgatory. In Canto IV Virgil encourages his pupil for the hard climb, and then they meet some indolent souls, who are lingering outside the gate because they postponed repentance until the end.*]

M Y GUIDE explained: "Such is this steep ascent,
That it is ever difficult at first,
But more a man proceeds, less evil grows.
When pleasant it shall seem to thee, so much

---

* Thereby forming the Mount of Purgatory.
† Each of the three parts of the *Divine Comedy* ends with this word, "stars," suggesting aspiration. It is now Easter morning.

That upward going shall be easy to thee
As in a vessel to go down the tide,
Then of this path thou wilt have reached the end.
There hope to rest thee from thy toil. No more
I answer, and thus far for certain know."
As he his words had spoken, near to us
A voice there sounded: "Yet ye first perchance
May to repose you by constraint be led."
At sound thereof each turned; and on the left
A huge stone we beheld, of which nor I
Nor he before was ware. Thither we drew;
And there were some, who in the shady place
Behind the rock were standing, as a man
Through idleness might stand. Among them one,
Who seemed to be much wearied, sat him down,
And with his arms did fold his knees about,
Holding his face between them downward bent.

"Sweet Sir!" I cried, "behold that man who shows
Himself more idle than if laziness
Were sister to him." Straight he turned to us,
And, lifting up his face, observed us,
Then in these accents spake: "Up then, proceed,
Thou valiant one." Straight who it was I knew;
Nor could the pain I felt (for want of breath
Still somewhat urged me) hinder my approach.

His lazy acts and broken words my lips
To laughter somewhat moved; when I began:
"Belacqua, now for thee I grieve no more.
But tell, why thou art seated upright there.
Waitest thou escort to conduct thee hence?
Or blame I only thine accustomed ways?"
Then he: "My brother! of what use to mount,
When, to my suffering, would not let me pass
The bird of God, who at the portal sits?
Behooves so long that Heaven first bear me round
Without its limits, as in life it bore;
Because I, to the end, repentant sighs
Delayed; if prayer do not aid me first,
That riseth up from heart which lives in grace.
What other kind avails, not heard in Heaven?"

*[An encounter with Sordello the poet (who, like Virgil, came
from Mantua) leads to an outburst against the warring factions of
Italy.]*

Ah, slavish Italy! thou inn of grief!
Vessel without a pilot in loud storm!
Lady no longer of fair provinces,
But brothel-house impure! this gentle spirit,
Even from the pleasant sound of his dear land
Was prompt to greet a fellow citizen
With such glad cheer: while now thy living ones
In thee abide not without war; and one
Malicious gnaws another; ay, of those
Whom the same wall and the same moat contains.
Seek, wretched one! around thy sea-coasts wide;
Then homeward to thy bosom turn; and mark,
If any part of thee sweet peace enjoy.

My Florence! thou mayst well remain unmoved
At this digression, which affects not thee:
Thanks to thy people, who so wisely speed.
Many have justice in their heart, that long
Waiteth for counsel to direct the bow,
Or ere it dart unto its aim: but thine
Have it on their lip's edge. Many refuse
To bear the common burdens: readier thine
Answer uncalled, and cry, "Behold I stoop!"

Make thyself glad, for thou hast reason now,
Thou wealthy! thou at peace! thou wisdom-fraught!
Facts best will witness if I speak the truth.
Athens and Lacedæmon, who of old
Enacted laws, for civil arts renowned,
Made little progress in improving life
Towards thee, who usest such nice subtlety,
That to the middle of November scarce
Reaches the thread thou in October weavest.
How many times within thy memory,
Customs, and laws, and coins, and offices
Have been by thee renewed, and people changed.
If thou remember'st well and canst see clear,
Thou wilt perceive thyself like a sick wretch,

Who finds no rest upon her down, but oft
Shifting her side, short respite seeks from pain.

[*Dante, asleep and dreaming, is carried up the mountain by St. Lucia.*]

When near the dawn the swallow her sad lay,
Remembering haply ancient grief, renews;
And when our minds, more wanderers from the flesh,
And less by thought restrained, are, as it were, full
Of holy divination in their dreams;
Then, in a vision, did I seem to view
A golden-feathered eagle in the sky,
With open wings, and hovering for descent;
And I was in that place, methought, from whence
Young Ganymede from his associates
Was snatched aloft to the high consistory.
"Perhaps," thought I within me, "here alone
He strikes his quarry, and elsewhere disdains
To pounce upon the prey." Therewith, it seemed
A little wheeling in his aëry tour,
Terrible as lightning, rushed he down,
And snatched me upward even to the fire.
There both, I thought, the eagle and myself
Did burn; and so intense the imagined flames,
That needs my sleep was broken off. As erst
Achilles shook himself, and round him rolled
His wakened eyeballs, wondering where he was,
That time his mother had from Chiron fled
To Scyros, with him sleeping in her arms;
There whence the Greeks did after sunder him;
E'en thus I shook me, soon as from my face
The slumber parted, turning deadly pale,
Like one ice-struck with dread. Sole at my side
My comfort stood: and the bright sun was now
More than two hours aloft: and to the sea
My looks were turned. "Fear not," my master cried,
"Assured we are at happy point. Thy strength
Shrink not, but rise dilated. Thou art come
To Purgatory now. Lo! there the cliff
That circling bounds it. See the entrance there,

Where it doth seem disparted. Ere the dawn
Ushered the day-light, when thy wearied soul
Slept in thee, o'er the flowery vale beneath
A lady came, and thus bespake me: 'I
'Am Lucia. Suffer me to take this man,
'Who slumbers. Easier so his way shall speed.'
Sordello and the other gentle shapes
Tarrying, she bore thee up: and, as day shone,
This summit reached: and I pursued her steps.
Here did she place thee. First, her lovely eyes
That open entrance showed me; then at once
She vanished with thy sleep." Like one, whose doubts
Are chased by certainty, and terror turned
To comfort on discovery of the truth,
Such was the change in me: and as my guide
Beheld me fearless, up along the cliff
He moved, and I behind him, towards the height.

[*Purgatory consists of seven ledges or rounds, one for each of the Seven Deadly Sins—pride, envy, anger, sloth, avarice, gluttony, incontinence, in ascending order. Purgatory is less populous than Hell and Heaven, being a way-station where souls that repent in time undergo punishment until they have been purged of their sins and are fit for entrance to an appropriate sphere of the Celestial Paradise.*

As usual Dante draws on both fable and recent history for his individual names or cases. One of the envious, in Canto XIII, is Sapia of Siena, who, at the battle of Colle in 1269, gloated over the defeat of her fellow-townsmen.]

A ghost I noted, in whose look was marked
Expectance. Ask ye how? The chin was raised
As in one reft of sight. "Spirit," said I,
"Who for thy rise art tutoring, (if thou be
That which didst answer to me,) or by place,
Or name, disclose thyself, that I may know thee."
    "I was," it answered, "of Siena: here
I cleanse away with these the evil life,
Soliciting with tears that He, who is,
Vouchsafe Him to us. Though Sapia named,
In sapience I excelled not; gladder far

Of other's hurt, than of the good befell me.
That thou mayst own I now deceive thee not,
Hear, if my folly were not as I speak it.
When now my years sloped waning down the arch,
It so bechanced, my fellow-citizens
Near Colle met their enemies in the field;
And I prayed God to grant what He had willed.
There were they vanquished, and betook themselves
Unto the bitter passages of flight.
I marked the hunt; and waxing out of bounds
In gladness, lifted up my shameless brow,
And, like the merlin cheated by a gleam,
Cried: 'It is over. Heaven! I fear thee not.'
Upon my verge of life I wished for peace
With God; not yet repentance had supplied
What I did lack of duty, were it not
The hermit Piero, touched with charity,
In his devout orisons thought on me.
But who art thou that questionest of our state,
Who goest, as I believe, with lids unclosed,
And breathest in thy talk?"—"Mine eyes," said I,
"May yet be here ta'en from me; but not long;
For they have not offended grievously
With envious glances. But the woe beneath
Urges my soul with more exceeding dread,
That nether load already weighs me down."

[*Statius, a Latin poet whom Dante treats as a Christian, joins the two for part of the way. Having been cleansed, he is going to Paradise.*

Canto XXIV, in which a number of those expiating the vice of gluttony are pointed out, ends with a paean to temperance:]

As when, to harbinger the dawn, springs up
On freshened wing the air of May, and breathes
Of fragrance, smelling sweet of herb and flowers;
E'en such a wind I felt upon my front
Blow gently, and the moving of a wing
Perceived, that, moving, shed ambrosial smell;
And then a voice: "Blessed are they, whom grace
Doth so illume, that appetite in them

Exhaleth no inordinate desire,
Still hungering as the rule of temperance wills."

[At the summit of the Mount of Purgatory is the Terrestrial Paradise.]

CANTO XXVIII

Dante wanders through the forest of the Terrestrial Paradise, till he is stopped by a stream, on the other side of which he beholds a fair lady gathering flowers. He speaks to her; and she, in reply, explains to him certain things about that place. She tells him that the water which flows between them is here called Lethe, and in another place has the name of Eunoe.

THROUGH that celestial forest, whose thick shade
With lively greenness the new-springing day
Illumined, eager now to roam, and search
Its limits round, forthwith I left the bank;
Along the meadow leisurely my way
Pursuing, o'er the ground, that on all sides
Delicious odor breathed. A pleasant air,
That intermitted never, never veered,
Smote on my temples, gently, as a wind
Of softest influence: at which the sprays,
Obedient all, leaned trembling to that part
Where first the holy mountain casts his shade;
Yet were not so disordered, but that still
Upon their top the feathered choristers
Applied their wonted art, and with full joy
Welcomed those hours of prime, and warbled shrill
Amid the leaves, that to their jocund lays
Kept tenor; even as from branch to branch,
Along the piny forests on the shore
Of Chiassi, rolls the gathering melody,
When Eolus hath from his cavern loosed
The dripping south. Already had my steps,
Though slow, so far into that ancient wood
Transported me, I could not see the place
Where I had entered; when, behold! my path

Was bounded by a rill, which, to the left,
With little rippling waters bent the grass
That issued from its brink. On earth no wave,
How clean soe'er, that would not seem to have
Some mixture in itself, compared with this,
Transpicuous clear; yet darkly on it rolled,
Darkly beneath perpetual gloom, which ne'er
Admits or sun or moon-light there to shine.

 My feet advanced not; but my wondering eyes
Passed onward, o'er the streamlet, to survey
The tender may-bloom, flushed through many a hue,
In prodigal variety: and there,
As object, rising suddenly to view,
That from our bosom every thought beside
With the rare marvel chases, I beheld
A lady all alone, who, singing, went,
And gathering flower on flower, wherewith her way
Was all o'er painted. "Lady beautiful!
Thou, who (if looks, that use to speak the heart,
Are worthy of our trust) with love's own beam
Dost warm thee," thus to her my speech I framed;
"Ah! please thee hither towards the streamlet bend
Thy steps so near, that I may list thy song.
Beholding thee and this fair place, methinks,
I call to mind where wandered and how looked
Proserpine, in that season, when her child
The mother lost, and she the bloomy spring."

 As when a lady, turning in the dance,
Doth foot it lightly, and advances scarce
One step before the other to the ground;
Over the yellow and vermilion flowers
Thus turned she at my suit, most maiden-like
Veiling her sober eyes; and came so near,
That I distinctly caught the dulcet sound.
Arriving where the limpid waters now
Laved the greensward, her eyes she deigned to raise,
That shot such splendor on me, as I think
Ne'er glanced from Venus' eyes when her son
Had sped his keenest weapon to her heart.
Upon the other bank she stood and smiled;

As through her graceful fingers shifted still
The intermingling dyes, which without seed
That lofty land unbosoms. By the stream
Three paces only were we sundered: yet,
The Hellespont, where Xerxes passed it o'er,
(A curb for ever to the pride of man,)
Was by Leander not more hateful held
For floating, with inhospitable wave,
'Twixt Sestos and Abydos, than by me
That flood, because it gave no passage thence.

    "Strangers ye come; and haply in this place
That cradled human nature in its birth,
Wondering, ye not without suspicion view
My smiles: but that sweet strain of psalmody,
'Thou, Lord! hast made me glad,' will give ye light,
Which may uncloud thee. The First Good, whose joy
Is only in himself, created man,
For happiness; and gave this goodly place,
His pledge and earnest of eternal peace.
Favored thus highly, through his own defect
He fell; and here made short sojourn; he fell,
And, for the bitterness of sorrow, changed
Laughter unblamed and ever-new delight.
That vapors none, exhaled from earth beneath,
Or from the waters, (which, wherever heat
Attracts them, follow,) might ascend thus far
To vex man's peaceful state, this mountain rose
So high toward the Heaven, nor fears the rage
Of elements contending; from that part
Exempted, where the gate his limit bars.

    "The water, thou beholdest, springs not from vein,
Restored by vapor, that the cold converts;
As stream that intermittently repairs
And spends his pulse of life; but issues forth
From fountain, solid, undecaying, sure:
And, by the Will Omnific, full supply
Feeds whatsoe'er on either side it pours;
On this, devolved with power to take away
Remembrance of offense; on that, to bring
Remembrance back of every good deed done.

From whence its name of Lethe on this part;
On the other, Eunoe: both of which must first
Be tasted, ere it work; the last exceeding
All flavors else. Albeit thy thirst may now
Be well contented, if I here break off,
No more revealing; yet a corollary
I freely give beside: nor deem my words
Less grateful to thee, if they somewhat pass
The stretch of promise. They, whose verse of yore
The golden age recorded and its bliss,
On the Parnassian mountain, of this place
Perhaps had dreamed. Here was man guiltless; here
Perpetual spring, and every fruit; and this
The far-famed nectar." Turning to the bards,
When she had ceased, I noted in their looks
A smile at her conclusion; then my face
Again directed to the lovely dame.

[*This lady's name, it develops, is Matilda. But the time has come
for Beatrice herself to take over as guide. Virgil vanishes, not without Dante's tears, even while the Lady who has come down from
Heaven to her adorer is awaiting recognition.*]

No sooner on my vision streaming smote
The heavenly influence, which, years past, and e'en
In childhood, thrilled me, than towards Virgil I
Turned me to leftward; panting, like a babe,
That flees for refuge to his mother's breast,
If aught have terrified or worked him woe:
And would have cried, "There is no dram of blood,
That doth not quiver in me. The old flame
Throws out clear tokens of reviving fire."
But Virgil had bereaved us of himself;
Virgil, my best-loved father; Virgil, he
To whom I gave me up for safety: nor
All, our prime mother lost, availed to save
My undewed cheeks from blur of tears.
"Dante! weep not that Virgil leaves thee; nay,
Weep thou not yet: behooves thee feel the edge
Of other sword; and thou shalt weep for that."
As to the prow or stern, some admiral

Paces the deck, inspiriting his crew,
When 'mid the sail-yards all hands ply aloof;
Thus, on the left side of the car, I saw
(Turning me at the sound of mine own name,
Which here I am compelled to register)
The virgin stationed, who before appeared
Veiled in that festive shower angelical.

Towards me, across the stream, she bent her eyes;
Though from her brow the veil descending, bound
With foliage of Minerva, suffered not
That I beheld her clearly: then with act
Full royal, still insulting o'er her thrall,
Added, as one who, speaking, keepeth back
The bitterest saying, to conclude the speech:
"Observe me well. I am, in sooth, I am
Beatrice. What! and hast thou deigned at last
Approach the mountain? Knewest not, O man!
Thy happiness is here?" Down fell mine eyes
On the clear fount; but there, myself espying,
Recoiled, and sought the greensward; such a weight
Of shame was on my forehead. With a mien
Of that stern majesty, which doth surround
A mother's presence to her awe-struck child,
She looked; a flavor of such bitterness
Was mingled in her pity.

CANTO XXX

[*Beatrice reproves Dante for his morally unworthy conduct in
the years following her death.*

*Matilda draws the poet through the waters of Lethe, and he
drinks of Eunoe, the mystical source of both streams being the
fountain of the grace of God. "Pure and made apt for mounting to
the stars"—such is the last line of the* Purgatory—*Dante is now
ready to visit Paradise.*]

PART THREE: Paradise

[With Beatrice as his escort Dante soars through the Ten Heavens. For, as in the Inferno *and in* Purgatory, *there are distinctions and degrees. Each soul in Paradise is perfectly blessed, according to its capacity, but there are degrees of glory, of nearness to the All-Encompassing Vision. No one can be anything but happy in his place. "In His will is our peace."*

The first Heaven is the sphere of the Moon, allotted to those who, after having made profession of chastity and a religious life, had been compelled to violate their vows. In the second, that of Mercury, are seen the spirits of those whom desire of fame incited to noble deeds—e.g., the Emperor Justinian. To the third Heaven, Venus, go the Lovers. The fourth sphere, that of the Sun, holds the Theologians and Church Fathers. Thomas Aquinas is their principal spokesman, but Solomon is also heard expatiating on the joys of Paradise.

In the fifth sphere, Mars, containing those who died fighting for the true faith, the poet discourses with his ancestor, Cacciaguida (who died in the Crusade of 1147), on the degeneracy of Florence —a recurring theme throughout the poem. Cacciaguida prophesies the poet's own exile, urges him to write his poem.

Jupiter, the sixth Heaven, has an array, in the form of an eagle, of the souls who administered justice rightly, such as Joshua and Charlemagne and Godfrey of Bouillon and Trajan. The seventh Heaven is the planet Saturn, dedicated to the spirits of those who had passed their lives in holy retirement and contemplation. Here St. Benedict gives explanations. On mounting to the eighth Heaven, or that of the Fixed Stars, where he will see the Triumph of Christ, Dante first looks back, reviewing all he has passed between his present station and the earth. In Canto XXIV he passes an examination by St. Peter on questions of faith. St. James and St. John follow with further questions, and Adam gives his history from creation till his admittance to Heaven.

In the ninth Heaven, the Primum Mobile which moves the first eight, Dante sees, in three hierarchies, the nine choirs of Angels. Finally, in the tenth Heaven, the motionless, all-encompassing Empyrean, the Heaven of Heavens, the ultimate Vision awaits him.]

560

The Poet expatiates further on the glorious vision described in the last Canto. On looking round for Beatrice, he finds that she has left him, and that an old man is at his side. This proves to be Saint Bernard, who shows him that Beatrice has returned to her throne, and then points out to him the blessedness of the Virgin Mother.

I N FASHION, as a snow-white rose, lay then
    Before my view the saintly multitude,
Which in His own blood Christ espoused. Meanwhile,
That other host, that soar aloft to gaze
And celebrate His glory, whom they love,
Hovered around; and, like a troop of bees,
Amid the vernal sweets alighting now,
Now, clustering, where their fragrant labor glows,
Flew downward to the mighty flower, or rose
From the redundant petals, streaming back
Unto the steadfast dwelling of their joy.
Faces had they of flame, and wings of gold;
The rest was whiter than the driven snow;
And, as they flitted down into the flower,
From range to range, fanning their plumy loins,
Whispered the peace and ardor, which they won
From that soft winnowing. Shadow none, the vast
Interposition of such numerous flight
Cast, from above, upon the flower, or view
Obstructed aught. For, through the universe,
Wherever merited, celestial light
Glides freely, and no obstacle prevents.
    All there, who reign in safety and in bliss,
Ages long past or new, on one sole mark
Their love and vision fixed. O trinal beam
Of individual star, that charm'st them thus!
Vouchsafe one glance to gild our storm below.
    If the grim brood, from Arctic shores that roamed,
(Where the Great Bear for ever, as she wheels,
Sparkles a mother's fondness on her son,)
Stood in mute wonder 'mid the works of Rome,
When to their view the Lateran arose

561

In greatness more than earthly; I, who then
From human to divine had passed, from time
Unto eternity, and out of Florence
To justice and to truth, how might I choose
But marvel too? 'Twixt gladness and amaze,
In sooth no will had I to utter aught,
Or hear. And, as a pilgrim, when he rests
Within the temple of his vow, looks round
In breathless awe, and hopes some time to tell
Of all its goodly state; e'en so mine eyes
Coursed up and down along the living light,
Now low, and now aloft, and now around,
Visiting every step. Looks I beheld,
Where charity in soft persuasion sat;
Smiles from within, and radiance from above;
And, in each gesture, grace and honor high.

 So roved my view, and in its general form
All Paradise surveyed: when round I turned
With purpose of my lady to inquire
Once more of things, that held my thought suspense.
But answer found from other than I thought;
For, Beatrice when I thought to see,
I saw instead a senior, at my side,
Robed, as the rest, in glory. Joy benign
Glowed in his eye, and o'er his cheek diffused,
With gestures such as spake a father's love.
And, "Whither is she vanished?" straight I asked.

 "By Beatrice summoned," he replied,
"I come to aid thy wish. Looking aloft
To the third circle from the highest, there
Behold her on the throne, wherein her merit
Hath placed her." Silently mine eyes I raised,
And saw her, where aloof she sat, her brow
A wreath reflecting of eternal beams.
Not from the center of the sea so far
Unto the region of the highest thunder,
As was my ken from hers; and yet the form
Came through that medium down, unmixed and pure.

 "O Lady! thou in whom my hopes have rest;
Who, for my safety, hast not scorned, in Hell

562

To leave the traces of thy footsteps marked;
For all mine eyes have seen, I to thy power
And goodness, virtue owe and grace. Of slave
Thou hast to freedom brought me: and no means,
For my deliverance apt, hast left untried.
Thy liberal bounty still toward me keep:
That, when my spirit, which thou madest whole,
Is loosened from this body, it may find
Favor with thee." So I my suit preferred:
And she, so distant, as appeared, looked down,
And smiled; then towards the eternal fountain turned.

　　And thus the senior, holy and revered:
"That thou at length mayst happily conclude
Thy voyage, (to which end I was dispatched,
By supplication moved and holy love),
Let thy upsoaring vision range, at large,
This garden through: for so, by ray divine
Kindled, thy ken a higher flight shall mount;
And from Heaven's Queen, whom fervent I adore,
All gracious aid befriend us; for that I
Am her own faithful Bernard." Like a wight,
Who haply from Croatia wends to see
Our Veronica *; and, the while 'tis shown,
Hangs over it with never-sated gaze,
And, all that he hath heard revolving, saith
Unto himself in thought: "And didst Thou look
E'en thus, O Jesus, my true Lord and God?
And was this semblance Thine?" So gazed I then
Adoring; for the charity of him,
Who musing, in this world that peace enjoyed,
Stood cheerfully before me. "Child of grace!"
Thus he began: "thou shalt not knowledge gain
Of this glad being, if thine eyes are held
Still in this depth below. But search around
The circles, to the farthest, till thou spy
Seated in state, the Queen, that of this realm

---

* The Veronica is an impression of the countenance of Christ that miraculously appeared on the handkerchief of a woman who wiped Jesus' face on the way to Calvary.

Is sovereign." Straight mine eyes I raised; and bright,
As, at the birth of morn, the eastern clime
Above the horizon, where the sun declines;
So to mine eyes, that upward, as from vale
To mountain sped, at the extreme bound, a part
Excelled in luster all the front opposed.
And as the glow burns ruddiest o'er the wave,
That waits the ascending team, which Phaëton
Ill knew to guide, and on each part the light
Diminished fades, intensest in the midst;
So burned the peaceful oriflamme, and slacked
On every side the living flame decayed.
And in that midst their sportive pennons waved
Thousands of Angels; in resplendence each
Distinct, and quaint adornment. At their glee
And carol, smiled the Lovely One of Heaven,
That joy was in the eyes of all the blest.
Had I a tongue in eloquence as rich,
As is the coloring in fancy's loom,
'Twere all too poor to utter the least part
Of that enchantment. When he saw my eyes
Intent on her that charmed him Bernard gazed
With so exceeding fondness, as infused
Ardor into my breast, unfelt before.

CANTO XXXII

Saint Bernard shows him, on their several thrones, the other blessed souls, of the old and the new Testament; explains that their places are assigned them by grace, and not according to merit; and lastly, tells him that if he would obtain power to descry what remained of the heavenly vision, he must unite with him in supplication to Mary.

FREELY THE sage, though wrapt in musings high,
Assumed the teacher's part, and mild began:
"The wound that Mary closed Eve opened first,
Who sits so beautiful at Mary's feet.
The third in order, underneath her, lo!
Rachel with Beatrice: Sarah next;

Judith; Rebecca; and the gleaner, Ruth,
Meek ancestress of him, who sang the psalms
Of sore repentance in his sorrowful mood.
All, as I name them, down from leaf to leaf,
Are, in gradation, throned on the rose.
And from the seventh step, successively,
Adown the breathing tresses of the flower,
Still doth the file of Hebrew dames proceed;
For these are a partition wall, whereby
The sacred stairs are severed, as the faith
In Christ divides them. On this part, where blooms
Each leaf in full maturity, are set
Such as in Christ, or e'er He came, believed.
On the other, where an intersected space
Yet shows the semicircle void, abide
All they, who looked to Christ already come.
And as our Lady on her glorious stool,
And they who on their stools beneath her sit,
This way distinction make; e'en so on his,
The mighty Baptist that way marks the line,
(He who endured the desert, and the pains
Of martyrdom, and, for two years, of Hell,
Yet still continued holy,) and beneath,
Augustine; Francis; Benedict; and the rest,
Thus far from round to round . . .
And, if thou mark and listen to them well,
Their childish looks and voice declare as much.
    "Here, silent as thou art, I know thy doubt;
And gladly will I loose the knot, wherein
Thy thoughts have bound thee. From this realm
Excluded, chance no entrance here may find;
No more than hunger, thirst, or sorrow can.
A law immutable hath stablished all;
Nor is there aught thou seest, that doth not fit,
Exactly, as the finger to the ring.
It is not, therefore, without cause, that these,
O'erspeedy comers to immortal life,
Are different in their shares of excellence.
Our Sovereign Lord, that settleth this estate
In love and in delight so absolute,

That wish can dare no further, every soul,
Created in His joyous sight to dwell,
With grace, at pleasure, variously endows;
And for a proof the effect may well suffice.
And 'tis moreover most expressly marked
In holy Scripture, where the twins are said
To have struggled in the womb.* Therefore, as grace
Inweaves the coronet, so every brow
Weareth its proper hue of orient light.
And merely in respect to his prime gift,
Not in reward of meritorious deed,
Hath each his several degree assigned.
In early times with their own innocence
More was not wanting, than the parents' faith,
To save them: those first ages past, behooved
That circumcision in the males should quicken
The flight of innocent wings: but since the day
Of grace hath come, without baptismal rites
In Christ accomplished, innocence herself
Must linger yet below. Now raise thy view
Unto the visage most resembling Christ:
For, in her splendor only, shalt thou win
The power to look on Him." Forthwith I saw
Such floods of gladness on her visage showered,
From holy spirits, winging that profound;
That, whatsoever I had yet beheld,
Had not so much suspended me with wonder,
Or shown me such similitude of God.
And he, who had to her descended, once,
On earth, now hailed in Heaven; and on poised wing,
Ave Maria, Gratia Plena, sang:
To whose sweet anthem all the blissful court,
From all parts answering, rang: that holier joy
Brooded the deep serene. "Father revered!
Who deignest, for me, to quit the pleasant place
Wherein thou sittest, by eternal lot;
Say, who that Angel is, that with such glee
Beholds our Queen, and so enamored glows
Of her high beauty, that all fire he seems."

* Jacob and Esau. Genesis XXV, 22.

566

So I again resorted to the lore
Of my wise teacher, he, whom Mary's charms
Embellished, as the sun the morning star;
Who thus in answer spake: "In him are summed,
Whate'er of beauty substantive
May be in spirit, or in Angel, met:
And so beseems: for that he bore the palm
Down unto Mary, when the Son of God
Vouchsafed to clothe Him in terrestrial weeds.
Now let thine eyes wait heedful on my words;
And note thou of this just and pious realm
The chiefest nobles. Those, highest in bliss,
The twain, on each hand next our Empress throned,
Are as it were two roots unto this rose:
He to the left, the parent, whose rash taste
Proves bitter to his seed; and, on the right,
That ancient father of the holy Church,
Into whose keeping Christ did give the keys
Of this sweet flower; near whom behold the seer,
That, ere he died, saw all the grievous times
Of the fair bride, who with the lance and nails
Was won. And, near unto the other, rests
The leader, under whom, on manna, fed
The ungrateful nation, fickle and perverse.
On the other part, facing to Peter, lo!
Where Anna sits, so well content to look
On her loved daughter, that with moveless eye
She chants the loud hosanna: while, opposed
To the first father of your mortal kind,
Is Lucia, at whose hest thy lady sped,
When on the edge of ruin closed thine eye.

"But (for the vision hasteneth to an end)
Here break we off, as the good workman doth,
That shapes the cloak according to the cloth;
And to the Primal Love our ken shall rise;
That thou mayst penetrate the brightness, far
As sight can bear thee. Yet, alas! in sooth
Beating thy pennons, thinking to advance,
Thou backward fallest. Grace then must first be gained;
Her grace, whose might can help thee. Thou in prayer

Seek her: and, with affection, whilst I sue,
Attend, and yield me all thy heart." He said;
And thus the saintly orison began.

CANTO XXXIII

Saint Bernard supplicates the Virgin Mary that Dante may have grace
given him to contemplate the brightness of the Divine Majesty, which is
accordingly granted; and Dante then himself prays to God for ability to
show forth some part of the celestial glory in his writings. Lastly, he is
admitted to a glimpse of the great mystery; the Trinity, and the Union of
Man with God.

O VIRGIN MOTHER, daughter of thy Son!
    Created beings all in lowliness
Surpassing, as in height above them all;
Term by the eternal counsel pre-ordained;
Ennobler of thy nature, so advanced
In thee, that its great Maker did not scorn
To make Himself his own creation;
For in thy womb rekindling shone the love
Revealed, whose genial influence makes now
This flower to blossom in eternal peace:
Here thou to us, of charity and love,
Art, as the noon-day torch; and art, beneath,
To mortal men, of hope a living spring . . .
Suppliant to thee he kneels, imploring grace
For virtue yet more high, to lift his ken
Toward the bliss supreme. And I, who ne'er
Coveted sight, more fondly, for myself,
Than now for him, my prayers to thee prefer,
(And pray they be not scant), that thou wouldst drive
Each cloud of his mortality away,
Through thine own prayers, that on the sovereign joy
Unveiled he gaze. This yet, I pray thee, Queen,
Who canst do what thou wilt; that in him thou
Wouldst, after all he hath beheld, preserve
Affection sound, and human passions quell.
Lo! where, with Beatrice, many a saint

568

Stretch their clasped hands, in furtherance of my suit."
    The eyes that Heaven with love and awe regards,
Fixed on the suitor, witnessed, how benign
She looks on pious prayers: then fastened they
On the everlasting light, wherein no eye
Of creature, as may well be thought, so far
Can travel inward. I, meanwhile, who drew
Near to the limit, where all wishes end,
The ardor of my wish (for so behooved)
Ended within me. Beckoning smiled the sage,
That I should look aloft: but, ere he bade,
Already of myself aloft I looked;
For visual strength, refining more and more,
Bore me into the ray authentical
Of sovereign light. Thenceforward, what I saw,
Was not for words to speak, nor memory's self
To stand against such outrage on her skill.
    As one, who from a dream awakened, straight,
All he hath seen forgets; yet still retains
Impression of the feeling in his dream;
E'en such am I: for all the vision dies,
As 'twere, away; and yet the sense of sweet,
That sprang from it, still trickles in my heart . . .
Yield me again some little particle
Of what Thou then appearedst; give my tongue
Power, but to leave one sparkle of Thy glory,
Unto the race to come, that shall not lose
Thy triumph wholly, if Thou waken aught
Of memory in me, and endure to hear
The tale I sing in this unequal strain.
    Such keenness from the living ray I met,
That, if mine eyes had turned away, methinks,
I had been lost; but, so emboldened, on
I passed, as I remember, till my view
Hovered the brink of dread infinitude . . .
    With fixed heed, suspense and motionless,
Wondering I gazed; and admiration still
Was kindled as I gazed. It may not be,
That one, who looks upon that light, can turn
To other object, willingly, his view.

For all the good, that will may covet, there
Is summed; and all, elsewhere defective found,
Complete. My tongue shall utter now, no more
E'en what remembrance keeps, than could the babe's,
That yet is moistened at his mother's breast.
Not that the semblance of the living light
Was changed, (that ever as at first remained,)
But that my vision quickening, in that sole
Appearance, still new miracles descried,
And toiled me with the change. In that abyss
Of radiance, clear and lofty, seemed, methought,
Three orbs of triple hue, clipped in one bond:
And, from another, one reflected seemed,
As rainbow is from rainbow: and the third
Seemed fire, breathed equally from both. O speech!
How feeble and how faint art thou, to give
Conception birth. Yet this to what I saw
Is less than little. O eternal Light!
Sole in Thyself that dwell'st; and of Thyself
Sole understood, past, present, or to come;
Thou smiledst, on that circling, which in Thee
Seemed as reflected splendor, while I mused;
For I therein, methought, in its own hue
Beheld our image painted: steadfastly
I therefore pored upon the view. As one
Who versed in geometric lore would fain
Measure the circle; and, though pondering long
And deeply, that beginning, which he needs,
Finds not: e'en such was I, intent to scan
The novel wonder, and trace out the form,
How to the circle fitted, and therein
How placed: but the flight was not for my wing;
Had not a flash darted athwart my mind,
And, in the spleen, unfolded what it sought.
   Here vigor failed the towering fantasy:
But yet the will rolled onward, like a wheel
In even motion, by the Love impelled,
That moves the sun in Heaven and all the stars.

Further Reading

LES MISÉRABLES by Victor Hugo

DUCLAUX, A. M. *Victor Hugo.* London: CONSTABLE AND CO., LTD., 1921.

GIESE, W. F. *Victor Hugo: The Man and the Poet.* N. Y.: THE DIAL PRESS, 1926.

GRANT, E. M. *The Career of Victor Hugo.* Cambridge, Mass.: HARVARD UNIVERSITY PRESS, 1945.

JOSEPHSON, M. *Victor Hugo.* New York: DOUBLEDAY, DORAN & CO., 1942.

THE AUTOBIOGRAHY OF BENJAMIN FRANKLIN

BRUCE, W. C. *Benjamin Franklin Self-Revealed.* 2 vols. 2nd revised edition. New York: G. P. PUTNAM'S SONS, 1923.

FORD, P. L. *The Many-Sided Franklin.* N. Y.: THE CENTURY CO., 1899.

PARTON, J. *Life and Times of Benjamin Franklin.* 2 vols. N. Y.: MASON BROTHERS, 1864.

VAN DOREN, CARL. *Benjamin Franklin.* N. Y. THE VIKING PRESS, 1938.

THE FRENCH REVOLUTION by Thomas Carlyle

CARLYLE, THOMAS. *Letters to His Wife.* Edited by Trudy Bliss. Cambridge, Mass.: HARVARD UNIVERSITY PRESS, 1953.

CAZAMIAN, L. F. *Carlyle.* Translated by E. K. Brown. N. Y.: THE MACMILLAN COMPANY, 1932.

FROUDE, J. A. *Thomas Carlyle.* 2 vols. N. Y.: C. SCRIBNER'S SONS, 1882.

RALLI, A. *Guide to Carlyle.* London: G. ALLEN & UNWIN, LTD., 1920.

THE DIVINE COMEDY by Dante Alighieri

BARBI, M. *Life of Dante.* Translated and edited by Paul Ruggiers. Berkeley: UNIVERSITY OF CALIFORNIA PRESS, 1954.

DINSMORE, C. A. *Aids to the Study of Dante.* Boston and New York: HOUGHTON MIFFLIN AND COMPANY, 1903.

ELIOT, T. S. "Dante," in *Selected Essays.* New York: HARCOURT BRACE AND COMPANY, 1932.

GRANDGENT, C. H. *Dante.* New York: DUFFIELD & COMPANY, 1916.